PLANE GEOMETRY

PLANE GEOMETRY

by John F. Schacht and Roderick C. McLennan

with the editorial guidance of
Alice L. Griswold

HENRY HOLT AND COMPANY, NEW YORK

ABOUT THE AUTHORS AND EDITOR OF *PLANE GEOMETRY*

John F. Schacht is Instructor in the Mathematics Department
Bexley High School
Bexley, Ohio

Roderick C. McLennan is Head of the Mathematics Department
Arlington High School
Arlington Heights, Illinois

Alice L. Griswold is Instructor in the Mathematics Department
Garden City High School
Garden City, New York

PREFACE

PLANE GEOMETRY, as usually taught, has several primary objectives. The most important are: (1) to develop an understanding of the meaning and nature of mathematical proof; (2) to improve the quality of thinking in non-mathematical situations; (3) to further develop mathematical concepts of an arithmetic and algebraic nature; and (4) to provide an understanding of plane and space relationships for a better appreciation of nature and the arts as they apply to daily life. In the preparation of this textbook, the authors were always mindful of the tried and tested procedures of the past in achieving these objectives. In addition, they wished to share with teachers some special features which have proved successful in their own classrooms and which are consistent with modern trends in teaching demonstrative geometry. They hope that the materials in this book will enable teachers to give students a significant foundation in the science of reasoning.

Considerable emphasis is given to the basic concepts. For example, in the first two chapters, the basis for a mathematically rigorous treatment of geometry is developed through the presentation of: (1) terms that are accepted without definition; (2) terms that are defined; and (3) assumptions (axioms and postulates) that are accepted without proof. Mathematical terms are carefully defined and their meanings are clarified before they are used in constructions, theorems, or the exposition.

Deduction is thoroughly explained and illustrated. Formal deductive proof is introduced by using familiar reasoning situations which are set up in the form of simple syllogisms. These are followed by proofs consisting of two or more syllogisms in which the sequence of the steps is represented by special devices the authors have called linkage lines. Formal proofs of theorems are not introduced until the student understands the nature of deduction. The proofs of the first theorems are simple extensions of algebraic proofs comparable to those with which the student has had some informal experience. These are followed by the parallel line theorems, the authors believing them to be less difficult for beginners than theorems involving the congruence concept. To furnish the student with models he can follow, some proofs are given in detail, others are partially completed, and still others are incomplete—most of the proof being left for the student to do himself.

Induction is suggested throughout the book, not only as an important and respectable method of arriving at conclusions, but also as a method for discovering geometric relationships. The challenge to discover is provided by such questions as: "On the basis of your experimental data, what seems to be true?" or: "What are the implications of these data?" The student is not always told what can be proved, either in the theorems or in the exercises. The experimental-inductive method is followed by deduction. This is good practice, psychologically, for concrete experience is frequently a good preparation for a general deductive proof. Concepts, meanings, and relationships are developed and clarified by such procedure. As a major help in experimental work, dynamic geometry instruments are suggested.

Emphasis is placed on reasoning in non-mathematical situations. Correct procedures for deducing conclusions implied by sets of data are presented, and the kinds of errors commonly found in arguments resembling deduction are illustrated. There are many exercises in which the student is instructed to judge the correctness of conclusions and to identify any errors in the argument.

Some theorems in this book are accepted without proof. In a school year it is hardly possible to consider proofs of all the theorems that may be needed in a well-rounded general course and still have time for the adequate development of other important aspects, such as applications, training in logical reasoning, three-dimensional geometry, co-ordinate geometry, and trigonometry. Moreover, after the student has thoroughly mastered the nature of proof, little is gained by endless repetition.

Many teachers believe that proofs based on superposition detract from, rather than add to, a student's concept of proof. For this reason, the theorems whose proofs would normally be based on superposition are postulated. The congruence and similarity concepts are introduced through inductive procedures. At times, statements which are traditionally propositions are labeled corollaries. Such corollaries are not always attached in the usual way to theorems. The decision as to whether or not proofs of corollaries are required is left to the judgment of the individual teacher.

Special emphasis is placed on the locus concept. This concept is introduced early and is used frequently throughout the text, since all constructions involve loci, and since the locus concept is basic to work in analytical geometry.

This book has been planned to meet the needs of *all* students, although the authors fully realize that in one school year no student can possibly cover the wealth of material herein presented. Therefore, they have provided graded exercises to take care of individual and class differences and have developed three levels of teaching materials: (1) the easier exercises, from which the teacher can make a selection for a minimum course, are designated by numerals printed in **black type**; (2) the more difficult exercises and those for enrichment are designated by numerals printed **in color**: and (3) certain topics and their exercises, not essential to the basic sequence of the course, which may either be omitted or taken up as time permits, are marked with a **colored star** (★). Certain other topics (three-dimensional geometry, applications to science, co-ordinate geometry, trigonometry, and computation with approximate data) are marked *Optional* and are included to provide for differences in local and state syllabi. With these three levels of material, the book will provide for a good general course and also be sufficiently thorough for the best preparation of students for college mathematics and the engineering professions.

Particular attention has been given to the integration of geometry with the other branches of mathematics. Algebraic proofs of theorems have been encouraged and numerous exercises which involve the use of algebra have been included. Co-ordinate geometry appears as an optional topic in each chapter in which it is appropriate. Some of the more elementary principles of trigonometry are included in Chapter 14, and these principles are applied in many exercises involving indirect measurement and the areas of polygons.

The text is written in clear language, geared to the reading ability of the average tenth-grade student. Explanations are always accompanied by appropriate illustrations and examples. To make the text especially interesting color is used frequently but judiciously. Color not only makes the book physically attractive, but also makes it more functional by focusing attention on the important parts of a figure such as right angles, equal segments, and loci.

The authors provide an abundance of exercises and also include short tests at the end of chapters. Numerous devices and materials for motivation are suggested. There are puzzle-type problems for recreation, and application problems in physics, astronomy, navigation, surveying, and carpentry. The authors hope that these will develop an appreciation for geometry and will interest the student in further study.

The entire manuscript was mimeographed and then subjected to the rigors of classroom teaching for three years. Many teachers of mathematics have read it and have offered numerous suggestions, for which the authors are most grateful. Special thanks are due to Mr. Edward Spacapan, Teacher of Mathematics in Arlington High School, Arlington Heights, Illinois; Dr. Clarence Heinke, Professor of Mathematics, Capital University, Columbus, Ohio; and Dr. Sheldon Myers, Educational Testing Service, Princeton, New Jersey for their kindness in giving invaluable assistance and advice during the early stages of the manuscript. The following persons have read the entire manuscript in final form and have given many helpful suggestions: Dr. John Kinsella, Professor of Mathematics Education, School of Education, New York University, New York City; Miss Elizabeth Roudebush, Director of Mathematics, Seattle Public Schools, Seattle, Washington; Mr. Robert Fertig, Chairman of the Mathematics Department, Burlingame High School, Burlingame, California; and Mr. Robert T.

Bateman, Teacher of Mathematics, Wellesley High School, Wellesley, Massachusetts. To each of these, the authors extend their grateful appreciation.

Thanks are due to the New York State Education Department for their kindness in giving permission to use certain materials from their publication entitled "Non-Mathematical Applications to Everyday Life."

Finally, to Alice Griswold, consulting editor and general advisor, herself an outstanding and long-successful author and classroom teacher, the authors express their sincere gratitude.

J. F. S.
R. C. McL.

CONTENTS

★ Starred material is optional (see Preface).

Congruent figures, 183—Corresponding parts of triangles, 183—
Combinations of equal parts that make triangles congruent,
184—Congruence postulates, 186—Proving triangles congruent,
187—Triangles with equal parts that are not corresponding parts,
188—Corresponding parts of congruent triangles, 189—The
isosceles triangle, 191—Deductive proof that the base angles of
an isosceles triangle are equal, 192—Three famous problems
(*Optional*), 195—Overlapping triangles, 196—Proofs of postulates (*Optional*), 198—Proofs of constructions, 199—Investigating
a triangle with a line segment from the vertex to some point on

the opposite side, 200—Investigating an isosceles triangle with altitudes and medians to the equal sides and bisectors of the base angles, 201—The 30°, 60° right triangle, 202—Two points each equidistant from the ends of a line segment, 204—The locus of points equidistant from two given points, 205—⋆Necessary and· sufficient conditions, 206—The locus of the vertex of a triangle having a given side, 207—Dynamic models of loci, 207—The locus of points equidistant from the sides of an angle, 208—Practical applications, 210—Jumping to conclusions, 212—Review of Chapter 7, 214

Dynamic quadrilaterals, 217—Quadrilaterals classified, 218—Relations of the angles of a parallelogram, 220—Relations of the sides of a parallelogram, 221—Relations of the diagonals of a parallelogram, 221—Sufficient conditions for a parallelogram, 222—The parallelepiped (*Optional*), 225—Properties of a rectangle, 225—Sufficient conditions for a rectangle, 226—Properties of a rhombus, 227—Sufficient conditions for a rhombus, 227—Drawing a straight line geometrically (*Optional*), 228—Properties of a square, 228—Sufficient conditions for a square, 228—The cube (*Optional*), 229—Properties of an isosceles trapezoid, 229—Sufficient conditions for an isosceles trapezoid, 230—The bisectors of the angles of a quadrilateral (*Optional*), 231—⋆Necessary and sufficient conditions, 232—Dividing a line segment into any number of equal parts, 233—A line segment joining the midpoints of two sides of a triangle, 235—The converses of Theorem 37, 236—The median of a trapezoid, 238—The median to the hypotenuse of a right triangle, 239—Properties of the quadrilateral formed by joining the midpoints of the consecutive sides of a given quadrilateral, 239—Quadrilaterals determined by their diagonals, 240—Practical applications, 242—Puzzles (*Optional*), 243—APPLICATION OF PARALLELOGRAMS TO VECTORS, 245—Direction of a ray (*Optional*), 245—Vectors (*Optional*), 245—Parallelogram of vector quantities (*Optional*), 246—Parallelogram of forces (*Optional*), 248—Resolution of forces (*Optional*), 249—CO-ORDINATE GEOMETRY, 250—Projection of a point and of a line segment (*Optional*), 250—The co-ordinates of the midpoint of a line segment (*Optional*), 251—The distance between two points (*Optional*), 252—Chapter Summary, 254—Review of Chapter 8, 255

PLANE GEOMETRY

Why study geometry? Here is one answer——This young scientist is working on the design and installation of radar units. These units are used to detect high-flying aircraft and to provide information on their speed, altitude, and flight direction. To participate in the development of such scientific advances, or even to appreciate and enjoy others like them, we must first gain a basic understanding of mathematics and science.

Chapter 1 POINTS, LINES, AND SURFACES

WELCOME to the study of geometry!

Have you been curious about the content of this mathematics course? If so, you might be interested in the following conversation that is developing between two high school boys, Jim Edwards and Tom Matthews, and their teacher, Mr. Thompson. Summer vacation is about to end, and the boys have sought out Mr. Thompson, Jim's neighbor, for questioning.

Tom says, "Jim and I were wondering if geometry has anything to do with the earth, because both geometry and geography begin with the letters, g-e-o."

"Yes," replied Mr. Thompson as he laid his hammer on a nearby workbench. "Plane geometry is a branch of mathematics that involves earth measure. The word *geometry* originates from the Greek words *geos* and *metron*, which mean *earth* and *measure*, respectively. Although these words are Greek, the Egyptians are probably more responsible for our association of geometry with the earth and measurement. Every year in ancient Egypt the Nile River overflowed its banks and flooded its valley. Methods for re-establishing landmarks had to be devised so that flooded lands could be returned to their rightful owners. Geometry began with these ancient efforts to survey the land."

'We still use geometry in many ways," continued Mr. Thompson. "In fact, I have been applying it as I make this gate. Notice that the gate isn't firm, for it can be moved out of shape. How could I remedy this situation, boys?"

Fig. 1

"Perhaps you should put more screws in it," Jim suggested.

"Or a brace," added Tom.

"A good suggestion, Tom," agreed Mr. Thompson. "A brace will form many triangles with the framework of the gate. Since a triangle is a rigid figure and will not change its shape, the gate will not be as flexible as it is without the brace.

Fig. 2

"We cannot escape the applications of geometry," continued Mr. Thompson. "The windows in most houses are rectangles or squares. Street curbs are parallel lines, and two cars colliding meet at a common point."

Mr. Thompson might have explained that geometry has been studied for centuries for still another purpose in addition to its practical applications. Geometry is an intellectual game where the players draw conclusions that are shown to be correct because they are the result of proper reasoning. We will often arrange facts in an order called a logical sequence and then draw one or more correct conclusions from these facts.

3

Why we study geometry

Geometry is the basis of many of the things that we use and enjoy today. It is a study of the *size, shape,* and *position* of figures in space. As we learn more about the properties of many of the geometric forms found in nature, we will become more appreciative of them. We can also learn to enjoy the geometric designs in art and architecture, and the applications of geometry used in the machines of industry and transportation.

Of even greater importance is the assistance that the study of geometry gives us as we seek an intelligent approach to the solution of the difficult problems of modern living. We shall improve our thinking habits by learning to apply good reasoning when we are solving geometric problems.

If all life's problems were as simple as tying a shoestring, we could rely on our memory and habit to solve them; but many of our problems are complex, and we are forced to study the many changing situations in our environment. These changing situations, or variables, must be examined as to their relationship to each other and the effect of certain conditions on all of them. Most important of all, we must learn how to control these variables to use them for our advantage and benefit.

For example, we often read of people being hurt by an explosion resulting from an attempt to kindle a fire by using gasoline. Although these people had control of the conditions up to a certain point, they had no control over the result. It is likely that the explosion could have been avoided if the people had learned to control the result by exercising the proper control of the conditions (gasoline, for one) that led to the result. Training and experience are required to adjust to new situations and to solve problems correctly.

The organization of geometry

Although geometry had been in existence for centuries before Euclid's time, he was the first one to successfully organize the subject. Euclid was a capable Greek mathematician who lived 300 years before the birth of Christ. He studied the geometric ideas that were used in various parts of the world including Greece, Egypt, and China, and organized all of them into a collection of books named *The Elements*. The geometry we study today is essentially the same as it was when Euclid organized it.

The vocabulary of geometry

Before we can learn the ideas of geometry, we must have a vocabulary of geometric terms. Words are very important, and every subject must have a beginning. In geometry we begin with the vocabulary and ideas we already have. We try to pin them down and make them definite so that each one will have exactly the same meaning to everyone. No doubt we have all heard of a *point*, but does the word have the same meaning for all of us? One of our objectives is to make clear-cut distinctions among the many geometric terms we use.

A point

Put a dot on your paper with a pencil. No matter how small you make it, it has length, width, and thickness. Now imagine a dot that gets smaller and smaller until it has neither length, width, nor thickness. It is not only invisible, but it does not exist. A *geometric point* is an *idea*, not a dot.

If you know your exact latitude and longitude, you know your position with reference to the earth. Your position is a geometric point that can be represented on a map by a visible mark such as a dot or a small *x*.

The characteristics of a geometric point

1. It has no size.
2. It indicates position only.

How to name a point

Capital letters of the alphabet are used to name points. For example, in Figure 3 below, the colored points are named *R*, *M*, *S*, and *Z*. The points are represented by visible dots.

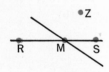

Fig. 3

Physical points

A dot, the point of a pin, the end of a sharpened lead pencil, the point of intersection of two streets, and the tip of a sawtooth are examples of real or physical points.

A straight line

We might think of a line as being the path of a moving point. Since the path of a geometric point is invisible, a geometric line is invisible. To represent a geometric line we draw a visible line. A geometric line is, or contains,

an infinite number of geometric points; it is endless in both directions; and there are no gaps in it.

A part of a line is a *line segment*. A stretched elastic cord is a physical representation of a *straight line segment*. A straight line segment has two end points. *RN* in Figure 4 is a straight line segment. The arrowheads on the extensions of *RN* are sometimes used to indicate that a straight line has no end points.

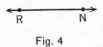

Fig. 4

A straight line that has only one end point and extends in only one direction is called a *ray*. The lines in Figure 5 represent rays.

Fig. 5

The characteristics of a straight line

1. It is a geometric figure of unlimited length.
2. It has length but no width or height.
3. It has an unlimited number of points on it.
4. It may have one end point or no end points, but it never has two end points. (Only a line segment has two end points.)

How to name a straight line

Any single *lower case* letter may be used to name a straight line, or a straight line segment. A line may also be named by using the names of any two of its points. For example, the name of the straight line in Figure 6 is either *d* or *MN*. In Figure 7, the name of the colored line segment which is a side of triangle *PQS* is either *b* or *PQ*.

Fig. 6

Unless otherwise specified, when we speak of a *line*, we mean a *geometric straight line;* when we speak of a *line segment*, we mean a *geometric straight line segment*. If we say *SN* meets *PQ* at *N*, in Figure 7, we mean that *PQ* and *SN* are straight line segments.

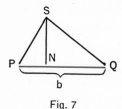

Fig. 7

Light traveling along a straight line

Because light normally travels along the path of a straight line, it is impossible for us to see directly an object that is around the corner of a building or that is on the other side of a high fence. To solve this problem, man invented the periscope. It is an instrument consisting of several mirrors which reflect into our eyes the light rays from objects that are not in our line of vision. Periscopes are used in submarines so that objects on the surface can be observed by the occupants of a submarine that is below the surface.

Exercises

1. Name (**a**) five physical points, (**b**) five physical straight line segments.

2. Distinguish between a physical point and a geometric point.

3. How many points are there on (**a**) a line? (**b**) a line segment?

4. Draw straight line segments *r* and *s* so that they intersect at *P*.

5. Draw a straight line segment and name it *b*. Name its end points *R* and *S*.

6. What geometric figure is represented by the crease in a folded piece of paper?

7. Name the straight line segments in each of these figures:

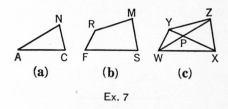

(a) (b) (c)

Ex. 7

8. Can a straight line be formed by placing straight line segments end to end? Why?

9. Is a straight line with one end point shorter than one with no end points?

10. If a candle burns at *C*, it will cast its image through the pinhole at *B* onto the screen at *A*. Can you explain why the image of the candle is upside down?

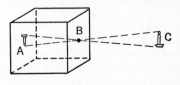

Ex. 10

11. Does a straight line segment that is two inches long contain any more points than a segment one inch long?

12. Light is shining toward an object through a small hole. Explain why the shadow on the screen is so much larger than the object.

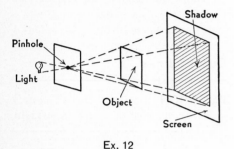

Ex. 12

Definitions

The definition of a term tells what that term is in such a way that it can be positively identified. Terms are defined in sequence, and each new term is defined by using terms that have been previously defined. We must not be guilty of circularity. For example, if we use the word "flat" in defining the word "plane", we cannot use the word "plane" in defining the word "flat." It is apparent that there must be some *first* terms in the sequence, the meanings of which must be accepted without formal definition. Terms such as point, line, straight line, and segment are examples of *undefined terms.*

Suppose we wish to define a fountain pen. We might say, "A fountain pen is an object used for writing." This statement does not give a clear picture of what a fountain pen is and how it differs from other similar things such as a quill, a pencil, a crayon, a piece of chalk, and a ball-point pen.

Let us try again: "A fountain pen is a metal or plastic writing instrument which uses ink." The class, "writing instrument," is certainly a smaller class than "object," and the characteristic, "uses ink," distinguishes it from some of the others in the writing instrument class; but it may not be necessary to specify the material with which the pen is made. Moreover, pens other than fountain pens may use ink.

For our third attempt to define a fountain pen, let us say, "A fountain pen is a writing instrument with a split metal point and a reservoir in the holder which furnishes a supply of ink." Does this third statement define a fountain pen in such a way that a person who has never seen one before would recognize it? If you think it does not, write a better definition.

A good definition has other requirements. The words used in a definition must have been previously defined or explained. Also, a definition is reversible; that is, it is true if the subject and predicate are interchanged. For example, if an assumption is defined as *a statement accepted as true without proof*, it must be true that *a statement accepted as true without proof is an assumption.*

People frequently disagree on some issue because there is not explicit agreement on the definitions of key words and phrases used in the statement of the issue. Suppose, for example, that a friend says, "Mr. Adams should be able to maintain a high standard of living because he earns more than $7,000 a year." *High standard of living* must be defined before you know whether or not you agree with your friend.

The properties necessary for a good definition are given on the following page.

The properties of a definition

1. The term that is being defined should be named.
2. The term should be placed in its nearest class.
3. The characteristics that distinguish the term from other members of its class should be given.
4. The statement should use only those terms that have previously been defined or accepted as undefined terms.
5. The statement should not contain any unnecessary information.
6. The reverse form of the definition must be a true statement.

Exercises

1. There is not always agreement on whether or not Abraham Lincoln was an educated man. Write a definition of *an educated man* which supports the contention that Lincoln was an educated man. Write one that does not support the contention. In your definition of an educated man, indicate the indefinite terms.
2. Some people argue that compulsory military training would be harmful to the youth of our country. Which words and phrases need careful and precise definition in order to reach agreement on the issue? Which words, if any, cannot be precisely defined?
3. Keeping in mind the properties of a good definition, write a good definition of a *ball*, as used to distinguish it from a *strike*, in baseball. In your definition, which terms are undefined?
4. Explain why this statement is not a good definition of a thermometer:

"A thermometer is a tube with mercury in it which is used for measuring temperatures."

5. Would you accept, "Brothers are people who have the same parents," as a good definition of brothers? If not, why?
6. Keeping in mind the properties of a good definition, explain why you would or would not accept the following as a definition: "A foal is a young horse."

Curved lines

DEFINITION A *curved line* or a *curve* is a line, no part of which is straight.

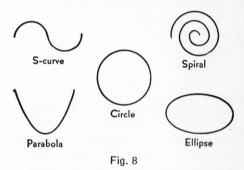

S-curve   Spiral   Circle   Parabola   Ellipse

Fig. 8

The definition of a curved line may also be written as follows: If a line is a curved line, it has no straight part.

Notice how the definition of a curved line satisfies the six properties of a definition:

1. The term is named: "*A curved line* is . . . . ."
2. The term is placed in its nearest class: "A curved line is a *line* . . . . ." It is not classified as a geometric figure because lines are a sub-class of geometric figures.
3. The term is distinguished from other members of its class: "It is a line, *no part of which is straight*."

4. The statement uses only geometric terms that have been accepted: namely, *line* and *straight*.

5. It is a concise statement: that is, no unnecessary information is given.

6. The reverse form is a true statement. Either of the following statements is the reverse form of the definition of a curved line:

   a. A line having no straight part is a curved line.

   b. If a line has no straight part, it is a curved line.

Broken lines

If two or more lines (or line segments) have a common point, they *intersect*.

Name the points of intersection of the segments in these figures:

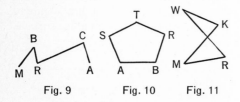

Fig. 9   Fig. 10   Fig. 11

DEFINITION A *broken line* is a line made up of straight line segments such that consecutive segments do not lie in the same straight line and are joined so that no more than two segments have a common end point.

Figure 9 is an illustration of an open broken line, and Figure 10 is an illustration of a closed broken line.

A broken line is named by using the names of the end points of the segments taken in succession. The name of the broken line in Figure 9 is *MBRCA* or *ACRBM*.

How might the broken line in Figure 10 be named?

Figure 11 is a special case of a closed broken line. It is made up of the four segments *MR*, *RW*, *WK*, and *KM*. If we begin at *M*, its name is either *MRWK* or *MKWR*.

The figures below were made by a geometry student. Although there seem to be many curves and "tunnels," he used only straight lines in making the drawing!

The linear motion of a molecule

What causes water to evaporate when it is put in an open container? If a small amount of dye is placed at the bottom of a pan of water, why does the water become colored even without stirring? Why does a container of pure gas soon lose its purity if a hole is punched in the container?

The answer to each of these questions is that the molecules of all substances are continually in motion, and the movement is usually in a zigzag path along a broken line. The molecules move along straight lines until they collide with others and then bounce away in different directions. As molecules of water reach the surface and mix with air, the water evaporates. The dye rapidly diffuses throughout the water in the pan because of the broken-line path of the molecules. In the same manner, gases become mixed if they are not kept in closed containers.

Exercises

In Exercises **1-6,** *which statements are acceptable definitions? By referring to the six properties of definitions, explain why the remaining ones are not acceptable.*

1. Corn is the seed of a cereal grass.
2. A high fever is dangerous.
3. An integer is a whole number.
4. A mayor is the top governing authority of a city or town.
5. A book is a collection of material that is bound within a cover.
6. An automobile is a vehicle that is powered by an engine.
7. Define the following terms and indicate how you have satisfied the properties of a definition: (**a**) chair, (**b**) clock, (**c**) arithmetic.

8. Name some examples of (**a**) physical broken lines, (**b**) physical curved lines.
9. Locate on a road map some of the geometric figures that we have studied.
10. Can a curve be part of a broken line? Explain.

Geometric surfaces

If the colored line moves as indicated in Figure 12, the successive positions form a path called a *geometric surface.* Curved line *a* moves from left to right to form a curved surface. Broken line *b* moves from left to right to form a surface like a folded paper. A surface may have unlimited length and width, but it has no thickness. Straight line *c* moves from left to right to form a curved surface. Straight line *d* moves from left to right to form a flat surface.

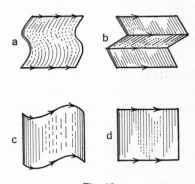

Fig. 12

When a straight line moves in a direction so that it forms what is commonly known as a flat surface, it is said to generate a *plane.* The area of a plane is infinite or limitless. Geometric figures are called plane figures if all their points lie in one plane.

DEFINITION   A *plane* is a surface such
that a straight line joining any two of
its points lies wholly in the surface.

Since many straight lines can be
drawn on a cylinder, such as a tin can,
why isn't the curved surface of a
cylinder a plane?

A part of a plane is called a *plane
segment*. It has finite (measurable)
area. A plane segment may be represented by any closed figure, but the
one shown below is generally used. The
name of the plane segment is *AB*.
Sometimes a single lower-case letter,
such as *m*, is used to name a plane.

Fig. 13

Exercises

1. Referring to a dictionary, find
several meanings for each of these
words: craft, plane, light, general,
file, post, fine, rate.

2. If possible, find a word in the
dictionary that has only one
meaning.

3. Is it possible for a curved line to
appear as a straight line?

4. When might a physical straight
line segment appear to be a physical point?

5. Draw and label the following
figures:

   a. Straight line *d* having one end
   point *X*.

   b. Curved line *e* if three of its
   points are common to a straight

line *k*. The three points of intersection are *M*, *N*, and *O*.

   c. Broken line *HJBK*.

6. Name several examples of plane
segments.

7. Does a moving straight line always
form a plane?

8. How many points are there on
(**a**) a surface? (**b**) a plane segment?

9. A line and a plane intersect if they
have only one point in common.
How many lines can intersect a
plane in the same point?

10. Discuss the number of planes that
can pass through: (**a**) a point in
space, (**b**) two points in space, (**c**)
three points in space, (**d**) a line in
space, (**e**) two intersecting lines in
space, (**f**) a line and a point in
space.

11. Describe the transformations illustrated in these figures:

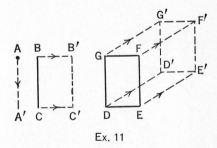

Ex. 11

12. Describe and name the figure
formed in each of the following:

    a. In a plane, the ray *m* rotates
    about point *P*.

    b. In a plane, the line *l* rotates
    about point *P*.

    c. In a plane, the path of the point
    B, as the segment *AB* rotates
    about the point *A*.

13. Repeat each part of Exercise **12** with the restriction, "in a plane," removed.

14. Cut out a triangular piece of cardboard as illustrated. Describe and name the path made by each of the following:

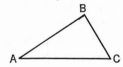

a. Point B as the cardboard is rotated about AC.

b. Side AB as the cardboard is rotated about AC.

c. Sides AB and CB as the cardboard is rotated about AC.

15. There is a book called *Flatland* by Edwin Abbott which describes life in the land of two dimensions. Read it and write a report for the class.

Geometric figures found in nature

Many of the shapes and forms found in nature resemble geometric figures. Curves and combinations of curves and straight lines occur more frequently than straight lines alone. For practical reasons, most of the figures found in buildings are composed of straight lines and planes.

In these photographs of insects, what geometric figures studied in this chapter can you identify?

Review of Chapter 1

General Questions

1. Does a line have area? Explain.
2. List some of the geometric figures that may have two end points.
3. List some geometric figures that have no end point.
4. Explain the difference between a ray and a straight line.
5. Do you think the shortest path between two points on a sphere is a straight line?
6. What is the shortest path between two points on a plane?
7. What geometric figures have measurable (**a**) length, (**b**) area, (**c**) volume?
8. What geometric figure is represented by:

   a. The intersection of the front and side wall of your classroom?

   b. The intersection of the ceiling, the front wall, and the side wall of your classroom?

9. Why isn't the surface of a pane of glass necessarily a plane?
10. State why important phrases and key words must be defined in both geometric and non-geometric situations.
11. Classify the following figures as zero-dimensional, one-dimensional, or two-dimensional: (**a**) point, (**b**) straight line, (**c**) the point of intersection of two rays, (**d**) plane segment, (**e**) circle, (**f**) broken line, (**g**) surface.

Chapter Test

1. Draw and label the following figures:

   a. Straight line f having one end point M.

   b. Point P located on the straight line segment CD and one inch from C.

   c. Curve e having three of its points common to the straight line k. The names of the points common to the two lines are J, F, and S.

   d. Open broken line RML.

   e. Closed broken line AXZ.

   f. Plane segment AM.

2. What geometric figure is suggested by the shadow of a building?
3. What geometric figure is suggested by a corner of a brick?
4. What geometric figure is suggested by an edge of a brick?
5. What geometric figure is suggested by one of the faces of a brick?
6. How can you test whether or not your desk top is a plane?
7. What properties other than length, width, and thickness does a real or physical solid possess?
8. How many geometric points are there on a line segment $\frac{1}{4}$ inch long? on a line segment $\frac{1}{2}$ inch long?
9. State the characteristics of a ray.
10. How are points named?

These men in the "Distortion Room" of Princeton University's Visual Perception Center are actually the same size! We are all fooled by the clever staging which makes one man seem much larger than the other. We are often fooled, too, by reasoning we hear or read in newspapers. It is one aim of this course in geometry to help you learn to reason correctly and to distinguish good reasoning from bad.

Chapter 2 BASIC ASSUMPTIONS AND DEFINITIONS

I N OUR everyday reasoning we take many things for granted. When we drive our car, we expect other drivers to obey traffic laws. We accept without question the rules that govern our social behavior. As citizens of the United States, we accept the basic principles of our form of government as they are set forth in the Declaration of Independence.

Assumptions

In arithmetic we base much of our reasoning on assumptions. For example, the reduction of ⅚ to ¾ is based on the assumption that the value of a fraction is unchanged if both the numerator and denominator of a fraction are divided by the same number.

If we agree to accept certain assumptions and definitions, we must accept the conclusions that follow from them. For example, *if* we agree that a reckless automobile driver is a violator of the law and also that violation of the law should be punished, *then* we must accept the conclusion that a reckless automobile driver should be punished.

In geometry we shall argue that certain statements are true because others that we have previously accepted are true. Obviously the first statements in this sequence cannot be proved. Some of the assumptions we accept without proof are called *postulates*, and others are called *axioms*. Geometric postulates are assumptions that apply only to the field of geometry. Axioms are assumptions that apply to quantities in general.

Note: Since one of the major objectives of this course is an elementary understanding and appreciation of mathematical rigor, the authors have developed a sequence of basic concepts of (a) terms that are accepted without definition, (b) definitions of terms, and (c) postulates. These fundamental ideas form the foundation of the logical structure of some of the more interesting and exciting aspects of geometry such as the constructions of figures and the proofs of theorems. For example, we cannot construct an angle equal to a given angle or prove that two angles are equal until we know the meaning of such terms as intersect, point, line, line segment, angle, circle, radius, center, and arc. We must also have a background of postulates relating these terms.

Implicative statements

We reason when we use certain facts, assumptions, and definitions, in order to get the conclusion *implied* by them. For example, if we know that $2x - 3 = 11$, then we should conclude that $x = 7$. This conclusion is the *implication* of the fact that $2x - 3 = 11$ and certain assumptions of algebra. Hence the statement, "If $2x - 3 = 11$, then $x = 7$," is an *implicative* statement.

If we assert that we have the right of free speech because we are Americans, our reasoning is based on the assumption that all Americans have the right of free speech; on the fact that we are Americans; on the definition of the word, American; and on the commonly accepted meanings of the defined and undefined words in the phrase, "have the right of free speech." Hence, the statement, "Since we are Americans, we have the right of free speech," is an implicative statement.

An implicative statement is not necessarily true. For example, the assertion, "If $x + 2 = 7$, then $x = 4$," is false. There is no necessary connection between the condition $x + 2 = 7$, and the conclusion, $x = 4$.

Assumptions and definitions are accepted without proof. Implicative statements require proof. An assumption states one or more properties of a thing, or of a class of things. A definition identifies what a thing is in a way that distinguishes it from other things. An implicative statement is an assertion that a certain conclusion is implied by a given set of conditions.

In geometry we shall learn how to prove implicative statements by using undefined terms, definitions, assumptions, and implicative statements which have been previously proved.

In everyday reasoning, we must be certain that the bases of our conclusions are true and acceptable. Consider the following examples:

1. Do you agree with this statement, "Since Mr. Rich is earning a good salary, he is able to give generously to charity"? The conclusion is based on the assumption that all men who earn good salaries are able to give generously to charities. Do you believe the assumption is true? Whether you do or not might depend upon your experience with people who have various financial obligations due to the size of the family, illness, social responsibilities, and the like. Moreover, your interpretation of "good salary," "able to give," and "generously" might influence your opinion.

2. Many people refuse to walk under a ladder. These people probably accept the false assumption that walking under a ladder is certain to bring bad luck.

3. Are you willing to accept the assumption that all electrical engineers are expert in the repair of radios? Suppose a friend said, "My brother, William, can fix your radio because he is an electrical engineer." Would you be likely to employ William without knowing more about his qualifications as a radio repairman?

Exercises

*Each of the statements in Exercises **1-10** is based on certain assumptions, definitions, and undefined terms. Write the assumption on which each statement is probably based.*

1. A baby shouldn't eat hamburgers.

2. Sam was in an automobile accident, but he will have good care because he has an accident insurance policy.

3. I will not take any more mathematics courses because I have decided not to be an engineer.

4. Sam cannot learn geometry because he had difficulty with algebra.

5. Brand X must be a good product because it is advertised widely.

6. In many schools the student council has delegated a group of

students to act as judge and jury in a student court.

7. Many people are worried when they break a mirror.

8. After a heavy rain, some people do not go fishing.

9. Study halls are provided for students in high schools.

10. The United States Senate approved the country's membership in the United Nations.

In Exercises **11-15,** *for the purpose of argument, accept the given statements and write the conclusions which must follow from them.*

11. All bears are animals. Buddy is a bear.

12. It never rains but it pours. It is raining.

13. It is bad luck to walk under ladders. Bob is walking under a ladder.

14. The bigger they are, the harder they fall. Boxer A is bigger than Boxer B.

15. Every cloud has a silver lining. This is a tornado cloud.

Assumptions concerning lines and points

In Figure 1, lines m and n intersect at the point P. Draw two intersecting lines on your paper. Can you make these lines intersect in a second point?

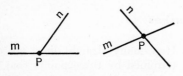

Fig. 1

POSTULATE 1.   If two straight lines intersect, (then) they have only one point in common.

Notice that the *if-clause* of Postulate 1 specifies the condition of two intersecting lines, and the *then-clause* specifies the consequence of the condition. The postulate may also be stated in this form: Two intersecting straight lines have only one common point.

On your paper, locate a point P. Draw three lines through P as shown in Figure 2. If possible, draw more such lines. How many can you draw?

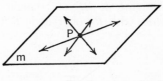

Fig. 2

POSTULATE 2.   An unlimited number of straight lines can pass through a point.

Locate two points P and Q on your paper. With a straightedge, draw a line connecting, or through, P and Q. Now try to draw a *different* straight line through P and Q. Can you do it? Remember that an extension of segment PQ is not considered a different line.

POSTULATE 3.   One, and only one, straight line can be drawn through two points.

Postulate 3 is sometimes stated as follows: Two points determine one straight line.

In Figure 3, the two points P and Q *determine* the line m.

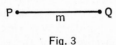

Fig. 3

The meaning of "coincide"

Two points *coincide* if one falls on the other. From Postulate 3 it is obvious that if the end points of two straight line segments *coincide*, the line segments *coincide* and are equal.

In Figure 4, RS of triangle RES coincides with RS of triangle RSC.

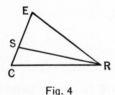

Fig. 4

Two straight line segments of the same length can be made to coincide if we agree that a line segment can be moved to a new position without changing its size and shape. Likewise, other geometric figures such as broken lines or curves can be made to coincide.

POSTULATE 4. The position of a geometric figure can be changed without changing its size and shape.

DEFINITION *Equal line segments* **are segments that have the same length.**

The distance between two points

DEFINITION **The *distance between two points* is the shortest path between them.**

Do you think the shortest path between the two points A and B in Figure 5 is the curved line segment ADB, the broken line segment ACB, or the straight line segment AB? Do you think the shortest path between two points on a sphere is a straight line segment?

Fig. 5

POSTULATE 5. In a plane, the distance (shortest path) between two points is the length of the straight line segment joining them.

In the definition above we *call* the shortest path between two points the distance between them. In Postulate 5 we *assume* that in a plane the distance between two points is the length of the straight line segment joining them.

Exercises

1. How many straight lines are determined by three points that do not lie in the same straight line?

2. How many straight lines are determined by four points, no three of which lie in the same straight line?

3. If a straight line intersects each of two intersecting lines, how many points of intersection can there be? Would a different arrangement give more points? fewer?

4. Can a segment 2 inches long be made to coincide with a segment 3 inches long?

Exercises—Space Geometry (*Optional*)

5. Two planes can intersect as shown in this figure. Complete this assumption: If two planes intersect, their intersection is . . . .

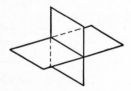

Ex. 5

6. Think of your pencil as being a segment of a straight line. Write an assumption that states how many planes can be passed through the line represented by the pencil.

7. Write an assumption about the number of straight lines that can pass through a point in space.

8. Hold your pencil so that it intersects or meets the top of your desk. How many points are common to the pencil and the desk? Complete: If a straight line intersects a plane . . . .

9. Explain why cameras, picture screens, surveyor's instruments, and other objects are often supported by tripods.

10. How many positions may a book take when placed on one point? on two points? on three points not in the same straight line? Write an assumption concerning the number of points required to determine a plane.

Ex. 10

11. Can you find three planes in your classroom that have a common point of intersection?

12. Fold a sheet of heavy paper to form two intersecting planes. Let *WK* be their line of intersection. Near the bottom of one plane place the point *A*, and near the top of the other plane place the point *B*. What is the shortest path that can be drawn on the paper between *A* and *B*, Sketch (a)?

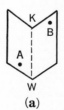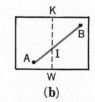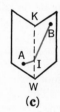

(**a**)   (**b**)   (**c**)

Ex. 12

Flatten out the paper and draw a straight line segment between *A* and *B*, Sketch (b). It will intersect *WK* in some point *I*. Refold the paper. The sum of the segments *AI* and *IB* is the shortest path on the planes from *A* to *B*, Sketch (c).

The circle

How advanced would our civilization be without the circle? It has been the greatest factor in the development of modern transportation. Primitive man moved things by the strength of his own body. It must have been a momentous day for the man who first experimented with a wheel. Legend tells us that the first wheel was not perfectly round. It took man some time to change the wheel to the more efficient circle. Yet the first wheel allowed man to cart his goods, rather than carry them on his back; and it allowed one man to pull the load of many.

DEFINITION A *circle* is a closed plane curve, all points of which are the same distance from a fixed point in that plane.

This is the symbol for a circle: ⊙. The plural symbol for circles uses an *s* instead of a dot: ⑤.

In the definition of a circle, the fixed point is called the *center* of the circle.

The length of a circle is its *circumference*. The unit of measurement of the circumference of a circle is some convenient linear unit such as the inch, foot, or centimeter.

The portion of the plane within a circle (measured in some convenient area unit such as the square inch, square foot, or square centimeter) is the *area* of the circle.

The name of a circle is the name of its center. The name of the circle in Figure 6 is ⊙O. Sometimes it is convenient to use the names of two or more points on a circle to name the circle. Thus ⊙O may be named ⊙ACM.

Fig. 6

DEFINITIONS A *radius* is a straight line segment that joins the center of a circle to any point on the circle.

A *diameter* is a straight line segment through the center of a circle having its end points on the circle.

The plural of radius is *radii*. In Figure 6, *OA*, *OM*, and *OC* are radii; *AC* is a diameter.

DEFINITION *Equal circles* are circles whose circumferences are equal.

POSTULATES 6. If circles have equal radii, they are equal.

7. Radii of the same circle or of equal circles are equal.

Exercises

1. Refer to the definition of a circle.
   a. How is a circle classified?
   b. Name the undefined and the defined words used in the definition.
   c. What are the characteristics that distinguish a circle from other closed curves?

d. The definition of a circle in the if-then form is: If a plane curve is a circle, all points of the curve are the same distance from a fixed point in the plane of the curve. Write the reverse form of this statement.

e. In **d**, what part of speech is the first word, "plane"? What does it tell you?

2. a. Locate a point on your paper and call it O. Now locate several points each 2 inches from O. On a circle whose center is O and whose radius is 2 inches, is every point 2 inches from O?

b. Locate a point on your paper and call it P. Now draw a circle whose center is P and whose radius is 2 inches. Is every point on the circle 2 inches from P?

3. If the radius of a circle is 3 inches long, how long is the diameter?

4. If the diameter of a circle is d inches long, how long is a radius?

5. What is the distinction between a circle, its circumference, and its area?

Static and dynamic figures

We learn in science that a static object is one that is at rest. It is fixed in size, shape, and position. An object is dynamic if there is some form of motion involved. You recall that we sometimes think of a line as being formed by a moving point, and a surface as being formed by a moving line. From a static viewpoint, a circle is a group of points in a given plane each of which is at a given distance from a given fixed point. From a dynamic viewpoint, a circle is the path of a moving point that is always a given distance from a given point in a

given plane. Sometimes we study geometric figures as though they were fixed in position, shape, and size. At other times it is advantageous to study figures as they are being formed or as one figure is changing its position with reference to another. Describe the figure formed by a dynamic circle rotating about one of its diameters as an axis.

Circles having common points

In Figure 7, circles O and P have equal radii. As the two circles approach each other, they finally have one point in common; then two points in common. As the motion continues, center O will finally coincide with center P. In this position, how are the circles related?

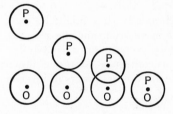

Fig. 7

Is it possible for two circles to have three common points? If two circles have more than two points in common, do the circles coincide?

If two circles have a common center, do the circles necessarily coincide? Draw two circles that have the same center but unequal radii. Do the circles coincide?

POSTULATE 8. **In a given plane with a given point as center and with a given radius, one, and only one, circle can be drawn.**

The intersection of a line and a circle

In Figure 8, line m intersects circle O in the two points C and D. Think of m as a line that can move away from center O in the direction indicated by arrow b. Can a straight line intersect a circle in more than two points? in fewer than two points? In general, m intersects the circle O in two distinct points. As m moves dynamically downward, as shown, there is one position where the two points become one.

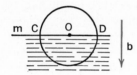

Fig. 8

Algebraically they might be the equal roots of an equation like $x^2 - 6x + 9 = 0$ whose roots are $x = 3$ and $x = 3$. As m continues to move downward there are no real points of intersection.

Exercises

1. Draw a straight line segment AB. Let P be the name of some point on AB. With A as center and with AP as radius, draw circle A. With B as center and BP as radius, draw circle B. How many points do the two circles have in common?

2. Draw a straight line segment MN 2 inches long. With M as center and radius $1\frac{1}{2}$ inches long draw circle M. With N as center and radius 1 inch long, draw circle N. How many points do the two circles have in common?

3. Draw a straight line segment RS $\frac{1}{2}$ inch long. With R as center and a radius 1 inch long, draw circle R. With S as center and a radius $1\frac{1}{2}$ inches long, draw circle S. How many points do the two circles have in common?

4. Draw a straight line segment CD so that it is $\frac{1}{2}$ inch long. With C as center and a radius 1 inch long, draw circle C. With D as center and a radius $\frac{1}{4}$ inch long, draw circle D. How many points do the two circles have in common?

5. Draw a straight line segment MN 2 inches long. If you use M and N as centers of circles that intersect in two points, the sum of their radii must be .... than .... inches.

An arc of a circle

The arch is a useful form found in many types of architecture. Notice that a geometric *arc* is spelled differently from its application in architecture, which is called an *arch*. The arch is used in the design of bridges, doorways, and ornaments not only because of its beauty but also because of its strength.

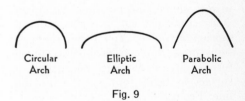

| Circular Arch | Elliptic Arch | Parabolic Arch |

Fig. 9

The circular arch, or arc, is the kind we shall study in plane geometry. The other arches are segments of the ellipse and the parabola.

In Figure 10, points A, J, and B divide circle O into parts called *arcs*. The shorter part of the circle between B and A is *minor arc BA*, and the longer part of the circle between A and B is *major arc AB*, or arc AJB. Observe that an arc is often named by reading the names of its end points. When an arc is read by two end points, the minor arc is indicated unless otherwise specified.

Fig. 10

This is the symbol for an arc: $\frown$. See $\overset{\frown}{BA}$ and $\overset{\frown}{AJB}$ in Figure 10.

DEFINITION An *arc of a circle* is a curve that is part of the circle.

A circle may be divided into any desired number of *equal* arcs. Each arc would then be a unit of the circle. The conventional unit of arc is $\frac{1}{360}$ of a circle. This unit of arc is called an *arc degree*. Hence, the measure of any circle, regardless of its circumference (or radius), is 360 arc degrees.

For greater accuracy in the measurement of an arc, an arc degree is divided into 60 equal parts, each of which is called a *minute of arc*. Each minute is divided into 60 equal parts each of which is called a *second of arc*.

An arc of 20 degrees 19 minutes and 16 seconds is written: 20° 19′ 16″.

Concentric circles

DEFINITION *Concentric circles* **are circles in the same plane that have the same center and different radii.**

The three circles in Figure 11 are concentric circles having the common center O. Lines OE and OF intersect each circle so that arcs AB, CD, and EF are each one-fourth of their respective circles. Hence, $\overset{\frown}{AB} = \overset{\frown}{CD} = \overset{\frown}{EF} = 90°$. An arc equal to one-fourth of a circle is sometimes called a *quadrant*.

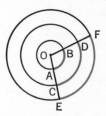

Fig. 11

The length of the radius of a circle does not affect the number of arc degrees in an arc, but it does affect the length of the arc. Although the three arcs AB, CD, and EF in Figure 11 have the same number of arc degrees, which of the three is the longest?

Exercises

1. How many arc seconds are there in one arc degree?
2. Find the number of arc degrees in:
   a. One-half of a circle.
   b. One-sixth of a circle.
   c. One-third of a circle.
   d. One-eighth of a circle.
3. What fraction of a circle is each of the following arcs: 45° ? 315° ? 180° ? 270° ? 90° ? 60° ?

4. How many degrees are there in each of the two arcs into which a circle is divided by a diameter?

The two circles in the figure for Exercises **5-9** *are concentric. Straight lines m and f pass through the common center O, and* $\overset{\frown}{AB} = 38°$. *Using this information, answer the questions in Exercises* **5-9.**

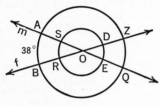

Ex. 5–9

5. How many degrees are there in $\overset{\frown}{SR}$?

6. How many degrees do you believe there are in $\overset{\frown}{ZA}$?

7. How are $\overset{\frown}{ZA}$ and $\overset{\frown}{DS}$ related in degrees? in length?

8. What is the linear relationship of $\overset{\frown}{AB}$ to $\overset{\frown}{SR}$?

9. How many degrees do you believe are in $\overset{\frown}{ED}$?

10. Explain how to produce concentric circles on the surface of a quiet lake.

11. Name a sport that involves the use of concentric circles.

12. Name some applications of concentric circles in industrial design, or bring to class some pictures showing such applications.

13. Make an original design using circles.

14. If one circle has a radius which is twice as long as another, how do you think their circumferences are related? their areas?

Angles

DEFINITIONS An *angle* is a figure formed by two rays from a common point.

The *size of an angle* is the amount of opening between the rays.

The *sides of an angle* are the rays which form the angle.

The *vertex of an angle* is the point of intersection of its sides. (The plural of vertex is vertices.)

This is the symbol for an angle: $\angle$.

In Figure 12, M is the vertex of $\angle CMD$, and CM and MD are its sides. The sides of an angle are not line segments; hence the size of an angle is not determined by the lengths of the designated sides.

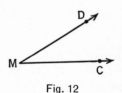

Fig. 12

How to name an angle

The common ways to name an angle are:
1. Place a number between the sides.
2. Place a lower-case letter between the sides.
3. Use the name of the vertex if only one angle has that vertex.
4. Use three capital letters. Be sure to put the vertex letter in the middle.

Since Z in Figure 13 is the vertex of more than one angle, we cannot name any one of the angles $\angle Z$.

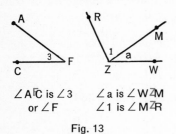

$\angle AFC$ is $\angle 3$ $\angle a$ is $\angle WZM$
    or $\angle F$ $\angle 1$ is $\angle MZR$

Fig. 13

Exercises

In Exercises **1-6,** *use this figure:*

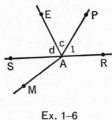

Ex. 1–6

1. Explain why none of the angles in the figure can be named $\angle A$.
2. Name $\angle c$ with three capital letters.
3. Name $(\angle 1 + \angle c)$ with three capital letters.
4. Name the angle whose sum is $\angle c + \angle d$ with three capital letters.
5. What is the name of the angle whose difference is $\angle EAM - \angle EAS$?
6. Name the angle whose sum is $\angle 1 + \angle c + \angle d$.
7. Draw an angle and place the letters K, L, and Z on the sides so that the name of the angle is ZKL.

Measure of an angle

If the vertex of an angle is the center of a circle and its sides are radii, the angle is called a *central* angle. The arc of the circle between the sides of a central angle is its *intercepted* arc.

If a circle is divided into 360 equal parts and radii are drawn to the points of division, there are 360 equal central angles. The size of each of these angles is one angle degree. An *angle degree* is a unit of angle. It is equal to a central angle that intercepts one arc degree on a circle. Thus the number of angle degrees in a central angle is the same as the number of arc degrees in its intercepted arc. In Figure 14 we can measure the number of angle degrees in $\angle EOC$ by measuring the number of arc degrees in $\widehat{EC}$. That is, $\angle EOC$ is *measured* by $\widehat{EC}$.

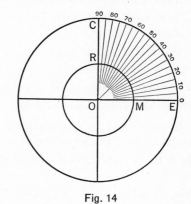

Fig. 14

The symbol for "is measured by" is $\stackrel{\circ}{=}$. In Figure 14, $\angle EOC \stackrel{\circ}{=} \widehat{EC}$.

DEFINITION   A *central angle* is an angle whose vertex is the center of a circle and whose sides are radii of the circle.

POSTULATE 9. A central angle is measured by its intercepted arc.

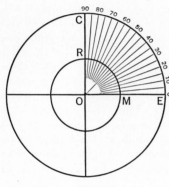

Fig. 14

In Figure 14 above notice that:

1. $\angle EOC$ is a central angle, and $\widehat{EC}$ is its intercepted arc.

2. $\angle MOR$ is a central angle, and $\widehat{MR}$ is its intercepted arc.

3. The linear measure of $\widehat{EC}$ is greater than the linear measure of $\widehat{MR}$.

4. The number of arc degrees in $\widehat{EC}$ is equal to the number of arc degrees in $\widehat{MR}$, for each is one-fourth of the circle.

5. The number of angle degrees in $\angle MOR$ is equal to the number of angle degrees in $\angle EOC$.

6. $\angle EOC$ is one-fourth of a complete angle about a point.

7. In a plane, the sum of the angles about a point is 360°.

8. An angle degree is constant in size; an arc degree is constant in relation to its circle, but is variable *in length* in circles with different radii.

Exercises

1. How many angle degrees are there in the central angles that intercept the following arcs?

   a. $\widehat{AB} = 70°$
   b. $\widehat{AC} = 180°$
   c. $\widehat{ABD} = 270°$
   d. $\widehat{DA} = 90°$
   e. $\widehat{ABCDA} = 360°$

Ex. 1–2

2. Using the figure above, answer the following questions:

   a. If $\angle AOB = 65°$, $\widehat{AB} = ?$
   b. If $\angle AOC = 180°$, $\widehat{AC} = ?$
   c. If $\angle DOA = 90°$, $\widehat{DA} = ?$
   d. If $\angle DOB = 155°$, $\widehat{DB} = ?$

3. Given: Two concentric circles have the common center O; $\angle AOB$ is a central angle of both circles; $\widehat{AB} = 76°\ 16'$. Find the angle degrees in:

   a. $\widehat{CD}$
   b. $\angle AOB$
   c. $\widehat{BXA}$
   d. $\angle COD$
   e. $\widehat{DYC}$

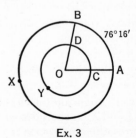

Ex. 3

4. If AOB is a straight line, estimate the sum of the angles e, f, and g.

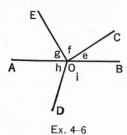

Ex. 4-6

5. If AOB is a straight line, estimate the sum of angles h and i.

6. What is the sum of the angles e, f, g, h, and i? Why?

7. Straight line KM intersects straight line RS at R. The number of degrees in $\angle SRK$ is x and the number of degrees in $\angle MRS$ is $x + 9°$. Find the number of degrees in each angle.

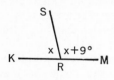

Ex. 7

8. Four straight lines OR, OE, OG, and OF intersect at O forming the angles indicated. Find the number of degrees in each angle.

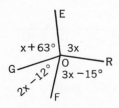

Ex. 8

9. If $\angle x + \angle y = 90°$, and if $\angle x - \angle y = 38°$, find the number of degrees in each angle.

Measuring and drawing angles with a protractor

A protractor is an instrument used to measure the number of degrees in an angle. Its semicircular scale is usually divided into 180 equal units, each an arc degree. Its use in measuring an angle is based on the principle that a central angle is measured by its intercepted arc.

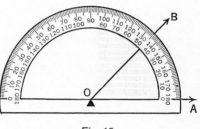

Fig. 15

Fig. 15 above shows the position of a protractor while measuring the size of $\angle AOB$. The arrowhead at the center of the diameter of the circular scale is placed at the vertex O of the angle, and the zero mark of the scale is on the side OA of the angle. The point of intersection of OB with the inner scale indicates that $\angle AOB = 45°$.

Suppose that we wish to draw a 32° angle. First draw a working line of a convenient length. Next, place the protractor so that the diameter of its circular scale coincides with the working line. Locate the vertex O of the angle at the center of the diameter of the circular scale. Using the inner scale, put a point at the 32° mark. Call this point B. Remove the protractor and draw a line through O and B.

Exercises

1. Draw several angles on a piece of paper. Estimate the size of each angle, and then check your estimates by measuring the angles with a protractor.

2. With a protractor draw angles of the following sizes: (**a**) 30° (**b**) 63° (**c**) 90° (**d**) 180° (**e**) 120° (**f**) 270° (**g**) 315°.

3. Use your protractor to draw arcs of the following sizes on a circle whose radius is 2 inches: (**a**) 30° (**b**) 45° (**c**) 75° (**d**) 210°.

4. With your straightedge draw angles that you estimate to be 45°, 90°, 135°, and 225°. Now measure the angles with your protractor to check your estimates.

5. How many degrees are there between the hour marks on the face of a clock?

6. How many degrees are there between the minute marks on the face of a clock? Is a time minute the same as an angular minute?

7. Is the angle between the hands of a clock when one is on top of the other 0°? 360°? or both?

8. Find the number of degrees between the hands of a clock when the time is:
   a. 3:00 A.M.
   b. 5:00 P.M.
   c. 6:00 P.M.
   d. 1:20 P.M.

9. If a fan turns at the rate of 1500 revolutions per minute, through how many degrees does a blade turn in one minute?

10. Find the number of degrees in the angle between these compass directions: (**a**) North and West (**b**) South and Northeast (**c**) Northwest and Northeast.

Angles of rotation   (*Optional*)

A *static* angle is an angle formed by two static rays that meet at a point. If a ray rotates about a point, a *dynamic* angle, called an angle of rotation, is formed.

In Figure 16, OB has rotated in a counter-clockwise direction about the point O forming $\angle AOB$. The arc with the arrowhead is used to indicate the amount and direction of rotation. The vertex O is the point of rotation, OA is the initial side, and OB is the terminal side of the angle.

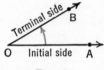

Fig. 16

If one is naming an angle of rotation with three capital letters, the initial side is named first, and the terminal side is named last. Of course, the name of the vertex is the middle letter. The name of the angle in Figure 16 is $\angle AOB$.

If the initial side and the terminal side of an angle lie along the same straight line in the same direction from the vertex, and if there hasn't been any rotation, the number of degrees in the angle is zero. In Figure 17, $\angle AOB = 0°$.

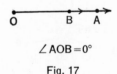

$\angle AOB = 0°$

Fig. 17

If the initial side and the terminal side of an angle lie along the same straight line in opposite directions from the vertex, and if there has been one-half of a complete rotation of the terminal side about the vertex, the number of degrees in the angle is 180. In Figure 18, $\angle DCN = 180°$.

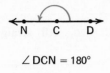

$\angle DCN = 180°$

Fig. 18

If the initial side and the terminal side of an angle lie along the same straight line in the same direction from the vertex, and if there has been one complete rotation of the terminal side, the number of degrees in the angle is 360. In Figure 19, $\angle TMR = 360°$.

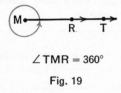

$\angle TMR = 360°$

Fig. 19

Positive and negative angles
(*Optional*)

In Figure 20, $\angle DCA$ has been formed by the rotation of a line in a clockwise direction. Angles formed in this manner are *negative* angles.

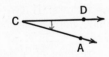

$\angle DCA$ is a negative angle

Fig. 20

Angle XBY in Figure 21 is a *positive* angle because it has been formed by

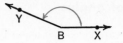

$\angle XBY$ is a positive angle

Fig. 21

the rotation of BY in a counter-clockwise direction.

Although the distinction between positive and negative angles is not an important one in plane geometry, it is a very significant one in trigonometry.

In this course we shall assume that all angles are positive unless otherwise designated.

Exercises (*Optional*)

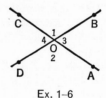

Ex. 1–6

1. Write the name of $\angle 2$ with three capital letters.
2. Is $\angle BOA$ a positive or a negative angle?
3. Which is larger, positive $\angle BOC$ or positive $\angle COB$?
4. Is the number of degrees in the positive $\angle COD$ numerically equal to the number of degrees in the negative $\angle DOC$?
5. If DOB is a straight line, what is the sum of the angles BOC and COD?
6. If DOB and COA are straight lines and if $\angle 1 = 120°$, how many degrees are there in $\angle 4$? in $\angle 3$?

Kinds of angles

Angles are classified according to the number of units, such as angle degrees, in them.

In Figure 22, $\widehat{AC}$ is ¼ of circle O. Hence $\angle AOC = 90°$. An angle of 90° is a *right* angle.

The symbol for right angle is ⌐ .

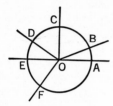

Fig. 22

An angle such as $\angle AOB$, which is greater than 0° but less than 90°, is an *acute* angle.

$\widehat{AE}$ is one-half of circle O. Hence $\angle AOE = 180°$ or a *straight angle*.

An angle such as $\angle AOD$, which is greater than 90° but less than 180°, is an *obtuse* angle.

An angle such as $\angle AOF$, which is greater than 180° but less than 360°, is a *reflex* angle.

DEFINITIONS   A *straight angle* is an angle whose sides extend in opposite directions from the vertex in a straight line.

A *right angle* is an angle that is one-half of a straight angle.

An *acute angle* is an angle that is less than a right angle.

An *obtuse angle* is an angle that is greater than a right angle, but less than a straight angle.

A *reflex angle* is an angle that is greater than a straight angle, but less than two straight angles.

Equal angles are angles which contain the same number of units of angle measure.

POSTULATE 10.   All straight angles are equal.

Since a right angle is one-half of a straight angle, all right angles are equal.

Perpendicular lines

DEFINITION   *Perpendicular lines* are two straight lines that intersect to form right angles.

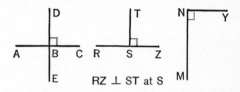

RZ ⊥ ST at S

AC ⊥ ED at B   MN ⊥ NY

Fig. 23

This is the symbol for "is perpendicular to": ⊥.

The definition of perpendicular lines can be stated in the *if-then* form of a sentence as follows: If two lines are perpendicular, they intersect to form right angles.

Since the reverse of a definition is true, then the statement, "If two lines intersect to form right angles, the lines are perpendicular," is a true statement.

In Figure 24, how many separate and distinct lines can be drawn perpendicular to AB from the external point P? at point P on the line?

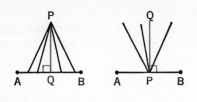

Fig. 24

POSTULATE 11. In a plane, through a given point there is one, and only one, perpendicular to a given line.

In each of the three sketches of Figure 25, the segment PA is perpendicular to the line through B and C. In each figure, which segment do you think represents the *distance* from P to BC?

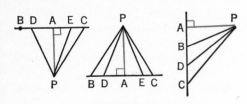

Fig. 25

DEFINITION *The distance from a point to a line* **is the shortest path from the point to the line.**

POSTULATES 12. The distance from a point to a line is the length of the perpendicular from the point to the line.

13. The length of the perpendicular from a point to a line is the distance from the point to the line.

Exercises

1. Is it possible for two perpendicular lines to form three right angles? Explain.

2. State the reverse of this definition: If the sides of an angle extend in opposite directions in a straight line, the angle is a straight angle.

3. Draw examples of the following angles with your protractor: (**a**) an acute angle; (**b**) a right angle; (**c**) an obtuse angle; (**d**) a straight angle. Could you have drawn any of these accurately with only a straightedge? If so, which ones?

In the figure for Exercises **4-7,** *EBG* $\perp$ *ABC, and BF, BD, and BH are straight lines.*

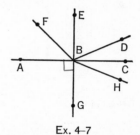

Ex. 4–7

4. Identify the following angles as acute, obtuse, etc.: (**a**) $\angle DBA$ (**b**) $\angle DBE$ (**c**) $\angle FBG$ (**d**) $\angle GBC$.

5. What is the sum of angles CBD and DBE?

6. What is the sum of angles CBF and FBA?

7. What is the sum of $\angle CBA$ and $\angle ABG$?

8. If a straight line is drawn through the point N perpendicular to OM, does it necessarily pass through the point P? Explain.

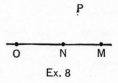

Ex. 8

9. It is a principle of physics that when a ray of light strikes a reflecting surface such as a mirror represented by AB, $\angle i = \angle r$. With your protractor draw the path of a ray if $\angle i$ is: **(a)** 45° **(b)** 60° **(c)** 90°.

Ex. 9

10. Explain the principle of a plumb bob and how it can be used to straighten a picture that is hanging askew on a wall.

Ex. 10

Angle bisector

Draw an angle on your paper and name it $\angle RMC$. Using a protractor, draw MD so that it divides $\angle RMC$ into two equal angles. The line MD is the *bisector* of $\angle RMC$.

In Figure 26, BE is the bisector of each of the angles. How many bisectors do you believe an angle can have?

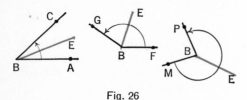

Fig. 26

DEFINITION An *angle bisector* is a line that divides an angle into two equal angles.

POSTULATE 14. **An angle has one, and only one, bisector.**

Exercises

1. Draw an angle on a piece of semi-transparent paper. Fold the paper through the vertex of the angle so that one side of the angle falls upon the other side. Does the crease bisect the angle?

2. What kind of angle do you get if you subtract an obtuse angle from a straight angle?

3. What kinds of angles can you get if you subtract an acute angle from an obtuse angle? Explain your answers.

4. Is the sum of two acute angles necessarily an obtuse angle? Explain.

5. Is the sum of an acute and an obtuse angle necessarily an obtuse angle? Explain.

6. Give an example in which the sum of an acute angle and an obtuse angle is a straight angle.

7. State in the if-then form: **(a)** the definition of an angle bisector **(b)** the reverse of the definition.

Midpoint and line bisector

In Figure 27, the point P is the *midpoint* of AB, and the line m is the *bisector* of AB. Hence, $AP = PB$, $AP = \frac{1}{2}AB$, $AB = 2AP$, etc. (The short marks crossing AP and PB are used as visual reminders that $AP = PB$.)

Fig. 27

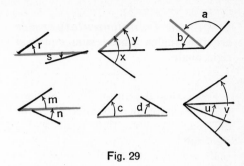

DEFINITIONS A *midpoint* is a point that divides a line segment into two equal segments.

A *line bisector* is a line that divides a line segment into two equal segments.

POSTULATE 15. A line segment has one, and only one, midpoint.

DEFINITION The *perpendicular bisector of a straight line segment* is the line that is perpendicular to the segment at its midpoint.

In Figure 28, the line CD bisects AB, and $CD \perp AB$. Hence CD is the perpendicular bisector of AB.

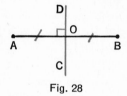

Fig. 28

How many perpendicular bisectors does a line segment have? Why?

Adjacent angles

There are six pairs of angles in Figure 29. The angles of certain pairs have a common side, a common vertex, or both. The angles of just one pair have a *common side* and a *common vertex*, and *do not overlap*. Such angles are called *adjacent* angles. Which angles of the six pairs are adjacent angles?

DEFINITION *Adjacent angles* are two angles that have the same vertex and a common side between them.

Fig. 29

The side that is common to two adjacent angles is called the *interior* side; the remaining two sides are called the *exterior* sides.

The definition of adjacent angles can be stated in the if-then form as follows: If two angles have the same vertex and a common side between them, they are adjacent angles. What is the reverse form of this definition?

Complementary angles

In Figure 30, $AO \perp OB$. Hence the sum of $\angle BOC$ and $\angle COA$ is a right angle. Angles BOC and COA are called complementary angles.

Fig. 30

In Figure 31, $\angle 3 + \angle 4 = 90°$. Angles 3 and 4 are complementary angles. Complementary angles are not necessarily adjacent.

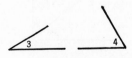

Fig. 31

DEFINITION *Complementary angles* are two angles whose sum equals a right angle.

From this definition it is obvious that the complement of an angle is the difference between that angle and a right angle.

If you are given the number of degrees in an angle, you find its complement by subtracting the number of degrees in the angle from 90°.

Example: Find the complement of 15° 20′ 13″.
Solution: Change 90° to 89° 59′ 60″.
Subtract: 89° 59′ 60″
            15° 20′ 13″
            ‾‾‾‾‾‾‾‾‾‾‾
            74° 39′ 47″ *Answer*

In Figure 32, ∠r is adjacent to ∠s, and ∠r + ∠s = 90°. How is OA related to OB?

Fig. 32

POSTULATE 16. **If two angles are complementary and adjacent, their exterior sides are perpendicular.**

In Figure 33, AO ⊥ OB, and ∠x is adjacent to ∠y. Are angles x and y complementary?

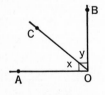

Fig. 33

POSTULATE 17. **If the exterior sides of two adjacent angles are perpendicular, the angles are complementary.**

Exercises

1. Draw a line segment AG on a piece of semi-transparent paper. Fold the paper so that point A coincides with point G. When the paper is unfolded, how do you think the crease is related to AG?

2. Find the complement of each of these angles: (**a**) 37° (**b**) 45° (**c**) 19° 26′ (**d**) 29° 59′ 43″ (**e**) 0° (**f**) 90°.

3. If two angles are equal and complementary, how many degrees are there in each angle?

*In the figure for Exercises **4** and **5**, lines RS, TS, and MS intersect at S, forming the adjacent angles m and n.*

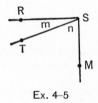

Ex. 4–5

4. If ∠m is the complement of ∠n, what is the relation of RS to MS? Does your answer necessarily follow from a postulate? If so, state the postulate.

5. If RS ⊥ MS, what is the relation of ∠m to ∠n? State the postulate from which your answer necessarily follows.

*In the figure for Exercises **6-12**, CBA is a straight line, and ∠NBA + ∠CBM = 90°.*

6. How many degrees are there in ∠CBA?

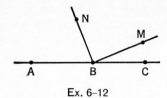

Ex. 6–12

7. How many degrees are there in ∠*MBN*?

8. How is *BM* related to *BN*?

9. What angle is adjacent to ∠*MBA*?

10. Are angles *CBM* and *NBA* adjacent? Explain.

11. Are angles *CBM* and *CBN* adjacent? Explain.

12. Which angle is the complement of ∠*CBM*?

13. Add:
   a. 4 ft. 7 in.   **b.** 38° 46′
      6 ft. 9 in.   49° 37′

14. Subtract:
   a. 8 ft. 3 in.   **b.** 124° 23′
      2 ft. 8 in.   49° 37′

15. a. Find one-half of 7 ft. 4 in.
    b. Find one-half of 35° 26′.

16. Find the average of 30° 21′ 4″ and 29° 56′ 44″.

Supplementary angles

In Figure 34, ∠*BOA* is a straight angle. ∠*BOC* is the *supplement* of ∠*COA*. In fact, angles *BOC* and *COA* are adjacent and supplementary.

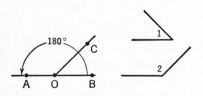

Fig. 34

The sum of angles 1 and 2 is 180°. Each angle is the supplement of the other.

DEFINITION *Supplementary angles* **are two angles whose sum equals a straight angle.**

Supplementary angles are not necessarily adjacent.

The supplement of an angle is the difference between that angle and a straight angle.

If you know the number of degrees in an angle, you find its supplement by subtracting the number of degrees in the angle from 180°.

Example: Find the supplement of 20° 18′ 53″.

Solution: 179° 59′ 60″
           20° 18′ 53″
          ———————
          159° 41′ 7″   *Answer*

Adjacent supplementary angles

In Figure 35, if ∠1 is adjacent to ∠2 and ∠1 is the supplement of ∠2, then ∠*ABC* is a straight angle, and *CBA* is a straight line. Why?

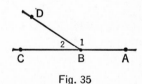

Fig. 35

In Figure 35, if *CBA* and *BD* are straight lines, how is ∠1 related to ∠2? Why?

POSTULATES 18. **If two angles are adjacent and supplementary, their exterior sides lie in a straight line.**

19. **If two angles are adjacent and their exterior sides lie in a straight line, the angles are supplementary.**

36 CHAPTER 2

Equal adjacent supplementary angles

In Figure 36, angles AOB and BOC are supplementary, adjacent, and equal. How many degrees are there in $\angle AOB$? How is CA related to OB?

Fig. 36

POSTULATES 20. If two straight lines intersect to form equal adjacent angles, the lines are perpendicular.

21. If two lines are perpendicular, they form equal adjacent angles.

Exercises

1. Find the supplement of each of these angles: (**a**) 30° (**b**) 135° (**c**) 90° (**d**) 123° 15′ (**e**) 145° 15′ 20″ (**f**) 25° 35′ 45″.
2. If two angles are equal and supplementary, how many degrees are there in each angle?
3. What kind of angle is the supplement of an acute angle?
4. What kind of angle is the supplement of an obtuse angle?

In the figure for Exercises 5 and 6, $\angle x$ is adjacent to $\angle y$.

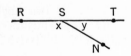

Ex. 5–6

5. If RST is a straight line, how are angles x and y related?

6. If $\angle x + \angle y = 180°$, how are the exterior sides of angles x and y related?

In the figure for Exercises 7 and 8, MO intersects NP at N.

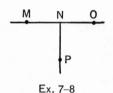

Ex. 7–8

7. If $MO \perp NP$, how is $\angle MNP$ related to $\angle PNO$?
8. If $\angle MNP = \angle PNO$, how is PN related to MO?
9. Write the reverse of the definition of supplementary angles. Explain why it is a true statement.
10. If there are $n°$ in an angle, how many degrees are there in its complement?
11. If there are $n°$ in an angle, how many degrees are there in its supplement?
12. If there are $n°$ in an angle, by how many degrees does its supplement exceed its complement?
13. If the number of degrees in an angle is twice the number of degrees in its complement, how many degrees are there in the angle?
14. If one angle is 20° larger than its complement, how many degrees are there in each angle?
15. If the number of degrees in an angle exceeds the number of degrees in its supplement by 10°, how many degrees are there in the smaller angle?
16. If there are three times as many degrees in the supplement of an angle as there are in its complement, how many degrees are there in the angle?

17. If there are two-fifths as many degrees in the complement of an angle as there are in its supplement, how many degrees are there in the angle?

Vertical angles

In Figure 37, AB and CD intersect at O forming angles 1, 2, 3, and 4 as indicated. Draw a figure such as this and measure each of the four angles. What do your measurements indicate about angles 1 and 3? about angles 2 and 4?

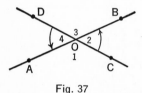

Fig. 37

The pairs of angles, 1 and 3, and 2 and 4, are called *vertical* angles. Do you think that vertical angles are equal?

DEFINITION   *Vertical angles* are two **non-adjacent angles formed by two intersecting straight lines.**

POSTULATE 22.   **Vertical angles are equal.**

Exercises

In the figure for Exercises **1-6,** *lines* AD, BE, *and* FC *intersect at* O.

1. Identify the following pairs of angles:

a. $\angle 1$ and $\angle 2$
b. $\angle 1$ and $\angle EOA$
c. $\angle 1$ and $\angle 4$
d. $\angle FOB$ and $\angle COE$

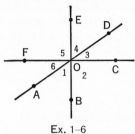

Ex. 1–6

2. Name six pairs of vertical angles.

3. Name six pairs of adjacent angles.

4. Name six pairs of supplementary angles.

5. Name six pairs of equal angles.

6. How is $\angle 1$ related to $\angle BOD$? How is $\angle 4$ related to $\angle BOD$?

7. In the photograph below find and identify at least one example of each of the following types of angles: straight, right, acute, obtuse, reflex. Find and identify each of the following pairs of angles: equal, adjacent, complementary, supplementary, vertical.

Axioms

The axioms which we used in algebra are also used in geometry. We should recall these axioms and learn how to apply them to geometric situations. Axioms are assumptions accepted without proof.

AXIOMS

1. The Substitution Axioms

a. If two quantities are equal, either quantity may be substituted for the other in an equation or other expression.

b. Quantities equal to the same or equal quantities are equal to each other.

2. The Addition Axiom

If equals are added to equals, the sums are equal.

3. The Subtraction Axiom

If equals are subtracted from equals, the differences are equal.

4. The Multiplication Axiom

If equals are multiplied by equals, the products are equal.

5. The Division Axiom

If equals are divided by equals, the quotients are equal. (The divisors must not be zero.)

6. The Whole-Parts Axioms

a. The whole is equal to the sum of its parts.

b. The whole is greater than any of its parts.

Exercises

In the if-clause of each of the statements which follow there is some **given** *information; and in the then-clause, there is*

a **conclusion**. *Write the axiom that is the authority for the conclusion.*

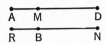

Example 1. If $AM = RB$, and $MD = BN$, then $AM + MD = RB + BN$. Authority: If equals are added to equals, the sums are equal.

Example 2. If $\angle a$, $\angle b$, and $\angle c$ are component parts of $\angle BOA$, then $\angle BOA = \angle a + \angle b + \angle c$.
Authority: The whole is equal to the sum of its parts.

In the figure for Exercises **1-5**, *AB, BC, AC, and DE are straight line segments; D is a point on AC and E is a point on BC.*

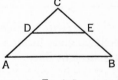

Ex. 1–5

1. If $\angle A = \angle B$, and $\angle A + \angle B = 80°$, then $\angle A + \angle A = 80°$.
2. If $2\angle A = 80°$, then $\angle A = 40°$.
3. If $AD = BE$, and $BE = DC$, then $AD = DC$.
4. If $AD = DC$, $BE = EC$, and $DC = EC$, then $AD = BE$.
5. If $AC = BC$, and $AD = BE$, then $DC = EC$.

In the figure for Exercises **6** *and* **7**, *the points* M *and* N *are on the straight line segment* AR.

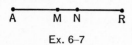

Ex. 6–7

6. If $AM = NR$, then $AN = MR$.

7. If $AN = MR$, then $AM = NR$.

In the figure for Exercises **8-12**, *PH, PF, PC, CF, and HF are straight line segments.*

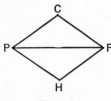

Ex. 8–12

8. If $\angle HPF = \angle PFH$, and $\angle FPC = \angle CFP$, then $\angle HPC = \angle CFH$.

9. If $\angle HPC = \angle CFH$, and $\angle FPC = \angle CFP$, then $\angle HPF = \angle HFP$.

10. If $\angle HPF = \frac{1}{2}\angle HPC$, $\angle HFP = \frac{1}{2}\angle HFC$, and $\angle HPF = \angle HFP$, then $\frac{1}{2}\angle HPC = \frac{1}{2}\angle HFC$.

11. If $\frac{1}{2}\angle HPC = \frac{1}{2}\angle CFH$, then $\angle HPC = \angle CFH$.

12. If $\angle HPC = \angle HFC$, then $\frac{1}{2}\angle HPC = \frac{1}{2}\angle HFC$.

In the following exercises certain information is given. Write the conclusions that are implied by the given information and the authorities for your conclusions.

13. If $x = \frac{1}{2}a$, $x = y$, and $y = \frac{1}{2}b$, then . . . . . Why? There are two conclusions: an immediate conclusion and a final one. Write the authority for each.

14. If $a = 2b$, $x = 2y$, and $a = x$, then . . . . . Why? Write the authorities for the immediate and for the final conclusion.

15. If $x + y = 10$, and $2x - y = 5$, then . . . . . Why?

In the figure for Exercises **16-18**, *AS, SC, AC, AJ, and JC are straight line segments.*

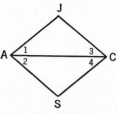

Ex. 16–18

16. If $\angle SAJ = \angle JCS$, and $\angle 1 = \angle 3$, then . . . . . Why?

17. If $\angle SAJ = 2\angle 1$, $\angle JCS = 2\angle 3$, and $\angle SAJ = \angle JCS$, then . . . . . Why? Write the authorities for the immediate and for the final conclusion.

18. If $\angle SAJ = \angle JCS$, AC bisects $\angle SAJ$, and AC bisects $\angle JCS$, then . . . . . Why?

In the figure for Exercises **19-21**, *all lines are straight line segments, P is on RN, and Q is on MN.*

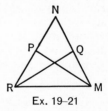

Ex. 19–21

19. If $\angle MRQ = \frac{1}{2}\angle MRP$, $\angle PMR = \frac{1}{2}\angle QMR$, and $\angle MRQ = \angle PMR$, then . . . . . Why? Write the authorities for the immediate and for the final conclusion.

20. If P is the midpoint of RN, Q is the midpoint of MN, and $RP = MQ$, then . . . . . Why?

21. If MP bisects RN, RQ bisects MN, and $RN = MN$, then . . . . . Why?

Polygons

These figures are polygons:

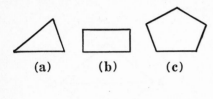

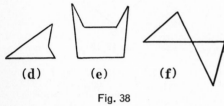

Fig. 38

DEFINITIONS   A *polygon* is a closed broken line in a plane.

A *convex polygon* is a polygon in which each angle is less than 180°.

A *concave polygon* is a polygon in which at least one angle is greater than 180°.

In Figure 38, polygons (a), (b), and (c) are convex polygons; (d) and (e) are concave polygons; (f) is a force-polygon encountered in engineering.

A vertex of one of the angles of a polygon is called a vertex of the polygon.

Unless otherwise specified, when the word "polygon" is used we shall assume that it is a convex plane polygon.

Polygons are classified according to the number of their sides as shown in the table at upper right.

DEFINITION   A *triangle* is a polygon of three sides.

NUMBER OF SIDES	NAME OF POLYGON
3	Triangle
4	Quadrilateral
5	Pentagon
6	Hexagon
7	Heptagon
8	Octagon
9	Nonagon
10	Decagon
12	Dodecagon
n	n-gon

Write a definition of each of the polygons listed above.

The sides of the polygons in Figure 39 are equal. Hence the polygons are *equilateral*.

Fig. 39

The angles of the polygons in Figure 40 are equal. Hence the polygons are *equiangular*.

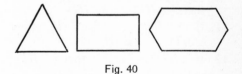

Fig. 40

The polygons in Figure 41 are both equilateral and equiangular.

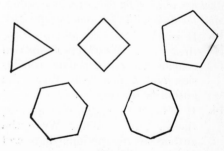

Fig. 41

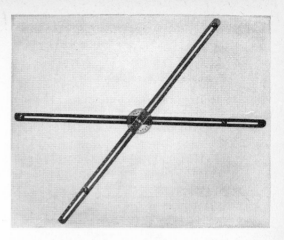

DEFINITIONS An *equilateral polygon* is a polygon whose sides are equal.

An *equiangular polygon* is a polygon whose angles are equal.

A *regular polygon* is a polygon that is both equilateral and equiangular.

Diagonal of a polygon

DEFINITION A *diagonal of a polygon* is a line segment joining any two non-consecutive vertices of the polygon.

Name the diagonals of quadrilateral *ABCD* in Figure 42. Explain why *AE* is not a diagonal.

How many diagonals does polygon *PQRSTU* have? Name them.

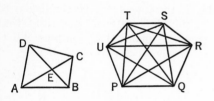

Fig. 42

Dynamic geometry instruments*

A dynamic device that shows the different parts of a figure changing shape, size, and position is a very useful learning aid. It has the same advantages over a static figure that a moving picture has over a slide.

If the device is made so that it is possible to read the measurements of the variables from calibrated scales, it is an instrument for obtaining data quickly and easily. These data can be used to investigate a problem situation inductively.

This picture shows an instrument with which you can investigate the relations of angles and their sides as they are being formed by two intersecting segments. You can make a model of it for yourself from two strips of cardboard, a protractor, and a round-head paper fastener.

Exercises

In Exercises **1-8**, *as you rotate one of the lines of the dynamic device with reference to the other, identify:*

1. The acute angles
2. The obtuse angles
3. The straight angles
4. The adjacent angles
5. The angles that are always supplementary
6. Supplementary adjacent angles
7. Vertical angles
8. The pairs of angles that are always equal
9. What is the situation when all the angles are equal?
10. What is the situation when the lines are perpendicular?

---

* For information concerning the dynamic instrument shown here, and others shown elsewhere in this book, write to W. M. Welch Scientific Company, 1515 Sedgwick Street, Chicago 10, Illinois.

Exercises—Space Geometry (*Optional*)

1. How many planes can pass through a given point in space? Illustrate with the tip of your finger and a book.

2. How many planes can pass through two given points in space? Illustrate.

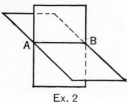
Ex. 2

3. If two points lie on a plane, does every point of the line determined by the two points lie on the plane? How can you test a surface to find out whether it is a plane?

4. If three points in space do not lie on the same straight line, do they determine one, and only one, plane? Illustrate.

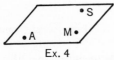
Ex. 4

5. Why are tripods used to support cameras, projection screens, and the like? Name other objects that are supported by three legs.

6. If three points not in the same straight line determine one, and only one, plane, explain why the following also determine a plane:
   a. Two intersecting lines.
   b. A line and a point external to it.

7. In space, how many lines can be perpendicular to a given line at a given point?

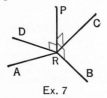
Ex. 7

8. By definition, a line is perpendicular to a plane if it is perpendicular to any line in the plane that passes through its foot. (The foot of a line is the point of intersection of the line and the plane.) However, it can be proved that if a line is perpendicular to each of two intersecting lines at their point of intersection, it is perpendicular to the plane of the lines.

   Explain how to erect a post perpendicular to a floor using a carpenter's square.

9. Write an assumption concerning the number of lines that can be drawn perpendicular to a given plane at a given point on the plane.

10. Write an assumption concerning the number of lines that can be drawn perpendicular to a given plane from a point external to the plane.

11. If the line AB is perpendicular to the plane MN, do you think that every plane that contains AB is perpendicular to plane MN?

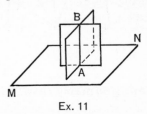
Ex. 11

12. If two planes are perpendicular, do you think that every line in one of them is perpendicular to the other plane?

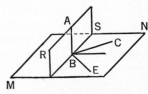
Plane RS ⊥ plane MN

When you open your book you can see two planes intersecting in a line. The angle formed by the two planes is called a *dihedral* angle. The common line of intersection is called the *edge*, and the two planes are called the *faces*.

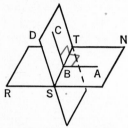

∠ ABC is a plane angle of
the dihedral angle D-ST-N

Dihedral angles are acute, right, and obtuse. There are also adjacent dihedral angles and vertical dihedral angles. Illustrate these angles with pieces of cardboard.

The angle formed by a line in each face perpendicular to the edge of a dihedral angle at the same point is called a plane angle of the dihedral angle.

A plane angle of the dihedral angle *D-ST-N* is ∠*ABC*. Angle *D-ST-N* is measured by ∠*ABC*.

13. Find some dihedral angles in your classroom.

14. How would you define the bisector of a dihedral angle?

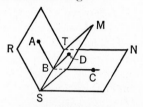

Plane SM bisects the
dihedral angle R-ST-N

Ex. 14

15. Explain why vertical dihedral angles are equal.

Review of Chapter 2

Definitions and Assumptions

QUOTATION FROM
DECLARATION OF INDEPENDENCE

"We hold these truths to be self-evident:—That all men are created equal; that they are endowed by their Creator with certain inalienable rights; that among these are life, liberty, and the pursuit of happiness. That, to secure these rights, governments are instituted among men, deriving their just powers from the consent of the governed; that, whenever any form of government becomes destructive of these ends, it is the right of the people to alter or to abolish it, and to institute a new government, laying its foundation on such principles, and organizing

its powers in such form, as to them shall seem most likely to effect their safety and happiness."

1. State the assumptions that are mentioned in the quotation from the Declaration of Independence.

2. Which words in the quotation from the Declaration of Independence need careful defining?

3. Are the assumptions in the quotation from the Declaration of Independence accepted as facts by the people of the United States?

4. Discuss how prejudice affects the assumptions we accept in life situations such as politics, games, war, and religion.

5. State the assumptions upon which your decision to study geometry is based.

6. State several assumptions that are common to persons of your age. Are they the result of convention, superstition, prejudice, tradition, or training?

7. In what ways are definitions like assumptions? How do they differ?

8. How can one distinguish between a general statement and a specific statement?

9. Give the meaning of each of the following in your own words: (**a**) consecutive; (**b**) bisect; (**c**) intersect; (**d**) intercept; (**e**) coincide; (**f**) concentric.

10. What assumptions are accepted by people whose policy is, "The customer is always right"?

11. What assumptions are in the minds of those who believe that the labor of persons under eighteen years of age should be regulated?

12. What assumptions are in the minds of those who believe that persons over eighteen years of age should be allowed to vote?

13. List the possible assumptions of a person who buys some particular make of automobile.

14. List the assumptions that are accepted by a lawbreaker.

15. What assumptions might be the basis of the decision of a young person to attend a university?

True-False Test

Write the numbers **1-15** *on your paper. After each number write* **True** *if the corresponding statement is always true; write* **False** *if the statement is not necessarily true.*

1. Two points determine one, and only one, straight line.

2. If the end points of a line segment are on a circle, the segment is a diameter.

In the figure for Exercises **3-10**, *the two circles have the same center O; AD is the diameter of the larger circle; AD intersects the smaller circle at B and C; OF is a radius of the larger circle; OF intersects the smaller circle at E.*

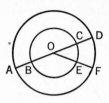

Ex. 3–10

3. $\overset{\frown}{EC}$ and $\overset{\frown}{FD}$ are equal in degrees.

4. If $\overset{\frown}{EC} = 47°$, $\overset{\frown}{AF} = 133°$.

5. The number of angle degrees in $\angle FOD$ is equal to the number of arc degrees in $\overset{\frown}{EC}$.

6. $\angle FOD$ is a central angle.

7. $\angle AOF$ is the complement of $\angle EOC$.

8. If $\overset{\frown}{EC}$ is less than 90°, $\angle AOF$ is obtuse.

9. $\overset{\frown}{AF}$ is the same length as $\overset{\frown}{BE}$.

10. The two circles are concentric.

11. If the number of degrees in an angle is y, its complement is $y - 90°$.

12. A quadrilateral has only one diagonal.

13. If $PQ \perp VT$, then PR is not $\perp$ VT.

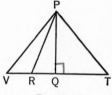

Ex. 13–15

14. If $PQ \perp VT$, the length of PQ is the distance from P to VT.

15. If $PQ \perp VT$, PQ is the only perpendicular from P to VT.

Completion Test

Write the numbers **1-15** *on your paper. After each number write the word or words that correctly complete the corresponding statement. Do not write in this book.*

1. The number of straight lines that can be drawn in one plane through a given point of that plane is . . . . .

2. A ray has one, and only one, ...

3. If two circles are equal, they have equal . . . . .

4. If two circles have the same center and unequal radii, the circles . . . . .

5. In a plane, all the points that are a given distance d from a given point P lie on a . . . . .

6. The number of arc degrees in two-thirds of a circle is . . . . .

7. The acute angle between the hands of a clock at 2:00 A.M. is . . . . .

8. The distance from a point to a line is the length of the . . . . . from the point to the line.

9. If the sides of an angle lie in a straight line in opposite directions from the vertex, the angle is . . . . .

10. If two angles are complementary and adjacent, their exterior sides are . . . . .

11. If two angles are supplementary and adjacent, the exterior sides of the angles . . . . .

12. If the exterior sides of two equal adjacent angles lie in a straight line, the angles . . . . .

13. If the exterior sides of two adjacent acute angles are perpendicular, the angles . . . . .

14. If two straight lines intersect, the . . . . . angles are equal.

15. A quadrilateral has . . . . . diagonals.

Drawing Exercises

In these exercises, you may use a protractor, ruler, straightedge, or a draftsman's right triangle.

1. Draw an obtuse angle on your paper and name it $\angle RET$.
   a. Measure $\angle RET$.
   b. Use your protractor to bisect $\angle RET$.

2. Draw a right angle ABC on your paper.
   a. Draw its supplement adjacent to it.
   b. Name it $\angle 1$.

3. Draw an angle of 35°.
   a. Name it $\angle x$.
   b. Draw $\angle y$ so that angles x and y are adjacent complementary angles.

4. Draw an acute angle on your paper and name it $\angle a$.
   a. Draw $\angle b$ so that it is the complement of $\angle a$ and adjacent to it.
   b. Draw $\angle c$ so that it is the supplement of $\angle a$ and adjacent to it.
   c. How many degrees are there in $\angle c - \angle b$?

5. Draw a line x on your paper.
   a. On it name some point P.
   b. Draw a line perpendicular to x at P.

6. Draw a vertical straight line m on your paper.
   a. Put the point P to one side of it.
   b. Draw the line that represents the distance from P to m.

7. Draw two intersecting straight lines on your paper so that a pair of vertical angles are supplementary. Name a pair of vertical angles a and b.

8. Draw two intersecting straight lines on your paper so that a pair of adjacent angles are equal. Name a pair of adjacent angles x and y.

Archimedes, a Greek mathematician who lived in the third century B. C., is given credit by historians for discovering many of the principles of geometry we study today. According to legend, he found certain geometric relationships by studying figures he drew in the sand. With the drawing instruments now available, we can draw our figures much more accurately.

THE MEANING OF PROOF

DO YOU remember Tom and Jim, the boys you met in the beginning of Chapter 1? Whether or not they realize it, Tom and Jim, as well as most of you, have been using informal proofs for some time. If you ever asked your parents for permission to go to the movies on a school night, you probably tried to *prove* to them that there were good reasons why you should be allowed to go. If Tom and Jim, or the students in your own high school, go to the principal to ask for special privileges, they try to persuade him by giving reasons in *logical order* to *prove* their point.

A district attorney trying a case in court works long and hard to collect all the facts and to present them in such a way as to convince the judge and jury that the accused man is guilty as charged. When the D.A. presents his facts, he tells how he knows them to be true; and when he presents opinions, he backs them up with the most convincing *reasons* he can command. *Geometric proofs* are not very different from the ones just described.

Few people, if any, would deny the *fact* that World War II was a bitter and costly struggle among leading world powers. Doubtless all of you accept as a *fact* that the sun will rise tomorrow morning just as it did today. On the other hand, if someone predicts that a storm is due we want him to tell us *why* he thinks so—we want his *reasons*—we want him to *prove* to us that the storm is likely to occur.

The need for logical reasoning

You recall that we have accepted without proof some statements of geometry which we called postulates.

However, we have many other statements which we do not accept unless we can prove them; that is, unless we can offer sufficient facts, or arguments, for which we can give sources or reasons. When these statements are gathered into a logical sequence and set down so that others can understand them and be convinced, they are called a formal proof. In this chapter you will learn how to set up such proofs.

To be sure that you are reasoning logically, you must observe certain cautions. Many of us are influenced by our own prejudices and experiences, and often we tend to accept as true those statements which we *wish* to believe. Watch out that you accept only such statements as can be verified by known facts and logical reasoning. Also be careful that you are not misled by the appearance of a figure. Did you ever put a long pencil in a glass of water and notice how the pencil appears to be bent? If you have never seen this, try it. This is only one of a number of optical illusions; some common ones are shown in Figure 1 below and Figure 2 on page 48. Perhaps you can collect other examples from newspapers and magazines.

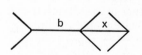

What is the comparative length of segments b and x?

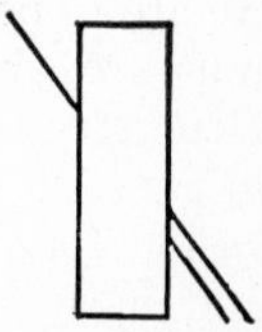

Which oblique line on the right is the prolongation of the oblique line on the left?

Fig. 1

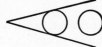

Are these circles equal?   Are these circles equal?
If not, which is larger?   If not, which is larger?
Which appears larger?   Which appears larger?

Fig. 2

Fig. 3

which are implied by sets of given conditions, using certain definitions, assumptions, and proved implicative statements.

Abraham Lincoln is remembered as a lawyer and a United States President whose ability to reason was beyond that of the average person. He would probably have given geometry some credit, for it is known that after he began the study of law in Springfield, Illinois, he discontinued his efforts for a short time and returned to his father's home where he studied Euclid's *Elements*. Lincoln's interest in geometry was motivated by his desire to learn to use the kind of proof used in geometry.

Cut out two figures shaped like the one in Figure 3, both of the same size. Hold these in several different positions, and you will see that sometimes one and sometimes the other looks larger. See if you can hold them so that they appear to be the same size. This should help to convince you that you cannot make decisions based on appearance alone. Careful measurement and correct reasoning are better tests.

Logic is the science of correct reasoning. In the study of geometry, we are to be scientists of a sort, for we must reason and learn to use logic. Geometry is ideally suited for practice in reasoning because there is no occasion for our emotions to affect us, and most situations in geometry are not open to prejudice. Although it is beyond the scope of this course to present all the rules of logic, some of the simpler ones will be given. Those rules of logic which are included in this chapter will help us get the conclusions

If-then statements

The *if-then* form of an implicative statement is a convenient one to use in geometry because the given conditions are usually all listed in the *if*-clause, and the implied conclusion, or conclusions, in the *then*-clause. For example, it is easy to find the given conditions and the conclusion in the statement, "If each of two angles is the supplement of a third angle, (then) the angles are equal." Of course, the subject-predicate form of the same statement, namely, "Supplements of the same angle are equal," contains the same information.

The statement, "All birds have feathers," has the same meaning as "If an animal is a bird, it has feathers." The if-clause of the latter contains the subject of the former, and the then-clause contains the predicate. The same given conditions and conclusions are present in both forms of the statement.

Exercises

Write **if-then** *sentences that have the same meaning as the following:*

1. Healthy and wealthy men are happy.
2. Supplements of equal angles are equal.
3. Two supplementary equal angles are right angles.
4. Students at Metropolis High School who have Room 303 for registration are freshmen.
5. A man living in the United States lives in North America.
6. Anyone who is twenty-one years old and is a citizen of the United States is legally of age.

Consistent conditions

Consistent conditions are conditions that are, or can be, true at the same time. The conditions of the following set are consistent (Figure 4):
1. $\angle s$ is adjacent to $\angle t$.
2. $\angle s$ is the supplement of $\angle t$.
3. $\angle s = \angle t$.

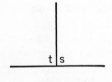

Fig. 4

The conditions of the next set are inconsistent (Figure 5):

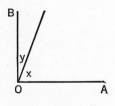

Fig. 5

1. $\angle x$ is adjacent to $\angle y$.
2. $\angle AOB = \angle x + \angle y$.
3. $AO \perp OB$.
4. $\angle x$ is not the complement of $\angle y$.

Deductive reasoning

Deductive reasoning is a method of using sets of consistent conditions together with certain definitions, assumptions, and implicative statements to get the conclusions which necessarily follow from them. For example, if we know that $x + y = 7$ and that $y = 2$, we are reasoning deductively when we conclude that $x = 5$. The conclusion is *implied* by the two given conditions and the subtraction axiom. To put it another way, the conclusion is deducible from the given conditions and the subtraction axiom.

As another example of deduction, let us assume that it is true that a man cannot vote in country C if he is an alien of that country. If Emil is an alien of country C, we can *deduce* that Emil cannot vote in that country.

Syllogisms

A simple deductive argument is called a *syllogism*. A syllogism consists of three parts:
1. The general statement called the *major premise*.
2. The particular statement called the *minor premise*.
3. The *conclusion* that necessarily follows from the first two statements.

The general statement of a syllogism is a definition, an assumption, or an implicative statement. The particular statement contains a set of consistent conditions which are relevant to the situation mentioned in the general statement. The conclusion is the implication of the other two.

Example 1

General Statement: (Major Premise)	If equals are subtracted from equals, the differences are equal.
Particular Statement: (Minor Premise)	$y = 2$ is subtracted from $x + y = 7$.
Conclusion:	$x = 5$.

Example 2

General Statement:	If a man is an alien of Country C, he cannot vote in that country.
Particular Statement:	Emil is an alien of country C.
Conclusion:	Emil cannot vote in country C.

Example 3

General Statement:	If an angle is a right angle, its sides are perpendicular.
Particular Statement:	$\angle y$ is a right angle.
Conclusion:	The sides of $\angle y$ are perpendicular.

The general statement of a syllogism, which is the authority for the conclusion, is not necessarily stated first. To illustrate, if angles r and s are right angles, the implication that $\angle r = \angle s$ can be deduced as follows:

Particular Statement:	Angles r and s are right angles.
Conclusion:	$\angle r = \angle s$.
General Statement:	If angles are right angles, the angles are equal.

Exercises

Write the conclusion that is deducible from the information given in each of Exercises **1-8.**

Example: If the sides of an angle extend in opposite directions in a straight line, the angle is a straight angle. The sides AO and OB of $\angle AOB$ extend in opposite directions in a straight line.

Conclusion: $\angle AOB$ is a straight angle.

1. If an animal is a dog, it is a quadruped. Sandy is a dog.

2. If soap is Beauty Soap, it is 98% pure. This soap is Beauty Soap.

3. All Eagle Scouts have passed a lifesaving test. Jim is an Eagle Scout.

4. If an angle is a straight angle, its sides extend in opposite directions in a straight line. $\angle EFG$ is a straight angle.

5. Vertical angles are equal. Angles x and y are vertical angles.

6. If the sides of an angle are perpendicular, the angle is a right angle. The sides of $\angle r$ are perpendicular.

7. If two angles are supplementary, their sum is 180°. $\angle A$ is the supplement of $\angle B$.

8. If the sum of two angles is 90°, the angles are complementary. $\angle x + \angle a = 90°$.

In each of Exercises **9-18**, *there is a particular statement and a conclusion. Write the general statement that gives the authority for the conclusion.*

Example:

Particular Statement: The central angle *AOB* intercepts $\overarc{AB}$.

Conclusion: $\angle AOB \doteq \overarc{AB}$.

General Statement: A central angle is measured by its intercepted arc.

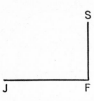

9. Particular Statement: $\angle SFJ$ is a right angle.
Conclusion: $FJ \perp FS$.

Ex. 9–10

10. Particular Statement: $JF \perp FS$.
Conclusion: $\angle JFS$ is a right angle.

11. Particular Statement: OE bisects $\angle COD$.
Conclusion: $\angle COE = \angle EOD$.

Ex. 11–12

12. Particular Statement: OE divides $\angle COD$ into two equal parts.
Conclusion: OE bisects $\angle COD$.

13. Particular Statement: $\angle CBD$ is the complement of $\angle DBA$, and $\angle CBD$ is adjacent to $\angle DBA$.
Conclusion: $AB \perp BC$.

Ex. 13–14

14. Particular Statement: $\angle CBD$ is adjacent to $\angle DBA$, and $AB \perp BC$.
Conclusion: $\angle CBD$ is the complement of $\angle DBA$.

15. Particular Statement: Straight lines CA and OB intersect to make $\angle AOB = \angle BOC$.
Conclusion: $OB \perp CA$.

Ex. 15–16

16. Particular Statement: CA is perpendicular to OB at O.
Conclusion: $\angle AOB = \angle BOC$.

17. Particular Statement: $\angle CBD$ is adjacent to $\angle DBA$, and $\angle CBD$ is the supplement of $\angle DBA$.
Conclusion: ABC is a straight line.

Ex. 17–18

18. Particular Statement: $\angle CBD$ is adjacent to $\angle DBA$, and ABC is a straight line.
Conclusion: $\angle CBD$ and $\angle DBA$ are supplementary.

Exercises Using Axioms

In each of Exercises **1-9,** *the particular statement of a syllogism is given. Write the implied conclusion and the general statement that gives the authority for it.*

1. Given: $MO = NO$, and $PO = SO$.
2. Given: $MP = \frac{1}{2} MO$, $NS = \frac{1}{2} NO$, and $MP = NS$.
3. Given: $MP = \frac{1}{2} MO$, $NS = \frac{1}{2} NO$, and $MO = NO$.
4. Given: $MP = PO$, $NS = SO$, and $MP = NS$.

Ex. 1–4

5. Given: $\angle FEH = \angle HGF$, and $\angle 1 = \angle 2$.
6. Given: $\angle 1 = \angle 2$, and $\angle 3 = \angle 4$.
7. Given: $\angle 1 = \angle 2$, $\angle 3 = \angle 4$, and $\angle 2 = \angle 4$.
8. Given: EG bisects $\angle FEH$, EG bisects $\angle HGF$, and $\angle FEH$ is equal to $\angle HGF$.

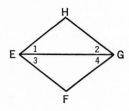

Ex. 5–8

9. Given: $y = 180° - a$, and $x = 90° - a$.
Conclusion: $y - x = ?$

Classification circles (*Optional*)

Classification circles are convenient enclosures that separate the members of one class from the members of another class. All the members that are within any circle have the same properties. Consider the following examples:

I. Definitions: One property of a definition is that a defined term must be placed in its nearest class. Figure 6 illustrates the classification of right angles.

(a) A large circle representing all geometric figures is drawn.

(b) Since angles are geometric figures, a circle representing all angles is drawn within the first circle.

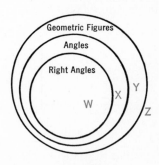

Fig. 6

(c) Since right angles are angles, a circle representing right angles is drawn within the angle circle.

It is obvious that W is a right angle; X is an angle, but not a right angle; Y is a geometric figure, but not an angle; and Z is not a geometric figure.

II. Geometric Deductions (Syllogisms): The circles are useful for illustrating the sequence of deductive reasoning in geometry.

Example 1:

General Statement: All right angles are equal.
(If angles are right angles, they are equal.)

Particular Statement: Angles R and M are right angles.

Conclusion: Angles R and M are equal.

(a) Draw a circle representing the class of things mentioned in the predicate of the general statement if it is a simple sentence, or in the then-clause if it is an if-then sentence.

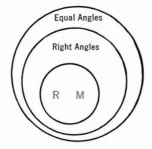

(b) Draw a second circle within the first representing the class of things mentioned in the subject, or in the if-clause of the general statement.

(c) If the pattern of the syllogism is correct, the individuals mentioned in the particular statement are members of the class represented by the second circle.

Example 2:

General Statement: Birds, and only birds, have feathers.

Particular Statement: Penguins are birds.

Conclusion: Penguins have feathers.

Notice that the circle including all birds is the same as the one including all feathered animals.

Example 3:

General Statement: No whales have gills.

Particular Statement: Jumbo is a whale.

Conclusion: Jumbo does not have
                              gills.

Example 4:

General Statement: Some angles are acute.

Particular Statement: x is an angle.

Conclusion: (No conclusion is possible.)

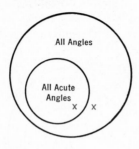

Angle x is not necessarily within the circle of acute angles.

Exercises   *(Optional)*

Use circles to classify the information given in Exercises **1-3**:

1. Plane geometry, mathematics, algebra, history, arithmetic, and subjects studied in school.
2. General statements, assumptions, definitions, postulates, and axioms.
3. Lines, curved lines, points, geometric figures, circles, acute angles, and straight angles.

In Exercises **4-7**, *write the conclusions and draw classification circles to illustrate the deductions:*

4. Vertical angles are equal. Angles x and y are vertical angles.
5. If angles are straight angles, they are equal. Angles m and n are straight angles.
6. All dogs are quadrupeds. Sandy is a dog.
7. If an animal is a fish, it can swim. Minnie is a fish.
8. How could circles be drawn to illustrate this syllogism?
   General Statement: No fish have lungs.
   Particular Statement: Chubby is a fish.

Conclusion: Chubby does not have lungs.

9. How could circles be drawn to illustrate this syllogism?
   General Statement: Right angles, and only right angles, have perpendicular sides.
   Particular Statement: Angle A is a right angle.
   Conclusion: Angle A has perpendicular sides.
10. Use circles to illustrate why this argument is false:
    General Statement: Some swimmers are fish.
    Particular Statement: A whale is a swimmer.
    Conclusion: A whale is a fish.

The form of a geometric proof

A geometric proof consists of one or more syllogisms arranged in logical sequence. It may be written in syllogistic form, paragraph form, or in the two-column form usually found in textbooks. Each of these forms is illustrated on the following pages.

Example 1. A proof consisting of only one syllogism.

In this figure, $\angle AOC$ is adjacent to $\angle COB$, and $\angle AOC$ is the complement of $\angle COB$.

What conclusion is deducible?

What general statement gives the authority for the conclusion?

SYLLOGISTIC FORM

General Statement: If two angles are adjacent and complementary, their exterior sides are perpendicular.

Particular Statement: $\angle AOC$ is adjacent to $\angle COB$, and $\angle AOC$ is the complement of $\angle COB$.

Conclusion: $AO \perp OB$.

PARAGRAPH FORM

Since the exterior sides of two adjacent complementary angles are perpendicular, and since angles AOC and COB are adjacent and complementary, then their exterior sides, AO and OB, are perpendicular.

TWO-COLUMN FORM

In this form the particular statements and the conclusions are arranged in logical sequence in a column on the left side of the page under the heading, "Statements." The general statements are arranged in another column on the right side of the page under the heading, "Authorities" or "Reasons." Each authority is numbered to correspond to the particular statement or conclusion it justifies.

Preceding the proof we write the particular conditions after the word "Given," and the deducible conclusion after the word "Prove."

Given: $\angle AOC$ is adjacent to $\angle COB$, and $\angle AOC$ is the complement of $\angle COB$.

Prove: $OA \perp OB$.

Proof

STATEMENTS	AUTHORITIES
1. $\angle AOC$ is adjacent to $\angle COB$, and $\angle AOC$ is the complement of $\angle COB$.	1. Given.
2. $\therefore OA \perp OB$. (The symbol for "therefore" is $\therefore$.)	2. If two angles are adjacent and complementary, their exterior sides are perpendicular.

Example 2. A proof consisting of two syllogisms.

In this figure, *OA*, *OC*, and *OB* intersect at *O* forming angles *AOC* and *COB*; ∠*AOC* is the complement of ∠*COB*.

What conclusion is deducible?

What general statements are used as authorities?

SYLLOGISTIC FORM

First syllogism:

General Statement: If two angles have a common vertex and a common side between them, the angles are adjacent angles.

Particular Statement: *OA*, *OC*, and *OB* intersect at *O* forming angles *AOC* and *COB*.

Conclusion: ∠*AOC* is adjacent to ∠*COB*.

Second syllogism:

General Statement: If two angles are adjacent and complementary, their exterior sides are perpendicular.

Particular Statement: ∠*AOC* is adjacent to ∠*COB*, and ∠*AOC* is the complement of ∠*COB*.

Conclusion: *AO* ⊥ *OB*.

PARAGRAPH FORM

Since any two angles having a common vertex and a common side between them are adjacent, and since *OA*, *OC*, and *OB* intersect at *O* forming angles *AOC* and *COB*, then angles *AOC* and *COB* are adjacent. Moreover, since the exterior sides of two adjacent complementary angles are perpendicular, and since angles *AOC* and *COB* are adjacent and complementary, then their exterior sides, *AO* and *OB*, are perpendicular.

TWO-COLUMN FORM

Given: *OA*, *OC*, and *OB* intersect at *O* forming angles *AOC* and *COB*; ∠*AOC* is the complement of ∠*COB*.

Prove: *OA* ⊥ *OB*.

Proof

STATEMENTS	AUTHORITIES
1. *OA*, *OB*, and *OC* intersect at *O* forming ∠*AOC* and ∠*COB*.	1. Given.
2. ∴ ∠*AOC* is adjacent to ∠*COB*.	2. If two angles have a common vertex and a common side between them, the angles are adjacent.
3. ∠*AOC* is the complement of ∠*COB*.	3. Given.
4. ∴ *AO* ⊥ *OB*.	4. If two angles are adjacent and complementary, their exterior sides are perpendicular.

Notice, below, how the parts of the proof of Example 2 are linked together.

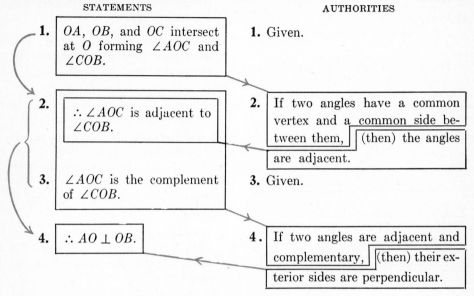

STATEMENTS   AUTHORITIES

1. | OA, OB, and OC intersect at O forming ∠AOC and ∠COB. | 1. Given.

2. | ∴ ∠AOC is adjacent to ∠COB. | 2. If two angles have a common vertex and a common side between them, (then) the angles are adjacent.

3. | ∠AOC is the complement of ∠COB. | 3. Given.

4. | ∴ AO ⊥ OB. | 4. If two angles are adjacent and complementary, (then) their exterior sides are perpendicular.

Here are some important facts concerning this proof:
1. There are two syllogisms in the proof.
    First syllogism:
    The general statement is Authority 2.
    The particular statement is Statement 1.
    The conclusion is Statement 2.
    Second syllogism:
    The general statement is Authority 4.
    The particular statement is a combination of Statements 2 and **3**.
    The conclusion is Statement 4.
2. The conclusion of the first syllogism is a part of the particular statement of the second syllogism.

Proof of a theorem

In mathematics, an implicative statement to be proved or a construction to be performed is called a *proposition*. A proposition to be proved is called a *theorem*. A theorem is an assertion that a certain conclusion is implied by a given set of conditions. It is proved by demonstrating that its conclusion is deducible from its given conditions, and from certain other theorems, definitions, axioms, and postulates that have preceded it.

For our first theorem we have chosen the implicative statement, "If two angles are complements of the same angle, the angles are equal." The if-clause states a relationship between each of two angles and a third angle; that is, it states the given conditions. The then-clause states a new relationship between the first two angles; that is, it states a conclusion. The theorem is an assertion that the set of given conditions implies the conclusion.

The procedure in writing the proof of Theorem 1 is as follows:

1. Draw an appropriate figure according to the directions found in the if-clause.

   Draw any acute angle and name it b.
   Then draw angles a and c so that each is the complement of $\angle b$.

   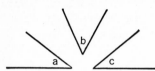

2. After the word "Given" write the conditions in terms of the figure.

   Given: $\angle a$ is the complement of $\angle b$, and $\angle c$ is the complement of $\angle b$.

3. After the word "Prove" write the conclusion in terms of the figure.

   Prove: $\angle a = \angle c$.

4. Decide upon a plan of proof. The plan may be the entire proof in paragraph form.

   If two angles are complementary, their sum is 90°. Hence, $\angle a + \angle b = 90°$, and $\angle c + \angle b = 90°$. Since quantities equal to the same quantity are equal, then $\angle a + \angle b = \angle c + \angle b$. Therefore, by the subtraction axiom, $\angle a = \angle c$.

5. Write the two-column form of a proof.

6. It is helpful, but not necessary, to draw linkage lines as you write the proof, in order to check for logical continuity.

THEOREM 1. If two angles are complements of the same angle, the angles are equal.

Given: $\angle a$ is the complement of $\angle b$, and $\angle c$ is the complement of $\angle b$.

Prove: $\angle a = \angle c$.

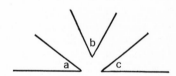

Proof

STATEMENTS	AUTHORITIES
1. $\angle a$ is the complement of $\angle b$, and $\angle c$ is the complement of $\angle b$.	1. Given.
2. $\therefore \angle a + \angle b = 90°$, and $\angle c + \angle b = 90°$.	2. If two angles are complementary, their sum is 90°.
3. $\therefore \angle a + \angle b = \angle c + \angle b$.	3. If two quantities are equal to the same quantity, they are equal.
4. $\angle b = \angle b$.	4. Identity ($\angle b$ is identical to itself).
5. $\therefore$ $\angle a = \angle c$.	5. If equals are subtracted from equals, the differences are equal.

Theorem 1 was proved by demonstrating that its conclusion is deducible from the given conditions and certain definitions and axioms.

There are three syllogisms in the proof. The particular facts of the minor premise of each syllogism are in agreement with the general conditions in the if-clause of the major premise; the particular conclusion of each syllogism is in agreement with the general conclusion in the then-clause of the major premise.

A linkage line drawn from one statement to another connects a minor premise to the conclusion of a syllogism. These lines are helpful but not necessary.

It should be noted that the given conditions of a theorem are consistent, that is, they all are, or may be true; they are independent, that is, none is implied by another or any combination of the others; they are relevant, that is, each is needed to deduce the conclusion.

Although a fixed figure is used, it represents *any* figure that satisfies the conditions. Hence, any deducible conclusion about the fixed figure is true about a variable figure that satisfies the conditions.

THEOREM 2. **If two angles are complements of equal angles, the angles are equal.**

Given: $\angle a$ is the complement of $\angle b$, $\angle c$ is the complement of $\angle d$, and $\angle b = \angle c$.

Prove: $\angle a = \angle d$.

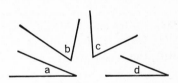

Proof

STATEMENTS	AUTHORITIES
1. $\angle a$ is the complement of $\angle b$, and	**1.** Given.
2. $\therefore \angle a + \angle b = 90°$, and . . .	**2.** Why?
3. $\therefore \angle a + \angle b = ?$	**3.** Why?
4. $\angle b = ?$	**4.** Given.
5. $\therefore \angle a = ?$	**5.** Why?

You write the complete proof.

THEOREMS 3. **If two angles are supplements of the same angle, the angles are equal.**

 4. **If two angles are supplements of equal angles, the angles are equal.**

The proofs of Theorems 3 and 4 are quite similar to the proofs of Theorems 1 and 2. You write the proofs of Theorems 3 and 4.

Deductive reasoning in the solution of algebraic equations

Although it is not customary to write the authorities for the steps in the solution of an algebraic equation, the solution can be written formally as follows:

Example 1.

Given: $2x + 3 = 11$.
Solve the equation for x.

Proof

STATEMENTS	AUTHORITIES
1. $2x + 3 = 11$	**1.** Given.
2. $\quad\ 3 = 3$	**2.** 3 is identical to itself (or Identity).
3. $\therefore\quad 2x = 8$	**3.** If equals are subtracted from equals, the differences are equal.
4. $\quad\ 2 = 2$	**4.** Identity.
5. $\therefore\quad\ x = 4$	**5.** If equals are divided by equals, the quotients are equal.

How many syllogisms are there in the proof? Identify the *general statement, particular statement,* and *conclusion* of each syllogism.

When we use the subtraction axiom, we must have a pair of *minuends,* a pair of *subtrahends,* and a pair of *differences.* Identify these in the first syllogism. Identify the *dividends,* the *divisors,* and the *quotients* in the last syllogism.

Only the outline of a proof is found in the next example. Copy it and complete the proof.

Example 2.

Given: $\angle x + \angle y = 180°$,
$\qquad \angle s + \angle r = 180°$, and
$\qquad\quad \angle x = \angle r$.

What can you prove about angles y and s?

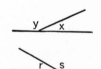

Proof

STATEMENTS	AUTHORITIES
1. $\quad \angle x + \angle y = 180°$, and $\angle s + \angle r = 180°$.	**1.** Why?
2. $\therefore \angle x + \angle y = $?	**2.** Why?
3. $\qquad\ \angle x = $?	**3.** Why?
4. $\qquad \therefore \angle y = $?	**4.** Why?

Proof patterns needed in the next list of exercises

Example 1.

Given: OA, OB, and OC intersect at O so that $OB \perp OA$.

Conclusion: $\angle AOC$ is the complement of $\angle COB$.

Proof

STATEMENTS	AUTHORITIES
1. OA, OB, and OC intersect at O.	**1.** Given.
These lines form angles AOC and COB that have a <u>common vertex</u> and a <u>common side</u> between them.	
2. ∴ $\angle AOC$ is <u>adjacent</u> to $\angle COB$.	**2.** If two angles have a common vertex and a common side between them, the angles are adjacent.
3. $OB \perp OA$.	**3.** Given.
4. ∴ $\angle AOC$ is the <u>complement</u> of $\angle COB$.	**4.** If the exterior sides of two adjacent angles are perpendicular, the angles are complementary.

Note: The sentence in the box under Statement 1 gives what is usually a mental operation and will not be included in a formal proof. It is written here to emphasize the implications of Statement 1.

Example 2.

Given: AB, OR, and OS intersect at O; $\angle 1 = \angle 4$.

Prove: $\angle 2 = \angle 3$.

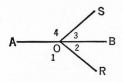

Proof

STATEMENTS	AUTHORITIES
1. AB, OR, and OS intersect at O.	**1.** Given.
2. ∴ $\angle 3$ is adjacent to $\angle 4$, and $\angle 2$ is adjacent to $\angle 1$.	**2.** If two angles have a common vertex and a common side between them, the angles are adjacent.
3. ∴ $\angle 3$ is the supplement of $\angle 4$, and $\angle 2$ is the supplement of $\angle 1$.	**3.** If two angles are adjacent and their exterior sides lie in a straight line, the angles are supplementary.
4. $\angle 1 = \angle 4$.	**4.** Given.
5. ∴ $\angle 2 = \angle 3$.	**5.** If two angles are supplements of equal angles, the angles are equal.

Example 3.

Given: $ES \perp EF$, $FE \perp FR$, and
$\angle FEM = \angle MFE$.

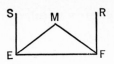

Prove: $\angle MES = \angle RFM$.

Proof

STATEMENTS	AUTHORITIES
1. $ES \perp EF$, and $FE \perp FR$.	1. Given.
2. $\therefore \angle FES$ is a right angle, and $\angle RFE$ is a right angle.	2. If two lines are perpendicular, they form a right angle.
3. $\therefore \angle FEM$ is the complement of $\angle MES$, and $\angle RFM$ is the complement of $\angle MFE$.	3. If the sum of two angles is a right angle, the angles are complementary.
4. $\angle FEM = \angle MFE$.	4. Given.
5. $\therefore \angle MES = \angle RFM$.	5. If two angles are complements of equal angles, the angles are equal.

Exercises

1. Given: AD is a straight line intersecting BE at B and CE at C; $\angle s = \angle m$.
   Prove: $\angle r = \angle n$.

Ex. 1

2. Given: $RB \perp BC$, $DC \perp BC$, and $\angle CBE = \angle ECB$.
   Prove: $\angle EBR = \angle DCE$.

Ex. 2

3. Given: ACD is a straight line and $\angle ACN = \angle FCA$.
   Prove: $\angle NCD = \angle DCF$.

Ex. 3

4. Given: AB and CD intersect EF at G and H, respectively; $\angle c$ is the supplement of $\angle b$.
   Prove: $\angle a = \angle c$.

Ex. 4

5. Given: $RU \perp RS$, $ST \perp TU$, and
$\angle UTR = \angle TRU$.
Prove: $\angle RTS = \angle SRT$.

Ex. 5

6. Given: SB and PD intersect EF
at R and Y, respectively; and
$\angle 1 = \angle 2$.
Prove: $\angle 1$ is the supplement of
$\angle 3$.

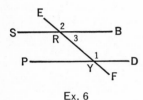

Ex. 6

7. Given: AJC is a triangle, AR
intersects JC at R, JS intersects
AC at S, and $\angle 1 = \angle 3$.
Prove: What you can about angles
2 and 4.

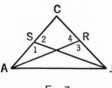

Ex. 7

8. Given: $AO \perp OC$, and $BO \perp OD$.
Prove: What you can about angles
AOB and COD.

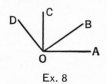

Ex. 8

9. Given: AB and CD intersect EF
at R and S, respectively; and
$\angle 3 = \angle 1$.
Prove: Anything you can about
angles 1 and 2.

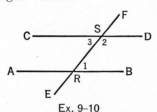

Ex. 9–10

10. Given: AB and CD intersect EF at
R and S, respectively, so that
$\angle 1 + \angle 2 = 180°$.
Prove: What you can about angles
1 and 3.

In Exercises **11-15** *facts given are
insufficient to prove the suggested conclusion. In each exercise a single
additional fact must be known. After
adding the necessary fact, prove the
conclusion.*

11. Given: RM, RW, RK, and RT
intersect at R; $RM \perp RK$.
Prove: $\angle MRW = \angle KRT$.

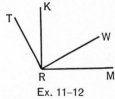

Ex. 11–12

12. Given: RM, RW, RK, and RT
intersect at R; $\angle KRT$ is the complement of $\angle WRK$.
Prove: $\angle MRW = \angle KRT$.

13. Given: $TW \perp WR$, $WR \perp RK$,
and WM intersects RM.
Prove: $\angle MWT = \angle KRM$.

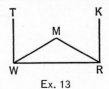

Ex. 13

14. Given: $\angle FMN$ is the supplement of $\angle EMF$, and MK intersects EK.

Prove: $\angle FMN = \angle NMK$.

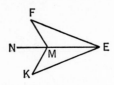

Ex. 14–15

15. Given: NM, KM, ME, and MF are straight line segments; $\angle EMF = \angle KME$.

Prove: $\angle FMN = \angle NMK$.

Synthesis and analysis

A synthetic proof is an orderly sequence of syllogisms that begins with the given conditions and by deduction proceeds to a logical conclusion. The proofs of Theorems 1 and 2 are synthetic proofs.

Analysis is the opposite of synthesis. We begin with what we are trying to prove and work backwards to the given conditions. Analysis is frequently used to determine the sequence of steps in a synthetic proof.

Analysis is a procedure whereby the plan of a proof is discovered by working backwards from the conclusion to the given conditions.

The analysis of a proof can generally be done mentally, but two examples are shown here to help you understand the method.

Example 1.

Given: $ST \perp SR$, $\angle n$ is adjacent to $\angle m$, and $\angle x$ is the complement of $\angle m$.

Prove: $\angle x = \angle n$.

Analysis:

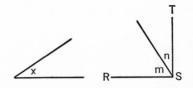

1. I can prove $\angle x = \angle n$ if I can prove
   - a. $\angle x$ is the comp. of $\angle m$ (Given).
   - b. $\angle n$ is the complement of $\angle m$.

2. I can prove $\angle n$ is the complement of $\angle m$ if I can prove
   - a. $\angle n$ is adjacent to $\angle m$ (Given).
   - b. $ST \perp SR$ (Given).

The plan suggested by analysis leads to the following synthetic proof:

Proof

STATEMENTS	AUTHORITIES
1. $\angle n$ is adjacent to $\angle m$, and $ST \perp SR$.	1. Given.
2. $\therefore$ $\angle n$ is the complement of $\angle m$.	2. If the exterior sides of two adjacent angles are perpendicular, the angles are complementary.
3. $\angle x$ is the complement of $\angle m$.	3. Given.
4. $\therefore$ $\angle n = \angle x$.	4. Complements of the same angle are equal.

Example 2.

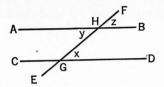

Given: *EF* intersects *CD* and *AB* at *G* and *H*, respectively; ∠*x* = ∠*z*.

Prove: ∠*x* = ∠*y*.

Analysis:

1. I can prove ∠*x* = ∠*y* if I can prove ⟨a. ∠*x* = ∠*z* (Given).
                                          ⟨b. ∠*y* = ∠*z*.

2. I can prove ∠*y* = ∠*z* if I can prove {∠*y* and ∠*z* are vertical angles.

3. I can prove ∠*y* and ∠*z* are vertical angles if I can prove {*AB* and *EF* are intersecting straight lines (Given).

You write the synthetic proof.

Exercises

Use analysis to discover a plan of proof in each of the following exercises and then write the proof:

1. Given: *EF* intersects *CD* at *G* and *AB* at *H*, ∠*x* = ∠*z*.

Prove: ∠*x* + ∠*w* = 180°.

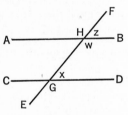

Ex. 1–2

2. Given: *EF* intersects *CD* at *G* and *AB* at *H*; ∠*x* is the supplement of ∠*w*.

Prove: ∠*x* = ∠*z*.

3. Given: *B* is the point of intersection of *RB*, *BF*, and *BC*; *C* is the point of intersection of *BC*, *FC*, and *DC*;

Ex. 3

BC ⊥ *DC*; ∠1 = ∠4; ∠2 = ∠3·

Prove: ∠*CBR* is a right angle.

4. Given: The straight line *AD* intersects *BN* at *B* and *CN* at *C*, and ∠2 = ∠3.

Prove: ∠1 = ∠4.

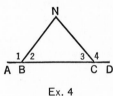

Ex. 4

5. Given: Straight lines *FD* and *CE* intersect at *B*, *CA* intersects *FD* at *A*, and ∠4 = ∠3.

Prove: ∠1 is the supplement of ∠2.

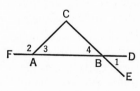

Ex. 5

Cautions in using deduction

Deduction is a powerful method of reasoning, but deducible conclusions may not be true; and arguments which resemble deduction may not fit into the pattern of a syllogism.

I. Unacceptable or false statements (General, G.S., or Particular, P.S.):

1. G.S.: If two angles are adjacent, their sum is 180°. (False)
   P.S.: Angles r and s are adjacent angles.
   $\therefore \angle r + \angle s = 180°.$
   (False)

2. G.S.: If an animal is a bird, it can fly.   (False)
   P.S.: Penny, the penguin, is a bird.
   $\therefore$ Penny can fly. (False)

3. G.S.: All birds have feathers.
   P.S.: A bat is a bird.   (False)
   $\therefore$ A bat has feathers.
   (False)

II. Arguments that do not fit into the pattern of a syllogism:

1. G.S.: All fish can swim.
   P.S.: Jumbo, the whale, can swim.
   $\therefore$ Jumbo is a fish.

Compare this argument with the syllogistic pattern and explain why the conclusion is not deducible.

2. G.S.: If two angles are equal and supplementary, the angles are right angles.
   P.S.: Angles CBD and DBA are supplementary.
   $\therefore$ Angles CBD and DBA are right angles.

The angles specified in the general statement must fulfill two requirements, or conditions. Angles CBD and DBA fulfill only one condition. The conclusion is not deducible.

Exercises

Study each of the following arguments and state whether or not the conclusion is deducible. If it is not, identify the error.

1. If two angles are complementary and adjacent, their exterior sides are perpendicular. Angles x and y are complementary. Therefore, the exterior sides of angles x and y are perpendicular.

2. If two angles have a common vertex and a common side between them, they are adjacent. Angles a and b have a common vertex. Therefore, angles a and b are adjacent.

3. All rainy days are disagreeable days. Wednesday was a disagreeable day. Therefore, Wednesday was a rainy day.

4. All milk sold by the Pure Dairy is pasteurized. This milk is not pasteurized. Therefore, this milk was not sold by the Pure Dairy.

5. Only persons who are at least 16 years of age may obtain a driver's license. Carl has not obtained a driver's license. Therefore, Carl is not 16 years old.

6. All school buses stop at railroad crossings. This vehicle stopped at the D. T. & I. railroad crossing. Therefore, this vehicle is a school bus.

7. No badly-worn tires are safe to use. This tire is badly worn. Therefore, this tire is not safe to use.

8. If a student at Metropolis High has Room 303 for registration, the student is a freshman. Bob Doak is a student and has Room 303 for registration. Therefore, Bob Doak is a freshman.

Arguments based upon unstated assumptions

In everyday reasoning, arguments are seldom stated in the form of a syllogism. It is a common practice to omit either the general statement or the particular statement. This practice makes it difficult to judge the correctness of the argument. In a critical analysis of the argument it is necessary to supply the missing assumption in order to judge whether it is acceptable or unwarranted and, finally, to decide whether the conclusion is deducible.

I. General statement omitted:

1. Argument: Mr. X must be a citizen of the United States since he is a United States senator.

   In syllogistic form this would be:

   General Statement: All United States senators are citizens of the United States.

   Particular Statement: Mr. X is a United States senator.

   Conclusion: Mr. X is a citizen of the United States.

   Is this argument correct? Is it acceptable if both of the statements are accepted?

2. Argument: Mary's father must be rich, for she wears pretty clothes.

   General Statement: If a girl wears pretty clothes, her father must be rich.

   Particular Statement: Mary wears pretty clothes.

   Conclusion: Mary's father must be rich.

   A critical analysis of this argument shows that it is based on an unacceptable assumption used as the general statement. Is the conclusion deducible?

II. Particular statement omitted:

   Argument: All college professors are absent-minded. Therefore, Mr. Brown is absent-minded.

   General Statement: All college professors are absent-minded.

   Particular Statement: ?

   Conclusion: Mr. Brown is absent-minded.

   What particular statement must be supplied to make a syllogism of the original argument? Is the conclusion deducible? Is it acceptable?

Exercises

Supply the missing assumptions in each of the arguments in Exercises 1-14 and write the arguments in syllogistic form. Judge the correctness of each argument.

1. Circles A and B are equal because they have equal radii.
2. Every rectangle has four right angles. Therefore, $ABCD$ has four right angles.
3. This stone is yellow and glitters. Therefore this stone is gold.
4. $3x = 12$. Therefore, $x = 4$.
5. I use "Silky" soap. Therefore, my skin will be soft as silk.
6. Central angles r and s are equal because they are central angles of the same circle.
7. Triangle ABC has one right angle. Therefore triangle ABC is a right triangle.
8. Sam must be an intelligent boy, for he is a member of the National Honor Society.
9. If the sum of two angles is 180°, the angles are supplementary. Therefore, angles a and b are supplementary.

10. Since $ABCD$ is a quadrilateral, the sum of angles A, B, C, and D is 360°.

11. This man is wealthy. Therefore, he is intelligent.

12. This solid is lighter than wood. Therefore, it will always float in water.

13. Jenny was elected Home-Coming Queen. Therefore, Jenny is glamorous.

14. If a student is not learning to think critically, he is not getting an education. Therefore, Bill is not getting an education.

15. An advertisement states that "The elite own Torpedo De Luxe automobiles." The reader might falsely reason as follows: "Since the elite own Torpedo De Luxe automobiles, it must be true that any person who owns a Torpedo De Luxe is a member of the elite. I want to be a member of the elite; so I'll buy a Torpedo De Luxe." Explain why this argument is not valid.

Induction

Induction is a type of reasoning in which a general conclusion is established on the basis of facts obtained through a systematic examination of many specific cases which are alike in certain respects. It is a logical process of proceeding from the particular to the general by a careful examination of many representative samples chosen at random. Induction is so widely used in science that it is commonly called the *scientific method*.

Induction is used in geometry to discover the relation of certain parts of a figure to others. For example, we can find out how the diagonals of a square are related by measuring them. However, an inductive discovery is not necessarily 100% correct, but only highly probable. There is always the chance of an exception. Moreover, since measurements are never exact, an inductive conclusion based on measurements is not a certainty.

Everyday reasoning is more often inductive than deductive. Public opinion polls are examples of induction. In the great research laboratories of our country both induction and deduction are used extensively. Theories based on induction are tested by deduction, and vice versa.

An inductive conclusion is a tentative statement of what seems to be true about an entire class. It is the result of experimentation with typical members of the class.

Cautions in using induction

Here is an example from algebra which shows how the inductive method might lead to a false conclusion:

You remember that a *prime number* is a whole number that has no integral factors except itself and one. For example, 3, 7, 11, and 23 are prime numbers.

You also know that an *integer* is a whole number such as 1, 2, 3, 4, 5, 7, etc.

Suppose we wish to determine whether the algebraic expression $n^2 + n + 17$ is prime for all positive integral values of n. When $n = 1$, the value of $n^2 + n + 17$ is $1^2 + 1 + 17$, or 19. Since 19 has no integral factors except itself and 1, it is a prime number.

Copy the table at the top of the next page and complete it. Do not write in this book.

n	1	2	3	4	5	6	7	8	9	10	11	12	13	14	15	16	17
$n^2 + n + 17$	19	?	?	?	?	?	?	?	?	?	?	?	?	?	?	?	?

By induction you might conclude that $n^2 + n + 17$ is a prime number for all positive integral values of n since the expression is prime for all numbers from 1 to 15.

When $n = 16$, $n^2 + n + 17 = 289$. Divide 289 by 17. Is 289 a prime number?

When $n = 17$, $n^2 + n + 17 = 323$. Is 323 divisible by 17? Is 323 prime?

Are you convinced that it is unsafe to be hasty in accepting a conclusion as a general truth, even if it happens to be true in a great many cases? Can one assume that because a great many cases seem to point to an inductive conclusion, it is acceptable?

Other examples:

1. You probably cannot recall having seen an animal with feathers that cannot fly. Is it safe to conclude that every animal with feathers can fly? Does a penguin have feathers? Can a penguin fly?
2. You might have observed that some of our past and present leaders in science, government, industry, and business have had little formal education. You might be tempted to conclude that formal education is not very important after all. What is wrong with this so-called argument?

Exercises

1. If a farmer moves to the State of Kansas, he expects to be in the midst of a wheat-growing area. What might account for this?

2. How may inductive reasoning influence the formulation of these statements?
   a. If it rains before 7:00, it will stop before 11:00.
   b. A rolling stone gathers no moss.
3. Travelers to New York City often make plans to go to the top of the Empire State Building. Why do they believe that such a trip is possible?
4. In what manner has inductive reasoning influenced the progress of air travel?
5. How has inductive reasoning influenced your selection of clothes?
6. How did inductive reasoning cause you to expect that the doors of your school would be open this morning?

The use of induction in geometry

We shall use induction in geometry primarily for the purpose of discovering relationships among the parts of geometric figures. We experiment with figures that are as different as possible so long as they fulfill the given conditions. All similar relationships in the various figures that seem to be the direct result of the given conditions are carefully noted for further investigation. When we are sure beyond any reasonable doubt what the implications of the given conditions are, we state our inductive conclusion. If we are able to prove these conclusions deductively, we are much more certain that they are correct.

Experiment 1

Given: Angles *CBD* and *DBA* are supplementary adjacent angles; *BE* bisects ∠*CBD*; and *BF* bisects ∠*DBA*.

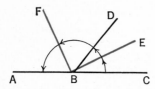

Problem: What, if any, is the relationship between the bisectors of two supplementary adjacent angles?

Procedure: Draw two supplementary adjacent angles. Bisect each of the angles with a protractor. Measure each of the angles. Draw several different figures, and measure the angles each time. Make a data table similar to the one shown here and record your measurements.

You are probably aware that you cannot bisect an angle exactly, nor can you measure it exactly. Although all measurements are approximate, you can reduce the error by using good instruments and by being extremely careful.

Data Table

Trial No.	∠CBD	∠DBA	∠EBF	Relation of *EB* to *FB*
1.	?	?	?	?
2.	?	?	?	?
3.	?	?	?	?
4.	?	?	?	?
5.	?	?	?	?
etc.	?	?	?	?

Conclusions: (Write a specific statement about ∠*EBF*. What seems to be the relationship of *EB* to *FB*?)

Inductive Conclusion: (Write a general word-statement about the bisectors of two supplementary adjacent angles.)

Are you positive that your conclusion is correct? Would you stake your life on it?

Now try to prove your conclusion deductively. Assuming that you are able to do so, would you now stake your life on it? Remember, deduction is a certain way of arriving at *deducible* conclusions, but the acceptability of the conclusions is based on the acceptability of the general and particular statements.

Experiment 2

Given: Polygons of different kinds and their diagonals.

Problem: What is the relationship, if any, between the number of sides of a polygon and

    a. the number of diagonals from any one vertex?

    b. the total number of diagonals from all vertices?

Procedure: Draw several of each of the different kinds of polygons. Count the diagonals in each polygon, and on your own paper record the numbers in a data table similar to the one on the following page. Do not write in this book.

It is impossible to draw all the polygons representing *n*-gons for which *n* is equal to all the positive whole numbers from 3 to infinity. Your conclusions must necessarily be based on some representative samples.

Data Table

Polygon	Number of Sides	Number of Diagonals From Just One Vertex	Number of Diagonals From All Vertices
Triangle	3	0	0
Quadrilateral	4	1	2
Pentagon	5	2	5
Hexagon	?	?	?
Heptagon	?	?	?
Octagon	?	?	?
Decagon	?	?	?
n-gon	?	?	?

Have you investigated a sufficient number of samples to be sure *beyond any reasonable doubt that:*

a. The number of diagonals from any one vertex of an n-gon is $n - 3$?

b. The total number of diagonals from all vertices of an n-gon is $\dfrac{n(n-3)}{2}$?

Exercises

1. How many diagonals are there from just one vertex of a 20-gon?

2. What is the total number of diagonals of a 20-gon?

3. If a polygon has 25 diagonals from just one vertex, how many sides has it?

4. By using the formula, show that a triangle has no diagonals.

5. If the total number of diagonals of an n-gon is 14, find n. (This problem involves the solution of a quadratic equation. Can you do it?)

6. Find, by experiment, the sum of the angles of a pentagon.

Review of Chapter 3

1. Distinguish between definitions, assumptions, and theorems.

2. Explain the meaning of: (**a**) deduction; (**b**) induction.

3. Discuss the pitfalls of: (**a**) deduction; (**b**) induction.

4. In what ways do undefined terms resemble assumptions?

5. Explain the differences between analysis and synthesis in geometry. State the purpose of analysis.

6. State the properties of a good definition.

7. Here is a "phony" proof that $2 = 1$. Can you find the false assumption?

1. Let $a = b = 1$.
2. Since $a = b$,
3. Then, $a^2 = ab$. (Multiply each side of step (2) by a.)
4. Then, $a^2 - b^2 = ab - b^2$. (Subtract b^2 from each side of step (3).)
5. Then, $\dfrac{(a-b)(a+b)}{(a-b)} = \dfrac{b(a-b)}{(a-b)}$. (Divide each side of step (4) by $(a-b)$.)
   or $a + b = b$.
6. Hence, $1 + 1 = 1$ (Substitute 1 for a and 1 for b.)
   or $2 = 1$.

---

8. If the following statements are not good definitions, which properties are violated?

a. A square is a figure that has four equal sides, four right angles, and two equal diagonals.

b. Adjacent angles are two angles that have a common side and the same vertex.

c. A fish is an animal with scales.

d. A circle is a round figure.

e. A chair is a piece of furniture with four legs.

9. Since a quadrilateral has a total of two diagonals, an octagon (which has twice as many sides as a quadrilateral) has a total of four diagonals. Do you agree with the conclusion of the argument?

10. Is there anything wrong with this inductive argument? I have been stung by bees many times and have never been poisoned by them. Therefore, I am immune to the poison of a bee sting.

11. Supply the assumption that makes this argument correct: John is an excellent mathematician. Obviously, he has an excellent memory.

12. Explain why the conclusion of this syllogism is or is not correct: All birds have wings. A robin has wings. Therefore, a robin is a bird.

In Exercises **13-16,** *judge whether the argument is correct or incorrect.*

13. All thieves are rascals. X is a thief. Hence, X is a rascal.

14. All fish breathe under water. Tadpoles breathe under water. Hence, tadpoles are fish.

15. Some supplementary angles are equal. Vertical angles are equal. Therefore, some vertical angles are supplementary.

16. The difference between the supplement of an angle and its complement is a right angle. $\angle x$ is the supplement of $\angle y$, and $\angle z$ is the complement of $\angle y$. Therefore, $\angle y$ is a right angle.

In Exercises **17-20,** *write a deducible conclusion if there is one. If there is none, write "None."*

17. The exterior sides of two supplementary adjacent angles lie in a straight line. Angles x and y are equal adjacent angles.

18. The exterior sides of some adjacent angles are perpendicular. Angles x and y are adjacent angles.

19. Only complementary adjacent angles have perpendicular exterior sides. Adjacent angles m and p have perpendicular exterior sides.

20. No acute angles are supplementary. Angles b and n are acute angles.

Cumulative Review

Chapters 2 and 3

Write the conclusions which can be deduced from the given information in Exercises **1-10** *and state your authorities for them:*

1. Given: Points A, B, and C are not in the same straight line.
Conclusion: The sum of AC and BC is . . . . .

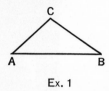

Ex. 1

2. Given: R is the midpoint of the straight line segment AB, and S is another point on AB.
Conclusion: S is not . . . . .

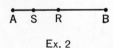

Ex. 2

3. Given: Circles O and S with equal radii r and s.

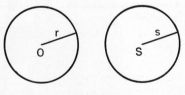

Ex. 3–4

4. Given: Equal circles with radii r and s.

5. Two angles are supplementary. The smaller angle is 10° less than the larger.

6. Given: Concentric circles (circles with the same center). $\overset{\frown}{CD} = 66°$.
Conclusion: $\overset{\frown}{AB} = ?$

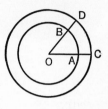

Ex. 6

7. Two angles are complementary. The larger angle is three times the smaller.

8. The complement of an angle is $\frac{2}{5}$ of the supplement of the angle.

9. Given: Angles x and y are complementary adjacent angles.

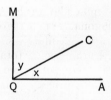

Ex. 9–10

10. Given: $\angle AQM$ is a right angle: AQ, CQ, and MQ intersect at Q.

In Exercises **11-12,** *write a deducible conclusion if there is one. If there is none, write "None."*

11. Only one perpendicular can be drawn from a point to a line. RM is a perpendicular from R to PQ.

12. The complements of some angles are equal. $\angle x$ is the complement of $\angle y$, and $\angle c$ is the complement of $\angle d$.

Wherever we look, we see parallel lines. This view of coke ovens at a Pennsylvania steel mill contains many sets of parallel lines. Can you locate and identify them?

PARALLEL LINES

So FAR in geometry we have considered only intersecting lines and the angles formed by them. In this chapter we shall study lines *in the same plane* that do not intersect.

Meaning of parallel lines

In Figure 1, m is a static line (fixed in position), n is a dynamic line through the fixed point P, and A is their point of intersection. Remember, m and n are geometric straight lines, not line segments.

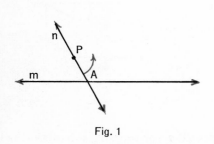

Fig. 1

Assume that n rotates counterclockwise about P as indicated in Figure 2. As n rotates to new positions, n_1, n_2, n_3, etc., A moves outward along m farther and farther to the right of P as indicated by the successive intersections A_1, A_2, A_3, etc.

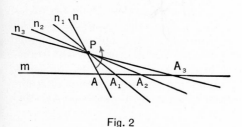

Fig. 2

In Figure 3, n has rotated until the point of intersection of m and n, which is A_5, is to the left of P. Since n cannot simultaneously intersect m at some point far to the right of P and at some point far to the left of P, we reason that at one, and only one, stage of the rotation of n the lines do not intersect at all. The line n_4 represents the stage in the rotation of n when it does not intersect m anywhere. When n is in the position n_4 we say the lines m and n are parallel.

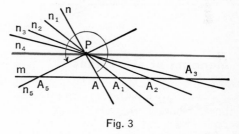

Fig. 3

DEFINITION *Parallel lines* **are straight lines in the same plane that do not intersect.**

The symbol $\parallel$ means "parallel" or "is parallel to." The arrows along the lines in Figure 4 are sometimes used to indicate that a is parallel to d.

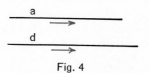

Fig. 4

75

Extending a line segment

There are occasions in geometry when it is convenient to show the extensions of line segments. The extensions are "dashed" as illustrated in Figure 5 where line segment XY is extended through both end points, and RS is extended through one end point. Because the definition of parallel lines applies to lines regardless of their *apparent* length, parallel line *segments* will not meet, no matter how far extended.

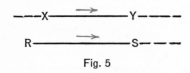

Fig. 5

Meaning of skew lines

Figure 6 illustrates two straight lines, x and y, that do not lie in the same plane and do not intersect. Lines x and y are *skew* lines.

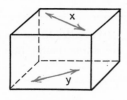

Fig. 6

DEFINITION *Skew lines* are straight lines in space that do not intersect and are not parallel.

Exercises

1. What three conditions are satisfied by parallel lines?

2. State the reverse of the definition of parallel lines. Is it acceptable? Why?

3. Why are objects such as slats in venetian blinds, the rails of a railroad track, and the yard lines of a football field not geometric parallel line segments?

4. This figure represents a rectangular box.
  a. Which lines are vertical?
  b. Are the vertical lines parallel?
  c. Which lines are horizontal?
  d. Are the horizontal lines parallel?
  e. Name several pairs of skew lines.

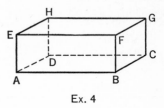

Ex. 4

Angles formed by a transversal

A *transversal* is a straight line that intersects two (or more) straight lines or straight line segments. In Figure 7, the lines a and c are intersected by the transversal t forming the following angles:

Exterior angles (outside a and c)— $\angle 1$, $\angle 2$, $\angle 7$, and $\angle 8$.

Interior angles (between a and c)— $\angle 3$, $\angle 4$, $\angle 5$, and $\angle 6$.

Corresponding angles—Pairs of angles that lie on the same side of the transversal and on corresponding sides of the lines cut by the transversal. Angles 4 and 8 are corresponding angles. Corresponding angles might be represented by this symbol:

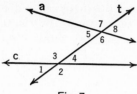

Fig. 7

Alternate interior angles—Pairs of angles that lie on opposite sides of the transversal and are interior, but not adjacent. Angles 4 and 5 are alternate interior angles. Alternate interior angles might be represented by this symbol:

Alternate exterior angles—Pairs of angles that lie on opposite sides of the transversal and are exterior but not adjacent. Angles 1 and 8 are alternate exterior angles.

Interior angles on the same side of the transversal—A pair of angles such as angles 4 and 6 are interior angles on the same side of the transversal.

In plane geometry a transversal and the lines it intersects lie in the same plane. The names of pairs of angles listed above do not apply to angles formed by two skew lines cut by a transversal.

Exercises

*Refer to Figure 7 for Exercises **1-6.***

1. Name the four pairs of corresponding angles.
2. Name the two pairs of interior angles on the same side of the transversal.
3. Name the two pairs of exterior angles on the same side of the transversal.
4. Name the pairs of alternate interior angles.
5. Name the pairs of alternate exterior angles.

6. Identify the following pairs of angles:
   a. 3 and 7   d. 3 and 2
   b. 3 and 6   e. 3 and 4
   c. 3 and 5   f. 2 and 7.
7. Consider AE to be the transversal of HB and FG.
   a. Name two pairs of alternate interior angles.
   b. Name two pairs of corresponding angles.
   c. Name two pairs of interior angles on the same side of the transversal.

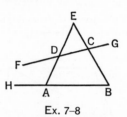

Ex. 7–8

8. Consider FG to be the transversal of AE and BE. Identify all the different pairs of angles formed by the three lines.
9. If AC is the transversal of FE and CD, identify the following pairs of angles:
   a. $\angle C$ and $\angle CBE$
   b. $\angle C$ and $\angle 1$
   c. $\angle C$ and $\angle FBC$.

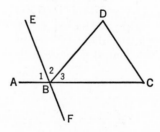

Ex. 9–10

10. If BD is the transversal of FE and CD, identify the following pairs of angles:
    a. $\angle D$ and $\angle FBD$
    b. $\angle 2$ and $\angle D$.

11. If *ABCD* is a quadrilateral, and *AC* is a diagonal, identify the transversal and the two lines intersected by the transversal when:

a. ∠1 and ∠3 are alternate interior angles.

b. ∠2 and ∠4 are alternate interior angles.

c. ∠*BAD* and ∠*ADC* are interior angles on the same side of the transversal.

d. ∠1 and ∠4 are interior angles on the same side of the transversal.

e. ∠3 and ∠*B* are interior angles on the same side of the transversal.

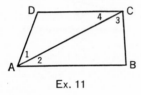

Ex. 11

Dynamic parallel lines instrument (*Optional*)

A dynamic instrument similar to the one shown in Figure 8 is very useful in studying relationships involving two lines cut by a transversal.

You can make this instrument from three strips of heavy cardboard or clear plastic about ½ inch wide and 15 inches long. Eyelets can be used to

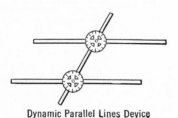

Dynamic Parallel Lines Device

Fig. 8

hold the strips together and to allow two of the strips to be rotated with reference to the third. Protractors mounted at the pivotal points are very convenient, but not essential.

Identifying angles

Use a dynamic instrument or a suitable drawing such as the one shown here to identify the following pairs of angles:

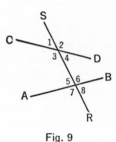

Fig. 9

1. Vertical angles. How many pairs are there?
2. Adjacent angles. Name eight pairs.
3. Supplementary adjacent angles. How many pairs are there?
4. Four pairs of corresponding angles.
5. Two pairs of alternate interior angles.
6. Two pairs of interior angles on the same side of the transversal.
7. Two pairs of alternate exterior angles.

Informal Experiments

For each of the experiments use either a dynamic instrument or a suitable drawing. The names used for the lines and angles are the same as those in Figure 9.

1. Arrange AB and CD with reference to RS so that a pair of corresponding angles such as $\angle 5$ and $\angle 1$ are equal. How does AB appear to be related to CD?

2. Make AB appear parallel to CD.
   a. How do the angles of the pairs of corresponding angles seem to be related? For example, how does $\angle 7$ seem to be related to $\angle 3$?
   b. How do the angles of the pairs of alternate interior angles seem to be related? For example, how does $\angle 6$ seem to be related to $\angle 3$?
   c. How do the angles of the pairs of interior angles on the same side of the transversal seem to be related? For example, how does $\angle 5$ seem to be related to $\angle 3$?

3. Make a pair of corresponding angles, such as $\angle 8$ and $\angle 4$, equal.
   a. How are the angles of the pairs of alternate interior angles related?
   b. How are the angles of the pairs of interior angles on the same side of the transversal related?
   c. How are the angles of the pairs of alternate exterior angles related?

4. Make both AB and CD perpendicular to RS. What seems to be the relation of AB to CD?

5. Make AB perpendicular to RS. Make CD appear parallel to AB. How does CD seem to be related to RS?

6. Make a pair of interior angles on the same side of the transversal supplementary.
   a. What seems to be the relation of AB to CD?
   b. What is the relation of $\angle 6$ to $\angle 2$?
   c. What is the relation of $\angle 6$ to $\angle 3$?
   d. What is the relation of $\angle 7$ to $\angle 2$?

Parallel line postulates

Are EF and RS in Figure 10 parallel? When we use the definition of parallel lines, it may be difficult to make certain that the lines will not intersect even if we could extend them indefinitely. In our development of geometry in this text, we shall assume that EF is parallel to RS if $\angle 1 = \angle 2$, and also that $\angle 1 = \angle 2$ if EF is parallel to RS.

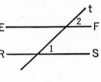

Fig. 10

In plane geometry we also assume that through the given point P in Figure 11 there is one, and only one, line parallel to x. Thus, if b is parallel to x, then b is the only line through P parallel to x.

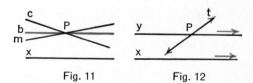

Fig. 11   **Fig. 12**

In Figure 12, x is parallel to y, and t intersects y at P. Since we have agreed that there is only one line through P parallel to x, then we must also agree that t is not parallel to x. That is, t and x intersect. Lines drawn on paper are of necessity line segments. Remember, x, y, and t represent lines and not line segments. Hence, t and x are intersecting lines, although the printed lines do not show the point of intersection.

POSTULATES 23. If two lines are cut by a transversal so that the corresponding angles are equal, the lines are parallel.

24. If two parallel lines are cut by a transversal, the corresponding angles are equal.

25. Through a given point there is one, and only one, line parallel to a given line.

26. In a plane, if a line intersects one of two parallel lines, it intersects the other, also.

Historical note

Postulate 25 is perhaps the most famous assumption in the history of mathematics. It is better known as Euclid's Fifth Postulate. As we shall learn later, this postulate is the basis of the proof that the sum of the angles of any triangle is 180°, and hence, of many of the other theorems of this course.

Nicholas Lobachevsky (1793-1856) and Johann Bolyai (1802-1860) each made the assumption that an infinite number of parallels can be drawn through a given external point. On the basis of this assumption, each of them proved that the sum of the angles of a triangle is less than 180°.

George Friedrich Riemann (1826-1866) assumed that any two lines will intersect. Thus he was able to prove that the sum of the angles of a triangle is greater than 180°.

If we assume that on a sphere the shortest path between two points is an arc of a great circle through the two points, then great circle arcs are analogous to straight lines in a plane. Hence, on a sphere where any two great circles intersect in two points, there are no parallel lines. As a matter of fact, if a triangle is drawn on a sphere, and if the sides of the triangle are arcs of great circles, the sum of its angles is greater than 180°, and the sum increases as its area increases.

Thus we see how really important definitions and assumptions are. Deducible conclusions change as definitions and assumptions are changed. If we agree to accept certain assumptions, we must accept the conclusions that necessarily follow from these assumptions.

Exercises

In the figure for Exercises **1-3**, *ABC is a triangle and D and E are points on AC and BC, respectively.*

1. If $AB \parallel DE$, then $\angle B = \ldots \ldots$
Why?

Ex. 1–3

2. If $\angle EDC = \angle A$, then $\ldots \ldots$ Why?

3. If $\angle B$ is the supplement of $\angle DEB$, prove:

   a. $\angle B = \angle CED$.

   b. $AB \parallel DE$.

In the figure for Exercises **4** *and* **5**, *lines x and y are cut by the transversal t.*

4. If $x \parallel y$, prove that $\angle 1 = \angle 3$.

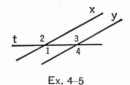

Ex. 4–5

5. If $\angle 2 = \angle 4$, prove that $x \parallel y$.

In the figure for Exercises **6-8**, *lines a and b are cut by the transversal t.*

6. If $\angle 1 + \angle 2 = 180°$, prove that $\angle 1 = \angle 3$.

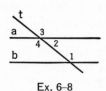

Ex. 6–8

7. If $\angle 1 = \angle 4$, prove that $a \parallel b$.

8. If $a \parallel b$, prove that $\angle 1$ is the supplement of $\angle 2$.

9. Parallel rules are convenient instruments for drawing parallel segments. Make a rule of strips of heavy cardboard or other material which will be satisfactory. The transverse segments are equal and parallel. The parts may be held together with eyelets or round-head paper fasteners.

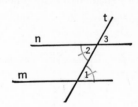

Ex. 9

Alternate interior angles

THEOREM 5. **If two lines are cut by a transversal so that the alternate interior angles are equal, the lines are parallel.**

Given: Lines m and n cut by the transversal t so that $\angle 1 = \angle 2$.

Prove: $m \parallel n$.

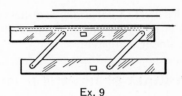

Proof

STATEMENTS	AUTHORITIES
1. Lines m and n are cut by t.	**1.** Given.
2. $\therefore \angle 2 = \angle 3$.	**2.** If two lines intersect, the vertical angles are equal.
3. $\angle 1 = \angle 2$.	**3.** Given.
4. $\therefore \angle 1 = \angle 3$.	**4.** If two quantities are equal to the same quantity, they are equal to each other.
5. $\therefore m \parallel n$.	**5.** If two lines are cut by a transversal so that the corresponding angles are equal, the lines are parallel.

Corollaries

The proofs of some theorems are so simple that there is no need to write a detailed formal proof. This is particularly true of a special case, or of a simple extension of another theorem.

DEFINITION A *corollary* is a theorem that is easily deducible from another theorem or statement.

COROLLARY OF THEOREM 5. If two lines in the same plane are perpendicular to the same line, they are parallel.

If a and b are each perpendicular to t, the alternate interior angles 1 and 2 are equal because they are right angles. Thus, a is parallel to b by Theorem 5.

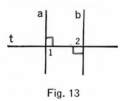

Fig. 13

Converses of implicative statements

An if-then statement, or one that can be written in the if-then form, is called an implicative statement. (See page 15.) The if-clause contains the given conditions and the then-clause specifies the conclusion. In a statement

having only one conclusion, if we interchange the conclusion and one of the given conditions, we get a new statement which is called a *converse* of the original. For example, the converse of Theorem 5 is "If two parallel lines are cut by a transversal, the alternate interior angles are equal." The condition "the alternate interior angles are equal" and the conclusion "the lines are parallel" were interchanged to form the converse.

Forming converses

It is easier to understand how the converses of a statement are formed if the verbal statement is analyzed in terms of a representative figure. To illustrate, we shall use the corollary of Theorem 5 and the figure that accompanies it (Figure 13).

Conditions: Lines a, b, and t are in the same plane.
    (a) $t \perp a$
    (b) $t \perp b$
Conclusion: (c) $a \parallel b$

A converse of the corollary:

Conditions: Lines a, b, and t are in the same plane.
    (a) $t \perp a$
    (c) $a \parallel b$
Conclusion: (b) $t \perp b$

Notice that condition (b) and conclusion (c) were interchanged to form the converse. The verbal statement of this converse is "If a line is perpendicular to one of two parallel lines, it is perpendicular to the other."

Another converse of the corollary could be formed by interchanging condition (a) and conclusion (c). However, the second converse does not yield anything new since its verbal statement is identical with that of the first converse.

The formation of converses of theorems is a convenient way to create important and interesting geometric situations. However, they cannot be accepted without proof. A statement and its converses are logically independent; that is, a converse of a true statement might be either true or false, and a converse of a false statement might be either true or false.

Particularly in non-mathematical situations, false converses of true statements are often inadvertently assumed to be true. Consider the following true statement and its converse:

Statement S: If a watch is an Enif, it is a fine watch.

Converse of S: If a watch is a fine watch, it is an Enif.

Although it might not be too obvious, the latter statement is probably false. In the next example it is immediately apparent that the converse is false.

Statement S: If a man lives in Ohio, he lives in the United States.

Converse of S: If a man lives in the United States, he lives in Ohio.

Exercises

Write the converses of the following statements and indicate whether or not they are true:

1. If an angle is a right angle, the sides of the angle are perpendicular.

2. If two lines in a plane are cut by a transversal so that the corresponding angles are equal, the lines are parallel.

3. If two angles are adjacent, they have the same vertex.

4. If two angles have a common side, they are adjacent. (This statement is false.)

5. If $\angle A = \angle B$ and if $\angle A$ is a right angle, then $\angle B$ is a right angle. This statement has two converses. Write the verbal statement of each.

6. If an animal is a dog, it has four legs.

7. If a man is an alien of country C, he cannot vote in country C.

8. If an animal does not have gills, it is not a fish.

9. If a boy is enrolled in plane geometry, he has credit in Algebra I.

10. If the fathers of Jim and Sam are brothers, then Jim and Sam are cousins.

The converse of Theorem 5

THEOREM 6. If two parallel lines are cut by a transversal, the alternate interior angles are equal.

Given: $m \parallel n$, and t is a transversal.

Prove: $\angle 1 = \angle 2$.

The proof is left for you.

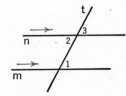

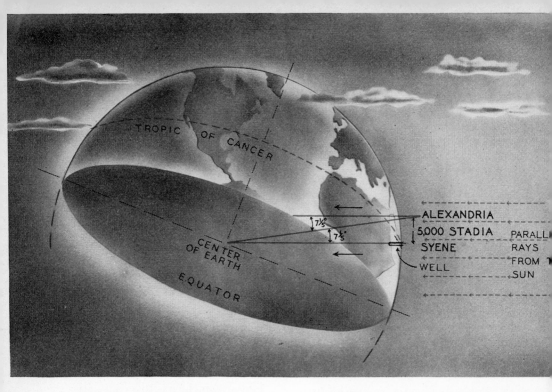

An ancient application of Theorem 6

Eratosthenes, a mathematical philosopher of the third century B.C., was the first to compute the approximate circumference of the earth.

At Syene, near the Tropic of Cancer, at noon on June 21, the summer solstice, the sun shone directly down into a deep well. Eratosthenes reasoned that the sun must be directly overhead. At Alexandria, approximately 5000 stadia to the north, he found the angle of the shadow of a vertical pole was 7.2°. He knew that light rays coming from a great distance appear to be parallel, and that the alternate interior angles of parallel lines are equal. Thus he reasoned that the angle at the center of the earth between the extensions of the well and the pole would be 7.2°. Since 7.2° is one-fiftieth of 360° and a central angle of a circle is numerically equal to its intercepted arc, the circumference of the earth must be 50 times 5000 stadia.

If stadia are converted to miles, his measurement is 25,000 miles—a remarkably close approximation to the actual circumference of the earth.

A converse of the corollary of Theorem 5

COROLLARY OF THEOREM 6. In a plane, if a line is perpendicular to one of two parallel lines, it is perpendicular to the other.

If $a \parallel b$, then $\angle 1 = \angle 2$. Since $t \perp a$, $\angle 1$ is a right angle. Therefore, $\angle 2$ is a right angle, and $t \perp b$.

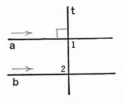

Fig. 14

Exercises

1. Given: $ABCD$ is a quadrilateral, AC is a diagonal, $DC \parallel AB$, and $\angle 1 = \angle 4$.

Deduce the implications.

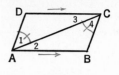

Ex. 1

Proof

STATEMENTS	AUTHORITIES
1. $DC \parallel AB$, and AC is a transversal.	1. Given.
2. $\therefore \angle 2 = \angle 3$.	2. Why?
3. AC is a transversal of AD and BC; $\angle 1 = \angle 4$.	3. Why?
4. $\therefore AD \parallel BC$.	4. Why?
5. $\therefore \angle 2 + \angle 1 = \angle 3 + \angle 4$.	5. Why?
6. $\therefore \angle BAD = \angle DCB$.	6. Why?

Questions on the proof:

a. How many syllogisms are there in this proof?

b. To what do the arrowheads on the linkage lines point?

c. How many conclusions were proved?

d. Is Statement 4 needed to prove Statement 5?

e. How are Authorities 2 and 4 related?

2. Given: $x \parallel y$, c and d are straight lines, and $\angle 1 = \angle 3$.
Deduce the relation of angles 2 and 3.

Ex. 2–3

3. Given: $x \parallel y$, c and d are straight lines, and $\angle 1 = \angle 3$.
What can you prove about angles 2 and 4?

4. Given: $ABCD$ is a quadrilateral, AD is extended to E, $AD \parallel BC$, and $\angle 1 = \angle 3$.
Deduce the implications.

Ex. 4

5. Given: Lines x, y, t, and m are straight lines, $\angle 1 = \angle 2$, $t \perp x$.
Deduce the implications.

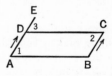

Ex. 5

6. Given: $x \parallel y$, $a \perp y$, and $b \perp y$.
Deduce the implications.

Ex. 6

7. Given: $\triangle ABC$ with AC extended to D, $CE \parallel AB$.
Deduce the implications.

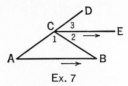

Ex. 7

8. Prove: If two parallel lines are cut by a transversal, the alternate exterior angles are equal.

9. Prove: If two parallel lines are cut by a transversal, the bisectors of a pair of alternate interior angles are parallel.

10. If $\angle 1 = \angle 2$, and $\angle 3 = 90°$, $\angle 4 = $?   Why?

Ex. 10

11. State and prove the converse of Exercise 8.

12. Prove: If two lines are cut by a transversal so that the corresponding angles are equal, the exterior angles on the same side of the transversal are supplementary.

Interior angles on the same side of the transversal

THEOREM 7. If two lines are cut by a transversal so that the interior angles on the same side of the transversal are supplementary, the lines are parallel.

Given: Lines r and s are cut by the transversal t, and $\angle 1$ is the supplement of $\angle 2$.

Prove: $r \parallel s$.

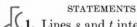

Proof

STATEMENTS	AUTHORITIES
1. Lines s and t intersect.	**1.** Given.
2. $\therefore$ $\angle 3$ is adjacent to $\angle 2$.	**2.** If two angles have a common vertex and a common side between them, then they are adjacent.
3. $\therefore$ $\angle 3$ is the supplement of $\angle 2$.	**3.** If the exterior sides of two adjacent angles lie in a straight line, the angles are supplementary.
4. $\angle 1$ is the supplement of $\angle 2$.	**4.** Given.
5. $\therefore$ $\angle 1 = \angle 3$.	**5.** If two angles are supplements of the same angle, they are equal.
6. $\therefore$ $r \parallel s$.	**6.** If two lines are cut by a transversal so that the alternate interior angles are equal, the lines are parallel.

The converse of Theorem 7

THEOREM 8. **If two parallel lines are cut by a transversal, the interior angles on the same side of the transversal are supplementary.**

Given: $a \parallel b$, and t is a transversal.

Prove: $\angle x$ is the supplement of $\angle y$.

The proof is left for you.

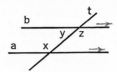

Exercises

In these numerical exercises, write the logical answers and an informal proof of each.

1. Given: $m \parallel n$, and t is a transversal.
  a. If $\angle 1 = 48° \, 15'$, then $\angle 2 = $?
  b. If $\angle 1 = 48° \, 15'$, then $\angle 3 = $?
  c. If $\angle 1 = 48° \, 15' \, 27''$, then $\angle 4 = $?

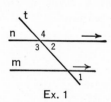

Ex. 1

2. Given: Triangle ABE, AB extended to C, and $BD \parallel AE$.
  a. If $\angle A = 70°$, then $\angle DBA = $?
  b. If $\angle E = 70°$, then $\angle 2 = $?
  c. If $\angle A = 70°$, then $\angle 1 = $?
  d. If $\angle 1 + \angle 2 = 140°$, then $\angle 3 = $?

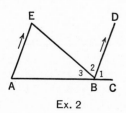

Ex. 2

3. Given: All the lines in the figure are intersecting straight lines.
  a. If $\angle A = 30°$, and $\angle ECA = 150°$, then . . . . .
  b. If $\angle ACG = 30°$, and $\angle CGF = 150°$, then . . . . .
  c. If $\angle A = 37°$, $AB \parallel ME$, and $AD \parallel FH$, evaluate each angle in the entire figure.

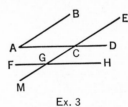

Ex. 3

4. Given: Triangle ABC with DE joining points D and E on BC and AC, respectively.
  a. If $\angle A = 59°$, and $\angle 1 = 121°$, then . . . . .
  b. If $\angle A = 59°$, and $\angle 1 = 121°$, then $\angle B + \angle 3 = $?
  c. If $\angle A = \angle 2$, and $\angle 3 = 130°$, then $\angle B = $?

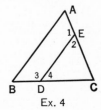

Ex. 4

Use algebraic equations to help you find answers to Exercises **5-12**.

5. If $r \parallel s$, and $\angle x$ is 72° less than $\angle y$, find the number of degrees in angles x and y.

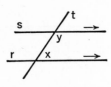

Ex. 5–7

6. If $r \parallel s$, and $\angle y$ is 60° greater than $\angle x$, how many degrees are there in each angle?

7. If $r \parallel s$, and $\angle x$ and $\angle y$ are in the ratio 4 : 5, how many degrees are there in each angle?

8. If a and b are cut by t so that $2\angle y - \angle x = 150°$, and $\angle y - \angle x = 40°$, then $\angle y + \angle x = $? How is a related to b?

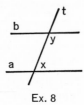

Ex. 8

9. If $k \parallel m$, and $\angle x = \frac{3}{5}\angle y$, find $\angle x$.

Ex. 9–10

10. If $k \parallel m$, and $\angle y = 2\angle z$, find $\angle x$.

11. If $AD \parallel BF$, and $\angle CEF$ exceeds twice $\angle DCE$ by 4°, find $\angle DCE$.

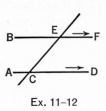

Ex. 11–12

12. If $AD \parallel BF$, $\angle CEF = 3x + 10°$, and $\angle ECA = 2x + 50°$, then $x = $?

The distance between two parallel lines

DEFINITION The *distance between two parallel lines* is the shortest path between them.

The distance from a point to a line is the length of the perpendicular segment from the point to the line. In Figure 15, if $PR \perp m$, the length of PR is the distance from P to m. We know that a line perpendicular to one of two parallel lines is perpendicular to the other. If m is parallel to n, then PR is also perpendicular to n. Hence, the length of PR is the distance from R to n. Therefore, the length of PR is also the distance between m and n.

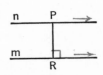

Fig. 15

POSTULATES 27. **The distance between two parallel lines is the length of the common perpendicular segment between the two lines.**

28. **If two lines are parallel, they are everywhere equidistant.**

Exercises

1. Draw a line on your paper. Through some point outside the line draw a line parallel to the given line. (Hint: Draw a transversal through the given point and line. Then use your protractor to draw equal corresponding angles or equal alternate interior angles.)

2. **a.** Draw an angle on your paper. Use your protractor to bisect the angle.
   b. Through some point on the angle bisector draw a line parallel to each side of the angle.

3. **a.** Draw two parallel lines on your paper that are two inches apart. Name the lines e and g.
   b. Find several points that are equidistant from e and g.

4. Draw a line on your paper and name it m. Locate several points one inch from m. Are all the points one inch from m on the same side of m?

Auxiliary lines

An *auxiliary* line is a line which we are allowed to add to a given figure to help us. It is customary to "dash" an auxiliary line to distinguish it from the given lines.

The postulate, "One, and only one, straight line can be drawn through

two given points," is the basic authority for drawing auxiliary lines. It gives us the right to draw the auxiliary line MN connecting the vertex N of $\triangle BXN$ and M, which is a point on BX.

Fig. 16

The postulates that justify auxiliary lines are:

1. One, and only one, straight line can be drawn through two given points. (Postulate 3)
2. Through a given point there is one, and only one, perpendicular to a given line. (Postulate 11)
3. An angle has one, and only one, bisector. (Postulate 14)
4. Through a given point there is one, and only one, line parallel to a given line. (Postulate 25)

From these postulates it is apparent that only two conditions can be imposed on an auxiliary line:

First condition—It can be drawn through a given point.

Second condition—Only one of the following:

a. It can be drawn through a second given point, *or*

b. It can be drawn perpendicular to a given line, *or*

c. It can bisect a given angle, *or*

d. It can be drawn parallel to a given line.

To illustrate the use of an auxiliary line, let us consider the example on the following page.

Example:

Given: $\triangle ABC$ with AC extended to E.

Prove: $\angle BCE = \angle A + \angle B$.

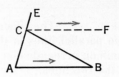

Proof

STATEMENTS	AUTHORITIES
1. Through C draw $CF \parallel AB$.	1. Through a given point there is one, and only one, parallel to a given line.
2. $\therefore$ With AE as the transversal, $\angle A = \angle FCE$.	2. Why?
3. $\therefore$ With BC as the transversal $\angle B = \angle BCF$.	3. Why?
4. $\therefore$ $\angle A + \angle B = \angle FCE + \angle BCF$.	4. Why?
5. $\therefore$ $\angle A + \angle B = \angle BCE$.	5. Why?

Two lines parallel to the same line

THEOREM 9. In a plane, if two lines are parallel to the same line, they are parallel to each other.

Given: $x \parallel y$, and $y \parallel z$.

Prove: $x \parallel z$.

Informal analysis: To prove two lines parallel, we need a transversal. If we draw a line t through P and Q, which are any points on x and y, respectively, it must intersect z at some point R. We can then prove $x \parallel z$ if we can prove $\angle 1 = \angle 3$.

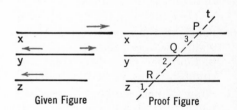

Given Figure   Proof Figure

Proof

STATEMENTS	AUTHORITIES
1. Draw the transversal t through the points P and Q on x and y, respectively.	1. A straight line may be drawn through two given points.
2. $y \parallel z$.	2. Why?
3. $\therefore$ t intersects z at some point R.	3. If a line intersects one of two parallel lines, ...

You complete the proof.

Exercises

1. Given: $AB \parallel ED$, and BC intersects CD.
Prove: $\angle DCB = \angle D + \angle B$.
Hint: Draw $CF \parallel AB$, and prove $CF \parallel ED$, etc.

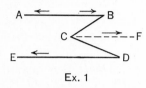

Ex. 1

2. Given: $AB \parallel ED$, and BC intersects DC.
Prove: $\angle D + \angle B + \angle BCD = 360°$.
Hint: Draw $FC \parallel AB$, etc.

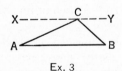

Ex. 2

3. Given: $\triangle ABC$.
Prove: $\angle A + \angle B + \angle C = 180°$.
Hint: Draw $XCY \parallel AB$.

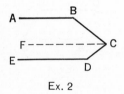

Ex. 3

Two angles with parallel sides

If you imagine yourself at the vertex of an angle with your arms extending along its sides, your right arm extends along the *right* side of the angle and your left arm extends along the *left* side of the angle. (The right side of a positive angle is its initial side, and its left side is its terminal side.)

In Figure 17, the sides of $\angle a$ are parallel to the sides of $\angle b$, and also to the sides of $\angle c$. The right side of $\angle a$ is labeled r_a, and the left side is labeled l_a. A similar notation is used for the sides of $\angle b$ and for the sides of $\angle c$. Notice the common side which is the left side of $\angle c$ and the right side of $\angle b$.

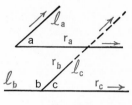

Fig. 17

It is apparent that the sides of angles a and c are parallel *right to right* and *left to left*. It can be proved that $\angle a = \angle c$.

The sides of angles a and b are parallel *right to left* and *left to right*. It can be proved that $\angle a$ is the supplement of $\angle b$.

In Figure 18, the sides of $\angle d$ are parallel to the sides of $\angle m$, and also to the sides of $\angle e$. Angles m and e are between the sides of $\angle d$.
How is $\angle d$ related to $\angle m$?
How is $\angle d$ related to $\angle e$?

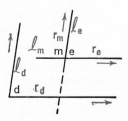

Fig. 18

THEOREMS 10. **If the sides of two angles are parallel right side to right side and left side to left side, the angles are equal.**

11. **If the sides of two angles are parallel right side to left side and left side to right side, the angles are supplementary.**

The proofs of these theorems are left for you.

Exercises

1. Given: The sides of angles *RST* and *TSW* are parallel to the sides of angle *B*.

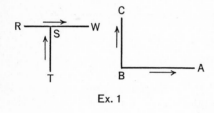

Ex. 1

a. Deduce the relation of ∠*RST* to ∠*B*.

b. Deduce the relation of ∠*TSW* to ∠*B*.

2. Given: *BC* ∥ *ST*, and *BA* ∥ *RS*. Deduce the relation of ∠*B* to ∠*S*.

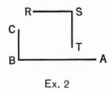

Ex. 2

3. Given: *BC* ∥ *ST*, and *BA* ∥ *SR*. Deduce the relation of ∠*B* to ∠*S*.

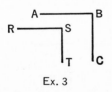

Ex. 3

4. Given: *ABCD* is a quadrilateral, *AB* ∥ *DC*, and *AD* ∥ *BC*.

a. Deduce the relation of ∠*A* to ∠*C*; of ∠*B* to ∠*D*.

b. Deduce the relation of ∠*A* to ∠*B*; of ∠*A* to ∠*D*.

Ex. 4

Space Geometry (*Optional*)

5. a. Do you think that a line and a plane might be located so that they do not intersect?

b. Write a definition of a *line parallel to a plane*.

c. According to your definition, how many lines may there be through a given point parallel to a given plane? Illustrate.

d. Hold your pencil so that it does not intersect your book. Are the pencil and book necessarily parallel? Explain.

6. a. Write a definition of parallel planes.

b. According to your definition, how many planes may there be through a given point parallel to a given plane?

7. If each of two planes is perpendicular to a given plane, are the planes necessarily parallel? Illustrate by using books to represent planes. (Refer to Chapter 2 for the definition of a dihedral angle. If the dihedral angle of two intersecting planes is a right angle, the planes are perpendicular.)

8. In plane geometry we know that if line x is perpendicular to line t, and line y is perpendicular to line t, then $x \parallel y$. Investigate the relation of x to y if:

   a. Line t is changed to plane t.

   b. Lines x and y are changed to planes x and y.

   c. Lines x and t are changed to planes x and t.

   d. Lines x, y, and t are changed to planes x, y, and t.

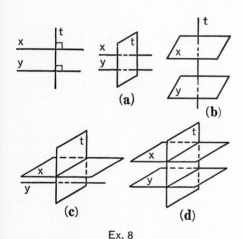

(a) (b) (c) (d)

Ex. 8

9. In plane geometry we know that if line x is parallel to line y, and line x is perpendicular to line t, then y is perpendicular to t. Draw appropriate figures and investigate the relation of y to t if:

   a. Line t is changed to plane t.

   b. Lines x and y are changed to planes x and y.

   c. Lines x and t are changed to planes x and t.

   d. Lines y and t are changed to planes y and t.

   e. All the lines are changed to planes.

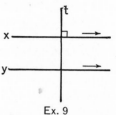

Ex. 9

10. Through the given point P, line m is the only line parallel to line x. Investigate the statements obtained by making the following changes:

    a. Line m is changed to plane m.

    b. Line x is changed to plane x.

    c. Lines m and x are changed to planes m and x.

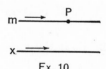

Ex. 10

11. Through the given point P, line t is the only line perpendicular to line x. Investigate the statements obtained by making the following changes:

    a. Line t is changed to plane t.

    b. Line x is changed to plane x.

    c. Lines t and x are changed to planes t and x.

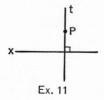

Ex. 11

⋆Transformations of implicative statements⋆

One of the most important values of geometry is the opportunity it affords for developing proper habits of clear thinking. We have seen how formal proof in geometry is based on the use of syllogisms. We know that sometimes even a deducible conclusion is not true. To be deducible a conclusion need only be the logical conclusion based on certain general and particular statements; if either of these statements is false, the conclusion is not necessarily true. All too often we base conclusions on false general statements, usually without realizing we are doing so. This occurs when we have in mind a true statement, but base our reasoning on another which, appearing to have the same meaning, actually is quite different.

Here are four statements that resemble one another and might appear to have the same meaning:

Statement A: If it is raining, the roads are wet.

Statement B: If the roads are wet, it is raining.

Statement C: If it is not raining, the roads are not wet.

Statement D: If the roads are not wet, it is not raining.

Statements A and D are true, but B and C are false. The roads might be wet from a previous rain, from the water of a road sprinkler, or for other reasons.

⋆Contradictory statements

An assertion that $\angle m = \angle n$ is contradicted by asserting that it is false that $\angle m = \angle n$, or simply that $\angle m$ and $\angle n$ are unequal. Likewise, an assertion that $a \parallel b$ is contradicted by asserting that it is false that $a \parallel b$, or simply that a and b are not parallel.

Contradictory statements occur in pairs. If either is true, the other must be false; if either is false, the other is true.

⋆Converses, inverses, and contrapositives

When a condition and the conclusion of an implicative statement are interchanged, the original statement has been transformed. We learned earlier that this particular transformation is called a converse. There are two other ways to transform an implicative statement. The three ways to transform an implicative statement S having only one condition and only one conclusion are shown at the top of the next page.

*Note to the teacher: Included in this section and in subsequent sections in this and in other chapters is a simplified explanation of the inverses and contrapositives of implicative statements and of necessary and sufficient conditions. Although there is no treatment of these concepts in some geometry textbooks, they are presented here, along with the converses of statements, for the benefit of those teachers who believe that the quality of one's thinking, in both mathematical and non-mathematical situations, is appreciably enhanced by an understanding of them.

Since these concepts are not essential to the basic sequence of this course, they may be omitted or they may be studied later in the course. They are designated by a star printed next to them on the left side of the column. All exercises based on them are similarly marked.

1. Converse of S: Interchange the condition and the conclusion.
2. Inverse of S: Contradict the condition and contradict the conclusion.
3. Contrapositive of S: Interchange the contradictory of the condition and the
                         contradictory of the conclusion.

These transformations are illustrated in the following examples:

Example 1

Statement S: If two lines in a plane are cut by a transversal so that
                         the alternate interior angles are equal, the lines are
                         parallel.

Converse of S: If two parallel lines are cut by a transversal, the
                         alternate interior angles are equal.

Inverse of S: If two lines in a plane are cut by a transversal so that
                         the alternate interior angles are not equal, the lines
                         are not parallel.

Contrapositive of S: If two non-parallel lines in a plane are cut by a trans-
                         versal, the alternate interior angles are unequal.

Since Statement S is Theorem 5 and Converse of S is Theorem 6, each is true.
Later we shall learn why Inverse of S and Contrapositive of S are true.

Example 2

Statement S: If an animal is a fish, it can swim.
Converse of S: If an animal can swim, it is a fish.
Inverse of S: If an animal is not a fish, it cannot swim.
Contrapositive of S: If an animal cannot swim, it is not a fish.

In Example 2, it is obvious that the statement and its contrapositive are both
true; the converse and the inverse are both false.

Most of the theorems in geometry have more than one condition and one or more conclusions. Any statement having more than one conclusion may be divided into as many statements as there are conclusions. For example, the statement, "In Figure F, if *a*, *b*, and *c* are true, then *x* and *y* are true" may be divided as follows:

1. In Figure F, if *a*, *b*, and *c* are true, then *x* is true.
2. In Figure F, if *a*, *b*, and *c* are true, then *y* is true.

In our simplified treatment of transformations, we shall deal with statements having only one conclusion.

★Exercises

1. Show that Postulates 23 and 24 are converses of each other.

2. Write the inverse of Postulate 23 and the inverse of Postulate 24.

3. Write the contrapositive of Postulate 24.

4. Write the inverse of Theorem 6. How is this statement related to the contrapositive of Theorem 5?

5. Write the three transformations of "If two parallel lines are cut by a transversal, the alternate exterior angles are equal."

*Multiple converses

A statement having more than one given condition and only one conclusion has as many converses as it has given conditions.

Example

Statement S:	If students attend Metropolis High and if they have Room 303 for registration, then they are freshmen. (Assumed to be true.)
Converse 1: (C₁ of S)	If students are freshmen and if they have Room 303 for registration, then they attend Metropolis High.
Converse 2: (C₂ of S)	If students attend Metropolis High and if they are freshmen, then they have Room 303 for registration.

Some or all of the converses of a true statement may be false. In the example, both converses of Statement S are false.

The converses of implicative statements having more than one given condition and only one conclusion are formed by interchanging one condition and the conclusion.

*Multiple inverses

A statement having more than one given condition and only one conclusion has as many inverses as it has given conditions.

Example

Statement S:	If students attend Metropolis High and if they have Room 303 for registration, they are freshmen. (Assumed to be true.)
Inverse 1: (I₁ of S)	If students do *not* attend Metropolis High and if they have Room 303 for registration, they are *not* freshmen.
Inverse 2: (I₂ of S)	If students attend Metropolis High and if they do *not* have Room 303 for registration, they are *not* freshmen.

Some or all of the inverses of a true statement may be false. Both of the inverses of Statement S are false.

The inverses of implicative statements having more than one given condition and only one conclusion are formed by contradicting one of the given conditions and contradicting the conclusion.

*Multiple contrapositives

A statement having more than one given condition and only one conclusion has as many contrapositives as it has given conditions.

Example

Statement S: If students attend Metropolis High and if they have Room
                            303 for registration, they are freshmen. (Assumed to be
                            true.)

Contrapositive 1:   If students are *not* freshmen and if they have Room 303
(Cp₁ of S)   for registration, they do *not* attend Metropolis High.

Contrapositive 2:   If students attend Metropolis High and if they are *not*
(Cp₂ of S)   freshmen, they do *not* have Room 303 for registration.

Both of the contrapositives of Statement S are true.

**The contrapositives of implicative statements having more than one condition
and only one conclusion are formed by interchanging the contradictory of one
given condition and the contradictory of the conclusion.**

★Equivalent statements

If two implicative statements are *equivalent*, one is true when the other is true;
one is false when the other is false. Although it can be proved by methods of
logic, in this course we shall assume that a statement and all its contrapositives
are equivalent.

**Law of Contrapositives—An implicative statement and its contrapositives are
equivalent; that is, if a statement is true, each of its contrapositives is true; if a
statement is false, each of its contrapositives is false.**

★Summary of transformations

I. Transformations of an implicative statement having one given condition and
one conclusion:

Let *s* represent the given condition, and let *c* represent the implied conclusion.
Statement S and its transformations are:

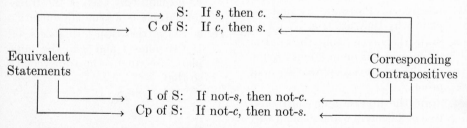

II. Transformations of an implicative statement having more than one given
condition and one conclusion:

In a statement having two given conditions, let s_1 and s_2 represent the conditions,
and let *c* represent the conclusion. Statement S and its transformations are
shown on the following page.

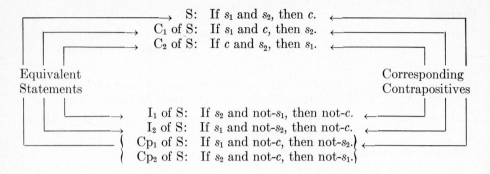

S: If s_1 and s_2, then c.

C_1 of S: If s_1 and c, then s_2.

C_2 of S: If c and s_2, then s_1.

Equivalent   Corresponding
Statements   Contrapositives

I_1 of S: If s_2 and not-s_1, then not-c.

I_2 of S: If s_1 and not-s_2, then not-c.

Cp_1 of S: If s_1 and not-c, then not-s_2.

Cp_2 of S: If s_2 and not-c, then not-s_1.

Converses and inverses of true statements may be false; converses and inverses of false statements may be true. If a true statement has multiple converses and inverses, some of them may be true and others may be false. However, the corresponding converses and inverses of a statement are equivalent because a converse is the contrapositive of the corresponding inverse, and vice versa.

A statement and its contrapositives are equivalent.

★**Exercises**

1. State the inverse and the contrapositive of Postulate 23 and explain why they are true.

2. State the inverse and the contrapositive of Postulate 24 and explain why they are true.

3. State the inverse and the contrapositive of Theorem 5 and explain why they are acceptable without proof.

4. State the inverse and contrapositive of Theorem 6 and explain why they are acceptable without proof.

5. State the three transformations of Theorem 8 and explain why all of them are true. Which statements are equivalent?

6. Prove: If two non-parallel lines in a plane are cut by a transversal, the alternate interior angles are unequal. Hint: Prove its contrapositive equivalent.

7. Prove the converse of the statement in Exercise 6.

8. State each of the transformations of: If $\angle a$ is the complement of $\angle b$, and if $\angle a$ is the complement of $\angle c$, then $\angle b = \angle c$.

9. State each of the transformations of: If $\angle x$ is the supplement of $\angle y$, if $\angle r$ is the supplement of $\angle z$, and if $\angle y = \angle r$, then $\angle x = \angle z$.

10. **a.** State the transformations of: If $\angle A$ is a right angle and if $\angle B$ is a right angle, then $\angle A = \angle B$.

    b. Write a verbal statement of each transformation.

    c. Explain why each of the transformations is a true statement.

11. **a.** State the transformations of: If two lines x and y in the same plane are cut by the transversal t so that

    $s_1 : x \parallel y$

    $s_2 : x \perp t$

    then $c : y \perp t$

    b. Write a verbal statement of each transformation.

    c. Explain why each transformation is, or is not, a true statement.

★Sufficient conditions

To clarify the meaning of sufficient conditions, we shall consider three examples:

1. If an $\underline{\text{animal is a dog}}$, it $\underline{\text{has four legs.}}$
   sc
   Condition s is sufficient for conclusion c because the presence of s means the presence of c. That is, the statement is true.

2. If students
   $\underline{\text{have Room 303 for registration}}$
   s_1
   $\underline{\text{and if they attend Metropolis High,}}$
   s_2
   $\underline{\text{they are freshmen.}}$
   c
   Condition s_1 is sufficient for conclusion c if, in the presence of s_2, the presence of s_1 means the presence of c. Likewise, condition s_2 is sufficient for conclusion c if, in the presence of s_1, the presence of s_2 means the presence of c.

3. Complements of the same angle are equal.
   Given: Three angles m, n, and s.
   s_1 : $\angle m$ is the complement of $\angle s$.
   s_2 : $\angle n$ is the complement of $\angle s$.
   Conclusion c : $\angle m = \angle n$.

Since condition s_1, in the presence of s_2, implies c, then s_1 is sufficient for c. Likewise, s_2 in the presence of s_1 is sufficient for c.

If an implicative statement or any of its contrapositives is true, the combination of conditions is sufficient for the conclusion.

To prove that a condition is sufficient for a conclusion, show that the conclusion is deducible from the condition.

★Necessary conditions

1. If an $\underline{\text{animal is a dog}}$, it has $\underline{\text{four legs.}}$
   sc
   Condition s is not necessary for c because the contradictory of s does not mean the contradictory of c. That is, the inverse of the statement is false.

2. If students
   $\underline{\text{have Room 303 for registration}}$
   s_1
   $\underline{\text{and if they attend Metropolis High,}}$
   s_2
   $\underline{\text{they are freshmen.}}$
   c
   Since both the inverses of the statement are false, neither condition s_1 nor s_2 is necessary for conclusion c. That is, the contradictory of s_1 does not mean the contradictory of c, and the contradictory of s_2 does not mean the contradictory of c.

A condition is necessary for the conclusion of an implicative statement if the inverse involving that condition is true. Since an inverse is the contrapositive of the corresponding converse, and vice versa, they are equivalent. Hence, a condition is proved to be necessary if either the inverse or the corresponding converse involving that condition can be proved.

In an implicative statement of the form, "If s, then c," if c is deducible from s, then s is a sufficient condition for c, and c is a necessary condition for s. To illustrate, consider the implicative statement, "If an animal is a cat, it has four feet." The fact that an animal is a cat is a sufficient condition that it be four-footed; however, in order for an animal to be a cat, it is necessary that it have four feet.

★Summary of necessary and sufficient conditions

| If s implies c
or
if not-c implies not-s | then | s is sufficient for c
and
c is necessary for s. |

| If not-s implies not-c
or
if c implies s | then | s is necessary for c
and
c is sufficient for s. |

★Exercises

*In the following statements decide whether the conditions are (**a**) sufficient but not necessary for the conclusion, (**b**) necessary but not sufficient for the conclusion, (**c**) both necessary and sufficient for the conclusion, or (**d**) neither necessary nor sufficient for the conclusion:*

1. If two parallel lines are cut by a transversal, the alternate interior angles are equal.

2. If two lines in a plane are cut by a transversal so that the corresponding angles are equal, the lines are parallel.

3. If $\angle A = 90°$ and if $\angle B = 90°$, then $\angle A = \angle B$.

4. If $\angle m$ is the supplement of $\angle s$, if $\angle x$ is the supplement of $\angle y$, and if $\angle m = \angle x$, then $\angle s = \angle y$.

5. If a man has 5 cents, he has enough money to buy a 3-cent stamp.

6. If an animal is a bird, it can fly.

7. If grass does not have water, it will not grow.

8. If it is raining, there are clouds in the sky.

9. If two angles are complementary, they are equal. (False)

10. If two angles are adjacent, they have the same vertex.

★General statements not in the if-then form

We have found the if-then form of theorems, assumptions, and definitions to be a convenient one to use in writing authorities in proofs of theorems and exercises. This form of general statement is also frequently used in reasoning about non-mathematical situations. However, many general statements may not be in the if-then form. Statements like the following are common ones:

a. All men are bipeds.
(All A is B.)

b. Some scholars are athletes.
(Some A is B.)

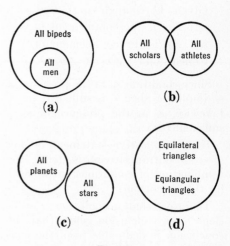

(a)

(b)

(c)

(d)

Fig. 19

c. No planets are stars.
(No *A* is *B*.)

d. If, and only if, a triangle is equilateral, then it is equiangular. (If, and only if, *A*, then *B*.)

In this section, we shall study the transformations of these forms of statements and learn which transformations are equivalent to the original ones.

★ Statements of the type "All A is B."

The following statements are equivalent to *All A is B*:

a. No *A* is non-*B*.
b. No non-*B* is *A*.
c. All non-*B* is non-*A*.

Fig. 20

The following statements are *not* equivalent to *All A is B*.

a. All *B* is *A*.
b. All non-*A* is non-*B*.
c. All non-*B* is *A*.

PRACTICE:

1. Which of these five statements are equivalent to the statement, *All Saxons are automobiles*?
   a. All automobiles are Saxons.
   b. No Saxon is not an automobile.
   c. Every non-automobile is a non-Saxon.
   d. Whatever is not a Saxon is not an automobile.
   e. No non-automobile is a Saxon.

2. Assume the truth of the statement, *All unkind people are rude*. (Also assume *impolite* is *rude*, and *polite* is *non-rude*.) Decide which of these five statements are equivalent to it:
   a. All kind people are polite.
   b. All impolite people are unkind.
   c. All polite people are kind.
   d. No unkind person is polite.
   e. No polite person is unkind.

★ Statements of the type "No A is B."

The following statements are equivalent to *No A is B*:

a. No *B* is *A*.
b. All *B* is non-*A*.
c. All *A* is non-*B*.

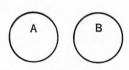

Fig. 21

The following statements are *not* equivalent to *No A is B*:

a. No non-*B* is *A*.
b. All non-*A* is *B*.
c. All non-*B* is *A*.

PRACTICE:

If we assume the truth of the statement, No worms are appetizing, *to which of the following would we have to agree?*

1. All non-worms are appetizing.
2. All worms are unappetizing.
3. All appetizing things are non-worms.
4. No appetizing things are worms.
5. All unappetizing things are worms.

★Statements containing the word "some"

Fig. 22

Original Statement	Equivalent Transformation
a. Some A is B.	Some B is A.
b. Some A is not B.	Some A is B.

PRACTICE:

Write the equivalent transformations of the following:

1. Some voters are intelligent people.
2. Some mules are not contrary animals.
3. Some swimmers are not fish.
4. Some flowers are roses.
5. Some equilateral polygons are equiangular.
6. Some equiangular polygons are not equilateral.

★Statements of the type "If, and only if, A is true, then B is true."

A is both sufficient and necessary for B. Hence, A implies B, and B implies A. The circles representing A and B are identical.

Fig. 23

PRACTICE:

Write all the equivalent transformations of the following statements:

1. If, and only if, an animal has feathers, it is a bird.
2. If, and only if, the sides of an angle are perpendicular, the angle is a right angle.
3. If, and only if, two sides of a triangle are equal, the angles opposite them are equal.
4. If, and only if, a point is equidistant from the sides of an angle, it is on the bisector of the angle.

★Exercises

In Exercises 1-2 write all the equivalent transformations:

1. If, and only if, a point is equidistant from two given points, it is on the perpendicular bisector of the segment joining the points.
2. Only equilateral triangles are equiangular.
3. Make as complete a list as you can of the logical conclusions that can be deduced from the following facts:

   a. All employees of the City Transit Company are members of the Transport Workers Union.

   b. No company can employ a member of the Transport Workers Union at wages less than $13 a day.

   c. No alien can be a member of the Transport Workers Union.

   d. Bill Smith is an employee of the City Transit Company.

   e. The combined wages of Bill Smith and his brother, Alex, are $25 a day.

4. What can be deduced from the following information?

a. No freshmen are permitted to take geometry at G. H. S.

b. Only students who have credit in Algebra I may take geometry at G. H. S.

c. Sam is taking geometry at G. H. S.

d. Bill is taking Algebra II.

e. Bill and Sam are brothers.

5. Consider this simple exercise in logic taken from a textbook on the subject by Lewis Carroll, mathematician and author of *Alice's Adventures in Wonderland*.

a. No kitten that loves fish is unteachable.

b. No kitten without a tail will play with a gorilla.

c. Kittens with whiskers always love fish.

d. No teachable kitten has green eyes.

e. No kittens have tails unless they have whiskers.

One, and only one, deduction can be drawn from this set of statements. What is it?

6. Are these two statements equivalent? Explain.

a. If a lamina is a drib, it has srehtaef.

b. If a lamina does not have srehtaef, it is not a drib.

7. If it is true that hsif can miws, does it necessarily follow that a buhc that can miws is a hsif?

8. Mary said, "Joe is the best halfback our school has ever had. If he does not play Friday, we shall lose the game." Sally replied, "You mean if he does play Friday, we shall win the game."

If Mary's statement is true, is Sally's statement necessarily true?

Chapter Summary

In this chapter we studied the conditions that make lines parallel and the properties of parallel lines. They were defined as straight lines in the same plane that do not intersect. For the purposes of demonstrative geometry, we agreed that parallel lines are lines that make equal corresponding angles with a transversal; and conversely, that if two lines are parallel, the corresponding angles which they make with a transversal are equal.

Two lines are parallel if:

1. The corresponding angles are equal.
2. The alternate interior angles are equal.
3. The interior angles on the same side of the transversal are supplementary.
4. They are both perpendicular to the same line and in the same plane.
5. They are both parallel to the same line.

If two lines are parallel, then:

1. The corresponding angles are equal.
2. The alternate interior angles are equal.
3. The interior angles on the same side of the transversal are supplementary.
4. A perpendicular to one of them is also perpendicular to the other if all three lines are in the same plane.
5. A line parallel to one of them is also parallel to the other.

Cumulative Summary

Two angles are equal if:

1. They are the results obtained by adding or subtracting equal angles, by multiplying or dividing equal angles by equals, or by substituting equal angles for equals.
2. They are parts of a bisected angle or of equal bisected angles.
3. They are adjacent angles formed by perpendicular lines.
4. They are both right angles or both straight angles.
5. They are complements or supplements of the same angle or of equal angles.
6. They are a pair of vertical angles of intersecting lines.
7. They are alternate interior angles or corresponding angles formed by two parallel lines cut by a transversal.

8. They are angles whose sides are parallel right side to right side and left side to left side.

Two angles are supplementary if:

1. Their sum equals a straight angle.
2. They are adjacent angles and their exterior sides extend in opposite directions in a straight line.
3. They are interior angles on the same side of a transversal that cuts two parallel lines.
4. They are angles whose sides are parallel right side to left side and left side to right side.

Two lines are perpendicular if:

1. They are the sides of a right angle.
2. They form equal adjacent angles.

Review of Chapter 4

General Questions

*In each of the Exercises **1-18**, certain conditions are given. You may be able to deduce more than one conclusion from each set of conditions. State the authority for each conclusion.*

*In the figure for Exercises **1-4**, RSTW is a quadrilateral.*

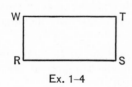

Ex. 1–4

3. If $\angle R$ is the supplement of $\angle S$, and $\angle S = \angle T$, then . . . . . Why?
4. If $WR \parallel TS$, and $WR \perp RS$, then . . . . . Why?

*In the figure for Exercises **5-8**, BDG, ABC, EDF, and CD are straight lines.*

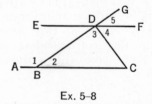

Ex. 5–8

1. If $WT \perp RW$, and $RS \perp RW$, then . . . . . Why?
2. If $\angle R$ is the supplement of $\angle S$, then . . . . . Why?

5. If $\angle 1 = \angle 3 + \angle 4$, then . . . . . Why?
6. If $\angle 2$ is the supplement of $\angle BDF$, then . . . . . Why?

7. If $EF \parallel AC$, then . . . . . Why?

8. If $\angle C = \angle 4$, then . . . . . Why?

In the figure for Exercises **9-12**, *ACE is a triangle; B and D are points on AC and EC, respectively.*

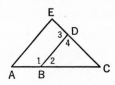

Ex. 9–12

9. If $\angle A = \angle 2$, then . . . . . Why?

10. If $\angle E$ is the supplement of $\angle 3$, then . . . . . Why?

11. If $\angle A$ is the supplement of $\angle 3$, and $\angle A = \angle E$, then . . . . . Why?

12. If $BD \parallel AE$, then . . . . . Why?

In the figure for Exercises **13-16**, *MNOP is a quadrilateral and MO is a diagonal.*

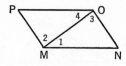

Ex. 13–16

13. If $\angle 1 = \angle 4$, then . . . . . Why?

14. If $\angle 2 = \angle 3$, then . . . . . Why?

15. If $\angle NMP$ is the supplement of $\angle P$, then . . . . . Why?

16. If $PO \parallel MN$, and $MP \parallel NO$, then . . . . . Why?

In the figure for Exercises **17** *and* **18**, *AB, DC, AD, and CB are straight lines.*

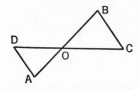

Ex. 17–18

17. If $DA \parallel BC$, then . . . . . Why?

18. If $\angle A = \angle B$, how are angles D and C related? Why?

19. Prove: If two lines are cut by a transversal so that the alternate exterior angles are equal, the lines are parallel.

20. Prove: If two parallel lines are cut by a transversal, the exterior angles on the same side of the transversal are supplementary.

21. Prove: If two lines are cut by a transversal so that the exterior angles on the same side of the transversal are supplementary, the lines are parallel.

22. Prove: If two parallel lines are cut by a transversal, the bisectors of a pair of corresponding angles are parallel.

23. Explain how a draftsman uses his straightedge and triangle to draw a line through P parallel to a given line l.

Ex. 23

24. The carpenter's bevel shown here was used to make parallel lines on a piece of wood. What other uses might it have?

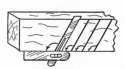

Ex. 24

Completion Test

Complete the following statements correctly. Do not write in this book.

1. If two lines in the same plane are perpendicular to the same line, they are . . . . .

2. If two lines are parallel to the same line, they are . . . . .

3. If a line is parallel to one of two perpendicular lines, it is . . . . to the other.

4. If a line is perpendicular to one of two parallel lines, it is . . . . to the other if all three lines are in the same plane.

5. Two . . . . are everywhere equidistant.

In the figure for Exercises 6-9, ABCD is a quadrilateral.

Ex. 6–9

6. If $AB \parallel DC$, then angles A and D are . . . . .

7. If $AB \parallel DC$, and $AD \parallel BC$, then $\angle A$ and $\angle C$ are . . . . .

8. If $\angle A$ is the supplement of $\angle D$, ... and . . . . are parallel.

9. If $AB \perp AD$, and $AB \perp BC$, ... and . . . . are parallel.

In the figure for Exercises 10-12, ABCD is a quadrilateral, and BD is a diagonal.

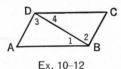

Ex. 10–12

10. If $\angle A + \angle 1 + \angle 2 = 180°$, ... and . . . . are parallel.

11. If $\angle 2 = \angle 3$, then . . . . and . . . . are parallel.

12. If $AB \parallel DC$, angles . . . . and . . . . are equal.

In the figure for Exercises 13-15, ABC is a triangle, AC is extended to D, and CE is a line through C.

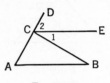

Ex. 13–15

13. If $AB \parallel CE$, angles . . . . and . . . . are supplementary.

14. If $AB \parallel CE$, and if $\angle A = \angle B$, then CE . . . . .

15. If $\angle A$ is the supplement of $\angle ACE$, then . . . . .

In the figure for Exercises 16-18, D and E are on the sides of △ABC as indicated.

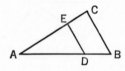

Ex. 16–18

16. If $DE \parallel BC$, $\angle B$ . . . . $\angle BDE$.

17. If $DE \parallel BC$, $\angle B$ is equal to . . . . .

18. If $\angle B = \angle C$, and if $DE \parallel BC$, $\angle EDA$ . . . . $\angle AED$.

In the figure for Exercises 19 and 20, m, n, x, and y intersect as indicated.

Ex. 19–20

19. If $m \parallel n$, and $x \parallel y$, $\angle a$ . . . . $\angle b$.

20. If $m \parallel n$, and $x \parallel y$, $\angle a$ . . . . $\angle c$.

True-False Test

Write the numbers **1-20** *on your paper. After each number write* **True** *if the corresponding statement is true; write* **False** *if the statement is never true; write* **Sometimes** *if the statement is not necessarily true.*

1. If two lines in the same plane are perpendicular to the same line, they are perpendicular to each other.

2. If two lines are parallel to the same line, they are parallel to each other.

3. If a line is parallel to one of two perpendicular lines, it is perpendicular to the other.

4. If a line is not perpendicular to one of two parallel lines, it is not perpendicular to the other.

5. Two lines are everywhere equidistant.

6. If the sides of two angles are respectively parallel, the angles are either equal or supplementary.

7. If two lines in space are perpendicular to the same line, they are parallel.

8. Two lines in space either intersect or they are parallel.

9. Horizontal lines are parallel.

10. Vertical lines intersect at the center of gravity of the earth.

11. If two lines in space are each parallel to the same line, they are parallel.

12. If two non-parallel lines are cut by a transversal, the alternate interior angles are unequal.

13. If two lines are cut by a transversal, the corresponding angles are equal.

14. If two parallel lines are cut by a transversal, any two interior angles are supplementary.

15. If two lines are cut by a transversal so that the alternate interior angles are equal, the corresponding angles are equal.

16. Two lines in a plane either are parallel or intersect.

17. The bisectors of a pair of corresponding angles of two parallel lines cut by a transversal are perpendicular.

18. If a line intersects one of two parallel lines, it intersects the other.

19. If a line intersects one of two perpendicular lines, it intersects the other.

20. When an auxiliary line is drawn through a given point, two additional conditions can be imposed upon it.

When highway engineers plan and build roads like this New York State Thruway, they make constant use of the basic geometric constructions and loci that you will study in this chapter. At this interchange cars enter and leave the thruway by a system of curves and an overpass.

Chapter 5   BASIC CONSTRUCTIONS AND LOCI

IF YOU were given the opportunity to choose only two instruments for constructing the figures of geometry, which two would you select? Plato, a famous Greek mathematician who lived after the time of Euclid, chose the straightedge and compass. He was in charge of a Greek school that emphasized the study of plane geometry. In fact, we are told by historians that Plato had a motto written over the entrance to his school that proclaimed, "Let no one who is ignorant of geometry enter these portals." Plato thought his students would learn to use deduction better if they were limited to the use of the straightedge and compass for constructions.

Even to this day, the distinction is made between *drawing* a figure and *constructing* a figure. When we draw a figure we may use a straightedge, a ruler, a compass, a protractor, a parallel rule, a draftsman's triangle and T-square, and/or any other convenient device, but when we construct a figure we are limited to the use of the straightedge and compass. The reason for this is that all constructions are based on Postulates 3 and 8:

A straight line can be drawn through two given points.

A circle can be drawn with a given point as center and a given radius.

Mathematicians agree that a straight line can be drawn with a straightedge, and a circle can be drawn with a compass.

Using the compass

To become skillful in constructing circles and arcs of circles with a compass requires practice. You may find these hints helpful: Hold the compass between the fingers at its top as illustrated; incline it slightly forward as you draw; keep a steady downward pressure on the sharp point and with a twisting motion turn the top between the fingers. The pencil should not extend beyond the sharp point when the compass is closed. The pencil should always be sharp.

Fig. 1

Construction assumptions

Before we could write the first proof in geometry, it was necessary to make some basic assumptions. In the same way, geometric constructions are based on other constructions, some of which we accept without proof.* Euclid, however, insisted upon proving every construction before he used it.

---

* **Note to the teacher:** In this chapter there are certain constructions which cannot be proved until after the study of congruent triangles. A careful analysis of the sequence reveals no circular reasoning. The study of congruence might have preceded the study of parallel lines; however, there are some good psychological and pedagogical reasons for studying parallel line relationships and constructions first.

Constructions dealing with points and segments

CONSTRUCTION 1.   Construct a line segment equal to a given segment.

Given: Segment AB.

Required: To construct a segment $RS = AB$.

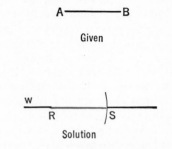

Given

Method: On w as a working line, with any point R as center and with a radius equal to AB, construct an arc intersecting w at S.

Can AB and RS be made to coincide? Does it seem reasonable to assume that $RS = AB$?

Solution

CONSTRUCTION 2.   Locate a point equidistant from two given points.

Given: Points R and S.

Required: To locate a point equidistant from R and S.

Method:

Given

1. With R as center and a radius greater than one-half RS, construct arc 1.
2. With S as center and the *same radius* with which arc 1 was drawn, construct arc 2.

Solution

   If arcs 1 and 2 intersect at P, then P is equidistant from R and S because $RP = SP$. Why?

Questions on the construction:

1. Would arcs 1 and 2 have intersected if we had used a radius less than one-half RS? Why?
2. How would arcs 1 and 2 have been related if we had used a radius equal to one-half RS? Why?
3. In Postulate 6, we learned that circles with equal radii are equal. How many pairs of equal circles can be drawn with R and S as centers? Explain.
4. How many pairs of points can be found which are equidistant from R and S?

CONSTRUCTION 3. Bisect a given straight line segment.

Given: The segment AB.

Required: To bisect AB.

Method:

1. Locate points X and Y equidistant from A and B.
2. Draw XY.

For the present, we shall assume that XY intersects AB at P, and that XY is the bisector of AB.

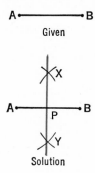

CONSTRUCTION 4. Construct the perpendicular bisector of a given line segment.

For the present, we shall assume that XY in Construction 3 is the perpendicular bisector of AB.

The following example illustrates how we can set up a construction problem that involves the use of line segments:

Example: Given two line segments m and n; construct a segment equal to $2m + n$.

Given: _____m_____

_____n_____

Required: A segment equal to $2m + n$.

Solution:

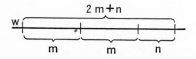

Be sure that you make a dot at your starting point on the working line.

Exercises

For Exercises **1-7** *draw two line segments m and n with m longer than n. Label the segments as in the example.*

1. **a.** Draw a segment equal to $m + n$.
   b. Construct a segment equal to $m + n$.
2. **a.** Draw a segment equal to $2m - n$.
   b. Construct a segment equal to $2m - n$.
3. Construct a circle whose diameter is m.
4. Bisect a line segment equal to the sum of m and n.
5. Construct a segment equal to $\frac{1}{2}(2m - n)$.
6. Construct the midpoint of $m + 2n$.
7. Divide $m + n$ into four equal parts with (**a**) a ruler; (**b**) a compass and straightedge. Is either (**a**) or (**b**) a construction? If so, which one?

Constructions dealing with angles

CONSTRUCTION 5.   **At a given point on a given line, construct an angle equal to a given angle.**

Given: $\angle ABC$ and a working line w with the point P on it.

Required: To construct an angle at P on the line w equal to $\angle ABC$.

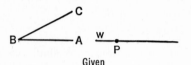

Given

Method:

1. With B as center and with a convenient radius, construct an arc that intersects BA at M and BC at N.
2. With P as center and with a radius *equal* to BM, construct arc 1 so that it intersects w at X.
3. With X as center and a radius *equal* to the straight line segment MN, construct arc 2 so that it intersects arc 1 at Y.
4. Draw PY.

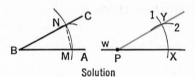

Solution

For the present, we shall assume that $\angle XPY = \angle ABC$.

CONSTRUCTION 6.   **Bisect an angle.**

Given: $\angle RST$.

Required: To bisect $\angle RST$.

Given

Method:

1. With S (the vertex) as center and with any convenient radius, construct an arc that intersects SR at M and ST at N.
2. Construct P equidistant from M and N.
3. Draw SP.

Solution

For the present we shall assume that SP bisects $\angle RST$.

Exercises

1. Draw an acute angle on your paper. Fold the paper so that the crease bisects the angle. Is this a construction?

2. Draw an obtuse angle. (**a**) Draw an angle equal to it, and bisect it with a protractor. (**b**) Construct an angle equal to it, and bisect it with a compass and a straightedge.

3. Draw an acute angle. Then (**a**) draw an angle twice as large as the given angle and, (**b**) construct an angle twice as large as the given angle. (Hint: Construct an angle adjacent to the given angle that is equal to it.)

4. Draw two angles on your paper.
   a. Measure each of the angles with your protractor and draw an angle equal to their sum.
   b. Construct an angle equal to the sum of the two given angles.

5. Draw an obtuse angle and an acute angle. Construct an angle equal to their difference. (Hint: Place the angles so that they have a common side and a common vertex and so that they overlap.)

6. Draw a reflex angle. Construct or draw an angle equal to it and bisect the angle.

For Exercises **7** *and* **8** *draw two angles on your paper. Let x be the number of degrees in the larger angle and let y be the number of degrees in the smaller angle.*

7. Construct an angle equal to $\frac{1}{2}(x + y)$.

8. Construct an angle equal to $\frac{1}{2}(x - y)$.

For Exercises **9** *and* **10** *draw a triangle ABC.*

9. Construct the sum of angles A, B, and C.

10. Bisect angles A, B, and C.

11. Divide an angle into four equal parts with:
    a. A protractor.
    b. A compass and straightedge.

12. Draw an obtuse angle. Construct its supplement.

13. Draw two intersecting straight lines. Bisect each angle of one pair of vertical angles. Prove that the bisectors lie in a straight line.

14. Draw two supplementary adjacent angles. Bisect both angles. Prove that the bisectors of two supplementary adjacent angles are perpendicular.

15. Through a given point P construct a line parallel to a given line m.

Men who draw the plans and work out construction details for buildings, bridges, automobiles, and airplanes are continually making the constructions which you are learning in your geometry course.

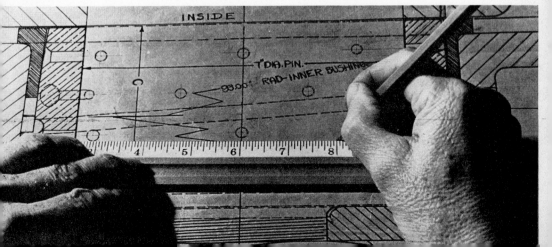

Constructing perpendiculars

CONSTRUCTION 7. **Through a given point, construct the perpendicular to a given line.**

Given: (**a**) Line m and point P on the line. (**b**) Line m and a point P outside m.

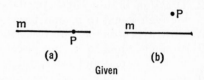

Given

Required: To construct a line through P perpendicular to m.

Method: The method of construction is the same for both parts (**a**) and (**b**).

Solution (a)

1. With P as center and a convenient radius, construct an arc that intersects m at two points R and S.

2. Construct point T equidistant from R and S.

3. Draw PT.

For the present, we shall assume that PT is perpendicular to m.

Solution (b)

Exercises

1. Fold a piece of paper so that you have a straight-line crease. Mark some point on the crease. Now the crease represents a straight angle. Fold again so that one side of the angle falls along the other side. When you unfold the paper, how are the creases related?

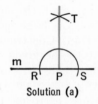

Ex. 2–3

Copy the figures for Exercises **2-10** *before starting each exercise. They must be made larger than they are shown here.*

2. Draw the perpendicular to AB at P.

3. Construct the perpendicular to AC at S.

4. Draw the segment that represents the distance from M to AB. Extend AB if necessary. (See figure at top of next page.)

Ex. 4–5

5. Find by construction the distance from M to AB.
6. Construct the perpendicular from P to AB.

Ex. 6–7

7. Construct the perpendicular to BR at P.
8. Find by construction the distance from S to RT.

Ex. 8–10

9. Find by construction the distance from T to RS.
10. Construct the perpendicular from R to ST.
11. Given a point D on line segment EF. Construct lines perpendicular to EF at E, D, and F. How are these perpendiculars related? Why?

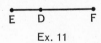

Ex. 11

12. Divide a circle into four equal arcs.
13. Divide a circle into eight equal arcs.
14. Construct a 45° angle.
15. Construct a 135° angle.
16. Draw an acute angle. Construct its complement.

Constructions dealing with parallel lines

When you construct a figure it is helpful first to draw a sketch of it. Suppose you want to construct a line r through P parallel to g. Recall the known ways of proving lines parallel. Each of the ways requires a transversal. A perpendicular transversal is required by some methods, but not by others.

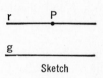

Sketch

Fig. 2

Suppose you decide to make a pair of corresponding angles equal. You need only to construct $\angle c$ at P equal to $\angle a$, one of the angles formed by t and g. The line through P and B must then be parallel to g. Why?

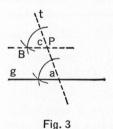

Fig. 3

Now draw a sketch to show how to construct r through P parallel to g, by:
1. Making a pair of alternate interior angles equal.
2. Using the corollary, "Lines perpendicular to the same line are parallel."

CONSTRUCTION 8. Construct a line parallel to a given line through a given point not on the line.

Given: Line m and point P not on m.

Required: To construct a line n through P parallel to m.

Method:

1. Draw any line t through P that makes any convenient angle such as $\angle x$ with m.
2. With t as one side, construct $\angle y$ equal to $\angle x$ and in such a position that $\angle x$ and $\angle y$ are corresponding angles.
3. The other side of $\angle y$, extended to form line n, is parallel to m.

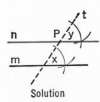

Given

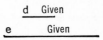

Solution

Proof

STATEMENTS	AUTHORITIES
1. $\angle y = \angle x$.	1. By Construction 5.
2. $\therefore n \parallel m$.	2. Why?

CONSTRUCTION 9. Construct lines parallel to a given line at a given distance from it.

Given: Line e and the segment d.

Required: To construct lines parallel to e at the distance d from e.

Method:

1. Construct a transversal t perpendicular to e at some point P.
2. From P, mark off on t segments PX and PY equal to d.
3. At X and Y construct perpendiculars to t.
4. Lines m and n are each parallel to e and at the distance d from e.

The proof of this construction is left for you.

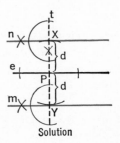

Solution

Exercises

For Exercises 1-7, draw figures on your paper similar to the given figures.

1. a. Through R construct a line parallel to s.

b. Through T draw a line parallel to s.

Ex. 1

2. a. Construct the midpoint of RS and name it M.

b. Through M construct a line parallel to RT.

c. Through M draw a line parallel to ST.

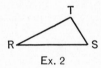

Ex. 2

3. Through A construct a line parallel to BC. Choose either AC or AB for the transversal. Extend the transversal if necessary.

Ex. 3

4. a. Construct the perpendicular to AB at C. Label it CF.

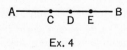

Ex. 4

b. Through D construct a line parallel to CF.

c. Through E construct a line parallel to CF by a method different from the one used in (**b**).

5. a. Bisect $\angle MKT$. Call the bisector KG.

b. Choose some point R on KG and through it construct a line parallel to KT.

Ex. 5

6. a. Through P construct a line parallel to MN.

b. Through N construct a line parallel to MP.

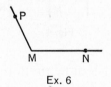

Ex. 6

7. a. Through P construct m parallel to n.

b. Through X construct a line parallel to m.

Ex. 7

8. Draw a line d on your paper. Construct two lines parallel to d, each $\frac{1}{2}$ inch from d.

9. Construct two parallel lines, m and n, on your paper. Construct a line that is parallel to them and midway between them.

Location of points that satisfy certain specified conditions

Imagine that you are in a physical education class in a gymnasium which has a straight line such as ML painted on the floor. After instructions by your teacher to stand 3 feet from the line, imagine that the members of the class took positions indicated by the dots A, B, C, etc. All the students except W, X, Y, and Z stood in the line represented by RA.

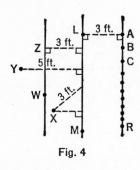

Fig. 4

What is meant by the distance from a point to a line? It is obvious that Y misunderstood the teacher's instructions, for he is more than 3 feet from ML. Suppose you are standing at X. Are you 3 feet from ML? Does Z satisfy the condition specified by the teacher?

If $ML \perp LA$, and $RA \perp LA$, then $ML \parallel RA$. Why? Why are ML and RA everywhere 3 feet apart?

Do all the students standing on RA fulfill the condition imposed by the teacher? Do any of the students not on RA satisfy the condition?

Can we be certain that all the students in either RA or WZ satisfy the condition?

Can we be certain that all the students who are 3 feet from ML are either on RA or WZ?

Can we be certain that the students not on RA or WZ do not satisfy the condition?

1. The teacher of your physical education class instructs everyone to stand 8 feet from him. Construct and describe the figure formed by the members of the class if they all follow the instructions.

2. Your physical education instructor asks you to walk around him so that you are always 8 feet from him. Construct and describe your path.

3. There are two parallel lines 4 feet apart on the gymnasium floor. What would be the path of the members of your physical education class if they were instructed to walk so that they were always equidistant from the two lines? Construct and describe their path.

4. James and Henry are standing 10 feet apart. All the other students in the class are instructed to stand so that they are as far from James as they are from Henry. Construct and describe the figure they form.

The meaning of locus

DEFINITION *A locus of points* **is a figure formed by all the points, and only those points, that satisfy certain conditions.**

The plural of locus is *loci* (pronounced: lō'-sī). From a dynamic viewpoint, a *locus of a point* is the path of a point that moves according to certain specified conditions.

Fig. 5

In Figure 5, $A, B, C, \ldots$ are static points in the same plane, each the distance r from the static point O in that plane. In Figure 6, A is a dynamic point that moves in a plane so that it is always the constant distance r from the static point O in that plane.

Fig. 6

In a plane, what is the locus of points at the given distance r from the given point O?

In a plane, what is the locus of the point A at the given distance r from the given point O?

Description of a locus

The description of a locus includes:

1. A statement of the conditions.
2. What the locus is (line, circle, pair of lines, ...).
3. Where the locus is (with reference to given point(s), line(s), ...).
4. How big the locus is, or what its dimensions are.

POSTULATE 29. In a plane, the locus of points (or the locus of a point) at a given distance from a given point is a circle with the given point as center and the given distance as radius.

☆Properties of a locus*

A locus has two properties:

FIRST PROPERTY:

It *includes* all the points that satisfy the given conditions. That is, the conditions are *sufficient* for the conclusion, as shown in **a** and **b**.

a. In a plane, if a point is the distance r from the point O, it is on the circle whose center is O and whose radius is r.

b. In a plane, if a point is not on the circle whose center is O, and whose radius is r, it is not the distance r from O. Statement **b** is the contrapositive equivalent of Statement **a**.

SECOND PROPERTY:

It *excludes* all the points that do not satisfy the given conditions. That is, the conditions are *necessary* for the conclusion, as shown in **c** and **d**.

c. In a plane, if a point is not the distance r from the point O, it is not on the circle with center O and with radius r.

d. In a plane, if a point is on a circle with center O and with radius r, it is the distance r from O.
Statement **c** is the inverse of **a**; Statement **d** is the converse of **a**; and Statement **d** is the contrapositive equivalent of **c**.

---

* See footnote on page 94 for an explanation of starred material.

Exercises

1. a. Which words of Postulate 29 state the given conditions?
b. Which words of Postulate 29 state what the locus is?
c. Which words of Postulate 29 state where the locus is?
d. Which words of Postulate 29 state how big the locus is?

2. The expressions *locus of a point* and *locus of points* are often used interchangeably, although they do not mean exactly the same thing. Explain how they differ.

3. Describe the locus of the tip of the second hand of a watch.

4. Describe the locus of a point on a fan blade 2 inches from the axis when the fan is in operation.

5. Describe the locus of the head of a screw on the handle of a revolving door.

6. Refer to Construction 1. Describe the locus of points AB units from R (page 110).

7. Refer to Construction 2. Describe the locus of points a given distance from R; from S. What is the locus of points a given distance from R *and* the same given distance from S?

8. Refer to Construction 3. Describe what you think is the locus of points equidistant from A and B.

9. Refer to Construction 6. Describe what you think is the locus of points equidistant from the sides of a given angle.

In Exercises **10-14** *explain whether or not the given conditions are* (**a**) *sufficient for the conclusion;* (**b**) *necessary for the conclusion.*

★**10.** If a man lives in New York, he lives in the United States of America.

★**11.** If a student did not receive excellent grades in algebra, he cannot get excellent grades in geometry.

★**12.** If a boy has good eyesight, he can drive an automobile.

★**13.** In space, if two straight lines are perpendicular to the same straight line, they are parallel.

★**14.** In a plane, if line x is perpendicular to line t, and if line y is not perpendicular to line t, then x is not parallel to y.

The locus of points at a given distance from a given line

POSTULATE 30. **In a plane, the locus of points at a given distance from a given line is a pair of lines parallel to the given line at the given distance from it.**

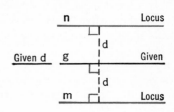

Fig. 7

Notice that the description of the locus in Postulate 30 contains the answers to these questions:

1. What conditions are imposed on the points?

a. They must be in a plane with the given line.

b. They must be at a given distance from the given line.

2. What is the locus?

The locus is a pair of lines.

3. Where is the locus?

The lines are parallel to the given line at the given distance from it.

4. How big is the locus?

The length of the locus is not explicitly stated, but we know that a line is of indefinite length.

Postulate 30 states:

1. In a plane, any point the distance d from g is on either m or n; or, any point not on either m or n is not the distance d from g.

2. In a plane, any point not the distance d from g is not on either m or n; or, any point on either m or n is the distance d from g.

The locus of points equidistant from two parallel lines

Lines r and s are parallel. Point P is midway between r and s on the perpendicular transversal t, and $h \perp t$ at P. Hence, h is parallel to both r and s.

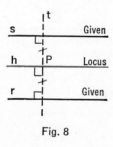

Fig. 8

If (1) every point equidistant from r and s is on h, and (2) every point on h is equidistant from r and s, then h is the locus of points equidistant from r and s.

★State the contrapositives of parts (1) and (2).

POSTULATE 31. In a plane, the locus of points equidistant from two given parallel lines is a third parallel midway between them.

Dynamic locus models

The dynamic models shown here can be made with heavy cardboard and round-head paper fasteners, or other suitable materials. The solid black parts represent the given figures, the red parts represent the loci, and the unshaded parts represent the framework of the model.

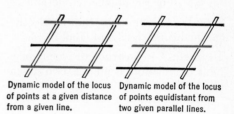

Dynamic model of the locus of points at a given distance from a given line.   Dynamic model of the locus of points equidistant from two given parallel lines.

Fig. 9

The distance from a point to a circle

How far are points P and Q from circle O? If OA is a radius, then QA is the shortest path from Q to the circle. If OP is a straight line intersecting circle O at B, then BP is the shortest path from P to the circle.

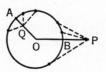

Fig. 10

DEFINITION The *distance from a point to a circle* is the shortest path from the point to the circle.

POSTULATE 32. The distance from a point to a circle is the length of the segment of the radius, or radius extended, from the point to the end of the radius on the circle.

The locus of a point equidistant from two concentric circles

Given: Two circles concentric at O; the radius of the larger circle is m and the radius of the smaller circle is n.

Note: We draw a figure that fulfills the specified conditions and label it.

Required: To construct the locus of a point equidistant from the two given circles.

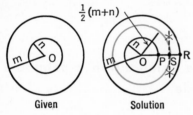

Given   Solution
Fig. 11

Method:

1. Draw OR a radius of the larger circle and intersecting the smaller circle at P. (The length of PR is the distance between the two circles. Why?)
2. Bisect PR. Call its midpoint S. (S is now equidistant from the two circles. Why?)
3. Construct the circle with O as center and OS as radius.

Description: The locus of a point equidistant from two given concentric circles, center O and radii m and n, is a circle whose center is O and whose radius is $\frac{1}{2}(m + n)$.

Answer the following questions:

1. Which part of the description states the *given conditions*?
2. Which words of the description tell us *what the locus is*?
3. Which words of the description tell us *where the locus is*?
4. Which words of the description tell us *how big the locus is*?
5. Why is $OS = \frac{1}{2}(m + n)$? Show algebraically.

Figures 12 and 13 picture dynamic locus models which you can make.

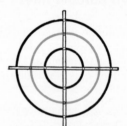

Model of the locus of points equidistant from two given concentric circles.

Fig. 12

Model of the locus of points at a given distance d from a given circle of radius r, when d is less than r.

Fig. 13

Exercises

1. Construct and describe the locus of a point that is the distance d from a circle of center O and radius r if d is less than r.

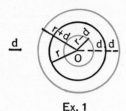

Ex. 1

2. Construct and describe the locus of a point that is ½ inch from a circle of center O and radius ½ inch.

3. Construct and describe the locus of a point that is the distance d from a circle of center O and radius r if d is greater than r.

4. Construct and describe the locus of a point that is ½ inch from a given line x.

5. Construct and describe the locus of a point that is equidistant from two parallel lines x and y which are 2 inches apart.

6. Construct and describe the locus of the midpoints of the radii of a circle of center O and radius r.

7. Construct the locus of a point that is the distance d from the sides of a triangle.

8. Construct the locus of a point that is the distance d from the sides of a quadrilateral.

9. Describe the locus of the center of a car wheel moving along a straight level track.

10. If you see a shelf in a library marked "Science," can you be sure that (**a**) all books on the shelf are science books? (**b**) all science books are on the shelf?

11. Do all the members of your geometry class satisfy a given condition? If so, what is it? Are all the students in your school who satisfy the same condition members of your geometry class?

12. Describe a non-mathematical situation that *includes* all the things or people that satisfy a specified condition and *excludes* all the things or people that do not.

13. Certain physical objects such as sidewalks along a street, the center line painted on a highway, and the pendulum bob of a clock, remind us of certain loci. Make a list of other objects that illustrate the loci we have described.

Exercises—Space Geometry (*Optional*)

1. Describe the locus, in space, of a point at the given distance r from the given point O.

2. Describe the locus, in space, of a point at the given distance d from a sphere whose center is O and whose radius is r if d is less than r.

3. Describe the locus, in space, of a point at the given distance d from a given line m.

4. Describe the locus, in space, of a point equidistant from two parallel lines.

5. Describe the locus, in space, of a point at the given distance d from a given circle whose center is O and whose radius is r.

6. Describe the locus, in space, of a point at the given distance d from a given plane.

7. Describe the locus, in space, of a point equidistant from two parallel planes.

Multiple loci (compound loci)

Sometimes it is necessary to locate points that satisfy two conditions simultaneously. Each condition determines a separate locus, which is constructed independently of the other. The points of intersection of the two loci, if any, are the required points.

If you want to plant a tree so that it is equidistant from two parallel sidewalks *and* 20 feet from a telephone pole, how might you locate the spot to plant the tree? In geometry, such problems are stated and solved as follows:

Example 1: Locate points that are (a) equidistant from two given parallel lines *and* (b) at a given distance from a given point.

Given: $m \parallel s$, point O, and the distance d.

Given

Required: Points equidistant from m and s *and* the distance d from O.

Possibility 1. The loci intersect in two points. In the solution figure, R_1 and R_2 are the required points. What is the distance of O from locus a?

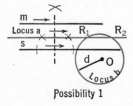

Possibility 1

Possibility 2. If point O happens to be exactly the distance d from locus a, the two loci have just one point R_1 in common.

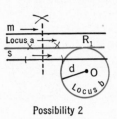

Possibility 2

Possibility 3. The loci do not intersect. If the distance from O to locus a is greater than the distance d, locus a and locus b do not intersect. The figure shows that there are no points that satisfy both conditions.

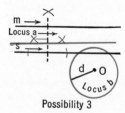

Possibility 3

Discussion:

There are three possibilities, depending upon the distance between the given lines m and s, the position of the given point O, and the length of the given segment d.

1. There may be two points that satisfy both conditions simultaneously.

2. There may be only one point that satisfies both conditions simultaneously.

3. There may be no points that satisfy both conditions simultaneously.

Example 2: Locate points that are on a given line g *and* at a given distance d from a second given line x.

Possibility 1. If x and g intersect, two points P_1 and P_2 satisfy both conditions simultaneously.

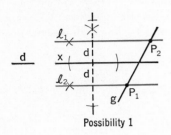

Possibility 1

Possibility 2. If g happens to be parallel to x and the distance d from x, an infinite number of points satisfy both conditions simultaneously; all of them lie on g.

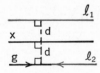

Possibility 2

Possibility 3. If x is parallel to g, and g is not the distance d from x, no points satisfy the conditions simultaneously (g might also lie between l_1 and l_2 or above l_1).

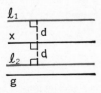

Possibility 3

Exercises

In each of the following exercises you are to locate points that satisfy two conditions simultaneously. Construct and discuss the possibilities of each.

1. The foreman of a crew of telephone maintenance men is instructed to place a service pole 70 feet from a designated point on a certain house *and* 10 feet from a street curb which is 50 feet from the house. Draw a figure and explain how he might use his knowledge of loci to find the place for the pole.

2. A dog is tied to a stake S in a yard which has parallel fences f_1 and f_2. The distance between f_1 and f_2 is 50 feet; S is 7 feet from f_2; and the dog's leash is 10 feet long. Draw a figure to show the portion of the yard over which the dog can exercise.

3. Locate the points that are $1\frac{1}{4}''$ from the given line g, *and* $1\frac{1}{2}''$ from the given point O which is $2''$ from g.

4. Locate the points that are $2.0''$ from the given line g, *and* equidistant from two given parallel lines a and b which are $1.0''$ apart.

5. Locate the points that are $2\frac{1}{2}''$ from the given point O_1, *and* $1\frac{1}{4}''$ from the given point O_2. Explain why the number of points that satisfy the two given conditions depends upon the distance between O_1 and O_2.

6. Locate the points that are equidistant from two given parallel lines a and b, *and* equidistant from two given parallel lines m and n.

7. Locate the points that are equidistant from two given parallel lines m and n *and* at the given distance d from the given point O.

8. Locate the points on the given segment AB that are the given distance d from the given line g.

9. Locate the points that are on a given circle, *and* are equidistant from two given parallel lines.

10. Locate the points that are equidistant from two given concentric circles, *and* equidistant from two given parallel lines.

11. Locate the points that are equidistant from two given concentric circles, *and* at a given distance from a third circle.

12. Locate the points that are equidistant from two given concentric circles, *and* at a given distance from a given line.

Symmetry and design

Many of the designs we see in architecture, tile, linoleums, fabrics, rugs, wallpapers, china, jewelry, insignia, etc., are based on geometric figures. In these designs there is often a kind of balance which we call symmetry. Geometric figures are classified as symmetrical or non-symmetrical. Symmetrical figures have either line, point, or plane symmetry or a combination.

We are accustomed to symmetrical designs in many natural forms, and we like man-made figures to be symmetrical with just enough variation to avoid monotony.

Line symmetry

A figure is *symmetric* with respect to a line as an axis if for every point of the figure there is another point such that the *axis* is the perpendicular bisector of the segment joining the two points. That is, a figure has line symmetry if there is a line along which

it can be folded so that the corresponding parts coincide. A figure may have more than one axis of symmetry. For example, an equilateral triangle has three axes of symmetry, and a circle has an infinite number. Because of the line which is used as an axis, line symmetry is also known as *axial symmetry*. In Figure 14, XY is the axis of symmetry for each design.

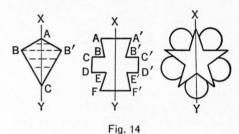

Fig. 14

In Figure 15, how many axes of symmetry has each design?

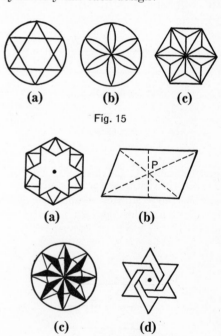

(a)   **(b)**   **(c)**

Fig. 15

(a)   **(b)**

(c)   **(d)**

Figures symmetric with respect to a point.

Fig. 16

Point symmetry

A figure is symmetric with respect to a point, called the *center of symmetry*, if for every point of the figure it is possible to find a second point such that the *center* bisects the segment joining the pair of points. That is, a figure has point symmetry if a line that joins any two corresponding points passes through and is bisected by the center of symmetry.

In the four illustrations of point symmetry shown in Figure 16, do you find any which also have line symmetry? If so, which ones?

Examine these three symmetrical designs made by geometry students. Which have point symmetry? Which have line symmetry? Can you tell if any of the three figures has more than one axis of symmetry? How many does it have?

The spindle of the steam turbine shown in this photograph is symmetrical with respect to a plane passed vertically through its center.

Plane symmetry

A solid figure may have point, line, or plane symmetry. A solid is symmetric with respect to a plane if this plane bisects all the line segments perpendicular to the plane and terminated by the corresponding points of the figure.

Regular polygons

Lattice work of squares and diamonds (rhombuses) and certain regular polygons such as triangles, pentagons, hexagons, and octagons form the framework of most of our symmetrical designs. Of course, the circle is the dominant feature of many of them. In fact, the knowledge of how to inscribe and circumscribe certain regular polygons is very helpful in copying and creating interesting figures.

The regular hexagon is the most important basic design because it occurs so frequently in nature. The honeycombs of bees are hexagonal. All snow crystals and those of many minerals exhibit the characteristics of the hexagon.

The regular pentagon and the five-pointed star are the basis for a great many attractive designs because five-pointed forms, such as five-petaled flowers and five-pointed leaves, are common in nature.

Exercises

1. Fold a piece of paper and place a drop of ink in the crease. Then press the paper together. Is the ink design on the paper symmetric with respect to the crease? Can you make an ink design in this manner that is symmetric with respect to a point?
2. Do you believe an automobile has a plane of symmetry? If so, where is the plane and what exceptions must you make?
3. Name two letters of the alphabet which have one axis of symmetry.
4. Name two letters of the alphabet which have two axes of symmetry.
5. Do any of the letters of the alphabet have a point of symmetry?

Co-ordinate Geometry

Locating points on a line
(Optional)

In Figure 17, we see how the positions of points A and B may be represented by numbers by selecting any point O on XX' as a point of reference. The point O is called the *origin*. Distances measured to the right of O are considered positive, and distances measured to the left of O are negative. Thus B, which is 2 units to the right of O, is represented by $+2$, and A, which is 4 units to the left of O, is represented by -4. We call XX' a number scale.

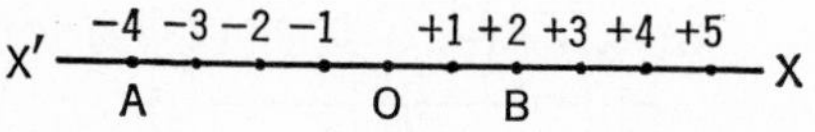

$$X' \quad \overset{-4\ -3\ -2\ -1 \quad\ +1\ +2\ +3\ +4\ +5}{\underset{A\qquad\qquad O\quad B}{\rule{7cm}{0.4pt}}} \quad X$$

Fig. 17

Choose some convenient unit such as $\frac{1}{4}$ inch, and make a number scale.

Locating points in a plane
(Optional)

To locate points in a plane, we draw two number scales perpendicular to each other so that their origins coincide and so that one is horizontal and the other is vertical. We call the horizontal scale the x-axis and the vertical scale the y-axis. Their point of intersection is called the *origin of the axes*.

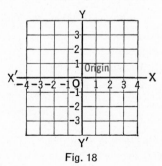
Fig. 18

Distances measured to the right of the y-axis, either along the x-axis or parallel to it are considered positive; distances measured to the left of the y-axis are negative. Distances measured above the x-axis are positive, and distances measured below the x-axis are negative.

In Figure 19, the point A is represented by $(6,5)$. That is, A is 6 units to the right of the y-axis and 5 units above the x-axis. We call the x-distance of a point its *abscissa*, and the y-distance of a point its *ordinate*. The abscissa and the ordinate of a point are called the *co-ordinates* of the point. The x-axis and the y-axis are called the co-ordinate axes.

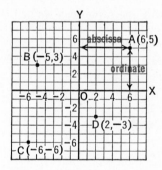
Fig. 19

To designate the position of a point, the abscissa and the ordinate are written in parentheses with a comma between them, the abscissa always being written first. Thus, $D(2, -3)$ means a point whose abscissa is $+2$ and whose ordinate is -3.

Explain the meaning of $B(-5, 3)$; of $C(-6, -6)$.

The process of locating a point on a set of axes as illustrated above is called *plotting a point*.

Exercises *(Optional)*

1. In the figure, give the abscissa and ordinate of each of the points A, B, D, and F if the distance between two consecutive parallel lines represents one unit.

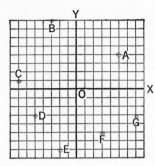

Ex. 1–2

2. Using the same scale as in Exercise **1**, what are the co-ordinates of points C, E, and G?
3. Draw co-ordinate axes and plot the following points:
   a. $L(2, 5)$
   b. $M(-3, 2)$
   c. $N(0, -4)$
   d. $P(-3, 0)$
   e. $Q(-3, -2)$
   f. $R(4, -5)$
4. Draw a triangle whose vertices are: $A(3, 2)$, $B(2, -3)$, and $C(-3, -3)$.
5. Draw a quadrilateral whose vertices are: $A(-3, -4)$, $B(2, -2)$, $C(3, 3)$, and $D(-2, -3)$.
6. Find the length of each side of the quadrilateral whose vertices are $W(4, -1)$, $B(4, 3)$, $N(-2, 3)$, and $S(-2, -1)$.
7. Estimate the co-ordinates of the midpoints of the sides of the triangle with vertices $R(2, -2)$, $K(4, 2)$, and $M(-2, 2)$.

The distance between two points having equal abscissas or equal ordinates *(Optional)*

In this elementary course, we shall assume that the distance between two points has no algebraic sign. To find the distance between two points having equal abscissas such as $B(3, 1)$ and $D(3, 6)$, subtract one ordinate from the other and ignore the algebraic sign of the answer. Thus, the distance between B and D is 5 units.

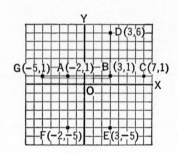

Fig. 20

To find the distance between $G(-5, 1)$ and $B(3, 1)$, which have equal ordinates, subtract one abscissa from the other and ignore the algebraic sign of the answer. Thus, the distance between G and B is 8 units.

Exercises *(Optional)*

Find the distance between the following pairs of points:
1. $B(3, 1)$ and $C(7, 1)$.
2. $D(3, 6)$ and $E(3, -5)$.
3. $A(-2, 1)$ and $F(-2, -5)$.
4. $E(3, -5)$ and $B(3, 1)$.
5. $F(-2, -5)$ and $E(3, -5)$.
6. $P(x_1, y_1)$ and $Q(x_1, y_2)$.
7. $P(x_1, y_1)$ and $S(x_2, y_1)$.

The straight line locus *(Optional)*

An equation such as $y = 2x - 4$ (or $2x - y = 4$) is called a *linear* equation because the locus of points whose co-ordinates satisfy the equation is a straight line.

To plot the locus (graph) of $y = 2x - 4$ we may assign to x any value we choose and solve the resulting equation for y; or we may assign to y any value we choose and solve the resulting equation for x.

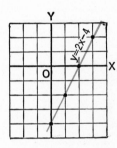

Fig. 21

The following table gives the co-ordinates of three points which satisfy the equation $y = 2x - 4$:

x	0	1	2
y	-4	-2	0

The straight line determined by any two of these points is a locus because:

1. The co-ordinates of any point on it satisfy the equation;

2. Any point whose co-ordinates satisfy the equation lies on the line.

1. a. Plot the points $A(-5, 2)$, $B(-3, 2)$, $C(0, 2)$, and $D(5, 2)$.
b. Do these points lie on a straight line? Do the co-ordinates of all the points on this line satisfy the condition that $y = 2$?
c. Do all the points whose ordinate is 2 lie on this line?
d. Is this line the locus of a point 2 units above the x-axis?

2. What is the equation of the locus of points 2 units below the x-axis?

3. What is the locus of a point that moves so that it is always 3 units to the left of the y-axis?

4. Draw the locus determined by each of the following equations:
a. $y = 2x$ **d.** $3x + 2y = 6$
b. $x + y = 0$ **e.** $x - 2y = 6$
c. $x + y = 2$ **f.** $y = 6x$

5. a. Plot the co-ordinates of two points each of whose abscissas is equal to twice its ordinate.
b. Select any other point on the line determined by the points in part **a** and verify that its abscissa is twice its ordinate.
c. Select any point not on this line and verify that its abscissa is not twice its ordinate.

6. Plot the locus of a point such that the sum of its co-ordinates is 6.

7. Plot the locus of a point such that its abscissa is half its ordinate, plus 6.

8. Plot the locus of a point such that its abscissa is equal to its ordinate diminished by 5.

9. Draw the graphs of $y = \frac{1}{2}x + 1$ and $y = \frac{1}{2}x - 2$ on the same set of co-ordinate axes. How do the two lines seem to be related?

10. Draw the graphs of $y = \frac{1}{3}x$ and of $y = -3x$ on the same set of co-ordinate axes. How do the two lines seem to be related?

Points that satisfy two linear equations simultaneously

(Optional)

If the loci of two linear equations intersect, the co-ordinates of their point of intersection satisfy both equations. These co-ordinates can be found (a) algebraically and (b) graphically.

Example: Find the co-ordinates of the point of intersection of (1) $x + 2y = 8$ and (2) $4y - x = 4$.

a. Algebraic solution:
  Solve (1) for x: $x = 8 - 2y$.
  For x in equation (2) substitute its equal, $8 - 2y$.
  $4y - (8 - 2y) = 4$
  $4y - 8 + 2y = 4$
  $\qquad\qquad 6y = 12$
  $\qquad\qquad\ y = 2$
  Substitute 2 for y in equation (1).
  $\qquad x + 2(2) = 8$
  $\qquad\qquad\quad x = 4$
  Thus the loci of the two equations intersect at $P(4, 2)$. Check this solution with the graphic solution.

b. Graphic solution:

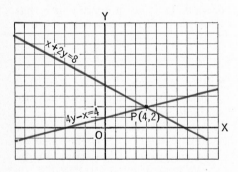

Notice that the graphic solution yields the same result as the algebraic solution.

Exercises *(Optional)*

Find the co-ordinates of the points of intersection, if any, of the loci of the following pairs of linear equations. (Solve them graphically and then algebraically.)

1. $3x - 2y - 4 = 0$
  $3x + 2y - 8 = 0$

2. $3x + 2y = 4$
  $\qquad\ x = 2y$

3. $3x - 2y = 8$
  $\qquad y = \dfrac{3}{2}x + 4$

4. $6x + 4y = 16$
  $\qquad y = -\dfrac{3}{2}x + 4$

5. $3x - 2y = 4$
  $\ x - 2y = 4$

6. $y = \dfrac{2}{3}x + 3$
  $\quad y = -\dfrac{3}{2}x + 3$

7. $.2x + .4y = 0$
  $.3x + .8y = .6$

The circle locus *(Optional)*

It can be proved that the locus of a point whose co-ordinates satisfy a quadratic equation of the form

$$x^2 + y^2 = r^2$$

is a circle with its center at the origin and r as radius.

Example 1: Draw the locus of points whose co-ordinates satisfy the equation $x^2 + y^2 = 25$.

There are two ways to do this:
Solution 1: We can plot many points that satisfy the equation and then draw a smooth curve through the points.

Table of values:

x	0	±2	±3	±4	±5
y	±5	±4.6	±4	±3	0

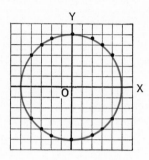

Notice that for one value of x, there are two values of y; for one value of y, there are two values of x. That is, this circle is symmetric with respect to its axes.

Solution 2: By inspection we find that $x^2 + y^2 = 25$ is of the same form as $x^2 + y^2 = r^2$. Hence, $r^2 = 25$, and $r = 5$. We simply draw a circle whose center is $O(0, 0)$ and whose radius is 5.

Example 2: What is the equation of the circle whose center is $(0, 0)$ and whose radius is 6?

Solution: Since $r = 6$ and its center is at the origin, the equation of the circle is $x^2 + y^2 = 36$. Since a circle is a locus, the co-ordinates of all the points on the circle satisfy the equation; and the co-ordinates of all the points not on the circle do not satisfy the equation.

If the center of a circle is $P(h, k)$, and its radius is r, it can be proved that the equation of the circle is

$$(x - h)^2 + (y - k)^2 = r^2.$$

Example 3: If the center of a circle is at $P(2, -4)$, and its radius is 3, the equation of the circle is
$$(x - 2)^2 + (y + 4)^2 = 9.$$

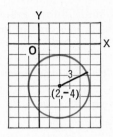

Ex. 3

Example 4: If the equation of a circle is $(x + 2)^2 + (y - 3)^2 = 16$, the co-ordinates of the center are $(-2, 3)$, and its radius is 4.

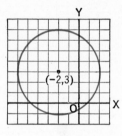

Ex. 4

Example 5: Find the center and radius of the circle whose equation is
$$x^2 + y^2 - 14x + 6y - 23 = 0.$$

Solution: Write the equation in the form
$$(x^2 - 14x + \ ?) + (y^2 + 6y + \ ?) = 23.$$
Complete the squares in the above equation.
$$(x^2 - 14x + 49) + (y^2 + 6y + 9) = 23 + 49 + 9.$$
From this we can write
$$(x - 7)^2 + (y + 3)^2 = 81.$$
Hence the center is the point $(7, -3)$ and the radius is 9.

Intersection of loci (*Optional*)

If the loci of two equations intersect, their common points satisfy both equations. These points may be found either algebraically, or graphically by drawing both loci on the same set of co-ordinate axes.

Example 1: Find the co-ordinates of the points common to the loci of:
(a) $x^2 + y^2 = 25$
(b) $3x = 4y$.

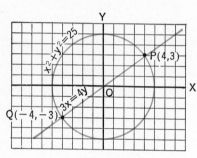

Fig. 22

Solution: Solving equation (b) for x,

$$x = \frac{4}{3}y.$$

Substituting $\frac{4}{3}y$ for x in equation (a),

$$\left(\frac{4}{3}y\right)^2 + y^2 = 25$$

$$\frac{16}{9}y^2 + y^2 = 25$$

$$16y^2 + 9y^2 = 225$$

$$25y^2 = 225$$

$$y^2 = 9$$

$$y = \pm 3$$

Substituting first $+3$ and then -3 in equation (b), $x = 4$, and $x = -4$, respectively. Hence the loci intersect at the points $P(4, 3)$ and $Q(-4, -3)$.

Example 2: Find the co-ordinates of the points common to the two loci:
(a) $x^2 + y^2 = 25$
(b) $(x - 6)^2 + y^2 = 13$.
Solution: Solving equation (a) for y^2, $y^2 = 25 - x^2$.
Substituting $25 - x^2$ for y^2 in equation (b),

$$(x - 6)^2 + 25 - x^2 = 13$$

$$x^2 - 12x + 36 + 25 - x^2 = 13$$

$$-12x = -48$$

$$x = 4$$

Substituting 4 for x in equation (a) and solving for y, $y = \pm 3$.
Hence, the two circles intersect at the points $P_1(4, 3)$ and $P_2(4, -3)$.

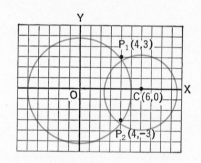

Fig. 23

Exercises (*Optional*)

1. The equation of a circle is
$$x^2 + y^2 = 4.$$
   a. Draw its locus.
   b. What is the abscissa of each of the points on the circle having the ordinate 1?
   c. Does the point $T(2, 2)$ lie on the circle?
   d. Does the point $S(2, 3)$ lie on the circle?

2. The equation of a circle is
$$(x + 1)^2 + (y - 2)^2 = 4.$$
   a. Draw its locus.

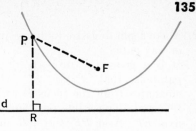

Fig. 24

b. What is the ordinate of each of the points on the circle having the abscissa -1?

c. Do the points $R(-3,\ 2)$ and $M(1,\ 1)$ lie on the circle?

3. Construct and describe the locus of points 2 units from the locus of $(x-7)^2 + (y+1)^2 = 100$.

4. Construct and describe the locus of points equidistant from the loci of $x^2 + y^2 = 49$ and $x^2 + y^2 = 9$.

5. Write the equation of the circle whose center is $C(-4,\ 5)$ and whose radius is equal to 8.

6. Find the center and radius of the circles whose equations are:

a. $x^2 + y^2 + 4x - 6y - 51 = 0$

b. $x^2 + y^2 - 10x + 12y + 45 = 0$

7. Find the points, if any, common to the locus of $x^2 + y^2 = 25$ and each of the following:

a. $y = -4$

b. $y - x = 7$

c. $4x + 3y + 25 = 0$

d. $y = x - 8$

e. $x - y = 1$

f. $x^2 + y^2 = 9$

g. $x^2 + (y-6)^2 = 13$

h. $(x-5)^2 + (y+5)^2 = 5$

The parabola (*Optional*)

The locus of a point which moves so that its distance from a fixed point is always equal to its distance from a fixed line is a *parabola*.

If P moves so that for any position of P, $PR = PF$, then P traces a parabola. The fixed point F is called the *focus* and the fixed line d is called the *directrix* of the parabola. (See Figure 24.)

Exercises (*Optional*)

1. Make a parabola with a piece of string and a draftsman's right triangle.

Let AB represent the directrix and F the focus of a parabola. Fasten a string to a right triangle at T and to the point F so that the length of the string equals ET. Hold a pencil point at P as you move the triangle along AB. Be sure that ES follows AB and that the string is kept taut.

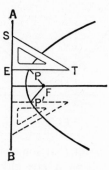

Ex. 1

As point P moves, according to the conditions described above, it traces a parabola. Explain why PE is the distance from P to AB, and also explain why $PE = PF$.

2. Make a parabola by folding a piece of wax paper.

It is a geometric property of any parabola that a ray FP which emanates from the focus F will be reflected along a line parallel to its axis EF. Also PF and PR make equal angles x and y with the tangent drawn to the curve at the point P. The converse of this relationship is also true.

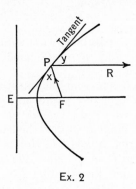

Ex. 2

The outline of a parabola can be made on a piece of wax paper as follows:

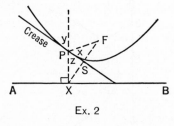

Ex. 2

Mark a point F at some convenient distance from a straight line AB which is drawn on the paper. Fold the paper so that some point X on AB coincides with F, and crease the paper. It can be proved that the crease is tangent to a parabola at P. By folding many points of AB on F, you make a series of creases (tangents) which form the outline of the parabola.

3. Draw a parabola with a compass. Use a sheet of lined paper or draw equally spaced parallel lines and number them as illustrated. Each number in the vertical column denotes in units how far the corresponding line is from AB. With F as center, draw circles with radii 1 unit, 2 units, 3 units, etc. The points of intersection of similarly numbered lines and circles are points on the parabola. Why?

Change the position of the focus F with reference to the directrix AB.

Is the shape of the parabola affected by the position of F relative to AB?

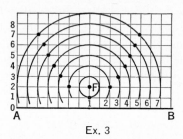

Ex. 3

4. Draw the axis of symmetry of a parabola. Is it symmetric with respect to a point?

5. Study the equations of parabolas in an algebra text. Also investigate the parabola's practical application to the path of a projectile.

The ellipse *(Optional)*

The locus of a point which moves so that the sum of its distances from two fixed points is constant is an *ellipse.*

Fig. 25

In Figure 25 the two fixed points
F and F' are called *foci* (pronounced
fō′-sī). $PF + PF' = P'F + P'F' = $ a
constant.

Exercises (*Optional*)

1. Draw an ellipse by the two-pin-
and-string method. Push two pins
into a board. Make a loop of string
which is greater than twice the
distance between the two pins. Loop
the string over the pins, and with a
pencil holding the loop taut, trace
an ellipse.

Ex. 1

2. Make an ellipse with a piece of wax
paper.
It is a geometric property of
an ellipse that if lines are drawn
from the two foci to any point on
the curve, they make equal angles
with the tangent to the curve at
that point.

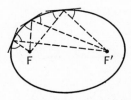

Ex. 2

By folding a piece of wax paper
so that the creases are tangents we
can form an ellipse. Draw a large
circle on a piece of wax paper.
Designate some point F within the
circle. Fold the paper so that any
point X on the circle coincides with

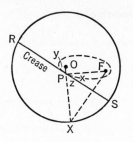

Ex. 2

F. We can prove that the crease RS
is tangent to an ellipse whose foci
are O and F. By folding many other
points of the circle onto F, a great
many creases are made. These
creases outline an ellipse.

3. Construct an ellipse with a compass.
Place two points F and F' on your
paper. Draw a straight line k longer
than FF'. If P is a point on the
ellipse, then $FP + F'P = k$. Points
on the ellipse are located by drawing
pairs of circles. One circle of the
pair has F as center and FP as
radius; the other has F' as center
and $F'P$ as radius. Repeat this
process, using one part of k as the
radius of one circle and the remaining part of k as the radius of the
other circle, until you have a great
many points through which you
can draw a smooth curve.

Ex. 3

4. Draw the axes of symmetry of an
ellipse. Is it symmetrical with
respect to a point?

5. Study the equations of ellipses in
an algebra text. Also investigate
such practical applications as whis-
pering galleries and the paths of
planets.

The hyperbola (*Optional*)

The locus of a point which moves so that the difference of its distances from two fixed points is a constant is a *hyperbola*.

In Figure 26, the two fixed points F and F' are foci; $F'P - FP$ is a constant k and $FP' - F'P'$ is the same constant k.

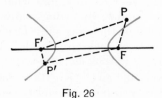

Fig. 26

Exercises (*Optional*)

1. Devise a method for drawing a hyperbola with two pins and a piece of string.

2. Make a hyperbola with a piece of wax paper. The method is similar to that of making an ellipse except that the point F is chosen outside the circle.

3. Draw the axis of symmetry of a hyperbola. Is it symmetrical with respect to a point?

4. In any advanced algebra book study the equations of hyperbolas.

5. Write to the United States Government Printing Office, in Washington, D. C., for the latest edition of CG 157 which explains Loran. The name "Loran" was derived from the words "LOng RAnge Navigation." The Loran system is a modern electronic aid to navigation by means of which navigators on or over the ocean can determine their position accurately and quickly, day or night, and under practically any condition of weather and sea.

6. Construct a hyperbola with a compass. Place two points F' and F on your paper. Draw a segment k shorter than FF'. To get one branch of the hyperbola, locate many points, such as P, by making $FP - F'P = k$; to get the other branch, locate many points by making $F'P - FP = k$.

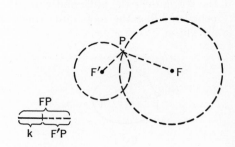

Ex. 6

Conics

Circles, ellipses, parabolas, and hyperbolas are called conics. As illustrated in these figures, conics are produced by the intersections of conical surfaces and planes.

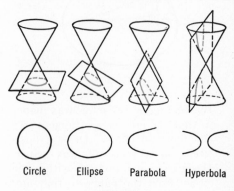

Circle   Ellipse   Parabola   Hyperbola

Fig. 27

Review of Some of the Concepts of Logic

Definitions

Review the properties of a definition before you do these exercises:

1. Explain why this series of definitions is circular.
   a. A house is a dwelling place.
   b. A dwelling place is a place where people live.
   c. A place where people live is a house.
2. When a term is defined, new terms are used. These, in turn, involve new terms in their definitions. Somewhere certain terms must be left without definition.

   Define a bicycle, then try to define each of the terms used in the definition. Continue this procedure until you arrive at the undefined terms. Make a list of these terms.
3. Explain why each of the following statements is, or is not, a good definition:
   a. Equal angles are angles having sides which can be made to coincide.
   b. A fish is an animal that has gills and can swim.
   c. Perpendicularity is a property of two perpendicular lines.
   d. A turnip is a vegetable that grows in the ground.
   e. A lazy person is one who is not industrious.
4. Define (a) street, (b) avenue, (c) boulevard, (d) alley, and (e) highway.
5. Quite often the meaning of a term or phrase is ambiguous. Indicate what this term or phrase is in each of the following:
   a. All men are created equal.
   b. Mr. X, who owns property in five different states, is a thrifty person.

c. All the angles of a triangle are equal to two right angles.
d. This is an inexpensive coat. It cost only $49.95.
e. Adjacent angles have a common vertex and a common side.
f. A certain club has 30 members. In an election for president, Sally received 12 votes, Mary 8 votes, and June 4 votes. Did Sally receive a majority of votes, a plurality of votes, or neither?

★Equivalent Statements

Decide whether or not the two statements in each of the exercises below are equivalent. If they are not equivalent, write a statement equivalent to the first one.

1. a. All unkind people are rude.
   b. All polite people are kind.
2. a. All worms are creepy.
   b. If a thing is not a worm, it is not creepy.
3. a. If a flower is a rose, it is not ugly.
   b. All roses are pretty things.
4. a. If a pen is a Fountain, it is a good pen.
   b. If a pen is not a Fountain, it is not a good pen.
5. a. If Henry passed his examination, he was given a trip to Europe.
   b. If Henry failed his examination, he was not given a trip to Europe.
6. a. If I go to bed early at night, I am happy when I get up the next morning.
   b. If I am grumpy when I get up in the morning, I have gone to bed late the night before.

7. a. If Harry refuses to do his homework, he is indolent.

b. If Harry does his homework, he is ambitious.

8. a. If two lines in the same plane are cut by a transversal so that a pair of alternate interior angles are not equal, the lines are not parallel.

b. The alternate interior angles of two parallel lines cut by a transversal are equal.

9. a. If a line does not bisect the angle between two equal sides of a triangle, it is not an altitude.

b. If an angle bisector of a triangle is an altitude, the triangle has two equal sides.

10. a. If the bisector of the exterior angle at the vertex of a triangle is not parallel to the opposite side, the triangle is not isosceles.

b. If a triangle is isosceles, the bisector of an exterior angle is parallel to the opposite side.

★ Necessary and Sufficient Conditions

Condition A is sufficient for B if it is correct to say, "If A is true, then B is true." Condition A is a necessary condition for B if it is correct to say, "If A is not true, then B is not true." (Or, "if B is true, then A is true.") Condition A is both a sufficient and a necessary condition for B if it is correct to say, "If, and only if, A is true, then B is true."

In each of the following exercises, there are two statements, A and B. Decide whether (**a**) *A is a sufficient condition for B,* (**b**) *A is a necessary condition for B,* (**c**) *A is both sufficient and necessary for B,* (**d**) *A is neither sufficient nor necessary for B.*

STATEMENT A	STATEMENT B
1. The street is icy.	1. The street is slippery.
2. The mothers of Mary and Sue are sisters.	2. Mary and Sue are cousins.
3. My watch is not running.	3. The main spring of my watch is broken.
4. Bill is driving his mother's car.	4. Bill has an automobile driver's license.
5. I can run faster than anyone in school.	5. I can win the 100-yard dash.
6. Mary is a charming girl.	6. Mary gets excellent grades in school.
7. This number is an even number.	7. This number is divisible by 2.
8. Sam was born on February 29th.	8. Sam has a birthday once in four years.
9. $x + 3 = 7$.	9. $x = 4$.
10. $ab = 8$.	10. $a = 4$ and $b = 2$.
11. Lines a and b are perpendicular to s.	11. Lines a and b are parallel.
12. The points on line t are equidistant from lines m and n.	12. The line t is midway between lines m and n.

Review of Chapter 5

1. Draw a triangle ABC. Construct the midpoint of AB and name it M. Through M construct a line parallel to AC.

2. Draw a triangle ABC. Through B construct a line parallel to AC.

3. Draw a triangle RST. Construct the segment that represents the distance from S to RT.

4. Draw a triangle RST. Construct the perpendicular to RT at T.

5. Draw a line AB. Construct two points equidistant from A and B.

6. Draw a line segment AB. Construct all the points that are the distance d from AB.

7. Construct and describe the locus of the midpoints of the radii of the circle of center O and radius 2 inches.

8. Construct and describe the locus of points one inch from a circle whose radius is one-half inch.

9. Construct and describe the locus of points at the given distance m from a given point R *and* midway between two given circles having the common center S and radii b and c. Discuss the possibilities.

10. Construct and describe the locus of points at the given distance r from the given point O *and* equidistant from two given parallel lines m and n. Discuss the possibilities.

In Exercises **11-14**, *the colored lines are loci. State the* **two** *conditions satisfied by the points of intersection P_1 and P_2.*

11.

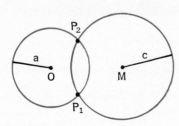

12.

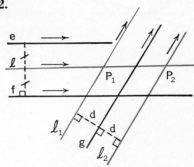

13.

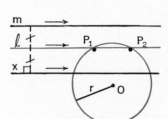

14.

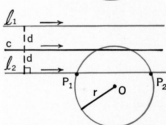

15. In the figure for Exercise **15**, x is a given line and the circle is a locus with center O and with radius r.

a. State the two conditions that P_1 and P_2 satisfy.

b. Explain how the distance from O to x must be related to r for x and the circle to have only one common point.

c. Explain how the distance from O to x must be related to r for x and the circle to have no common points.

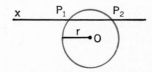

The triangle is an indispensable geometric figure. Steel framework usually contains an arrangement of triangles which makes it rigid. These high-voltage wires are hung on steel supports. Note how triangles are used to brace the towers.

TRIANGLES

TRIANGLES are familiar figures. We see them in the framework of almost every structure such as buildings, electrical transmission lines, and bridges. The triangular framework and bracing make the structure strong because a triangle is a rigid figure. That is, it does not change its size and shape when force is applied to it unless the force is sufficient to bend or break its sides.

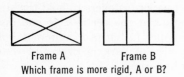

Frame A   Frame B
Which frame is more rigid, A or B?

Fig. 1

How to name the sides of a triangle

A triangle is a polygon of three sides. As the name "triangle" implies, it has three angles and, hence, three vertices. A triangle is named by using the names of the vertices in any order. Thus the name of the triangle in Figure 2 is $\triangle STR$ or $\triangle TRS$, etc.

The names of the sides of $\triangle STR$ are ST, TR, and SR. For simplicity and convenience, we frequently name

a side by using the lower-case form of the capital letter that denotes the opposite vertex. Thus we name the sides s, t, and r.

The perimeter of a polygon

The *perimeter of a polygon* is known to be the sum of the lengths of its sides.

The sum of the sides of the pentagon $ARCGM$ is its perimeter. If we denote the perimeter by the letter p, $p = AR + RC + CG + GM + MA$. Similarly, the perimeter p of $\triangle STR$ in Figure 2 is $s + t + r$.

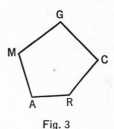

Fig. 3

Exercises

1. **a.** What is the difference between a physical triangle and a geometric triangle?

   b. Are pictures of triangles physical or geometric?

   c. Are triangles made of cardboard, wood, or metal geometric triangles?

   d. Are draftsman's triangles geometric triangles?

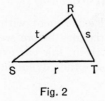

Fig. 2

2. Find the perimeters of the following triangles:

   a. $\triangle ABC$ if $a = 2.10''$, $b = 2.03''$, and $c = 1.98''$.

   b. $\triangle CDE$ if $c = 3\frac{1}{4}'$, $d = 4\frac{3}{4}'$, and $e = 4\frac{0}{4}'$.

   c. $\triangle RST$ if $r = 12.0$ cm., $s = 7.0$ cm., and $t = 9.5$ cm.

3. How many sides has a polygon if each of its sides is 6 in. long and its perimeter is 48 in.?

4. Draw a large triangle on your paper. Measure its perimeter (**a**) to the nearest $\frac{1}{4}$ inch, (**b**) to the nearest $\frac{1}{8}$ inch, and (**c**) to the nearest $\frac{1}{16}$ inch. If you consider all the possible errors, which of these measurements is the most reasonable?

5. Make a list of five objects in which triangles are used to make them rigid and strong.

6. Make a list of objects in which triangles are used for reasons other than strength and rigidity.

In Exercises **7-9**, *write the appropriate equations and algebraic solutions.*

7. The perimeter of $\triangle ABC$ is $30''$. Sides a and b are equal, and each is twice as long as c. Find the length of each side.

8. The perimeter of $\triangle ABC$ is $36''$. The sides a, b, and c are to each other as 2 to 3 to 4. Find the length of each side of the triangle.

9. The perimeter of $\triangle ABC$ is $27''$. Side a is twice side b, and side c is three-halves side b. Find a, b, and c.

10. Is it possible for the sides of a triangle to be $2.0''$, $3.0''$, and $5.0''$? Explain your answer.

11. Is it possible for the sides of a triangle to be $1.5''$, $3.0''$, and $1.0''$? Explain.

Static and dynamic triangles

When we study triangles, we often use static triangles in which the sides and angles are fixed. A triangle drawn on paper is a static triangle. Dynamic triangles are triangles in which the parts are changing or being formed; the three sides and the three angles are variables.

You can make a triangle that is semi-dynamic from three strips of heavy cardboard or plastic, each about 18 inches long. Punch holes in the strips at regular intervals. Use round-head paper fasteners to hold the strips together at the vertices. If you insert the paper fasteners in different holes, triangles of various sizes and shapes can be formed.

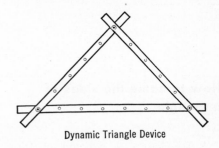

Dynamic Triangle Device

Fig. 4

Classification of triangles

In order to study triangles systematically, we must classify and name them. Triangles may be classified according to their sides, their angles, or their sides and angles.

Experiments *(Optional)*

We shall experiment with different kinds of triangles before we attempt to classify them. For our experiments we may use either dynamic or static triangles.

1. Make a triangle, if possible, having:
   a. Three equal sides
   b. Two equal sides
   c. No equal sides
2. Make a triangle, if possible, having:
   a. Three acute angles
   b. One or more right angles
   c. One or more obtuse angles
   d. Two equal angles
   e. Three equal angles
3. Make a triangle, if possible, having:
   a. No equal sides and all angles acute
   b. No equal sides and one right angle
   c. No equal sides and one obtuse angle
   d. Two equal sides and all angles acute
   e. Two equal sides and one right angle
   f. Two equal sides and one obtuse angle
   g. Three equal sides and one right angle

Questions on the Experiments
(*Optional*)

1. If a triangle has three equal sides, can it have one right angle?
2. If a triangle has three equal sides, what seems to be true about its angles?
3. If a triangle has three equal angles, do the sides seem to be equal?
4. If a triangle has two equal sides, do you think the angles opposite them are necessarily equal?
5. If a triangle has two equal angles, which, if any, of its sides seem to be equal?
6. Do you think it is possible to make a triangle with more than one obtuse angle?
7. Do you think it is possible for a triangle to have more than one right angle?

Triangles classified by their sides

Classified according to their sides, the three kinds of triangles are:
1. Equilateral triangles
2. Isosceles triangles
3. Scalene triangles

DEFINITIONS An *equilateral triangle* is a triangle that has three equal sides.

An *isosceles triangle* is a triangle that has two equal sides.

A *scalene triangle* is a triangle that has no equal sides.

If $AB = BC = AC$, $\triangle ABC$ is equilateral.

If $RT = ST$, $\triangle RST$ is isosceles.

The equal sides are called the *legs*. RT and ST are the legs of $\triangle RST$. The third side is called the *base*. RS is the base of $\triangle RST$.

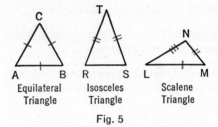

| Equilateral Triangle | Isosceles Triangle | Scalene Triangle |

Fig. 5

The angles at either end of the base are the *base angles*. Angles R and S are the base angles of $\triangle RST$. The angle opposite the base is called the *vertex angle*. Angle T is the vertex angle of $\triangle RST$.

The vertex of the vertex angle is called the *vertex* of the triangle. Point T is the vertex of $\triangle RST$.

The symbol for "is not equal to" is: $\neq$.

If $LM \neq MN \neq NL \neq LM$, $\triangle LMN$ is scalene.

Unless otherwise specified, when we speak of a triangle, we mean a scalene triangle.

Unlike an isosceles triangle, a scalene triangle may have any one of its sides as its base.

Triangles classified by their angles

Classified according to their angles, the four kinds of triangles are:
1. Acute triangles
2. Obtuse triangles
3. Right triangles
4. Equiangular triangles

DEFINITIONS   An *acute triangle* is a triangle in which all angles are acute.

An *obtuse triangle* is a triangle in which one angle is obtuse.

A *right triangle* is a triangle in which one angle is a right angle.

An *equiangular triangle* is a triangle in which all three angles are equal.

If angles A, B, and C are each acute, $\triangle ABC$ is acute. An acute triangle may be scalene, isosceles, or equilateral, as shown in Figure 6.

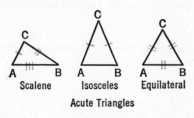

Acute Triangles

Fig. 6

If $\angle B$ is obtuse, $\triangle ABC$ is obtuse. An obtuse triangle may be scalene or isosceles, as shown in Figure 7.

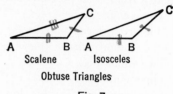

Obtuse Triangles

Fig. 7

If $\angle C$ is a right angle, $\triangle ABC$ is a right triangle. The sides of the right angle of a right triangle are called *legs*, and the side opposite the right angle is called the *hypotenuse*. A right triangle may be scalene or isosceles, as shown in Figure 8.

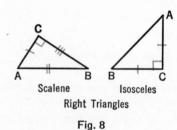

Right Triangles

Fig. 8

If $\angle A = \angle B = \angle C$, $\triangle ABC$ is equiangular (Figure 9).

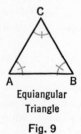

Equiangular Triangle

Fig. 9

Exercises

*In the figure for Exercises **1-3**, Y is the vertex of the isosceles triangle XYZ.*

1. Which sides of △XYZ are its legs?

Ex. 1–3

2. What is the side XZ called?

3. Which angles of △XYZ are its base angles?

*In the figure for Exercises **4-6**, CAB is a triangle, and ∠C = 90°.*

4. Which sides of △CAB are its legs?

Ex. 4–6

5. Which side of △CAB is its hypotenuse?

6. If △CAB is isosceles, which sides are equal?

7. Identify each of the following triangles:

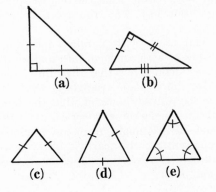

*For Exercises **8-15** refer to the classification circles diagram. (Optional)*

8. Why is the circle for triangles placed within the circle for polygons?

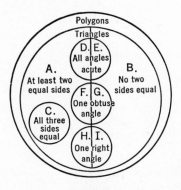

Ex. 8–15

9. Are all triangles either isosceles or scalene?

10. Are all equilateral triangles isosceles?

11. Are all isosceles triangles equilateral?

12. Can a triangle be both acute and isosceles?

13. Can a triangle be both acute and obtuse?

14. Can a triangle be both right and obtuse?

15. Identify the triangles in each of the classes designated by the capital letters.

The sum of the angles of a triangle

In order to study triangles we must know whether the sum of the angles varies in different kinds of triangles, or whether the sum is a constant (always the same). From a dynamic viewpoint, we wish to learn how the sum of the angles of a triangle is affected by transforming the triangle from one kind into another.

We will do an experiment that will give us some information about the sum of the angles of triangles.

Experiment

Given: Any triangle ABC.

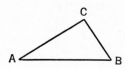

Problem: What is the sum of the angles of any triangle?

Procedure: Make each of the triangles named in the data table any convenient size. Measure each of the angles of each triangle. Enter the angle measurements, together with their sum, in a data table similar to the one shown below. (Do not write in this book.)

Data table:

Kind of Triangle	$\angle$ A	$\angle$ B	$\angle$ C	$\angle A +$ $\angle B +$ $\angle C$
Acute scalene	?	?	?	?
Obtuse scalene	?	?	?	?
Right scalene	?	?	?	?
Acute isosceles	?	?	?	?
Obtuse isosceles	?	?	?	?
Right isosceles	?	?	?	?
Equilateral	?	?	?	?

Conclusion: (What seems to be true about the sum of the angles of $\triangle ABC$?)

General inductive conclusion: (Generalize your conclusion in terms of any triangle.)

Induction versus deduction

The great advantage of the inductive method, or experimental method, is that we can readily discover relationships for ourselves. One disadvantage of the method is that an inductive conclusion is only a theory. There is always a possibility that an exception can be found that will disprove the theory.

If we measured the angles of hundreds of triangles, we would seldom find the sum to be exactly 180°. We cannot obtain exact measurements with a protractor for two reasons: (1) the protractor is not a perfect instrument, and (2) there is always a human error involved in placing the instrument on the angle, and in reading it.

The deductive method, based as it is upon the use of previously proved theorems and acceptable assumptions, not only tells us what the relationships are, but also why the relationships exist.

Our work with parallel lines furnishes us with sufficient information to prove deductively that the sum of the angles of a plane triangle is 180°. It can be proved, however, that the sum of the angles of a spherical triangle such as we might draw on a globe representing the earth's surface is always greater than 180° and less than 540°.

THEOREM 12. **The sum of the angles of a triangle is a straight angle, or 180°.**

Given: Any triangle ABC.

Prove: $\angle A + \angle B + \angle C = $ a straight angle (180°).

Plan: If we draw the auxiliary line RS through C, $\angle RCS$ is a straight angle. Hence $\angle 1 + \angle ACB + \angle 3 = 180°$. If RS is parallel to AB, there are two pairs of equal alternate interior angles, one angle of each pair being an angle of the triangle.

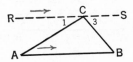

Proof

STATEMENTS	AUTHORITIES
1. Draw RS through C parallel to AB.	1. Through a given point, there is one line parallel to a given line.
2. ∴ with AC as the transversal, $\angle A = ?$ With BC as the transversal, $\angle B = ?$	2. Why?
3. ∴ $\angle RCS$ is a straight angle.	3. Why?
4. ∴ $\angle 1 + \angle ACB + \angle 3 = ?$	4. Why?
5. ∴ ?	5. Why?

COROLLARIES 1. **If one angle of a triangle is either a right angle or an obtuse angle, the other two angles are acute.**

2. The acute angles of a right triangle are complementary.

Exercises

Use algebraic equations in numerical problems if you cannot obtain the answer mentally.

1. In $\triangle ABC$, if $\angle C = 90°$ and $\angle A = a°$, then $\angle B = ?$

2. If each of two angles of a triangle is 57°, what is the size of the third angle?

3. If a triangle is equiangular, what is the size of each angle?

4. If one angle of a triangle is $x°$, the second angle is $2x°$, and the third angle is $3x°$, find the size of each angle.

5. One angle of a triangle is 40°. The difference between the other two is 15°. Find the number of degrees in each angle.

6. One acute angle of a right triangle is twice the other. Find the number of degrees in each angle.

7. One acute angle of a right triangle is 12° less than the other. Find the number of degrees in each angle.

8. Given: $\triangle ABC$ in which $\angle ACB = 90°$, and $CH \perp AB$ at H. Deduce the relationship of $\angle A$ to $\angle 1$; of $\angle B$ to $\angle 2$.

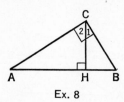

Ex. 8

9. Given: $\triangle ABC$ in which $\angle A = \angle B$, and CD bisects $\angle ACB$.
Prove: $CD \perp AB$.

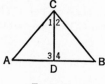

Ex. 9–11

10. Given $\triangle ABC$ in which $\angle A = \angle B$, and $CD \perp AB$. Deduce the implications. (This exercise is a converse of Exercise 9.)

11. Given: $\triangle ABC$ in which CD bisects $\angle ACB$, and $CD \perp AB$. Deduce the implications. (Exercise 11 is a converse of Exercises 9 and 10.)

12. Given: $\triangle ABC$ and ABD in which AD bisects $\angle BAC$, BD bisects $\angle CBA$, and $\angle C = 50°$. Find $\angle D$.

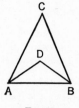

Ex. 12

13. Given: The sides of $\angle A$ are respectively perpendicular to the sides of $\angle B$. How is $\angle A$ related to $\angle B$? Why?

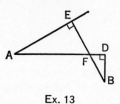

Ex. 13

14. Given: $\triangle ABD$ in which $\angle A = \angle B$, C and E are points on AD and BD, respectively, and $\angle ECD = \angle DEC$. Deduce the implications.

Ex. 14

15. ABC represents a right-angled plane mirror. A ray of light from M to the mirror at K is reflected to W so that $\angle x = \angle x'$. From W it is again reflected to N so that $\angle y' = \angle y$. (This is one of the properties of a plane mirror.) Prove that $\angle x$ is the complement of $\angle y$ and that $MK \parallel WN$.

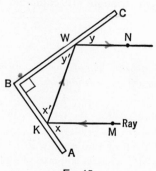

Ex. 15

Two angles of one triangle equal, respectively, to two angles of another

Since the sum of the angles of a triangle is a constant, does the size of two of them determine the third? If two angles of a triangle are $x°$ and $y°$, what is the number of degrees in the third angle?

If we think of a dynamic triangle in which two angles remain constant as the triangle gets larger or smaller, does the third angle also remain constant? Why?

If we have two static triangles ABC and RST in which $\angle A = \angle R$ and $\angle B = \angle S$, how is $\angle C$ related to $\angle T$?

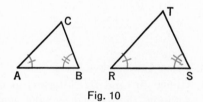

Fig. 10

COROLLARY 3. **If two angles of one triangle are equal respectively to two angles of another triangle, the third angles are equal.**

Exercises

1. Prove the corollary stated above.

2. First draw and then construct a triangle ABC so that $\angle C = 90°$ and $\angle B = 45°$. Draw or construct several other triangles with the same two angles. Are they exactly alike? Explain.

3. Draw or construct a triangle RST so that $\angle R = 45°$ and $\angle S = 45°$. Are all triangles having two 45° angles exactly alike? Explain.

4. Construct triangle LMN so that $\angle M = 135°$. Does this one angle determine the size of either of the other two angles? Explain.

5. Given: Side AB of $\triangle ABC$ is extended to X.

a. How is $\angle XBC$ related to $\angle CBA$?

b. How is $\angle XBA$ related to the sum of the angles of $\triangle ABC$?

c. What can you prove about $\angle XBC$ and the sum of $\angle A$ and $\angle C$?

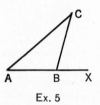

Ex. 5

6. Given: $\triangle ABC$, AC is extended to D, $CE \parallel AB$, $\angle A = \angle B$.

a. Prove that $\angle BCD = 2\angle A$.

b. Prove that CE bisects $\angle BCD$.

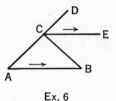

Ex. 6

7. Given: $\triangle ABC$ with the sides extended in succession as shown. What can you prove about the sum of angles x, y, and z?

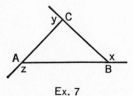

Ex. 7

Exterior angles of polygons

The sides of the quadrilateral *ABCD* are extended in succession through the vertices. The numbered angles are called *exterior angles*.

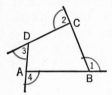 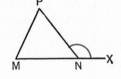

Fig. 11

∠*XNP* is an exterior angle of △*MNP*. ∠*PNM* is the adjacent interior angle, and ∠*M* and ∠*P* are the non-adjacent, or opposite, interior angles. How is ∠*XNP* related to the sum of ∠*M* and ∠*P*?

DEFINITION An *exterior angle of a polygon* is an angle formed by one side of the polygon and another side extended.

COROLLARY 4. An exterior angle of a triangle is equal to the sum of the two opposite interior angles.

Exercises

1. Given: ∠*y* is an exterior angle of △*MCR*.
Prove: ∠*M* = ∠*y* − ∠*C*.

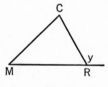

Ex. 1

2. Each side of △*ABC* is extended through both vertices as indicated.

a. Is ∠*DAE* an exterior angle of △*ABC*? Why?

b. How many exterior angles may a triangle have?

c. If ∠*EAB* is one of the exterior angles formed by extending the sides of the triangle in succession, name the other two angles of its set.

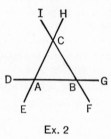

Ex. 2

3. Prove Corollary 4.

4. Given: *AC* and *BD* intersect at *O* forming the triangles *ABO* and *OCD*, and ∠*A* = ∠*D*.

a. How is ∠*DOA* related to other angles in the figure?

b. How is ∠*B* related to ∠*C*?

Ex. 4

5. Prove: If two parallel lines are cut by a transversal, and a pair of interior angles on the same side of the transversal are bisected, the bisectors are perpendicular to each other.

6. Given: $\triangle ABC$, $\angle ACB = 92°$, $\angle A = 45°$, and CD bisects $\angle ACB$. Evaluate each of the other angles in the figure.

Ex. 6–7

7. If $\angle ACB = 90°$, $CD \perp AB$, $\angle A = \angle B$, evaluate all the angles in the figure.

8. Given: $ABCDE$ is a pentagon, and PA, PB, PC, PD, and PE are straight line segments.

   a. What is the sum of angles BAE, CBA, DCB, EDC, and AED?

   b. What is the sum of the interior angles of an n-gon? Prove it.

Ex. 8

9. a. Given: $ABCD$ is a quadrilateral with its sides extended in succession to form the exterior angles x, y, z, and w. What is the sum of x, y, z, and w? Prove your answer.

   b. If the sides of an n-gon are extended in succession, what is the sum of the exterior angles?

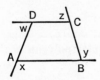

Ex. 9

The sum of the interior angles of a convex polygon

Now that we know that the sum of the angles of a triangle is 180°, we should be concerned about the sum of the interior angles of other polygons. As before, we shall consider only convex polygons, that is, polygons whose interior angles are each less than 180°.

We shall investigate numerous special cases to get information about the general n-gon. By observing how the sum of the interior angles is related to the number of sides in many special cases, we might reach a conclusion that applies to an n-gon.

From an examination of Figures 12 and 13, we see that any polygon can be divided into triangles by joining an internal point to each of the vertices. How is the number of triangles related to the number of sides? Can you be certain that there is one triangle for each of the sides?

Triangle   Quadrilateral

Fig. 12

Pentagon   N-gon

Fig. 13

POSTULATE 33. **If lines are drawn from a point within a polygon to the vertices of the polygon, they form with the sides as many triangles as there are sides.**

Make a table similar to the one below. Draw each of the polygons mentioned in the table. (See Figures 12 and 13, page 153.) Write the correct numerical values where there are question marks. (Do not write in this book.)

Polygon	No. of Sides	No. of △	Sum of All ∠s of All the △	Sum of ∠s at P	Sum of ∠s of Polygon
Triangle	3	3	$3 \times 180°$	$2 \times 180°$	$(3-2)180°$
Quadrilateral	4	4	$4 \times 180°$	$2 \times 180°$	$(4-2)180°$
Pentagon	?	?	?	?	?
Hexagon	?	?	?	?	?
Octagon	?	?	?	?	?
Decagon	?	?	?	?	?
N-gon	?	?	?	?	?

If you have the correct answer in the last space of the right-hand column, you have a formula for finding the sum of the interior angles of a polygon of n sides.

THEOREM 13.   **The sum of the interior angles of a convex polygon is $(n - 2)\ 180°$.**

Given: The polygon $ABCDE$ . . . . of n sides.

Prove: The sum of angles A, B, C, D, E, ... is $(n-2)180°$.

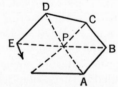

Suggestion: Divide the polygon into triangles by drawing lines from some point within the polygon to each of the vertices.

The proof is left for you to do.

COROLLARY   **The size of each angle of an equiangular polygon is**
$$\frac{(n-2)180°}{n}.$$

The solution of numerical problems

These three examples illustrate how numerical problems involving the interior angles of a polygon are solved.

Example 1: If the sum of the interior angles of a polygon is 720°, how many sides has the polygon?

Solution: Sum of interior angles $= (n - 2)180°$ Formula

$$720 = (n - 2)180$$ Substitute

$$720 = 180n - 360$$ Remove parentheses

$$1080 = 180n$$ Addition axiom

$$6 = n$$ Division axiom

The polygon has 6 sides.

Example 2: Each interior angle of an equiangular polygon is 108°. How many sides has the polygon?

Solution: Each interior $\angle = \dfrac{(n - 2)180°}{n}$ Formula

$$108 = \frac{(n - 2)180}{n}$$ Substitute

$$108n = \frac{(n - 2)180 \cdot \cancel{n}^{1}}{\cancel{n}_{1}}$$ Multiplication axiom

$$108n = 180n - 360$$ Remove parentheses

$$360 = 72n$$ Addition axiom

$$5 = n$$ Division axiom

The polygon has 5 sides.

Example 3: A regular polygon has 12 sides. How many degrees are in each angle?

Solution: Each interior $\angle = \dfrac{(n - 2)180°}{n}$ Formula

$$= \frac{(12 - 2)180}{12}$$ Substitute

$$= 150$$ Simplify

There are 150° in each interior angle.

Exercises

1. How many sides has an equiangular polygon if each angle is 120°?

2. How many sides has a regular polygon if each angle is 165°?

3. How many sides has a polygon in which each angle is 144°?

4. How many sides has a polygon if the sum of the angles is 540°?

5. What is the size of each angle of a regular octagon?

6. How many sides are there in a polygon in which the sum of the angles is 1080°?

7. What is the size of each angle of an equiangular quadrilateral? Why is it not necessarily a regular quadrilateral?

8. In considering a polygon of n sides, why must n always represent a positive whole number?

9. Prove Theorem 13 again by using this new figure:

10. Given: $ABCDEF$ is a regular hexagon, AP bisects $\angle BAF$, PB bisects $\angle CBA$, and $\angle XBC$ is an exterior angle.
   Prove: $\angle XBC = \angle P$.

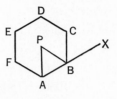

Ex. 10   Ex. 11

11. A pentagram is a five-pointed star formed by extending the sides of a regular pentagon. What is the sum of the angles at the points of the star?

The sum of the exterior angles of a convex polygon formed by extending the sides in succession

THEOREM 14.   **If the sides of a convex polygon are extended in succession, the sum of the exterior angles is 360°.**

Given: Polygon $ABCD$ .... of n sides with exterior angles e_1, e_2, e_3, ... e_n.

Prove: $e_1 + e_2 + e_3 + ... + e_n = 360°$.

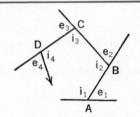

Proof

STATEMENTS		AUTHORITIES
1. $\angle e_1 + \angle i_1 = ?$ $\angle e_2 + \angle i_2 = ?$ $\angle e_3 + \angle i_3 = ?$ . . . . $\angle e_n + \angle i_n = ?$		**1.** ?
2. ∴ Sum of e angles + sum of i angles $= ?$		**2.** ?
3. Sum of i angles $= ?$		**3.** ?
4. ∴ Sum of e angles $= ?$		**4.** ?

COROLLARIES 1. If an _n_-gon is equiangular, the size of each exterior angle is $\dfrac{360°}{n}$.

2. If an _n_-gon is equiangular, the number of degrees in each interior angle is $180° - \dfrac{360°}{n}$.

Exercises

1. If you know how many sides an equiangular polygon has, how can you find the number of degrees in each exterior angle?

2. If you know how many degrees there are in each exterior angle of an equiangular polygon, how can you find how many sides the polygon has?

3. In any polygon, what is the relation of an exterior angle to the adjacent interior angle?

4. If a pentagon is equiangular, how many degrees are there in each exterior angle? in each interior angle?

5. A surveyor frequently measures the exterior angles rather than the interior angles of a polygon-shaped piece of land. To check the correctness of his measurements, he finds the sum of the exterior angles. What should be their sum? Explain why, in general, it might be more difficult to check his work if he had measured the interior angles. A surveyor might measure an angle several times and find the average, even though he is using the very accurate protractor of his transit. Explain why the average of several trials is more reliable than a single trial.

6. How many degrees are there in each exterior angle of an equiangular (a) triangle, (b) quadrilateral, (c) pentagon, (d) hexagon, (e) decagon?

7. How many sides does a polygon have if each exterior angle is 45°? 24°? 18°?

8. If a regular polygon has 12 sides, how many degrees are there in each interior angle?

9. Is it possible to make a polygon in which each exterior angle is 15°? 50°? Explain.

10. Is it possible to make a polygon in which each interior angle is 150°? 80°? Explain.

11. Think of a dynamic polygon that is changing its size and shape, but not the number of sides. As some exterior angles get larger, others must get smaller. Explain.

12. The sum of the interior angles of a polygon is a function of the number of its sides. Explain.

Two angles that have their sides respectively perpendicular

If the sides of two angles are perpendicular, they are perpendicular in one of two ways as follows:

1. The right side of the first is perpendicular to the right side of the second, and the left side of the first is perpendicular to the left side of the second, _or_

2. The right side of the first is perpendicular to the left side of the second, and the left side of the first is perpendicular to the right side of the second.

Case 1:

Given: *PM* and *TN* intersect at *P* to form ∠1 and ∠2; *RL* ⊥ *PM* at *B*, and *RS* ⊥ *TN* at *A*, intersect to form ∠*R*.

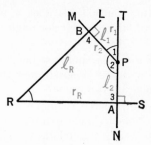

Deduce the relation of
   a. ∠*R* to ∠2
   b. ∠*R* to ∠1.

Hint: What is the sum of the angles of the quadrilateral *RAPB*?
   ∠3 + ∠4 = ? Etc.

Notice that the sides of ∠*R* and ∠2 are perpendicular *right to left* and *left to right;* the sides of ∠*R* and ∠1 are perpendicular *right to right* and *left to left.*

Case 2:

Given: ∠*R*, ∠1, and ∠2 with *RS* ⊥ *NT* at *A*, and *RL* ⊥ *MP* at *B*.

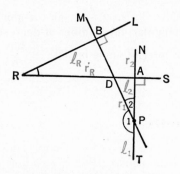

Deduce the relation of

   a. ∠*R* to ∠2

   b. ∠*R* to ∠1.

The sides of ∠*R* and ∠2 are perpendicular right to . . . . and left to . . . . ; the sides of ∠*R* and ∠1 are perpendicular right to . . . . and left to . . . . .

THEOREMS 15. **If the sides of two angles are perpendicular right to right and left to left, the angles are equal.**

     16. **If the sides of two angles are perpendicular right to left and left to right, the angles are supplementary.**

Exercises

1. Given: △*ABC*; ∠*ACB* = 90°, and *CH* ⊥ *AB* at *H*.

   a. Prove ∠*A* = ∠1 by using Theorem 15.

   b. Prove ∠*A* = ∠1 without using Theorem 15.

c. Which angle in the figure is equal to ∠2? Prove your answer.

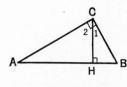

Ex. 1

2. Given: Angles AOB and BOC in which $CA \perp OA$, $CB \perp OB$, and $BD \perp CA$ at D. (Note: This figure is sometimes used in proving certain important trigonometric relationships which are later used in engineering, electronics, and other fields.)

a. Deduce the relation between $\angle a$ and $\angle x$.

b. Deduce the relation between $\angle x$ and $\angle w$.

c. Deduce the relation between $\angle y$ and $\angle z$.

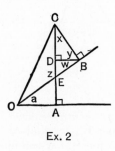

Ex. 2

3. Given: Angles EOB and BOC in which $CA \perp EO$, extended, at A, $CB \perp OF$ at B, and $BD \perp AC$ at D.

a. Deduce the relation between $\angle ACB$ and $\angle EOB$.

b. Deduce the relation between $\angle BOA$ and $\angle ACB$.

c. Deduce the relation between $\angle DBO$ and $\angle DCB$.

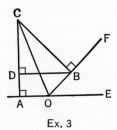

Ex. 3

Secondary lines in triangles

In the geometry of a triangle we frequently use four kinds of lines that are particularly important. We call them the secondary lines of the triangle. These four kinds of lines are:

1. Bisectors of the angles
2. Altitudes to the sides
3. Perpendicular bisectors of the sides
4. Medians

Bisectors of the angles of a triangle

DEFINITION An *angle bisector of a triangle* is a line segment bisecting an angle of the triangle and extending to the opposite side.

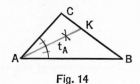

Fig. 14

It is convenient to designate the bisectors of the angles of a triangle in terms of the names of the angles bisected. Thus the bisector of $\angle A$ of $\triangle ABC$ is called t_A. The symbol is read, "t-sub A." Because the bisector of $\angle A$ meets side a, the bisector is sometimes referred to as t_a.

Exercises

1. Construct the bisectors of the angles of any scalene $\triangle RST$. Name the bisectors. Do they seem to meet at a common point?

2. Do the bisectors of the angles of an obtuse triangle seem to meet at a point?

Altitudes to the sides of a triangle

DEFINITION An *altitude of a triangle* is a line segment from a vertex of the triangle perpendicular to the opposite side or the opposite side extended.

The letter h is often used to denote an altitude. The name of the side to which it is drawn is used as a subscript. Thus in $\triangle ABC$, h_c is the altitude to the side c; and h_b is the altitude to the side b.

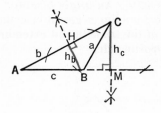

Fig. 15

Perpendicular bisectors of the sides of a triangle

Perpendicular bisectors of the sides of a triangle are named with reference to the names of the sides to which they are drawn. Thus the perpendicular bisector of side b of $\triangle ABC$ is p_b.

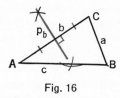

Fig. 16

Remember, the perpendicular bisector of a side of a triangle is not a line segment.

Medians to the sides of a triangle

DEFINITION A *median of a triangle* is a line segment from a vertex to the midpoint of the opposite side.

Medians are named with reference to the names of the sides to which they are drawn. The median to the side c of $\triangle ABC$ is m_c.

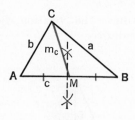

Fig. 17

Exercises

1. Draw an acute scalene $\triangle MNR$. Construct h_m, h_n, and h_r. Do they seem to meet at a common point?

2. Draw $\triangle ABC$ so that $\angle C = 90°$. Do h_a, h_b, and h_c intersect at a common point? Where?

3. Draw $\triangle EFC$ so that $\angle E$ is obtuse. Construct and name the altitudes. Which ones lie outside $\triangle EFC$?

4. Draw an acute $\triangle MRN$. Construct p_m, p_n, and p_r. Do they seem to have a common point of intersection?

5. Draw $\triangle XYZ$ so that $\angle X$ is obtuse. Construct p_x, p_y, and p_z. Where do they seem to intersect?

6. Draw any $\triangle ABC$. Construct m_a, m_b, and m_c. Do they seem to have a point in common?

7. Draw an isosceles $\triangle EMC$ so that EM is its base. Construct t_C, h_c, m_c, and p_c. What seems to be true?

8. Draw an equilateral triangle and construct all of the secondary lines. What seems to be true?

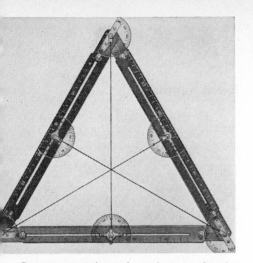

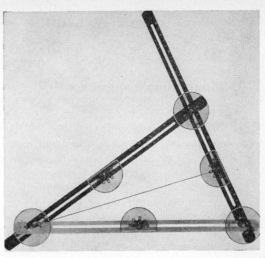

Dynamic triangle with midpoints of sides maintained mechanically. The medians to the three sides are shown.

Dynamic triangle with movable points on its sides. One angle bisector is shown.

Measurement and Computation with
Approximate Numbers*

Linear measurement means the comparison of an unknown distance with a selected standard unit by finding the number of times the standard unit is contained in the unknown distance. To measure a line segment, use a scale on a straightedge. Units of length are marked on this scale. We are familiar with such units of linear measure in the English system as the inch, foot, yard, rod, and mile. The longer the distance to be measured, the longer is the unit of measure used. For example, the distance between two cities is measured in miles; the length of a field, in rods; the length of a pencil, in inches. On most English scales, the inch is divided into halves, fourths, eighths, and sixteenths. On some scales, the foot is divided into tenths and hundredths; on others, the inch is divided into tenths.

Units of measure (*Optional*)

A *unit of measure* is the smallest unit used in making a measurement. If the length of a pencil is found to be $7\frac{3}{4}$ inches, the unit of measure is $\frac{1}{4}$ inch and the measure (or number of units) is 31. Again, if the length of a pencil is expressed as 7.75 inches, the unit of measure is 0.01 inch and the measure is 775 units.

The *precision* of a measurement depends upon the size of the unit used. The smaller the unit of measure used, the more precise is the measure obtained. Since $0.01''$ is smaller than $\frac{1}{4}''$, $7.75''$ is a more precise measure than $7\frac{3}{4}''$; since $0.001''$ is smaller than $0.01''$, $7.750''$ is a more precise measure than $7.75''$.

---

* Although this section is not usually included as an essential topic in plane geometry, reference to it in connection with drawing and measuring line segments and angles and in the solution of numerical problems containing approximate data will help to make geometry more practical.

Approximate numbers (*Optional*)

When a quantity is measured, errors may arise from imperfections in the measuring instrument and from inexperience or carelessness of the person using the instrument. Hence, any number obtained by measurement is an approximate number.

Numbers which are rounded are approximate numbers. The decimal value of $\frac{10}{11}$, rounded to *any* number of decimal places, is an approximate number since 10 is not exactly divisible by 11.

The decimal equivalent of an irrational number such as $\sqrt{2}$ is approximate since there is no rational number which when multiplied by itself is exactly 2.

This machinist is using spring calipers to measure a part which he is turning on a lathe. Calipers are precision-made instruments which, when properly used, help obtain measurements with very little error.

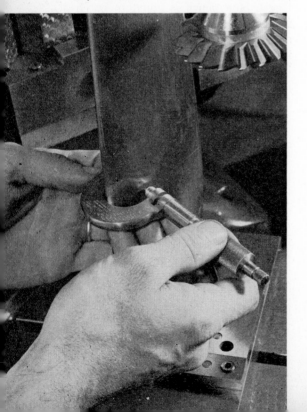

Exact numbers (*Optional*)

A number obtained as the result of counting is an exact number. The numbers in the following quantities are exact: 12 boys, 8 pencils, 512 pages, and 5 dimes. The *constants* found in many formulas such as the 2 in $C = 2\pi r$, and the 1 and 2 in $A = \frac{1}{2}bh$ are exact numbers.

Some numbers are exact from one viewpoint and approximate from another. The 2 in 2 pints of ice cream is an exact number in terms of counting containers. But it is impossible to put exactly one pint of ice cream in a container, and so, in terms of the quantity of ice cream, the 2 is an approximate number. Although the ratio of the circumference of a circle to its diameter is the exact number π, approximate values of π such as $\frac{22}{7}$, 3.14, and 3.14159 are used in computing with it.

Possible error in measurement (*Optional*)

If we say that, to the nearest inch, the length of a pencil is 7″, the true length might be anywhere between $6\frac{1}{2}$ inches and $7\frac{1}{2}$ $(7 \pm \frac{1}{2})$ inches. A measurement of $7\frac{0}{2}$″ implies a *possible* error of $\frac{1}{4}$″; a measurement of $7\frac{0}{4}$″ has a *possible error* of $\frac{1}{8}$″, and a measurement of 7.00 inches has a *possible* error of 0.005″. The approximate measurements 7″, $7\frac{0}{2}$″, $7\frac{0}{4}$″, and 7.00″ are not equally precise because the units of measure are respectively 1″, $\frac{1}{2}$″, $\frac{1}{4}$″, and 0.01″. Notice that the smaller the unit of measure used, the smaller is the possible error.

Assuming that the instrument used is perfect, the greatest possible error in a measurement is an error that never exceeds one-half the unit of measure used.

Relative error in measurement
(*Optional*)

The relative error of a measurement is the quotient of the possible error and the measurement. If 93,000,000 miles is the distance from the earth to the sun, correct to the nearest 1,000,000 miles, there is a possible error in the measurement of 500,000 miles. That is, the distance is 93,000,000 miles $\pm$ 500,000 miles. Hence the relative error is $\frac{500,000}{93,000,000}$ or $\frac{5}{930}$, which is approximately 0.5%.

If a boy is timed at 9.3 seconds for the 100-yard dash, the possible error is 0.05 second. That is, the boy's time is 9.3 seconds $\pm$ 0.05 second. The relative error is $\frac{0.05}{9.3}$ or $\frac{5}{930}$, which is approximately 0.5%.

Although the unit used in measuring the distance from the earth to the sun was very large (1,000,000 miles), and the possible error is 500,000 miles, the relative error is not very great (0.5%). The unit used in timing the boy in the 100-yard dash was very precise (0.1 second), but the relative error is exactly the same as that for the earth-to-the-sun measurement. In each case the possible error is 0.5 unit, and the measure is 93 units. Hence both measurements are equally accurate.

Significant digits and accuracy
(*Optional*)

A measurement of 3.46 feet implies that the unit of measure is 0.01 foot, and that there are 346 of these units. In this measure, the digits 3 and 4 are correct; and the possible error in the last digit 6 is no more than one-half 0.01 foot ($\frac{1}{2}$ of 0.01 = 0.005). Since the measurement 3.46 contains three digits, it is said to be *accurate* to three *significant* digits.

Here the machinist uses a micrometer caliper to measure an airplane propeller part. His instrument can be read to the nearest 0.01 millimeter or to the nearest 0.001 inch.

All the digits in an approximate number are significant if all the digits in the number are correct except the last one, and if the error in the last one does not exceed one-half the unit of measure used.

In a measurement such as $8\frac{3}{16}$ inches, the unit of measure is $\frac{1}{16}$ inch, and the number of units is 131. Hence there are three significant digits in $8\frac{3}{16}$.

Digits that express how many units there are in a measurement are significant digits. The accuracy of a measurement is determined by the number of significant digits in the measurement. The more significant digits there are in an approximate number, the more accurate is the number.

When zeros are not significant digits (*Optional*)

To the nearest 1,000 miles, the speed of light is 186,000 miles per second. The three zeros following the 6 are not significant because there are 186 units of 1,000 miles each in the measurement. A convenient way to indicate that 186,000 is correct to the nearest 1,000 is to write 186,000 as 1.86×10^5. If 186,000 is correct to the nearest 100, the first zero following the 6 will be significant. The number will then be 1.860×10^5. Similarly, if 186,000 is correct to the nearest 10, the number will be written 1.8600×10^5. With this system of writing a number, it is easy to tell which zeros at the right-hand end of a number are significant.

In a measurement such as 0.003 inch, the zeros are not significant because they serve only to locate the decimal point. In 0.003 inch, the unit of measure is 0.001 inch ($\frac{1}{1,000}$ inch), and there are three units.

If a number such as 2,046 is rounded to 2,050 (correct to the nearest 10), the zero following the 5 is not significant; if it is rounded to 2,000 (correct to the nearest 100), the last two zeros are not significant because they take the place of the 4 and the 6 in the original number. The first zero following the 2, however, is significant. To avoid confusion concerning which zeros at the right-hand end of a number are significant, a number such as 2,000 may be written as $2.0 \times 1,000$ or 2.0×10^3 if it has been obtained by rounding the number to the nearest 100.

Metric units of linear measure (*Optional*)

The metric system of units was adopted in the United States in 1866. Although it is used in this country in practically all scientific work, most of our common measurements are expressed in the more familiar English system.

The standard unit of linear measure in the metric system is the meter. To the nearest ten-thousandth of an inch, the meter is 39.3702 inches long.

TABLE OF METRIC LINEAR MEASURE

10 millimeters (mm.) = 1 centimeter (cm.)

10 centimeters (cm.) = 1 decimeter (dm.)

10 decimeters (dm.) = 1 meter (m.)

1000 meters (m.) = 1 kilometer (km.)

TABLE OF EQUIVALENTS

1 cm. = 0.3937 in.
1 m. = 39.3702 in.
1 km. = 0.6214 mi.
1 in. = 2.5400 cm.
1 mi. = 1.6093 km.

If the length of an object is expressed in millimeters, its length may be expressed in terms of a larger metric unit by dividing by the proper multiple of 10. For example: 1,492 mm. = 149.2 cm. = 14.92 dm. = 1.492 m. = 0.001492 km.

In the above example, notice that the unit of measure of 1,492 mm. is 1 mm.; the unit of measure of 149.2 cm. is 0.1 cm. or 1 mm.; the unit of measure of 14.92 dm. is 0.01 dm., or 1 mm.; etc. Hence, each measure has the same precision.

If the distance between two points is measured in a large unit such as the kilometer, the same distance may be converted to a metric measure in terms of a smaller unit by multiplying by the proper multiple of 10. For example:

8.05 km. = 8,050 m. = 80,500 dm. = 805,000 cm. = 8,050,000 mm.

It is important to note in the preceding example that the unit of measure in each case is 0.01 km. or 10 m. That is, the precision of the measure is not increased or decreased by converting a number of one denomination to a number of another denomination. Hence, 8,050 m. is correct to the nearest 10 m.; 805,000 cm. is correct to the nearest 1,000 cm. (or 10 m.); and 8,050,000 mm. is correct to the nearest 10,000 mm. (or 10 m.).

Exercises (*Optional*)

In each of Exercises **1-10** *state* (**a**) *the unit of measure;* (**b**) *the possible error and the relative error in each measurement;* (**c**) *the number of significant digits in each measurement.*

1. 6,250 in.
2. 6.25 in.
3. 0.625 in.
4. 0.0625 in.
5. $6\frac{1}{4}$ in.
6. $6\frac{2}{8}$ in.
7. $6\frac{4}{16}$ in.
8. $5\frac{8}{32}$ in.
9. 2 yd. 1 ft. 3 in.
10. 4 ft. $6\frac{1}{2}$ in.

11. Measure the line AB to:
    a. The nearest 1 inch
    b. The nearest $\frac{1}{2}$ inch
    c. The nearest $\frac{1}{4}$ inch
    d. The nearest $\frac{1}{8}$ inch
    e. The nearest $\frac{1}{16}$ inch
    f. The nearest 1 cm.
    g. The nearest 1 mm.

A ————————————————————— B

Ex. 11

12. Which measure of Exercise **11** is the most precise? What is the possible error in each measurement? In which is the relative error greatest?

13. Express 100 meters in yards to the nearest 0.01 yards.

14. Express 100 yards in meters to the nearest 0.01 meter.

15. If the distance between two cities is 26.5 miles, what is the distance in kilometers between the cities?

16. If the distance between two cities is 26.5 kilometers, what is the distance in miles?

17. Draw a line $3\frac{5}{16}$ inches long. Measure the line to the nearest millimeter. Convert $3\frac{5}{16}$ inches to millimeters. How does this answer compare with the measure in millimeters?

18. If the distance between two points, correct to the nearest 10 ft., is 3,600 ft., how many significant digits are there in the measure? What is the possible error? the relative error?

19. If the distance between two points, correct to the nearest 1 ft., is 3,600 ft., how many significant digits are there in the measure? What is the possible error? the relative error?

20. If the distance between two points, correct to the nearest 100 ft., is 3,600 ft., how many significant digits are there in the measure? What is the possible error? the relative error?

21. The vernier on a certain vernier protractor can be read to the nearest minute. How many significant digits are there in 15° 48'? What is the possible error? the relative error?

22. The vernier on a certain vernier caliper can be read to the nearest $\frac{1}{128}$ in. How many significant digits are there in a measure of $1\frac{32}{128}$ in.? What is the possible error? the relative error?

Addition and subtraction of approximate numbers (*Optional*)

In making a *set* of linear measurements, we usually use the same unit of measure. The unit to be used depends upon the degree of precision the occasion demands. The length of a table top need not be measured as precisely as some part of a mechanism in which the error must not exceed 0.001 inch.

If the length of a rectangle is 4 feet 5 inches, or 53 inches, and the width is 4 inches, the sum or difference of those measures has the same precision as the numbers added or subtracted. That is, the sum or difference of these measures is correct to the nearest 1 inch, and the possible error is $\frac{1}{2}$ inch.

Multiplication of approximate numbers (*Optional*)

The measure of the true area of a rectangle 53 inches by 4 inches is a number between 53.5×4.5 and 52.5×3.5. Hence, the area is a number between 240.75 and 183.75, or approximately 200 square inches. To obtain this answer we proceed as follows:

$$
\begin{array}{r}
53 \\
\times\ 4 \\
\hline
212 \\
\end{array}
$$

or 200 as the best approximation.

Since the last digit of a measure has a possible error of $\frac{1}{2}$, the digits in italics have a possible error of $\frac{1}{2}$. Hence the last two digits of the product are not exact.

In the above example, there are two significant digits in the measure 53 and only one significant digit in the measure 4. Hence there is only one significant digit in the product, and it should be rounded to 200.

Here is another example:

Find the product of the two approximate numbers 38.6 and 2.4.

$$
\begin{array}{r}
38.6 \\
\times 2.4 \\
\hline
1544 \\
772\ \ \\
\hline
92.64 \text{ or } 93
\end{array}
$$

The digits in italics are almost certain to be in error. Hence the product is rounded off to 93. The number of significant digits in 93 is the same as the number of significant digits in 2.4.

Since the accuracy of a measure is determined by the number of significant digits in it, 2.4 is less accurate than 38.6. It follows that the product of two or more approximate numbers is no more accurate than the least accurate of the numbers multiplied.

The product of two or more approximate numbers should be rounded off so that it has only as many significant digits as there are in the number with the fewest significant digits.

Division of approximate numbers (*Optional*)

The rule for rounding off the product of approximate numbers applies to rounding off the quotient of approximate numbers.

Note: In this text, if the data of an exercise are given without stating the units of measure, the data are assumed to be exact; and the results of computations involving these data need not be rounded according to the rules governing computations with approximate data.

Exercises *(Optional)*

1. To the nearest 10 miles, the distance between two cities is 430 miles. How many significant digits are there in the measurement? What is the possible error? the relative error?

2. To the nearest 1,000,000 miles, the sun is 93,000,000 miles from the earth. Name the significant and non-significant digits.

3. Round off 3.14159 to (**a**) 2 digits, (**b**) 3 digits, (**c**) 4 digits, (**d**) 5 digits.

In Exercises **4-9**, *give the results to the accuracy justified by the following approximate data:*

4. 234.15×2.40
5. 13.576×0.034
6. 6.00×70.00
7. $3.14 \times 0.02 \times 51.00$
8. $182.35 \div 2.00$
9. $0.73 \div 0.01$

In Exercises **10-16**, *the numbers* $2, \frac{1}{2}, \frac{4}{3}$, *and 4 are exact numbers and the values of b, h, r, and π are approximate numbers. Find the products indicated and round them off to the accuracy justified.* $(\pi = 3.14159)$.

10. If $A = \frac{1}{2}bh$, find A when $b = 13.42$, and $h = 1.06$.
11. If $C = 2\pi r$, find C when $r = 1.5$.
12. If $C = 2\pi r$, find C when $r = 1.500$.
13. If $A = 4\pi r^2$, find A when $r = 3$.
14. If $A = 4\pi r^2$, find A when $r = 3.0$.
15. If $A = 4\pi r^2$, find A when the value of $r = 3.000$.
16. If $V = \frac{4}{3}\pi r^3$, find V when $r = 3.00$.

Construction of Triangles

Combinations of three of the six parts of a triangle

Although a triangle has six parts (three sides and three angles), it is possible to construct a triangle if only three of its parts are given.

The combinations of three of the six parts of a triangle are:

1. Three sides. (Abbreviation: s, s, s).
2. Two sides and the included angle (s, a, s).

   In $\triangle ABC$, b, $\angle A$ and c; c, $\angle B$, and a; and a, $\angle C$, and b are s, a, s, combinations.
3. Two angles and the included side (a, s, a).

   In $\triangle ABC$, which combinations of parts are a, s, a?

4. Two angles and a side opposite one of them (a, a, s).

   In $\triangle ABC$, which combinations of parts are a, a, s?

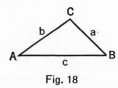

Fig. 18

5. Two sides and an angle opposite one of them (s, s, a).

   In $\triangle ABC$, which combinations of parts are s, s, a?
6. Three angles (a, a, a).

Constructing a triangle, given three sides

CONSTRUCTION 10. Construct a triangle, given three sides (s, s, s).

Given: The segments a, b, and c.

Required: To construct $\triangle ABC$ with sides a, b, c.

Method: Draw a sketch to show the relative positions of the three given parts of the triangle.

1. Draw a working line w. With any point A on w as center and with radius c, construct $\overset{\frown}{1}$ intersecting w at B. (Describe the locus of points which are c units from A.)
2. With A as center and with radius b, construct $\overset{\frown}{2}$.
3. With B as center and with radius a, construct $\overset{\frown}{3}$ intersecting $\overset{\frown}{2}$ at C. (What is the locus of points b units from A and a units from B?)

$\triangle ABC$ is the required triangle.

Explain why the sum of the two shorter given segments must be greater than the longest given segment.

Given

Sketch

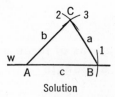

Solution

Exercises

1. With a given segment s, construct an equilateral triangle. Construct or draw all the angle bisectors, altitudes, medians, and perpendicular bisectors of the sides. What seems to be their relationship in this very special case?

2. Draw the segments $d = 2\frac{1}{2}''$, $e = 2\frac{0}{2}''$, and $f = 1\frac{1}{2}''$ on your paper. With them, construct $\triangle DEF$. Measure the angles. Do any of them seem to be equal? Which one seems to be the largest? the smallest?

3. Construct triangles, if possible, with the following sets of given segments as sides:
   a. $e = 3.0''$, $f = 4.0''$, and $g = 5.0''$.
   b. $h = 2.5''$, $i = 1.5''$, and $j = 1.0''$.
   c. $k = 2.5''$, $m = 2.5''$, and $n = 4.5''$.
   d. $x = 3.0''$, $y = 1.0''$, and $z = 1.5''$.
   With which of the above sets of segments could you not construct a triangle? Why?

4. Draw the segments $r = 2.0''$, $s = 2.0''$, and $t = 1.5''$ on your paper. With these segments construct $\triangle RST$. What kind of triangle is it? Measure the angles. Which angles, if any, seem to be equal?

5. With a given segment s, construct an equilateral triangle. Measure the angles. What seems to be true about the angles?

6. Construct an isosceles triangle with a given segment l as one of the legs and a given segment b as the base.

7. Construct a triangle with the given segments x, y, and z as sides. Construct several more triangles with the same given segments as sides. Measure all the corresponding angles of the triangles. What seems to be true about the corresponding angles?

Constructing a triangle, given side, angle, side

CONSTRUCTION 11. Construct a triangle, given two sides and the included angle (s, a, s).

Given: The segments s and t and $\angle R$.

Given

Required: To construct $\triangle RST$ with the parts s, $\angle R$, and t.

Method: The method is left for you to write.

Sketch

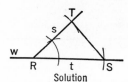

Solution

Exercises

Construct triangles with the following combinations of given parts:

1. An obtuse angle N, side MN, and side NO.

2. An obtuse angle R and equal sides RS and RT.

3. An acute angle A and equal sides AB and AC.

4. A right angle C and sides CA and CB.

5. One of the legs of an isosceles right triangle.

6. The vertex angle of an isosceles triangle equal to $135°$ and one of the legs equal to $2\frac{1}{2}''$.

Constructing a triangle, given angle, side, angle

CONSTRUCTION 12.   Construct a triangle, given two angles and the included side (a, s, a).

Given: The angles M and N, and the segment e.

e

Sketch

Given

Required: To construct $\triangle MNE$ with the parts $\angle M$, side e, and $\angle N$.

Method: This is left for you to do.

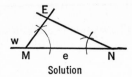

Solution

Explain why the sum of the two given angles must be less than a straight angle.

Exercises

Construct triangles with the following combinations of given parts:

1. $\angle A = 45°$, $\angle B = 90°$, $AB = 2.0''$.
2. An obtuse $\angle R$, an acute $\angle S$, and side RS. What restriction is there on $\angle R + \angle S$?
3. Two equal angles and the side between them. Measure the sides of the triangle. What seems to be true?
4. Angles A and B, and the side AB.

Construct several more triangles with the same parts arranged in the same order. Measure the other three parts of each of the triangles. Do they seem to be respectively equal?

5. An angle $A = 45°$, $AB = AC = 2.0''$.
6. Side MN, side MO, and $\angle M$. Construct several more triangles with the same parts arranged in the same order. Measure the remaining three parts of each triangle. Do they seem to be respectively equal?

Constructing a triangle, given angle, angle, side

CONSTRUCTION 13. **Construct a triangle, given two angles and a side opposite one of them (a, a, s).**

Given: The angles A and C, and the segment c.

Given

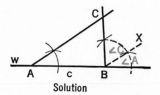

Sketch

Required: To construct $\triangle ABC$ with the parts $\angle A$, $\angle C$, and c.

Method: Draw a sketch to show the relative positions of the three given parts.

Since we do not know how long AC is, we do not know where to place $\angle C$ on AC. However, we can find $\angle B$ by subtracting the sum of angles A and C from a straight angle. We then have the combination a, s, a, and we can proceed as in Construction 12.

Solution

Exercises

1. In the solution figure of Construction 13, how is the dashed line BX related to AC?

2. Construct $\triangle OMN$, if $\angle O = 90°$, $\angle N = 45°$, and $OM = 2.0''$.

3. Construct $\triangle DEF$, given $\angle D$, $\angle F$, and DE. What restriction is there on $\angle D + \angle F$?

4. Construct a right triangle, given its hypotenuse and one acute angle.

5. Construct isosceles $\triangle RST$, given the base RS and the $\angle T$.

6. Construct obtuse $\triangle EFG$, given obtuse $\angle G$, $\angle E$, and side e.

7. Construct $\triangle ABC$, given $\angle A$, $\angle B$, and side AC. Construct several more triangles with the same parts arranged in the same order. Measure the other three parts of the triangles. Do they seem to be respectively equal?

Constructing a triangle, given side, side, angle

CONSTRUCTION 14. **Construct a triangle, given two sides and an angle opposite one of them (s, s, a).**

Given: The segments a and b and $\angle A$.

Required: To construct $\triangle ABC$ with the given sides a and b, and $\angle A$.

Case 1. *The given angle is obtuse.*

A. The given angle is obtuse, and the segment that lies opposite the given angle is longer than the other given segment. (a is greater than b.)

Given   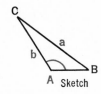 A Sketch

Method:

1. At any point A on the working line w, construct $\angle A$.
2. With A as center and b as radius, construct $\overarc{1}$, intersecting one side of $\angle A$ at C.

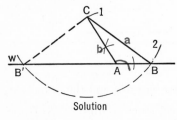

Solution

3. With C as center and a as radius, construct $\overarc{2}$ intersecting the other side of $\angle A$ at B. Arc 2 also intersects w at B'.
4. Draw CB.
It is obvious that $\triangle AB'C$ does not satisfy the given conditions. Explain.

B. $\angle A$ is obtuse and $a = b$.

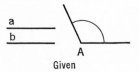

Given

Explain why $\triangle AB'C$ does not satisfy the given conditions and, hence, why there is no solution.

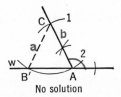

No solution

C. $\angle A$ is obtuse, and a is less than b.

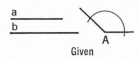

Given

Explain why no triangle can be constructed with these given parts.

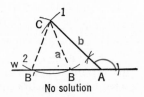

No solution

Case 2. *The given angle is a right angle.*

A. The given angle is a right angle, and the segment that lies opposite the given angle is greater than the other given segment. (*a* is greater than *b*.)

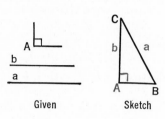

Given   Sketch

You write the method of construction.

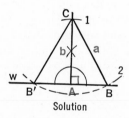

Solution

It is obvious that $\overset{\frown}{2}$ intersects w at two points B and B'.
Either $\triangle ABC$ or $\triangle AB'C$ satisfies the given conditions. It can be proved, however, that they are not different triangles, but the same triangle in different positions.

B. $\angle A$ is a right angle, and either $a = b$ or a is less than b.

Explain why no triangle can be constructed with these given parts. Remember, the perpendicular segment from a point to a line is the shortest path from the point to the line.

Case 3. *The given angle is acute.*

A. The given angle is acute, and the segment that lies opposite the given angle is longer than the other given segment. (*a* is greater than *b*.)

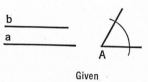

Given

You write the method of construction. Explain why $\triangle AB'C$ does not satisfy the given conditions.

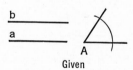

Solution

B. $\angle A$ is acute, and $a = b$.

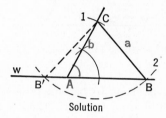

Given

Explain why it is possible to construct only one triangle with these given parts.

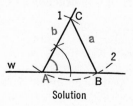

Solution

C. $\angle A$ is acute, and a is less than b.

Given

It is obvious that not only $\triangle ABC$ but also $\triangle AB'C$ satisfies the given conditions. For this reason, this combination of parts is called the *ambiguous case.*

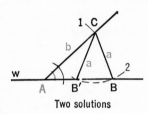

Two solutions

If a_2 happens to be equal to h_c (the distance from C to w), there is only one triangle, which is a right triangle.

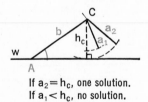

If $a_2 = h_c$, one solution.
If $a_1 < h_c$, no solution.

If a_1 is less than h_c, no triangle is possible.

Summary of Construction 14:

If the given angle of the side, side, angle combination is obtuse or right, the three given parts determine no more than one triangle; if the given angle is acute, the given parts might determine two different triangles.

Exercises

In Exercises **1-6**, *draw the given parts to measure, and then construct as many triangles as possible with the given parts:*

1. Construct $\triangle ABC$ with $\angle A = 30°$, $b = 2\frac{1}{2}''$, and $a = 1\frac{1}{2}''$.

2. Construct $\triangle MNO$ with $\angle M = 30°$, $n = 2\frac{1}{2}''$, and $m = 1''$.

3. Construct $\triangle XYZ$ with $\angle X = 30°$, $y = 2\frac{1}{2}''$, and $x = 2\frac{1}{2}''$.

4. Construct $\triangle RST$ with $\angle R = 120°$, $r = 2\frac{1}{2}''$, and $s = 1\frac{1}{2}''$.

5. Construct $\triangle ABC$ with $\angle A$ obtuse, $a = 3.0$ cm., and $b = 2.0$ cm.

6. Construct $\triangle XYZ$ with $\angle Y = 90°$, $z = 2.0''$, and $y = 2.5''$.

7. Construct $\triangle DEF$ with $\angle F$ an obtuse angle, and $f = d$.

8. Construct $\triangle RST$ with $\angle S$ an acute angle and s greater than t.

9. If possible, construct $\triangle ABC$ with $\angle A = 30°$, $b = 2\frac{1}{2}''$, and $a = 1\frac{0}{2}''$.

When three angles are given

Since the third angle of a triangle is determined by the other two angles, we cannot make a triangle from three angles chosen at random. If two angles are given and none of the sides, we do not know where to place them on a working line. Thus we can make as many triangles as we wish if only two angles are given.

To prove this to yourself, draw a working line and place two given angles on it at random. Extend the sides which are not on the working line until they meet. How many triangles can you draw having the two given angles?

More about the Meaning of Proof

We have studied how fallacies are likely to occur when we reason from an assumed converse, an assumed inverse, and faulty definitions. We shall now consider other types of fallacies.

Analogy

The type of reasoning that attempts to prove a statement by making a comparison between a given situation and another which bears some resemblance to the given situation is called reasoning by analogy.

For example, the rectangle and the parallelogram have certain properties in common. To conclude, however, that the diagonals of a parallelogram are equal merely because the diagonals of a rectangle are equal is incorrect. In other words, two situations are not necessarily alike in *all* respects just because it can be shown that they are alike in a *large number* of respects.

Consider this example: "All right," said John, "I'll clean up the yard if you pay me a quarter. Dad gets paid for his work; if you want me to work, I ought to be paid, too."

Here John is making a comparison between two situations which he asserts are alike. The situations, however, are not really alike. John's mother cooks and serves his food, clothes him, and without pay, looks after him in other ways. John's father, although he is similarly cared for, contributes by supporting the household. There is no such arrangement in the firm for which John's father works. John's father receives pay for his work, but there is no other obligation between them.

Exercises

In each of the following statements, examine the analogy and tell why you consider the conclusion true or false:

1. All equilateral triangles are regular; therefore, all equilateral polygons are regular.

2. Jerry and Susan are both known to be excellent dancers. George decides that they are also good skaters.

3. Because the League of Nations failed, the United Nations will fail.

4. Since a quadrilateral has one more side than a triangle, and since the sum of the interior angles of a quadrilateral is twice the sum of the interior angles of a triangle, then the sum of the interior angles of a pentagon should be twice the sum of the interior angles of a quadrilateral.

Circular reasoning

Circular reasoning, or, as it is often called, begging the question, is a fallacious type of reasoning in which the statement to be proved is implicitly taken for granted. In other words, circular reasoning assumes, in one form or another, the truth of the very statement being proved. Obviously, an argument of this kind is worthless. In geometry, this error sometimes is made when one of the authorities cited in the proof of a theorem is a statement of what was to be proved.

In everyday life this type of reasoning is often used, sometimes unwittingly, sometimes with evil design, in a discussion which is so long that by the time the offender reaches his conclusion his original statement is forgotten; and he uses as his final authority the statement he started out to defend.

Illustration: "This is a very accurate steel rule," said Walter. "I have used it and no other for years." "What makes you think it is accurate?" asked Evan. "Well, let's test it," returned Walter. "I measured the length of this desk very carefully last week, and it was exactly 37 inches long." Walter proceeded to measure the length of the desk and found it to be 37 inches. Evan was quite convinced of the rule's accuracy.

Exercises

In each of the following, explain how circular reasoning makes the conclusion the result of poor reasoning:

1. Many students in High School X wish to elect a course in photography, but are told that it is not taught because there is not enough demand for it; hence, they must decide on some other course.
2. It is a waste of money for me to have my brakes checked so frequently, since they never have failed to stop the car immediately.
3. It is fun to go to the movies because movies are entertaining.
4. The fact that the Fourth of July always falls on a holiday is a happy coincidence.

Hidden assumptions

Many times, our arguments are based on assumptions that are not explicitly stated. These hidden assumptions may be true, or they may be false; hence, they should be evalu-

ated carefully before deciding whether or not to accept the conclusions which depend on them.

Exercises

In Exercises 1-10, write the assumptions on which the argument depends, and explain why the argument is acceptable or unacceptable.

1. This soap must be good because we sell more of it than any other kind.
2. John is not a good citizen because he did not exercise his franchise at the last election.
3. Henry is a trustworthy person because he is kind to animals.
4. Jane is a lazy person. She won't succeed in geometry because it is a rigorous subject.
5. Our neighbor is a poor housekeeper because she always stacks her breakfast dishes unwashed.
6. Two straight lines cannot enclose a surface.
7. Point A is 6 inches from B, and C is 2 inches from B; hence, AC is 4 inches long.
8. Mr. Wise must be a socialist because he believes in government ownership of public utilities.
9. Sam didn't speak to me today. I must have done something to make him angry.
10. "You should wash the dishes, Sis. After all, you are a girl."
11. From the following list, choose the assumption that best justifies the statement, "The hypotenuse of a right triangle is longer than either leg":

    a. There is one, and only one, perpendicular from a point to a line.

b. The distance from a point to a line is the length of the perpendicular segment from the point to the line.

c. If two angles of a triangle are unequal, the sides opposite them are unequal.

d. The perpendicular segment from a point to a line is the shortest path from the point to the line.

12. From the following list, choose the assumption that best justifies the statement, "The sum of the lengths of two sides of a triangle is greater than the length of the third side":

a. There is one, and only one, straight line through two given points.

b. The distance between two points is the length of the straight line segment joining the two points.

c. A straight line segment is the shortest path between two given points.

d. The difference between the lengths of any two sides of a triangle is less than the third side.

13. Which one of the following statements is the best authority for drawing a straight line joining two given points?

a. Two points determine one, and only one, line.

b. A straight line segment is the shortest path between two points.

c. The distance between two points is the length of the straight line segment joining them.

d. There is one, and only one, straight line segment through two given points.

14. Which one of the following statements is the best authority for drawing the bisector of a given angle?

a. An angle has one, and only one, bisector.

b. The bisector of an angle is the locus of a point equidistant from the sides.

c. The bisector of an angle divides the angle into two equal parts.

d. If a line divides an angle into two equal parts, it bisects the angle.

Irrelevancy (non-sequitur reasoning)

In this day of keen competition and high-pressure salesmanship, it is essential that one be able to distinguish between those facts which have a bearing on, or are pertinent to, a given situation or product and those which are not. In other words, one should be able to sift and sort out all material so that only those facts remain which are relevant to the question at hand. Extravagant advertising heard so frequently on television and elsewhere affords ample illustrations of the very common practice of using irrelevant facts to influence the listeners to buy special products.

Illustration 1: If a polygon is a pentagon, the sum of its exterior angles is 360°. The conclusion is true, but the fact that the polygon has five sides is irrelevant.

Illustration 2: An advertisement shows a wealthy society woman in the garden of her beautiful estate and contains a statement to the effect that she uses a certain product. While it is quite possible that all such facts may build up an atmosphere which might impel one to buy the product, it is certainly obvious that they are irrelevant to the question.

Exercises

In each of the following statements select the fact or facts which you consider irrelevant, and explain:

1. Mary thinks that Jack is the best candidate for senior class president because he is intelligent, popular, good-looking, and a good athlete.

2. If a polygon is equilateral, the sum of its interior angles is $(n - 2)$ straight angles.

3. Since $\triangle EFG$ is isosceles, and since GH is the altitude from point G to side EF, then $\angle FHG = \angle GHE$.

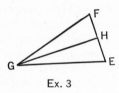

Ex. 3

4. James decided to go to a certain college because it has outstanding professors, is located near a big city, and has a fine athletic record.

5. "And now, class, we are going to read *The Mill on the Floss* because it is a good example of the work of George Eliot. I'm sure you are going to enjoy this book, for it gives an excellent picture of middle-class English home life in the nineteenth century. You will probably be especially interested in Maggie; she is such a self-sacrificing person. Every high-school boy and girl should become acquainted with this dramatic story in order to be well-informed."

6. In City High School where Louise is a student, members of the Honor Society are not required to take final examinations. Since Louise is an honor student, she will not be required to take final examinations.

7. Since Mr. J speaks foreign languages fluently and has been a great student of European history, he will enjoy traveling in Europe and would be a good representative of the United States in European countries.

Reasoning from special cases

Reasoning that since a certain conclusion is true in one or more cases it is necessarily true for all cases, is a common form of fallacy. For example, maybe it is true that in certain triangles the altitudes meet at a point within the triangle; but if we conclude that the altitudes of any triangle meet within the triangle, we are guilty of reasoning from special cases.

If one small group of boys from a neighboring school misbehaves while attending a basketball game at your school, are you justified in assuming that all boys from that school are equally discourteous?

Exercises

In each of the following, explain how the exercise illustrates the drawing of a conclusion from a special case, and tell whether you think the conclusion is or is not warranted:

1. Three planes coming from South American ports to the United States were found to have carried the yellow fever mosquito. As a result, the United States Government ordered that all such planes be searched and fumigated.

2. In the words, "deceive," "seize," and "receipt," the *e* precedes the *i*. Therefore, in any word where *e* and *i* occur consecutively, the *e* should precede the *i*.

3. President Eisenhower was a high military officer before being elected to the presidency. Therefore, to be successful, a party should have as its candidate a former high-ranking military officer.

4. After six o'clock, in City K, drivers do not have to insert coins in parking meters. I am safe, therefore, in parking in City M at seven o'clock without putting a coin in the meter.

Chapter Summary

Triangles classified according to their sides:

1. Equilateral—all sides equal.
2. Isosceles—two sides equal.
3. Scalene—no two sides equal.

Triangles classified according to their angles:

1. Acute—all angles acute.
2. Obtuse—one angle obtuse.
3. Right—one angle right.
4. Equiangular—all angles equal.

Angle sums:

1. The sum of the angles of a triangle is 180°.
2. The sum of the angles of an n-gon is $(n-2)180°$.
3. The sum of the exterior angles of an n-gon is 360°.
4. The sum of two interior angles of a triangle is equal to the non-adjacent exterior angle.

Angle sizes:

1. The number of degrees in each interior angle of an equiangular polygon having n sides is $\dfrac{(n-2)180°}{n}$.
2. The number of degrees in each exterior angle of an equiangular polygon having n sides is $\dfrac{360°}{n}$.

Secondary lines in triangles:

1. Median—a line segment from a vertex to the midpoint of the opposite side.

2. Altitude—a line segment from a vertex perpendicular to the opposite side, or opposite side extended.

3. Angle bisector—a line segment bisecting an angle of a triangle and extending to the opposite side.

4. Perpendicular bisector of a side—a line bisecting a side of a triangle and perpendicular to it.

Construction of triangles with given parts:

1. Three sides (s, s, s).

2. Two sides and the included angle (s, a, s).

3. Two angles and the included side (a, s, a).

4. Two angles and a side opposite one of them (a, a, s).

5. Two sides and an angle opposite one of them (s, s, a). (Ambiguous case.)

Review of Chapter 6

Algebraic Exercises

Copy the following table, writing the correct numerical values in the place of the question marks (do not write in this book):

Name of Polygon	Sum of the Interior ∠s	Sum of the Exterior ∠s	Size of Each Interior ∠ if Equiangular	Size of Each Exterior ∠ if Equiangular
1. Quadrilateral	?	?	?	?
2. Pentagon	?	?	?	?
3. Hexagon	?	?	?	?
4. Octagon	?	?	?	?
5. Decagon	?	?	?	?
6. ?	1260°	?	?	?
7. ?	1440°	?	?	?
8. ?	1800°	?	?	?
9. ?	?	360°	?	?
10. ?	?	?	144°	?
11. ?	?	?	165°	?
12. ?	?	?	162°	?
13. ?	?	?	?	18°
14. ?	?	?	?	20°
15. ?	?	?	?	24°

Constructions

1. Construct an equilateral triangle ABC, given side AB.
2. Construct an isosceles triangle ABC, given the base AB and the leg AC.
3. Construct a triangle ABC, given $\angle A$, side b, and side c.
4. Construct a triangle ABC, given $\angle A$, $\angle B$, and side c.
5. Construct a triangle RST, given $\angle R$, $\angle S$, and side s.

6. Construct a triangle DEF, given $\angle D$, side e, and side d.

7. Draw a scalene triangle ABC. Construct h_c.

8. Draw a scalene triangle DEF. Construct m_e.

9. Draw an obtuse triangle RST. Construct p_r.

10. Draw triangle XYZ. Construct t_X.

Proofs

1. Given: $\triangle ADF$ in which AH bisects $\angle FAD$, and AH is the altitude to FD.
Prove: $\angle F = \angle D$.

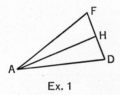

Ex. 1

2. Given: $ABCD$ is a quadrilateral with AD extended to E, $AE \perp AB$, and $BC \perp DC$.
Prove the relation of $\angle B$ to $\angle CDE$.

Ex. 2

3. Given: $\triangle SRC$; D and E are points on sides SR and SC, respectively;

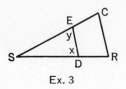

Ex. 3

$DE \parallel RC$, and $\angle R = \angle C$.
Deduce the relation between $\angle x$ and $\angle y$.

4. Given: Lines AB, AC, and AD so that $CD \perp AC$, and $BD \perp AB$. Deduce the relation between $\angle m$ and $\angle n$.

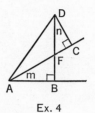

Ex. 4

★Transformations of Implicative Statements*

1. Write the converse, inverse, and contrapositive of Theorem 12.

2. Prove the two converses, the two inverses, and the two contrapositives of the exercise below.

The side BF of $\triangle BEF$ is extended to G.
If (s_1) $FH \parallel BE$, and
if (s_2) FH bisects $\angle EFG$,
then (c) $\angle B = \angle E$.

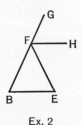

Ex. 2

Explain why all seven exercises can be proved by proving the original exercise and its two converses.

---

* See footnote on page 94 for an explanation of starred material.

The mass production of automobiles on an assembly line requires the use of many congruent figures. Notice that each chassis is congruent to the others in the group, and each one contains hundreds of congruent interchangeable parts.

Chapter 7　CONGRUENCE

THIS IS the age of assembly lines and mass production. Henry Ford is given credit for being the first industrialist to use assembly-line techniques to produce automobiles quickly and cheaply. Mass production of our necessities and luxuries of life depends upon the ability to make parts that are almost exactly alike. These parts are then assembled by people who are trained to perform one or more relatively simple operations. If the parts were not almost exact duplicates, they would not be interchangeable, and they would not fit together with other parts to make a complete functional unit.

Congruent figures

Patterns that are repeated in painted, printed, or woven designs on china, rugs, wallpaper, fabrics, etc., are copies or duplicates of a given design. In the clothing industry, many thicknesses of material are cut simultaneously from the same pattern. Each piece is an exact copy of the pattern, and any piece can be made to coincide with any other piece.

DEFINITION　*Congruent figures* are figures that can be made to coincide.

The symbol for "congruent" or "is congruent to" is: $\cong$. The definition of congruent figures implies that:

1. If two figures are congruent, the corresponding sides and angles are respectively equal.
2. If the corresponding sides and angles of two or more figures are respectively equal, the figures are congruent.
3. Congruent figures have the same size and shape.

Corresponding parts of triangles

In triangles AEB and RFN of Figure 1, if $\angle A = \angle N$, and if $\angle E = \angle R$, then side a corresponds to side n, side e corresponds to side r, and side b corresponds to side f.

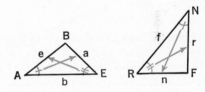

Fig. 1

In triangles MCD and GHQ of Figure 2, if $\angle D = \angle G$, $MD = GQ$, and $CD = GH$, then $\angle C$ corresponds to $\angle H$, MC corresponds to HQ, and $\angle M$ corresponds to $\angle Q$.

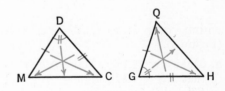

Fig. 2

If two triangles are congruent, corresponding sides are those that are opposite equal angles, and corresponding angles are those that are opposite equal sides.

Combinations of equal parts that make triangles congruent

In the last chapter we learned that under certain conditions a triangle can be constructed if only three of its parts are given. This suggests the possibility that two triangles are congruent if only three parts of one are equal, respectively, to the corresponding three parts of the other.

Experiment

Given: Three parts of △ABC are equal, respectively, to corresponding parts of △RST.

Problem: Which combinations of three pairs of equal parts, if any, are sufficient to make △$ABC \cong$ △RST?

Procedure: For this experiment we may use a pair of dynamic triangles, or we may draw or construct triangles that fulfill the given conditions.

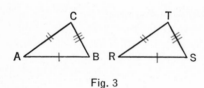

Fig. 3

COMBINATION 1: $s, s, s = s, s, s$ (Figure 3).

a. Make any △ABC. Make △RST so that $RS = AB$, $RT = AC$, and $ST = BC$.

b. Measure the corresponding angles. Do they seem to be respectively equal?

c. Repeat this experiment several times with different kinds of triangles. Do you get the same results as you did in **b**?

d. Complete the statement that seems to follow by induction from the experiment: *If three sides of one triangle are equal, respectively, to three sides of another, the triangles* . . . . .

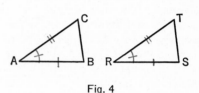

Fig. 4

COMBINATION 2: $s, a, s = s, a, s$ (Figure 4).

a. Make any △ABC. Make △RST so that $RS = AB$, $\angle R = \angle A$, and $RT = AC$.

b. Measure ST and BC; $\angle S$ and $\angle B$, $\angle T$ and $\angle C$. What seems to be true?

c. Repeat the experiment several times with different kinds of triangles.

d. Complete this inductive conclusion: *If two sides and the included angle of one triangle are equal, respectively, to* . . . . .

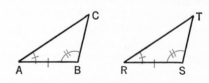

Fig. 5

COMBINATION 3: $a, s, a = a, s, a$ (Figure 5).

a. Make any △ABC. Make △RST so that $\angle R = \angle A$, $RS = AB$, and $\angle S = \angle B$. Can you be certain that $\angle T = \angle C$?

b. Compare RT with AC, and ST with BC.

c. Repeat the experiment several times. What do you discover?

d. Complete this inductive conclusion: *If two angles and the included side of one triangle are equal, respectively, to . . . . .*

Fig. 6

COMBINATION 4: $a, a, s = a, a, s$ (Figure 6).

a. Make any $\triangle ABC$. Make $\triangle RST$ so that $\angle R = \angle A$, $\angle T = \angle C$, and $ST = BC$.

b. Measure the remaining corresponding parts. Do they seem to be equal?

c. Repeat the experiment several times. Are the results consistent with those in b?

d. Complete this inductive conclusion: *If two angles and a side opposite one of them of one triangle are equal, respectively, to . . . . .*

COMBINATION 5: $s, s, a = s, s, a$.

We shall consider three cases as follows:

Case 1. The equal angles are acute. (Figure 7).

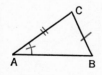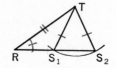

Fig. 7

a. Make $\triangle ABC$ with AC longer than BC. Make $\triangle RST$ so $\angle R = \angle A$, $RT = AC$, and $ST = BC$.

b. Can ST take the position of either S_1T or S_2T?
Is $\triangle ABC \cong \triangle RS_2T$?
Is $\triangle ABC \cong \triangle RS_1T$?

This combination of equal pairs of parts is called the *ambiguous* combination.

The triangles are sometimes congruent but not always.

Fig. 8

Case 2. The equal angles are right angles (Figure 8). In this case the hypotenuse and a leg of one triangle are equal, respectively, to the hypotenuse and a leg of the other triangle.

a. Make $\triangle ABC$ so that $\angle A = 90°$. Make $\triangle RST$ so that $\angle R = 90°$, $RT = AC$, and $ST = BC$.

b. Compare RS with AB, $\angle S$ with $\angle B$, and $\angle T$ with $\angle C$.

c. Repeat the experiment several times. What seems to be true?

d. Complete this generalization: *If the hypotenuse and a leg of one right triangle are equal, respectively, to the hypotenuse and a leg of another right triangle, the triangles . . . . .*

Case 3: The equal angles are obtuse (Figure 9).

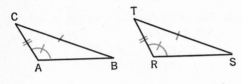

Fig. 9

a. Make △ABC so that ∠A is obtuse. Make △RST so that ∠R = ∠A, RT = AC, and ST = BC.

b. Measure the remaining parts. Do they seem to be respectively equal?

c. Repeat the experiment several times.

d. Complete this statement: *If the obtuse angles of two obtuse triangles are equal, if the sides opposite the obtuse angles are equal, and if another pair of sides are equal, the triangles* . . . . .

Congruence postulates

As the result of our experiments with triangles having three pairs of parts respectively equal, it seems reasonable to postulate the following statements:

POSTULATE 34. **If three sides of one triangle are equal, respectively, to three sides of another triangle, the triangles are congruent.**

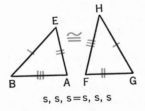

s, s, s=s, s, s

POSTULATE 35. **If two sides and the included angle of one triangle are equal, respectively, to two sides and the included angle of another triangle, the triangles are congruent.**

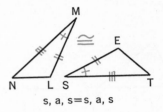

s, a, s=s, a, s

POSTULATE 36. **If two angles and a side of one triangle are equal, respectively, to two angles and a corresponding side of another triangle, the triangles are congruent.**

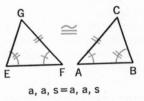

a, s, a=a, s, a

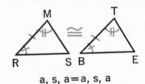

a, a, s=a, a, s

POSTULATE 37. **If the hypotenuse and a leg of one right triangle are equal, respectively, to the hypotenuse and a leg of another right triangle, the triangles are congruent.**

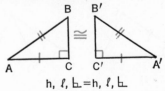

h, ℓ, ∟=h, ℓ, ∟

Proving triangles congruent

When you are proving triangles congruent, it is advisable first to look for equal sides. If there are three pairs of equal sides, you do not need any equal angles. If there are two pairs of equal sides, you must also have equal included angles unless the triangles are right triangles. If there is only one pair of equal sides, you must have two pairs of corresponding angles that are respectively equal. If there are no equal sides, the triangles cannot be proved congruent.

Example of proving triangles congruent

Given: RN and GS bisect each other at E to form with RG and SN the $\triangle$ REG and ESN.

Prove: $\triangle REG \cong \triangle ESN$.

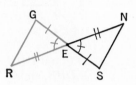

Proof

STATEMENTS	AUTHORITIES
1. RN and GS bisect each other at E.	1. Given.
2. $\therefore$ $RE = EN$, and $GE = ES$.	2. If a line is bisected, ...
3. $\therefore$ $\angle REG = \angle SEN$.	3. If two straight lines intersect, ...
4. $\therefore$ $\triangle REG \cong \triangle ESN$.	4. $s, a, s = s, a, s$ (RE, $\angle REG$, $GE = EN$, $\angle SEN$, ES)

Exercises

In Exercises **1-6**, *draw figures on your paper like the ones shown. Mark the parts of the triangles that are given equal. If the conditions are sufficient to make the triangles congruent, write the postulates that justify your conclusions. Do not assume that parts are equal because they appear to be equal.*

1. Given: $\triangle$ ABO and ODC in which $AO = OC$, $\angle AOB = \angle DOC$, and $\angle B = \angle D$.

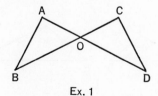

Ex. 1

2. Given: $\triangle AEG$ in which H and F are on AG and EG, respectively, $HM \perp AE$ at M, $FN \perp AE$ at N, $AH = EF$, and $AM = NE$.

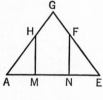

Ex. 2–3

3. Given: $\triangle AEG$ in which H and F are on AG and EG, respectively, M and N are on AE, $AH = EF$, and $AM = NE$.

4. Given: ⚗ ABC and DEF in which $\angle A = \angle D$, $AB = DE$, and $BC = EF$.

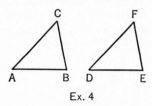

Ex. 4

5. Given: ⚗ APC and PDB in which $\angle CPA = \angle DPB$, and $CP = PD$.

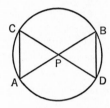

Ex. 5

6. Given: ⚗ ABC and ACD in which $AB = AD$, and $BC = CD$. (AC is common to the two triangles.)

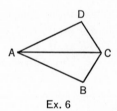

Ex. 6

In Exercises **7-10**, *if two triangles can be proved congruent, write the proof.*

7. Given: Quadrilateral $ABCD$ in which AC is a diagonal, $\angle 1 = \angle 4$, and $\angle 2 = \angle 3$.

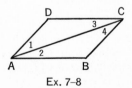

Ex. 7–8

8. Given: Quadrilateral $ABCD$ in which AC is a diagonal, $AD = BC$, and $\angle 3 = \angle 2$.

9. Given: $\triangle ABC$ in which $CD \perp AB$ at D, and $\angle A = \angle B$.

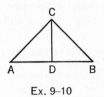

Ex. 9–10

10. Given: $\triangle ABC$, CD bisects AB at D, and CD bisects $\angle ACB$.

Triangles with equal parts that are not corresponding parts

Three parts of $\triangle ABC$ are equal to three parts of $\triangle DEF$. The pairs of equal parts, however, are not arranged in the same order. That is, there are not three pairs of equal *corresponding* parts. Are the triangles necessarily congruent?

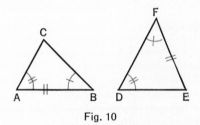

Fig. 10

Five parts of $\triangle TSR$ are respectively equal to five parts of $\triangle BCA$. Are there five pairs of equal corresponding parts? Are the triangles necessarily congruent?

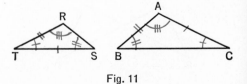

Fig. 11

Corresponding parts of congruent triangles

If we have enough information to prove triangles congruent, we can prove sides and angles equal by proving that they are corresponding parts of congruent triangles. Sometimes it is a little difficult to group corresponding parts, but just remember that corresponding sides are opposite angles known to be equal, and that corresponding angles are opposite sides known to be equal.

Example 1. If $\triangle ABC \cong \triangle RST$ because $\angle B = \angle R$, $\angle C = \angle S$, and $a = t$, then $b = r$, $c = s$, and $\angle A = \angle T$.

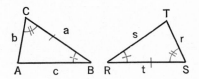

Example 2. Given: $\triangle ABC$ and $\triangle ACE$, AC is extended to D, $\angle 1 = \angle 2$, and $BC = CE$.

Deduce the implications.

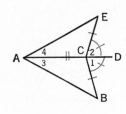

Proof

STATEMENTS	AUTHORITIES
1. ACD is a straight line.	**1.** Why?
2. $\therefore$ $\angle 1$ is the supplement of $\angle ACB$, and $\angle 2$ is the supplement of ?	**2.** If the exterior sides of two adjacent angles lie in a straight line, ...
3. $\angle 1 = $?	**3.** Why?
4. $\therefore$ $\angle ACB = $?	**4.** Why?
5. $AC = AC$.	**5.** Identity. (AC is identical to itself.)
6. $BC = $?	**6.** Why?
7. $\therefore$ $\triangle ABC \cong$?	**7.** $s, a, s = s, a, s.$ $(BC, \angle ACB, AC = CE, \angle ECA, AC)$
8. $\therefore$ $AB = $?	**8.** If two triangles are congruent, the corresponding parts are equal.
9. $\therefore$ $\angle 3 = $?	**9.** Why?
10. $\therefore$ AC bisects $\angle BAE$.	**10.** Why?
11. $\therefore$ $\angle B = \angle E$.	**11.** Why?

Exercises

1. Given: Quadrilateral $PQRS$, the diagonal PR bisects $\angle QPS$, and $PQ = PS$.

Prove: PR bisects $\angle SRQ$.

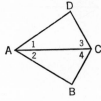

Ex. 1

2. Given: $ABCD$ is a quadrilateral, and the diagonal AC bisects both $\angle BAD$ and $\angle DCB$.

Deduce the implications.

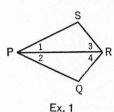

Ex. 2–3

3. Given: $ABCD$ is a quadrilateral, the diagonal AC bisects $\angle BAD$, and $\angle D = \angle B$.

Deduce the implications.

4. Given: AB bisects CD at O, and $AC \parallel BD$.

Prove: **a.** CD bisects AB.
　　　　b. $AC = BD$.

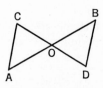

Ex. 4–6

5. Given: AB and CD bisect each other at O.

Prove: $AC \parallel BD$.

6. Given: AB and CD intersect at O, $AC = BD$, and $AC \parallel BD$.

Deduce the implications concerning AB and CD.

7. Given: $\triangle NBS$ in which $NS = BS$, and SY bisects NSB.

Prove: **a.** $\triangle NSB$ is isosceles.
　　　　b. $\angle N = \angle B$.
　　　　c. SY is an altitude.
　　　　d. SY is a median.

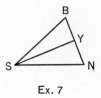

Ex. 7

8. Given: $ABCD$ is a quadrilateral, AC is a diagonal, $AD \parallel BC$, and $AD = BC$.

Prove: **a.** $DC = AB$.
　　　　b. $DC \parallel AB$.

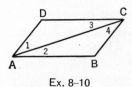

Ex. 8–10

9. Given: $ABCD$ is a quadrilateral, AC is a diagonal, $AD \parallel BC$, and $AB \parallel DC$.

Prove: **a.** $AD = BC$.
　　　　b. $AB = DC$.

10. Given: $ABCD$ is a quadrilateral, AC is a diagonal, $AD = BC$, and $AB = DC$.

Deduce new implications concerning AD and BC, also concerning AB and DC.

11. Given: $\triangle ABC$ in which $\angle A = \angle B$; D and E are points on AB; G and F are points on AC and BC, respectively; $AE = DB$; $GD \perp AB$; and $FE \perp AB$.

    Deduce the implications concerning AG and BF, also concerning DG and EF.

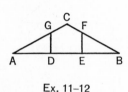

Ex. 11–12

12. Given: $\triangle ABC$ in which $AG = BF$, $AE = BD$, $GD \perp AB$, and $FE \perp AB$.

    Deduce the implications concerning $\angle A$ and $\angle B$, also concerning DG and EF.

13. Prove: If two triangles are congruent, any pair of corresponding medians are equal.

14. Prove: If two triangles are congruent, any pair of corresponding altitudes are equal.

15. Prove: If two triangles are congruent, any pair of corresponding angle bisectors are equal.

16. Prove: If the perpendicular bisector of one side of a triangle passes through the opposite vertex, the triangle is isosceles.

17. Prove: Oblique line segments drawn to a given line from any point on the perpendicular to the line so that they intersect the given line equidistant from the foot of the perpendicular are equal.

The isosceles triangle

Since an isosceles triangle has two equal sides, it seems reasonable to expect other parts to be related in some particular way. We shall use induction to explore the possibilities.

Experiment

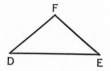

Given: Isosceles triangle DEF in which $DF = EF$.

Problem: How are the other parts of $\triangle DEF$ related?

Procedure: You may use a dynamic triangle, or you may construct triangles that fulfill the given condition. Measure the relevant parts of representative samples of different kinds of triangles. Record your data in a table.

Conclusion: (In terms of $\triangle DEF$, what did you discover?)

Inductive conclusion: (In terms of *any* isosceles triangle, what did you discover?)

Does the length of DE or the size of $\angle F$ seem to affect the relation of $\angle D$ to $\angle E$? If not, then these data are *irrelevant* to that relationship. Would your conclusions be more significant if all the other members of your class had results identical to yours? What is the procedure when you find a sample that seems to be an exception?

Deductive proof that the base angles of an isosceles triangle are equal

---

THEOREM 17. If two sides of a triangle are equal, the angles opposite these sides are equal.

Given: Isosceles $\triangle DEF$; $DF = EF$.

Prove: $\angle D = \angle E$.

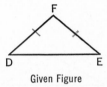

Given Figure

Informal analysis: None of the ways to prove two angles equal seems to apply here. To prove that they are corresponding parts of congruent triangles, we must have two triangles with $\angle D$ in one of them and $\angle E$ in the other. We can make two triangles by drawing an auxiliary line through F so that it intersects DE at some point A. We know that only two conditions can be imposed on an auxiliary line. Think of three ways to draw auxiliary line through F and intersecting DE. Draw FA one or more of these three ways and prove $\triangle DAF \cong \triangle AEF$.

The proof is left for you to write.

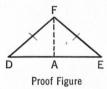

Proof Figure

Another way to state Theorem 17 is: The base angles of an isosceles triangle are equal.

Converse of Theorem 17

THEOREM 18. If two angles of a triangle are equal, the sides opposite these angles are equal.

Draw a general figure that represents the conditions of the theorem. Draw an auxiliary line as suggested for Theorem 17 and prove the resulting triangles congruent.

The proof is left for you to write.

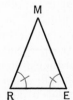

COROLLARIES 1. If a triangle is equilateral, it is equiangular.

2. If a triangle is equiangular, it is equilateral.

Exercises

1. Is an isosceles triangle symmetrical? Explain.

2. Is an equilateral triangle symmetrical with respect to a point? to one or more lines? Explain.

3. Given: $ABCD$ is a straight line, BCE is a triangle, and $\angle x = \angle y$.
   Prove: $\triangle BCE$ is isosceles.

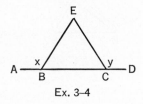

Ex. 3–4

4. Given: $ABCD$ is a straight line, and BC is the base of the isosceles $\triangle BCE$.
   Deduce the implications.

5. Given: AB is the base of the isosceles $\triangle ABC$; D and E are points on AC and BC, respectively; and $DE \parallel AB$.
   Prove: $\triangle DEC$ is isosceles.

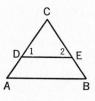

Ex. 5–7

6. Given: AB is the base of the isosceles $\triangle ABC$; D and E are points on AC and BC, respectively; and DE is the base of the isosceles $\triangle DEC$.
   Prove: $AB \parallel DE$.

7. Given: $\triangle ABC$; D and E are points on AC and BC, respectively; $\angle A = \angle B$; and $\angle A = \angle EDC$.
   Prove: $\triangle DEC$ is isosceles.

8. Given: NF is a diagonal of the quadrilateral $NBFD$, $NB = BF$, $BN \perp ND$, and $BF \perp FD$.
   Prove: $\triangle NFD$ is isosceles.

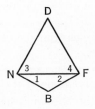

Ex. 8–9

9. Given: NF is the diagonal of the quadrilateral $NBFD$, $\angle 1 = \angle 2$, $\angle 1$ is the complement of $\angle 3$, and $\angle 2$ is the complement of $\angle 4$.
   Deduce the implications.

10. Given: $\angle URW$, S and V are on RU, T is on RW, and $RS = ST = TV$.
    Prove: $\angle 8 = 3\angle 1$.

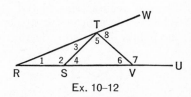

Ex. 10–12

11. In the same figure, evaluate all the angles if $\angle 1 = 30°$.

12. In the same figure, evaluate all the angles if $\angle 8 = 60°$.

13. Given: *M* is a point on the side *AB* of △*ABG*, and *GA* = *GM* = *MB*.

Prove: ∠*A* = 2∠*B*.

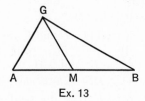

Ex. 13

14. Construct a 60° angle, a 30° angle, an angle of 120°.

15. Construct a 30°, 60° right triangle having a given hypotenuse.

16. Given the perimeter and base of an isosceles triangle, construct the triangle.

17. Construct an isosceles right triangle, given one of the legs.

18. Given the base and the altitude to the base of an isosceles triangle, construct the triangle.

19. Divide a circle into six equal parts.

20. Draw a symmetrical design based upon the equilateral triangle. You may use circles in the design.

21. Construct a right triangle, given the hypotenuse and one of the acute angles.

22. Construct an isosceles triangle, given the base and the vertex angle.

23. Draw a regular six-pointed star. What is the sum of the angles at the points of the star? Is the star

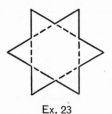

Ex. 23

symmetrical? Is it symmetrical with respect to a point? How many axes of symmetry does it have?

24. Draw a symmetrical design based upon a regular hexagon.

25. Through a given point, construct a line making equal angles with the sides of a given angle.

26. Given an angle of a triangle, an adjacent side, and the sum of the other two sides, construct the triangle.

Given: Side *g*, ∠*E*, and *e* + *f*.

Construct: △*EFG*.

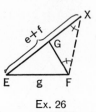

Ex. 26

27. Given an angle of a triangle, an adjacent side, and the difference of the other two sides, construct the triangle.

28. Prove: In an isosceles triangle, the perpendiculars drawn from the midpoints of the equal sides to the base are equal.

29. Prove: If the bisectors of two angles of a triangle intersect at a point equidistant from the vertices of those angles, the triangle is isosceles.

30. Prove: The median to the hypotenuse of an isosceles right triangle is one-half the hypotenuse.

31. Prove: The perpendicular segments from the midpoint of the base of an isosceles triangle to the equal sides are equal.

32. Prove the following theorems:

a. Theorem A: If a line bisects an exterior angle at the vertex of an isosceles triangle, it is parallel to the base.

In $\triangle ABD$ with exterior angle CBD.

if   (s_1) $AB = BD$, and

if   (s_2) BE bisects $\angle CBD$,

then (c) $BE \parallel AD$.

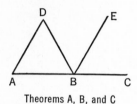

Theorems A, B, and C

b. Theorem B (First converse of Theorem A):

In $\triangle ABD$ with exterior angle CBD,

if   (c) $BE \parallel AD$, and

if   (s_2) BE bisects $\angle CBD$,

then (s_1) $AB = BD$.

State Theorem B.

c. Theorem C (Second converse of Theorem A):

In $\triangle ABD$ with exterior angle CBD,

if   (s_1) $AB = BD$, and

if   (c) $BE \parallel AD$,

then (s_2) BE bisects $\angle CBD$.

State Theorem C.

★ **d.** * Write each of the contrapositives of Theorem A. Does either of them require proof? Explain.

★ **e.** Write each of the inverses of Theorem A. Does either of them require proof? Explain.

★ **f.** In Theorem A, is the combination of given conditions s_1 and s_2 sufficient for conclusion c? Explain.

★ **g.** In Theorem A, is the condition s_1 necessary for c? Explain. Is the condition s_2 necessary for c? Explain.

★ **33.** Write the converse, the inverse, and the contrapositive of: If a triangle is not equilateral, it is not equiangular. Explain why each of these statements is true.

★ **34.** Write the inverse and the contrapositive of Theorem 17. Explain why each of them is true.

Three famous problems (*Optional*)

Three famous problems have claimed the interest and attention of mathematicians since ancient times. Restricting themselves to the compass and straightedge, they have tried to find ways to (a) *trisect an angle*, (b) *duplicate a cube*, and (c) *square a circle*. To trisect an angle means to divide an angle into three equal parts; to duplicate a cube means to find the length of a side of a cube whose volume is some integral multiple of the volume of a given cube; to square a circle is to find the length of the side of a square whose area is equal to the area of a given circle. We shall restrict our discussion to the trisection problem.

Although it has been mathematically proved to be impossible with compass and straightedge, the problem of trisecting an angle is still popular even today. It can be solved by using certain types of complex curves which require complicated instruments for their construction. It can also be solved by a number of mechanical devices, the simplest of which is a straightedge having only two marks on it, as in Figure 12 on the following page. The solution is:

* See footnote on page 94 for an explanation of starred material.

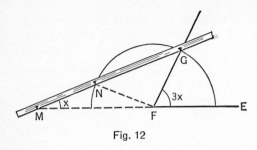

Fig. 12

Put two marks M and N on a straight-edge. The angle to be trisected is $\angle EFG$. With F as center and a radius equal to MN, construct a circle. Slide the straightedge about so that M falls on the extension of EF, N falls on the circle, and the edge of the straightedge passes through the intersection of the side of the angle and the circle at G. Then $FG = FN = MN$. Hence, $\angle EMG = \frac{1}{3} \angle EFG$. Why?

Note: For a complete discussion of the trisection problem, read a book entitled *The Trisection Problem* by Robert C. Yates, published by Edwards Brothers, Inc., Ann Arbor, Michigan.

Overlapping triangles

When you work with triangles that overlap, it is helpful to draw the triangles separately. You may also trace the triangles with colored pencils to distinguish one from another.

Example:

Given: $\triangle ABC$ with $\angle BAC = \angle CBA$; R and S are on AC and BC, respectively; $AR = BS$; and AS and BR intersect at O.

Prove: $\triangle ABO$ is isosceles.

Separate the given figure into four triangles and mark the known equal parts.

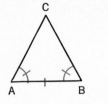

We see at once that $\triangle ABR \cong \triangle ABS$. Why? Therefore, $\angle 2 = \angle 1$. Why? Hence, $\triangle ABO$ is isosceles. Why?

Exercises

1. Given: AC and BD are the diagonals of the quadrilateral $ABCD$, $AD = BC$, $DA \perp AB$, $CB \perp AB$.

   a. Deduce the implications concerning AC and BD.

   b. Is the figure symmetrical with respect to any lines now drawn?

   c. Can you draw two axes of symmetry through O? Explain.

   d. Is the figure symmetrical with respect to a point? Explain.

Ex. 1

2. Given: AB is the base of the isosceles $\triangle ABC$; E and D are points on AC and BC, respectively; and $EC = DC$.

Ex. 2

Prove: **a.** $\angle 1 = \angle 2$.
     b. $\angle 3 = \angle 4$.
     c. $\triangle ABO$ is isosceles.
     d. A line through C and O is an axis of symmetry.

3. Given: $ADEB$ is a straight line segment, DE is the base of the isosceles $\triangle DEC$, and $AE = DB$. Prove: $\triangle ABC$ is isosceles.

Ex. 3

4. Given: AB is the base of the isosceles $\triangle ABC$, and CA and CB are extended to D and E, respectively, so that $AD = BE$.

    a. Deduce the implications concerning DB and AE, also AO and BO.

    b. Prove that a line through C and O is an axis of symmetry.

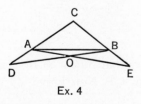

Ex. 4

5. Prove: If the altitudes to two sides of an acute triangle are equal, the triangle is isosceles.

6. Prove: If the altitudes to two sides of an obtuse triangle are equal, the triangle is isosceles.

7. Given: $\triangle ABC$; D and E are points on AC and BC, respectively; $AD = BE$; and $AE = BD$.
Prove: $AB \parallel DE$.

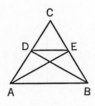

Ex. 7

8. Given: AB is the base of the isosceles $\triangle ABC$; CA is extended to D, and CB is extended to E so that $AD = BE$.

Prove: $\angle BAC = \angle CBA$, without using Theorem 17.

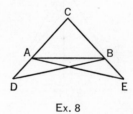

Ex. 8

9. Given: $ABCD$ is a quadrilateral, $AD = BC$, E and F are on AB, $DE \perp AB$, $CF \perp AB$, $DC \parallel AB$.
Prove: $AC = BD$.

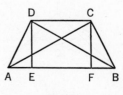

Ex. 9

10. Given: *AB* is the common base of the isosceles triangles *ABC* and *ADB*.

Prove whichever is correct:

a. *CD* is the perpendicular bisector of *AB, or*

b. *AB* is the perpendicular bisector of *CD.*

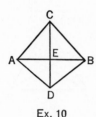

Ex. 10

11. Given: *AB* is the common base of the isosceles triangles *ABC* and *ABD.*

Prove: *CD* extended is the perpendicular bisector of *AB.*

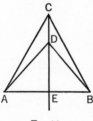

Ex. 11

12. Given: Points *B* and *A* are on *TR* and *TS*, respectively; *TB* = *TA*; *AR* and *BS* intersect at *C*; and ∠1 = ∠2.

Deduce the implications concerning *BC* and *CA.*

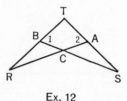

Ex. 12

Proofs of postulates (*Optional*)

In an ideal course in plane geometry, a statement that can be proved is not postulated. In such a system there are more theorems to be proved. Consequently, there is less time for exercises and optional topics such as coordinate geometry and numerical trigonometry.

In this course certain theorems are postulated because their proofs require special procedures which are seldom employed thereafter; however, the informal proofs of two postulates are presented below because the special techniques employed may be of particular interest to students.

1. Proof of Postulate 34:

Place △*RST* along △*ABC* so that *R* falls on *A*, *RS* falls along *AB*, and *T* and *C* lie on opposite sides of *AB.*

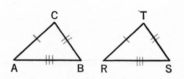

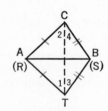

Fig. 13

Prove that *S* falls on *B.*

Draw *CT*. Now prove ∠1 = ∠2, and ∠3 = ∠4.

Hence, ∠*BTA* = ∠*ACB.*

∴ △*ATB* (△*RTS*) ≅ △*ABC* by Postulate 35.

2. Proof of Postulate 37:

Place $\triangle A'B'C'$ along $\triangle ABC$ so that C' falls on C, $C'B'$ falls along CB, and A' and A are on opposite sides of CB.

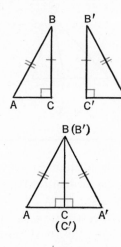

Fig. 14

Prove that B' falls on B.

Prove that ACA' is a straight line and, hence, $ACA'B$ is a triangle.

Now prove $\angle A' = \angle A$.

Therefore, $\triangle ACB \cong \triangle CA'B$ by Postulate 36.

Proofs of constructions

In Chapter 5, certain constructions were presented without proof. If we had chosen to precede them by certain postulates which are now available, they could have been proved at that time. Suggestions for a proof of each construction are presented in this section. After you have completed these proofs, examine them for violations of logical sequence and rigor.

1. Proof of Constructions 3 and 4 (Figure 15):

Draw AX, BX, AY, and BY.

∴ $\triangle AYX \cong \triangle BXY$.

∴ $\angle 1 = \angle 2$.

∴ $\triangle APX \cong \triangle PBX$.

You complete the proof that XY is the perpendicular bisector of AB.

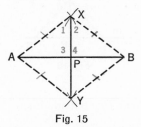

Fig. 15

2. Proof of Construction 5 (Figure 16):

Draw MN and XY.

You write the proof that $\angle P = \angle B$.

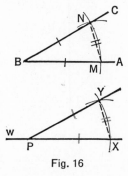

Fig. 16

3. Proof of Construction 6 (Figure 17):

Draw MP and PN.

You write the proof that SP bisects $\angle RST$.

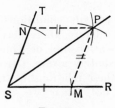

Fig. 17

4. Proof of Construction **7:**

a. Point P is on the line m (Figure 18).

Draw RT and ST.
You prove that $TP \perp RS$.

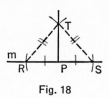

Fig. 18

b. Point P is outside line m (Figure 19).

Draw RP, SP, RT, and ST.
You prove that $PA \perp RS$.

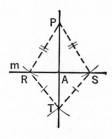

Fig. 19

Investigating a triangle with a line segment from the vertex to some point on the opposite side

When certain conditions are imposed on a figure, there may be some implied relationships of which we are not immediately aware. Often we can discover these relationships by deduction. If not, then we should use induction.

Consider the $\triangle ABC$ that has a segment CH from C to some point H on AB. The parts of the figure might be related in one or more of the following ways:

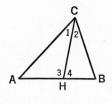

Fig. 20

a. $AC = BC$.

b. CH is the altitude to AB.

c. CH is the median to AB.

d. CH bisects $\angle ACB$.

We shall investigate each of these possibilities in the next group of exercises.

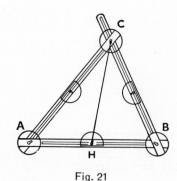

Fig. 21

Exercises

1. In Figure 20, is the position of CH determined by making $AC = BC$?

2. If we make CH an altitude, is AC necessarily equal to BC? Is an altitude necessarily a median or an angle bisector?

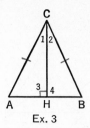

Ex. 3

3. If we make $AC = BC$ *and CH* the altitude to AB, of what can we be certain? To answer this question you may use either induction or deduction. If you use induction, you may use either dynamic triangles (formed by a device like that shown in Figure 21), or static line drawings that fulfill the given conditions. Measure the segments and angles listed in the table below. Why do we not need to include $\angle A$ and $\angle B$ in our investigation?

Data table:

$\triangle ABC$	AH	HB	$\angle 1$	$\angle 2$
Acute	?	?	?	?
Obtuse	?	?	?	?
Right	?	?	?	?
Equilateral	?	?	?	?

Conclusions: (What seems to be the relation of CH to AB and to $\angle ACB$?)

Inductive conclusion: (Write a word statement about *all* isosceles triangles having an altitude to the base.)

Prove your inductive conclusion deductively.

Investigate Exercises 4-8 in a manner similar to Exercise 3.

4. $AC = BC$, and CH is the median to AB.

5. $AC = BC$, and CH bisects $\angle ACB$.

6. CH is the altitude to AB, and CH is the median to AB.

7. CH bisects $\angle ACB$, and CH is the altitude to AB.

8. CH bisects $\angle ACB$, and CH is the median to AB. You may have difficulty proving your inductive conclusions at this time. What combination of parts of the two triangles do you find to be respectively equal?

Investigating an isosceles triangle with altitudes and medians to the equal sides and bisectors of the base angles

In $\triangle RST$, suppose that $RT = ST$, and RN and SM are altitudes, medians, or angle bisectors. Does it seem reasonable that each of these combinations of conditions would produce some equalities among the various segments and angles of the figure?

Fig. 22

Exercises

1. Given: RN and SM are altitudes to the equal sides RT and ST of $\triangle RST$.

   Discover and prove the implications concerning RN and SM, and angles 1 and 2. Consider acute, right, and obtuse triangles. State the theorem that you have proved.

2. Given: *RN* and *SM* are the medians to the equal sides *RT* and *ST* of △*RST*.

Discover and prove the implications. State the theorem that you have proved.

3. Given: *RN* and *SM* are the bisectors of the base angles *R* and *S* of the isosceles triangle *RST*.

Discover and prove the implications. State the theorem that you have proved.

Fig. 22

The 30°, 60° right triangle

Theorems about congruent triangles and the isosceles triangle are very useful in proving other relations. We are going to use some of them to prove a very important property of a right triangle which has acute angles of 30° and 60°.

THEOREM 19.   **If the acute angles of a right triangle are 30° and 60°, the side opposite the 30° angle is one-half the hypotenuse.**

Given: △*ABC* with ∠*C* = 90°, ∠*A* = 30°, and ∠*B* = 60°.

Prove: $BC = \frac{1}{2}AB$.

Plan: By extending *BC* its own length to *B'* and drawing *B'A* to make △*CB'A*, we can prove *B'B* = *AB* and, hence, $BC = \frac{1}{2}AB$.

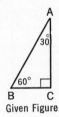

Given Figure

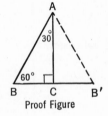

Proof Figure

Proof

STATEMENTS		AUTHORITIES
1. Extend *BC* to *B'* so that *CB'* = *BC*.	**1.** ?	
2. Draw *AB'* to make △*CB'A*.	**2.** ?	
3. ∠*ACB* = 90°.	**3.** ?	
4. ∴ *AC* ⊥ *BB'*.	**4.** ?	
5. ∴ ∠*ACB* = ∠*B'CA*.	**5.** ?	
6. *AC* = *AC*.	**6.** ?	
7. ∴ △*BCA* ≅ △*CB'A*.	**7.** ?	

You complete the proof.

The converses of Theorem 19

The conditions and conclusion of Theorem 19 may be written as follows:

In $\triangle ABC$,
if (s_1) $\angle A = 30°$, and
if (s_2) $\angle C = 90°$,
then (c) $BC = \frac{1}{2}AB$.

The theorem has two converses as follows:

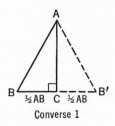

Converse 1

Converse 1:

In $\triangle ABC$,
if (s_2) $\angle C = 90°$, and
if (c) $BC = \frac{1}{2}AB$,
then (s_1) $\angle A = 30°$.

Extend BC its own length to B'. Draw $B'A$.

You write the proof and state the theorem you have proved.

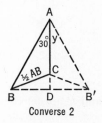

Converse 2

Converse 2:

In $\triangle ABC$,
if (s_1) $\angle A = 30°$, and
if (c) $BC = \frac{1}{2}AB$,
then (s_2) $\angle C = 90°$.

Make $\angle y = 30°$, and $AB' = AB$. Draw CB'.

Prove $\triangle BCA \cong \triangle CB'A$ and, hence, $\angle ACB = \angle B'CA$, and $BC = CB'$.

Since we are not certain that BCB' is a straight line, we are not certain that $\angle ACB = 90°$. If, however, we draw BB', we can prove each of the following:

a. $\triangle BB'A$ is equiangular.
b. $BB' = AB$.
c. $AD \perp BB'$.
d. $BC + CB' = AB = BB'$.
e. BCB' coincides with BB' ($BCB' = BB'$, and BB' is the shortest path from B to B').
f. $\angle ACB = 90°$.

Exercises

1. If a 30°, 60° draftsman's triangle has a hypotenuse of $6\frac{3}{4}$ inches, what is the length of the shortest side of the triangle?

2. In a scale drawing of a bridge truss, if a 30°, 60° triangle has a perimeter of 4.732 inches, and the hypotenuse is 2.000 inches long, what is the length of each of the legs?

3. In $\triangle ABC$, CH is the altitude to AB, $\angle A = 30°$, and $AC = 1\frac{1}{4}''$. How long is CH?

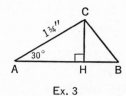

Ex. 3

4. ACD is an equilateral triangle in which DB is the altitude to AC. How long is AB if DC is 3.96 inches?

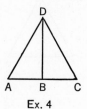

Ex. 4

5. Is a 30°, 60°, 90° triangle symmetrical with respect to a point? to a line? Explain.

6. $ABCD$ is a quadrilateral, $AC \perp BD$, $AB = AD = 2.0$ cm., and $\angle BAD = 60°$. **(a)** How long is BD? **(b)** Is the figure necessarily symmetrical with respect to a point? to a line? Explain.

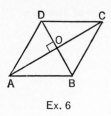

Ex. 6

Two points each equidistant from the ends of a line segment

THEOREM 20. **If two points are each equidistant from the ends of a line segment, they determine the perpendicular bisector of the segment.**

Given: Line segment AB, P is equidistant from A and B, and Q is equidistant from A and B.

Prove: PQ is the perpendicular bisector of AB.

There are three cases to consider. You write the proof for each case.

Case 1. Q is on AB.

Case 2. Q and P are on opposite sides of AB.

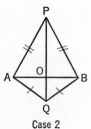

Case 2

Case 3. Q and P are on the same side of AB.

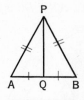

Case 1

Case 3

Exercises

1. Given: Isosceles triangles AEF and AGF have the common base AF; GE extended intersects AF at R. Deduce the relation of GR to AF. Is the figure symmetric with respect to RG?

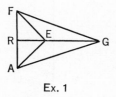

Ex. 1

2. Given: Quadrilateral $EFGH$ in which $EF = FG$, and $HG = HE$. Draw the diagonals and deduce their relationship.

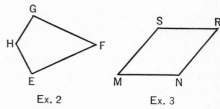

Ex. 2   Ex. 3

3. Given: $MNRS$ is an equilateral quadrilateral.

How are its diagonals related?

The locus of points equidistant from two given points

THEOREM 21.   **In a plane, the locus of points equidistant from two given points is the perpendicular bisector of the line segment joining the points.**

The proof consists of two parts:

Part 1: In a plane, if a point is equidistant from two given points, it is on the perpendicular bisector of the segment joining the points.

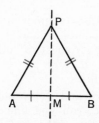

Given: P is equidistant from A and B ($PA = PB$).

Prove: P is on the perpendicular bisector of AB.

You write the proof.

Hint: Let M be the midpoint of AB. Draw MP, and prove that MP is the perpendicular bisector of AB.

Part 2: In a plane, if a point is on the perpendicular bisector of a line segment, it is equidistant from the ends of the segment.

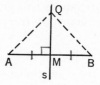

Given: Q is on s, the perpendicular bisector of AB.

Prove: Q is equidistant from A and B.

You write the proof.

*Necessary and sufficient conditions

To prove the theorem "The locus of points equidistant from two given points is the perpendicular bisector of the line segment joining the points" we need to prove that the condition, *points equidistant from two given points*, is both sufficient and necessary for the conclusion.

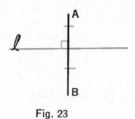

Fig. 23

The proof consists of two parts as follows:

Part 1: To prove the condition is sufficient for the conclusion, prove either Theorem A or its contrapositive equivalent, Theorem B:

Theorem A: In a plane, if a point is equidistant from two given points, it is on the perpendicular bisector of the segment joining the two points.

Theorem B: In a plane, if a point is not on the perpendicular bisector of the segment joining two given points, it is not equidistant from the given points.

Part 2: To prove the condition is necessary for the conclusion, prove either Theorem C or its contrapositive equivalent, Theorem D:

Theorem C: In a plane, if a point is on the perpendicular bisector of a line segment, it is equidistant from the ends of the segment.

Theorem D: In a plane, if a point is not equidistant from the ends of a line segment, it is not on the perpendicular bisector of the segment.

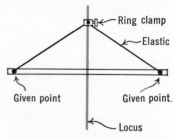

Dynamic model of the locus of points equidistant from two given points.

Fig. 24

Exercises

1. Draw an acute triangle. Construct the locus of points equidistant from the ends of each of the three sides. Do the three loci seem to have a common point of intersection?

2. Repeat Exercise **1** with an obtuse triangle.

3. Repeat Exercise **1** with a right triangle.

4. Locate points equidistant from two given points M and N *and* equidistant from two other given points R and S. Discuss the possibilities.

5. If R, S, and T are points on an arc RT, can you find the center and radius of the arc?

6. Locate points equidistant from two given points E and G *and* at a given distance d from a given point O. Discuss the possibilities.

7. Locate points equidistant from two given points C and F *and*

equidistant from two given parallel lines *s* and *t*. Discuss the possibilities.

8. Locate points equidistant from two given points *X* and *Y and* at a given distance *r* from a given line *c*. Discuss the possibilities.

9. Locate points equidistant from two given points *and* equidistant from two given concentric circles. Discuss the possibilities.

The locus of the vertex of a triangle having a given side

If one side of a triangle is fixed in length and position, and the vertex opposite that side moves according to some specified condition, the vertex generates a locus. The following loci are examples:

1. In a plane, the locus of the vertex of an isosceles triangle having a given base is the perpendicular bisector of the base (Figure 25).

2. In a plane, the locus of the vertex of a triangle having a given base and a given median to that base is a circle whose center is the midpoint of the given base and whose radius is the given median (Figure 26).

3. In a plane, the locus of the vertex of a triangle having a given side and a given altitude to that side is a pair of lines parallel to the given side at the distance equal to the given altitude from the given side (Figure 27).

Dynamic models of loci

Dynamic models may be used to give concrete meaning to the loci mentioned above. The solid black part(s) of each model represent the given figure; the colored part(s) represent the locus; the unshaded part(s) represent the framework of the model; and the narrow black lines, which are elastic, represent the two variable sides of the given triangle.

To locate the vertex of a triangle that satisfies two conditions at the same time, it is necessary to construct two loci. The points of intersection of the two loci are the desired vertices. Here again the models may be helpful. Models with equal bases should be used. Place one model over the other so that the equal bases coincide. Adjust the movable points on their respective loci until they coincide. Thus the vertex of the required triangle is located.

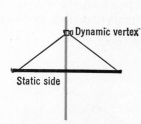

Dynamic model of the locus of the vertex of an isosceles triangle having a given base.

Fig. 25

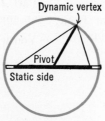

Dynamic model of the locus of the vertex of a triangle having a given side and given median to that side.

Fig. 26

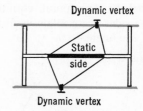

Dynamic model of the locus of the vertex of a triangle having a given side and a given altitude to that side.

Fig. 27

Example: Locate the vertex of a triangle that has a given side, a given median to that side, and a given altitude to that side.

Given: Side KR; median m, and altitude h, both to side KR.

With these given parts there are four vertices that satisfy both given conditions. Which points are they? Discuss the relation of m to h when there are only two points that satisfy both conditions. Discuss the relation of m to h when there are no points that satisfy both conditions.

The locus of points equidistant from the sides of an angle

Point P is on the bisector t_B of angle ABC, $PR \perp BA$ at R, and $PS \perp BC$ at S.

If Q is equidistant from BA and BC, can you prove that it is on t_B?

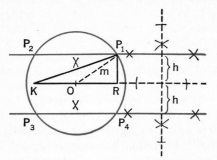

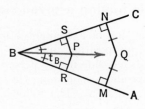

Fig. 28

Can you prove that P is equidistant from BA and BC?

Can you prove that t_B is the locus of points equidistant from AB and BC?

THEOREM 22. **In a plane, the locus of points equidistant from the sides of an angle is the bisector of the angle.**

The proof consists of two parts:

Part 1: Any point equidistant from the sides of an angle is on the bisector of the angle.

You write the proof.

Part 2: Any point on the bisector of an angle is equidistant from the sides.

You write the proof.

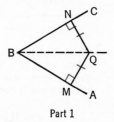

Part 1

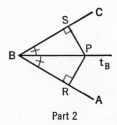

Part 2

COROLLARY In a plane, the locus of points equidistant from two intersecting lines is a pair of lines bisecting the angles formed by the given lines.

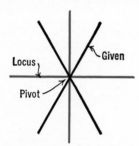

Dynamic model of the locus of points equidistant from two intersecting straight lines.

Fig. 29

Exercises

1. How are the statements of Parts 1 and 2 of the proof of Theorem 22 related?

2. Explain why there are two parts to the proof of Theorem 22.

3. Prove: If the bisector of an angle of a triangle is a median, the triangle is isosceles.

   Hint: Draw $ME \perp BD$, and $MF \perp CD$. What locus theorem can be used to prove $ME = MF$?

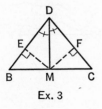

Ex. 3

4. Construct the locus of points equidistant from the sides of each of the three angles of a triangle. Do the three loci seem to have a common point of intersection?

5. Construct the locus of points equidistant from the sides of each of the angles of a quadrilateral. Do the four loci seem to have a common point of intersection?

6. Locate points equidistant from two given points *and* equidistant from two given intersecting lines. Discuss the possibilities.

7. Locate points equidistant from two given intersecting lines *e* and *m and* equidistant from two other given intersecting lines *r* and *s*. Discuss the possibilities.

8. Locate points equidistant from two given intersecting lines *and* at a given distance from a given point. Discuss the possibilities.

9. Locate points equidistant from two given parallel lines *and* equidistant from two given intersecting lines. Discuss the possibilities.

10. Locate points at a given distance from a given line *and* equidistant from two intersecting lines. Discuss the possibilities.

Space Loci (*Optional*)

11. Describe the locus, in space, of points equidistant from two given points.

12. Describe the locus, in space, of a point equidistant from two given intersecting lines.

13. Describe the locus, in space, of points equidistant from two given intersecting planes.

Practical Applications

1. There is an obstruction between the points A and B. How can straight line segments be constructed through A and B so that they lie in the same straight line?

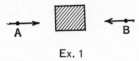

Ex. 1

2. Two points P and Q are on the same side of m. Find a point T on m so that $PT + QT$ is a minimum. (Hint: Construct $QQ' \perp m$ so that $Q'S$ equals QS. Draw PQ' intersecting m at T. Draw QT. Can you prove line PTQ' equal to broken line PTQ? Is PQ' the shortest path from P to Q'?)

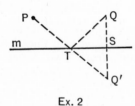

Ex. 2

3. When we see the image of an object in a plane mirror, rays of light follow the shortest path from the object to the mirror and then to the eye. Use the method suggested in Exercise **2** to locate on the mirror the point P where a ray of light from an object is reflected to the eye.

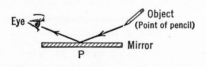

Ex. 3

4. The carpenter's level shown here is made of three strips of wood so that $AC = EC$, and $BC = DC$. A plumb line CG is attached at C. How can this instrument be used to tell whether AE is horizontal?

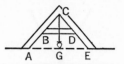

Ex. 4

5. Show how you could use the method suggested by the figure to find the distance NB across an impassable marsh. What measuring instruments would you need?

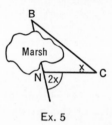

Ex. 5

6. Suppose that it is necessary to find the distance from R to the inaccessible point I. How would you lay out $\triangle RST$ so that the length of one of its sides would give you the distance from R to I? What measuring instruments would you need?

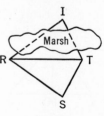

Ex. 6

7. Read Edgar Allan Poe's story, "The Gold Bug," and write a brief explanation of the locus problem described in the story. (See also the drawing above, made by a geometry student.)

8. Explain how you could measure RS indirectly by the method suggested in this figure.

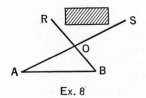

Ex. 8

9. Explain how to use a carpenter's square to bisect an angle.

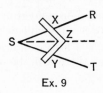

Ex. 9

Space Geometry *(Optional)*

10. Given: AC and AB in the plane m are perpendicular to AD, and $AC = AB$.
Prove: $CD = BD$.

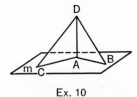

Ex. 10

11. Given: MO and NO in the plane x are perpendicular bisectors of AB.
Prove: $\angle NMA = \angle BMN$.

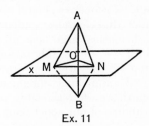

Ex. 11

12. Given: Plane m is the perpendicular bisector of AB.

Prove: Any point P in plane m is equidistant from A and B. (You may assume that if $AB \perp m$ at R, it is perpendicular to every line in m that passes through R.)

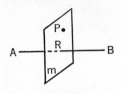

Ex. 12

13. Given: PC, PD, and PE are in the plane MN; PC and PE are perpendicular bisectors of AB; and CDE is a straight line segment.

Prove: PD is a perpendicular bisector of AB.

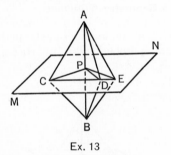

Ex. 13

Jumping to conclusions

Reaching a conclusion concerning a given question without sufficient evidence to justify that conclusion is characteristic of an untrained mind. The study of geometry should serve to counteract this common tendency. In any mathematical argument all given data must be thoroughly examined, each step in the argument carefully scrutinized, and final judgment reserved until we are reasonably certain of the validity of our conclusion.

ILLUSTRATION 1. In determining whether two triangles are congruent, we note that three parts of one triangle must be equal to the corresponding three parts of the other, and that one of the three parts must be a side. Frequently students "jump to the conclusion" that under such conditions two triangles are *always* congruent. That such a conclusion is false is immediately evident if we consider the case in which the given parts are two sides and the angle opposite one of these sides.

ILLUSTRATION 2. The number of persons dying from heart trouble has greatly increased within recent years. Some people draw the conclusion that modern life tends to create heart trouble. However, due to improvements in sanitation and medicine, many more people reach middle and old age now; and from this latter group, heart trouble is to be expected. A similar situation may explain the increase in the number of cases of cancer.

Exercises

In each of the following exercises which illustrate jumping to conclusions, state the reason why you consider the conclusion true or false; if false, tell what other conditions should be known before a conclusion can be reached:

1. Dr. Mason has three college degrees, so she will be a good teacher.

2. Because Tom was the first-ranking student in the graduating class from law school, he will be the most successful of his classmates in the practice of law.

3. If we had more playgrounds, there would be less juvenile delinquency.

4. If there is a heavy snowstorm this evening, there will be no school tomorrow.

5. John is a very lucky boy, for he has a car and plenty of money to spend.

6. I am going to vote for Henry for president of the Student Council. He is popular, bright, good-looking and a smooth dancer.

7. Since the altitude to the hypotenuse of a right isosceles triangle is one-half the hypotenuse, the altitude to the hypotenuse of any right triangle is one-half the hypotenuse.

8. If the water is roily, the fishing is poor; hence, the fishing will be good today because the water is clear.

9. Since the altitudes of a triangle are concurrent, the medians are concurrent.

10. A father is reproving his son for having cut classes in school. The son asks if his father didn't cut classes when he went to school.

11. If each of two points on the same side of a line segment is equidistant from the ends of the segment, they determine the perpendicular bisector of the segment; hence, any two points, each equidistant from the ends of a line segment, determine the perpendicular bisector of the segment.

12. An ambulance driver should not go through a red light, because driving through a red light is unlawful.

13. All unkind people are rude; hence, all kind people are polite.

14. If you saw a drowning man, you would feel obliged to try to save him. When a fellow student is in danger of failing, you have an obligation to give him help.

15. The following information is known about Miss Smith, the teacher of French in our school: She was born in this town; she has traveled in France; she majored in Romance languages in college; she has taught Latin and English; she is a good disciplinarian; she has a pleasing personality. Miss Smith should, therefore, be a good teacher of French.

16. All democracies have elective legislative assemblies. Since country M has an elective legislative assembly, it is a democracy.

17. Consider for re-election Councilman O'Berg: He has the unique record of being the only Republocrat to carry the 10th, 14th, and 16th wards in the same election; the cornerstone of the new city hall was laid by him; his zeal for the voters is shown by two new playgrounds in the West Side; he is a popular member of many social and fraternal organizations; his city-wide vision transcends all party lines, and qualifies him to represent the city as a whole.

18. It is wrong to cheat in an examination, because the answer you copy might be wrong.

19. This article is the best, since it is the most expensive.

20. In $\triangle GHE$, $GE = HE$, and M is a point on GH; hence, $\angle 3 = \angle 4$ because they are angles opposite equal sides.

Ex. 20–21

21. In $\triangle GHE$, EM bisects $\angle GEH$; hence, $GM = MH$ because sides opposite equal angles are equal.

Review of Chapter 7

Algebraic Exercises

1. If the number of degrees in one base angle of an isosceles triangle is x, find the number of degrees in the vertex angle.

2. If the number of degrees in the vertex angle of an isosceles triangle is y, find the number of degrees in each base angle.

3. If the vertex angle of an isosceles triangle is twice as large as one of the base angles, find the size of each angle of the triangle.

4. The number of degrees in each base angle of an isosceles triangle is $2x + 30$, and the number of degrees in the vertex angle is $x - 10$. Find the number of degrees in each angle of the triangle.

5. The vertex angle of an isosceles triangle is 40°. Find the size of the angle at the point of intersection of the bisectors of the base angles.

6. One angle of a scalene triangle is 58°. Find the size of the angle at the point of intersection of the bisectors of the other two angles.

Construction Exercises

1. Construct an angle of 75°.

2. Construct an equilateral triangle, given an altitude.

3. Construct an isosceles triangle, given its base and its vertex angle.

4. Construct a right triangle, given its hypotenuse and one acute angle.

5. Construct an isosceles right triangle, given its hypotenuse.

6. Construct a right triangle, given its hypotenuse and one leg.

7. Construct an isosceles triangle, given a leg and a base angle.

Congruent Triangles

In the following figures, equal parts of the triangles are similarly marked. (Braces are used to indicate equal sides when the triangles overlap.) Write the numbers **1-12** *on your paper, and after each number write an abbreviation such as* **s, a, s = s, a, s** *to indicate which congruence postulate you would use in proving the specified triangles congruent; if it cannot be proved, write "not necessarily congruent."*

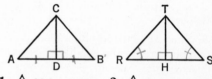

1. △ ADC and DBC   **2.** △ RHT and HST

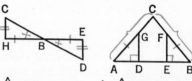

3. △ HBC and BDE   **4.** △ ADG and EBF

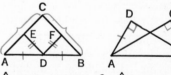

5. △ ADE and DBF   **6.** △ ABD and ABC

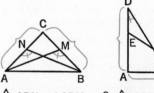

7. △ ABN and ABM   **8.** △ ACE and ABD

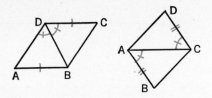

9. △ ABD and BCD   **10.** △ ABC and ACD

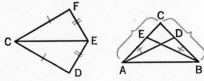

11. △ CDE and CEF   **12.** △ ADC and BCE

Proofs

1. Prove: The triangle formed by joining the midpoints of the sides of an equilateral triangle is also equilateral.

2. Prove: If the perpendiculars to a diameter of a circle are drawn through points on the diameter equidistant from the center, the segments of the perpendiculars cut off by the circle are equal.

3. Prove: If the bisector of an exterior angle of a triangle is parallel to one side of the triangle, the triangle is isosceles.

4. Prove: If one leg of a right triangle is one-half the hypotenuse, the acute angles are 30° and 60°.

5. Prove: The midpoint of the base of an isosceles triangle is equidistant from the legs of the triangle.

Symmetry

1. Construct a triangle symmetrical with respect to one of its altitudes.

2. Construct a triangle symmetrical with respect to each of two of its medians.

3. Construct a quadrilateral symmetrical with respect to one, and only one, of its diagonals.

4. Construct a quadrilateral symmetrical with respect to both its diagonals.

5. Draw a regular eight-pointed star. Designate the point of symmetry, if any. Designate the lines of symmetry, if any.

6. Draw a regular five-pointed star. Designate its point of symmetry, if any.

7. Draw a triangle, and draw another triangle within it by joining points on the sides of the first so that the figure is symmetrical with respect to a line.

8. Make a design based on two triangles that is symmetrical with respect to a point.

9. Make a design based on two squares that is symmetrical with respect to a point.

10. Make a design that is symmetrical with respect to a point, but not to a line.

This plane cruising over snow-capped Mount Rainier is America's first jet transport. It can fly as either a military or commercial plane at speeds of more than 550 miles per hour and at altitudes above 42,000 feet. Many geometric concepts are used by the engineers and designers who develop such a plane.

Chapter 8 QUADRILATERALS

WHAT makes a kite fly? What keeps an airplane in the air? If the air speed and heading of an airplane and the velocity (speed and direction) of the wind are known, can the track of the airplane over the ground be found? On the other hand, if the air speed and course of an airplane and the velocity of the wind are known, how can the required heading (to make good its course) be found? To understand these problems, and many other practical ones, we must know the parallelogram law of vectors. The parallelogram is one of the quadrilaterals we are going to study in this chapter.

Dynamic quadrilaterals

Dynamic quadrilaterals are devices for making quadrilaterals of different sizes and shapes. They can be made with strips of heavy cardboard and round-head paper fasteners. An inductive study of the relationships of the sides and angles is greatly facilitated if the holes on the sides are spaced according to scale, and if there are protractors at the vertices.

Of course, it is not necessary to have a dynamic device to do an experiment. Data can be obtained from carefully drawn or constructed figures.

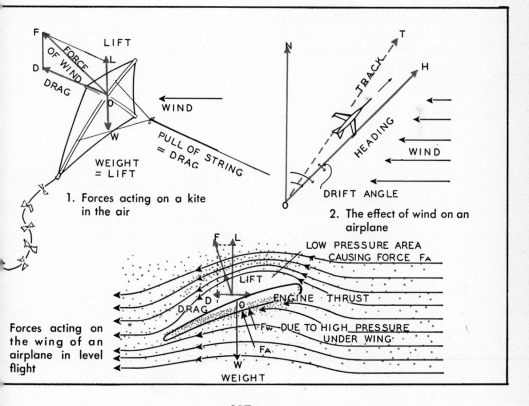

1. Forces acting on a kite in the air

2. The effect of wind on an airplane

Forces acting on the wing of an airplane in level flight

217

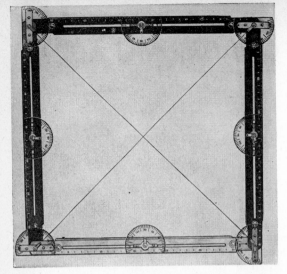

A dynamic quadrilateral instrument for investigating the angle, side, and diagonal relations of the different kinds of quadrilaterals.

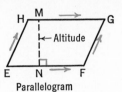

Parallelogram

Fig. 1

The quadrilateral $EFGH$ is a parallelogram.

The pairs of angles such as E and H are *consecutive* angles of $EFGH$.

The pairs of angles such as E and G are *opposite* angles of $EFGH$.

Either pair of opposite sides of $EFGH$ such as EH and FG are its *bases*.

An *altitude* of a parallelogram is a segment included between the bases and perpendicular to either one of them. MN is an altitude of $EFGH$.

In a reliable experiment many figures of different sizes and shapes which satisfy the given conditions are examined. A class can do this quickly if students, working independently or in small groups, collect sets of data and tabulate them on the blackboard for class discussion.

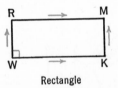

Rectangle

Fig. 2

DEFINITIONS A *rectangle* is a parallelogram with one of its angles a right angle.

A *rhombus* is a parallelogram with two equal adjacent sides.

A dynamic quadrilateral device which you can make.

Quadrilaterals classified

DEFINITION A *parallelogram* is a quadrilateral that has both pairs of opposite sides parallel.

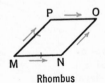

Rhombus

Fig. 3

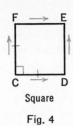

Square

Fig. 4

DEFINITIONS   A *square* is a rectangle with two equal adjacent sides.

A *trapezoid* is a quadrilateral with one, and only one, pair of parallel sides.

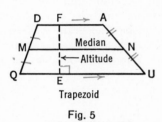

Trapezoid

Fig. 5

The quadrilateral $QUAD$ is a trapezoid.

The *bases* of a trapezoid are the two parallel sides. QU and DA are the bases of $QUAD$.

The *base angles* of a trapezoid are the angles at the ends of either base. Either $\angle Q$ and $\angle U$ or $\angle D$ and $\angle A$ are base angles of $QUAD$.

An *altitude* of a trapezoid is a segment included between the bases and perpendicular to either one of them. EF is an altitude of $QUAD$.

The *legs* of a trapezoid are the non-parallel sides. QD and UA are the legs of $QUAD$.

The *median* of a trapezoid is the line segment joining the midpoints of the non-parallel sides. MN is the median of $QUAD$.

DEFINITION   An *isosceles trapezoid* is a trapezoid with equal legs.

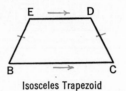

Isosceles Trapezoid

Fig. 6

The sides of a kite are equal in pairs as indicated in Figure 7. You write a suitable definition for this kite.

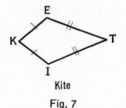

Kite

Fig. 7

Exercises (*Optional*)

In the following exercises, use the given classification diagram.

1. Write the names of the quadrilaterals designated by A, B, C, ... , I.

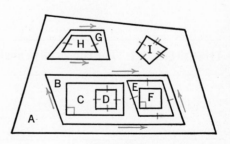

Ex. 1–8

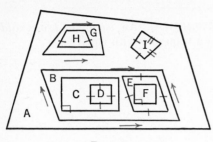

Ex. 1–8

★7. Is the combination of conditions imposed on B sufficient for C? Is each condition necessary for C? Explain your answers.

★8. Is the combination of conditions imposed on C sufficient for B? Is each condition imposed on C necessary for B? Explain your answers.

2. Can you be certain that all D's are B's? Explain.

3. Define D by classifying it as a B. Does your definition violate one of the properties of a good definition?

4. If F represents a square, and if E represents a rhombus, define a square by classifying it as a rhombus.

5. Some B's are C's, and some B's are E's. Does this necessarily mean that some C's are E's? Are all B's equilateral? Are some B's equilateral? Use the diagram to explain your answers.

★6.*Write the converse, inverse, and contrapositive of this statement: If a quadrilateral is a C, then it is a B. Is the original statement true? Is its contrapositive true? Is its converse true? Is its inverse true? Explain your answers.

Relations of the angles of a parallelogram

Substitute 4 for n in the formula $s_i = (n - 2)180°$, and find the sum of the interior angles of a parallelogram.

In the parallelogram $EFGH$, since $EH \parallel FG$, then $\angle E$ is the supplement of $\angle F$. Why? How is $\angle H$ related to $\angle G$?

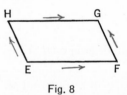

Fig. 8

Which angles are supplementary because $EF \parallel HG$?

If $\angle E$ is the supplement of $\angle F$, and $\angle F$ is the supplement of $\angle G$, how is $\angle E$ related to $\angle G$? Why?

THEOREM 23. **The consecutive angles of a parallelogram are supplementary.**

Write the proof of Theorem 23.

---

*See footnote on page 94 for explanation of starred material.

COROLLARY   The opposite angles of a parallelogram are equal.

Relations of the sides of a parallelogram

Induction: Make or construct several different parallelograms, and measure their opposite sides. Do they seem to be equal?

Deduction: Can you deduce the relation of the opposite sides of a parallelogram by adding one diagonal to the figure?

Complete Theorem 24 and write the proof.

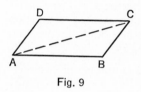

Fig. 9

THEOREM 24.   The opposite sides of a parallelogram are . . . . .

Relations of the diagonals of a parallelogram

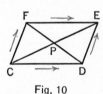

Fig. 10

Induction: Make or construct several parallelograms, and measure the segments of the diagonals from the vertices to their point of intersection. How do these segments seem to be related?

Do the diagonals of a parallelogram necessarily bisect its angles? Are the diagonals necessarily equal? Are the diagonals necessarily perpendicular? Do they necessarily bisect each other?

Deduction: To deduce the relation of *CE* and *DF*, prove a pair of triangles congruent.

Complete Theorem 25 and write the proof.

THEOREM 25.   The diagonals of a parallelogram . . . . .

Exercises

1. Prove: The bisectors of the opposite angles of a parallelogram are parallel.

2. Prove: The bisectors of two consecutive angles of a parallelogram are perpendicular.

3. Find the lengths of the sides of a parallelogram if one of its sides is 4 inches more than three times another, and its perimeter is 24 inches.

4. The number of degrees in one angle of a parallelogram is $a + 6$ and the number of degrees in another is $2a - 3$. Find the number of degrees in each angle. Are two solutions possible? If so, get both sets of answers.

5. There are one-third as many degrees in one angle of a parallelogram as there are in another. Find the number of degrees in each of the angles.

6. Construct a parallelogram, given two adjacent sides and the included angle. Explain why these three parts determine the size and shape of the parallelogram.

7. Given: Parallelogram $ABCD$; diagonals AC and BD intersect at P; line EF passes through P and terminates at F on DC and at E on AB. Imagine FE to be a dynamic line.

Deduce the implications concerning PF and PE.

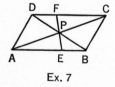

Ex. 7

8. Construct parallelogram $ABCD$, given AB, AC, and $\angle B$. If $\angle B$ is acute, and if AC is less than AB, explain why there may be two solutions. If $\angle B$ is obtuse, and if AC is greater than AB, explain why there is only one solution.

9. Given: Parallelogram $MPQR$; diagonal MQ intersects at S line DE joining the midpoints of opposite sides MP and RQ.

Deduce the implications concerning MS and SQ.

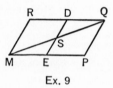

Ex. 9

10. Given: Parallelogram $ABCD$; E and F are points on AB and DC, respectively; and $AE = CF$.

Deduce the implications concerning AF and CE.

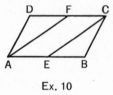

Ex. 10

Sufficient conditions for a parallelogram

From the definition, we know that a quadrilateral is a parallelogram if we know that its opposite sides are parallel. We shall now consider other combinations of conditions that are sufficient for a parallelogram.

THEOREM 26. If the opposite sides of a quadrilateral are equal, the quadrilateral is a parallelogram.

Given: Quadrilateral $ABCD$, such that $AB = DC$, and $AD = BC$.

Prove: $ABCD$ is a parallelogram.

You write the proof.

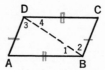

THEOREM 27. If two sides of a quadrilateral are equal and parallel, the quadrilateral is a parallelogram.

Given: Quadrilateral $EFGH$, such that $EF \parallel HG$, and $EF = HG$.

Prove: $EFGH$ is a parallelogram.

You write the proof.

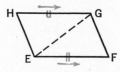

THEOREM 28. If the diagonals of a quadrilateral bisect each other, the quadrilateral is a parallelogram.

Given: Quadrilateral $MNRS$ in which the diagonals MR and NS bisect each other at P.

Prove: $MNRS$ is a parallelogram.

You write the proof.

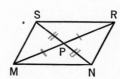

THEOREM 29. If the opposite angles of a quadrilateral are equal, the quadrilateral is a parallelogram.

You write the proof of Theorem 29.

THEOREM 30. If the consecutive angles of a quadrilateral are supplementary, the quadrilateral is a parallelogram.

You write the proof of Theorem 30.

Exercises

*In the figure for Exercises **1-3**, ABCD is a quadrilateral, and AC is a diagonal.*

1. Given: $AB = DC$, and $\angle 1 = \angle 2$. Deduce the implications concerning angles 4 and 3.

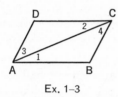

Ex. 1–3

2. Given: $AD \parallel BC$, and $\angle 1 = \angle 2$. Deduce the implications concerning $ABCD$.

3. Given: $\angle 1 = \angle 2$, and $\angle 3 = \angle 4$. Deduce the implications.

4. **a.** Does a parallelogram have an axis of symmetry? Explain.
   b. Does a parallelogram have a point of symmetry? Explain.

5. Construct a parallelogram, given two adjacent sides and the angle between them. Base your construction on Theorem 26. Then use Theorem 27, and do it again. If you think one method is better than the other, explain why you think so.

6. Construct a parallelogram, given its diagonals and one of the angles between them. Is this construction based on Theorem 25 or Theorem 28? Explain.

7. Construct a parallelogram, given its diagonals and one side. Describe the loci used in the construction.

8. Construct a parallelogram, given two adjacent sides and one diagonal. Explain why these three parts determine one, and only one, parallelogram.

9. In parallelogram $WKRD$,
$$\angle W = 2x + 32° \, 18',$$
$$\text{and } \angle K = 5x - 109° \, 40'.$$
Find the number of degrees in $\angle W$.

10. The median RN of a triangle ERF is extended its own length through N to K. What can you prove about the quadrilateral $ERFK$?

11. Given: $\triangle ABC$; D and E are midpoints of AC and BC, respectively; DE is extended its own length to F. What can you prove about $ABFD$?

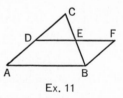

Ex. 11

12. Given: $\square ABCD$; the number of degrees in $\angle A$ is $x + y$, the number of degrees in $\angle C$ is $2x - 3y$, and $\angle D = 110°$.
Find x and y.

13. Given: $\square ABCD$; $AB = 2y + 4$, $AD = \frac{1}{2}x + 8$, $x = 2y$, and the perimeter of $ABCD$ is 96.
Find x and y.

★**14.** Prove: In quadrilateral $ABCD$,
  if   (s_1) AC bisects BD, and
  if   (s_2) BD bisects AC,
then (c) $AB \parallel DC$.

Prove the two converses of the above theorem.

Write the two inverses of the original theorem. If you have proved its two converses, explain why the inverses are true.

The parallelepiped (*Optional*)

A parallelepiped is shown in Figure 11. Each of the six faces is a parallelogram, and the opposite faces are parallel plane segments.

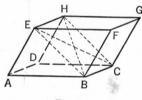

Fig. 11

Assume:

a. Two parallel lines determine a plane.

b. If two parallel planes are cut by a third plane, the lines of intersection are parallel.

Deduce the implications concerning:

a. EH and BC

b. EB and HC

c. EC and HB

Calcite is a mineral whose crystals are parallelepipeds. If one of these crystals is broken, each of the fragments will be a smaller parallelepiped.

Properties of a rectangle

Since a rectangle is a parallelogram, it has all of the properties of a parallelogram; but it has additional properties because, by definition, one of its angles is a right angle.

COROLLARY **The angles of a rectangle are right angles.**

This view of one of New York's most unusual skyscrapers shows how the rectangle has been used as the unifying theme of its design. Notice, too, that the building is composed of two rectangular parallelepipeds, one atop the other.

THEOREM 31. **The diagonals of a rectangle are equal.**

Write the proof of Theorem 31.

Sufficient conditions for a rectangle

If a parallelogram has a right angle, it is a rectangle. However, sets of conditions other than the set found in its definition are sufficient for a rectangle.

COROLLARY **If the angles of a quadrilateral are equal, the quadrilateral is a rectangle.**

THEOREM 32. **If a parallelogram has equal diagonals, the parallelogram is a rectangle.**

Write the proof of Theorem 32.

Exercises

1. Construct or draw a rectangle, given two adjacent sides. With the instruments you have, which of the methods do you think is more accurate? Why?

2. Construct a rectangle, given one diagonal and an angle between the diagonals. Is this construction based on Theorem 31 or on Theorem 32? Explain.

3. Construct a rectangle, given one diagonal and one side. What locus is used in the construction?

4. Construct the rectangle $ABCD$, given the diagonal AC and $\angle BAC$. First, construct $\triangle ABC$. What combination of parts of the triangle is given?

5. Construct and describe the locus of the point of intersection of the diagonals of a rectangle having one side fixed in length and position.

6. Using an *algebraic* method, prove: If the angles of a quadrilateral are equal, the quadrilateral is a rectangle.

7. A cabinetmaker sometimes makes a rectangular frame as follows: He cuts two pairs of equal pieces of any desired length. Then he dowels and glues them together so that the frame is a parallelogram. How does he arrange the pieces? Before the glue sets, he clamps the pieces so that the diagonals of the frame . . . . . (Complete the sentence). What geometric principles does he apply?

8. Prove: If the diagonals of a rectangle are perpendicular, the rectangle is equilateral.

9. (a) How many axes of symmetry does a rectangle have? Explain.

   (b) Is a rectangle symmetrical with respect to a point? Explain.

10. Complete and prove: If one of the angles at the point of intersection of the diagonals of a rectangle is 60°, each diagonal is . . . . as long as one of the sides of the rectangle.

11. Complete and prove: The four bisectors of the angles of a parallelogram form a . . . . .

Properties of a rhombus

A rhombus has all the properties of a parallelogram. Since it has two equal adjacent sides, it has additional properties.

COROLLARIES 1. **A rhombus is equilateral.**

2. **The diagonals of a rhombus are perpendicular.**

3. **The diagonals of a rhombus bisect the angles.**

Sufficient conditions for a rhombus

If a quadrilateral is a parallelogram with a pair of equal adjacent sides, it is a rhombus. The specified conditions are sufficient for a rhombus. However, there are sets of conditions other than the set in its definition that are sufficient for a rhombus.

COROLLARIES 1. **If a quadrilateral is equilateral, it is a rhombus.**

2. **If the diagonals of a parallelogram are perpendicular, the parallelogram is a rhombus.**

3. **If the diagonals of a parallelogram bisect the angles, the parallelogram is a rhombus.**

Exercises

1. Construct a rhombus, given one side and one angle. Is this construction based on the definition of a rhombus or on Corollary 1 above? Explain.

2. Construct a rhombus, given one side and one diagonal. Describe the locus used in this construction.

3. Construct a rhombus, given its diagonals. State the authorities for your construction.

4. a. Does a rhombus have an axis of symmetry? Explain.
   b. Is a rhombus symmetrical with respect to a point? Explain.

5. How many degrees are there in each angle of a rhombus if one of its diagonals is equal to a side?

6. In rhombus $WDKR$, if $\angle W = 30°$, and WD is 12 in., how long is the altitude from R to WD?

7. In rhombus $AEFG$, the number of degrees in $\angle A$ is 12° more than three times the number of degrees in $\angle E$.
   Find the number of degrees in each angle of rhombus $AEFG$.

8. If the diagonals MP and NS of the rhombus $MNPS$ intersect at O, if $\angle NMS = 60°$, and if $MS = 10$, how long is NO?

Drawing a straight line geometrically (*Optional*)

Euclid postulated that a straight line can be drawn through two points. He apparently had no geometrical method of doing it. A carpenter sights along the edge of a board to test its straightness; if he can see the whole edge as a point, he is satisfied that the edge is straight. This optical method is based on the assumption that a ray of light is straight.

In 1846, Peaucellier invented a linkage with which a straight line could be generated. Since that time, other linkages have been devised to produce straight lines geometrically.

Peaucellier's linkage is easily made from strips of cardboard and eyelets as follows:

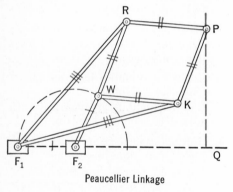

Peaucellier Linkage

Fig. 12

1. F_1 and F_2 are fixed points on some suitable backing material.
2. F_2 is a pivotal point of a link WF_2. $WF_2 = F_1F_2$.
3. W is a pivotal point of one vertex of rhombus $WKPR$ formed by four equal links. Link F_1K = link F_1R.
4. Links F_1K and F_1R are connected to the opposite vertices K and R of the rhombus.

5. The links are joined with eyelets so that the device can move freely about the pivotal points in the plane of the backing material.

It can be proved that as W describes an arc of a circle, the locus of P is perpendicular to the extension of F_1F_2 at Q and that F_2Q is constant in length; hence, PQ is a straight line generated by P.

Properties of a square

Since a square is a rectangle, it has all the properties of a rectangle. Additional properties can be proved because it also has two equal adjacent sides.

COROLLARIES 1. **A square is equilateral.**

2. **The diagonals of a square are perpendicular.**

3. **The diagonals of a square make 45° angles with the sides (or bisect the angles).**

Sufficient conditions for a square

By definition, if two adjacent sides of a rectangle are equal, the rectangle is a square. There are other sets of conditions sufficient for a square.

COROLLARIES 1. **If the diagonals of a rectangle are perpendicular, the rectangle is a square.**

2. **If the diagonals of a rhombus are equal, the rhombus is a square.**

3. **If an angle of a rhombus is 90°, the rhombus is a square.**

Exercises

1. Is a square symmetrical with respect to a line? If so, how many axes of symmetry does it have?

2. Is a square symmetrical with respect to a point? Explain.

3. Draw a symmetrical design based on the square.

4. Construct a square, given its perimeter. Is the construction based on the definition of a square or on a corollary? Explain.

5. Construct a square, given its diagonal. Write the authorities for your construction.

6. Draw a symmetrical design based on a regular octagon.

7. Prove: If a median of a triangle is also the bisector of an angle, the triangle is isosceles. (Hint: Through the midpoint of the side, extend the median its own length.)

8. Complete and prove: If the diagonals of a quadrilateral are unequal, perpendicular, and bisect each other, the quadrilateral is a . . . . .

9. $ABCD$ is a rhombus. The number of degrees in $\angle CAD$ is $x - y$, the number of degrees in $\angle ADB$ is $2x - 3y$, and $x = 2y$. Find x and y.

10. $ABCD$ is a parallelogram. The number of degrees in $\angle BAC$ is $2x + 5$, the number of degrees in $\angle CAD$ is $3x - 5$, and the number of degrees in $\angle ADC$ is $13x$.
    a. Find x.
    b. What kind of parallelogram is $ABCD$?

The cube (*Optional*)

A cube is shown in this figure.

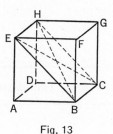

Fig. 13

Assume:

   a. A cube is a parallelepiped.

   b. The six faces of a cube are squares.

   c. Two intersecting lines determine a plane.

   d. If a line is perpendicular to each of two intersecting lines, it is perpendicular to the plane of the two lines.

   e. If a line is perpendicular to a plane, it is perpendicular to every line in the plane that passes through its foot.

Deduce the implications concerning:

   a. HE and EB.

   b. EC and HB.

   c. Quadrilateral $EBCH$.

Properties of an isosceles trapezoid

By definition, the bases of an isosceles trapezoid are parallel and the legs are equal. There are other properties we can prove (see next page).

THEOREM 33. **The base angles of an isosceles trapezoid are equal.**

Write the proof of Theorem 33.

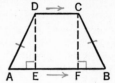

THEOREM 34. **The diagonals of an isosceles trapezoid are equal.**

Write the proof of Theorem 34.

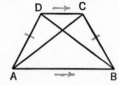

Sufficient conditions for an isosceles trapezoid

By definition, if the legs of a trapezoid are equal, it is isosceles. There are other sets of conditions sufficient for an isosceles trapezoid.

THEOREM 35. **If the base angles of a trapezoid are equal, the trapezoid is isosceles.**

COROLLARY **If the diagonals of a trapezoid are equal, the trapezoid is isosceles.**

Write the proof of Theorem 35.

Exercises

1. If one of the angles of an isosceles trapezoid is 40°, how many degrees are there in each of the other angles?

2. Prove: If the opposite angles of a trapezoid are supplementary, the trapezoid is isosceles.

3. If the number of degrees in one angle of an isosceles trapezoid is x and the angle opposite it contains $x + 20°$, how many degrees are there in each angle?

4. Prove: If a trapezoid is isosceles, the opposite angles are supplementary.

5. Is an isosceles trapezoid symmetrical with respect to a line? Is it symmetrical with respect to a point? Explain your answers.

6. Construct an isosceles trapezoid, given its bases and its altitude. What loci are used in this construction?

7. What is the altitude of a trapezoid if one of the non-parallel sides is 9 and the angle it forms with the base is 30°?

8. Find the number of degrees in the angles of an isosceles trapezoid if the legs are 6 in. long and the bases are 8 in. and 14 in. long.

9. One base of an isosceles trapezoid is twice as long as the other, and each leg is as long as the shorter base. Find the size of the angles.

In Exercises **10-12**, *ABCD is an isosceles trapezoid, the diagonals AC and BD intersect at P, AB is fixed in length and position, and DC is fixed in length.*

10. As DC moves with reference to AB, what is the locus of C?

11. As DC moves with reference to AB, what is the locus of P?

12. Measure AP, PC, BP, and PD. Compare $\dfrac{AP}{PC}$ with $\dfrac{BP}{PD}$. What seems to be true?

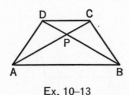

Ex. 10–13

13. If ABCD in the figure is a trapezoid that is not isosceles, how does $\dfrac{AP}{PC}$ seem to be related to $\dfrac{BP}{PD}$?

14. Construct a trapezoid, given its four sides.

15. Find the number of degrees in each angle of an isosceles trapezoid if two of its angles are in the ratio of 2 to 3.

★16. In quadrilateral $WMRK$, if (s_1) $WM \parallel KR$, and if (s_2) $WR = KM$, is (c) $WK = MR$? Is either of its two converses true? Explain. Is either of its two inverses true? Explain. Is either of its two contrapositives true? Explain.

The bisectors of the angles of a quadrilateral (*Optional*)

The bisectors of the angles A, B, C, and D of the quadrilateral $ABCD$ in Figure 14 intersect to form the quadrilateral $MNOP$. The following group of exercises will help you discover and prove the properties, if any, of quadrilateral $MNOP$.

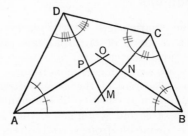

Fig. 14

Exercises (*Optional*)

1. Bisect all the angles of a square. Can you prove that they intersect at a point?

2. Bisect all the angles of a rhombus. Describe how the angle bisectors are related.

3. Bisect all the angles of a rectangle. What can you prove about the figure formed by the bisectors?

4. Bisect all the angles of a parallelogram. Is the figure formed by the bisectors different from the one in Exercise **3**? Explain.

5. Bisect all the angles of an isosceles trapezoid. What can you prove about the figure formed by the bisectors?

6. Bisect all the angles of a trapezoid. How does the figure formed by the bisectors differ from the one in Exercise **5**?

7. Bisect all the angles of any convex quadrilateral. What can you prove about the figure formed by the bisectors? Write a theorem that states the relationships in the figure formed by the angle bisectors of *any* quadrilateral.

★Necessary and sufficient conditions

The relationships of the parts of different kinds of quadrilaterals provide good material for a review of necessary and sufficient conditions.

In a theorem of the general form, "If s_1 and if s_2, then c," if the combination of s_1 and s_2 implies c, that is, if c is deducible from s_1 and s_2, then each condition in the presence of the other is sufficient for c. Or, if either contrapositive of the theorem can be proved, the condition involved in the transformation is sufficient for c. If an inverse or the corresponding converse of the theorem can be proved, the condition involved in the transformation is necessary for the conclusion. The use of these principles is illustrated in the following example:

Example

THEOREM: If two sides of a quadrilateral are equal and parallel, the other two sides are parallel.

Are the conditions specified in the *if*-clause of the theorem sufficient for the conclusion? Is either condition necessary for the conclusion?

Draw a figure on your own paper and identify the conditions and the conclusion as illustrated below.

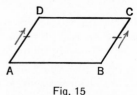

Fig. 15

THEOREM: If $ABCD$ is a quadrilateral in which

(s_1) $AD = BC$, and

(s_2) $AD \parallel BC$,

then (c) $AB \parallel DC$.

Since, by Theorem 27, conclusion c is true, condition s_1 in the presence of condition s_2 is sufficient for conclusion c. Similarly, condition s_2 in the presence of condition s_1 is sufficient for conclusion c.

Inverse 1. In quadrilateral $ABCD$,

if $(\text{not-}s_1)$ AD is not equal to BC,

and if (s_2) $AD \parallel BC$,

then $(\text{not-}c)$ AB not $\parallel DC$.

Fig. 16

The proof of this theorem is difficult; so we shall examine its contrapositive equivalent which is a converse of the original theorem.

Converse 1. In quadrilateral $ABCD$,
if (c) $AB \parallel DC$, and
if (s_2) $AD \parallel BC$,
then (s_1) $AD = BC$.

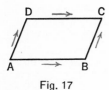

Fig. 17

Since, by Theorem 24, Converse **1** is true, Inverse 1 is true. Hence, condition s_1 is necessary for conclusion c.

Inverse 2. In quadrilateral $ABCD$,
if (s_1) $AD = BC$, and
if   (not-s_2) AD not $\parallel BC$,
then   (not-c) AB not $\parallel DC$.

Fig. 18

This theorem is obviously false since $ABCD$ might be an isosceles trapezoid. Hence s_2 is not necessary for conclusion c.

★Exercises

State whether the given conditions in the following statements are (**a**) *sufficient but not necessary,* (**b**) *necessary but not sufficient,* (**c**) *necessary and sufficient,* (**d**) *neither necessary nor sufficient for the conclusion:*

1. If two sides of a quadrilateral are parallel and equal, the other two sides are equal.

2. If two sides of a quadrilateral are equal, the diagonals are equal.

3. If the diagonals of a quadrilateral are perpendicular, they are equal.

4. If the opposite sides of a quadrilateral are equal, the diagonals are perpendicular.

5. If the diagonals of a parallelogram are equal, the diagonals are perpendicular.

Dividing a line segment into any number of equal parts

We have already learned how to bisect a line segment. Thus, by the same construction, we can divide a line segment into 4, 8, 16, ... , 2^n equal parts (where n is any positive integer greater than 1). We shall now learn how to divide a line segment into any number of equal parts.

THEOREM 36.   **If three or more parallel lines cut off equal segments on one transversal, they cut off equal segments on any transversal.**

Given: Parallel lines a, b, and c cutting off equal segments RS and ST on the transversal t; LM and MN are segments of any other transversal x, cut off by a, b, and c.

Prove: $LM = MN$.

You write the proof. (Hint: Through L, draw $LE \parallel RS$; and through M, draw $MF \parallel ST$. Then prove $\triangle EML \cong \triangle FNM$, etc.)

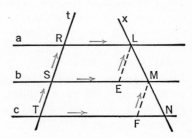

CONSTRUCTION 15. Divide a line segment into n equal parts.

Given: Line segment AB.

Required: To divide AB into n equal parts.

Method: (In this example, we shall divide AB into three equal parts. We can use the same method for any integral value of n.)

1. Draw any line AX, and on it lay off from A three *equal* segments of any convenient length.
2. Draw line l from the end of the last segment to B.
3. Construct parallels to l through the points of division on AX, intersecting AB at C and D.
4. AC, CD, and DB are the required segments.

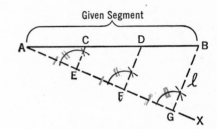

To prove the construction, draw a line through A parallel to l, then use Theorem 36.

Exercises

1. Divide a given line segment XY into five equal parts.
2. Construct three-sevenths of a given line segment.
3. Use a ruler to find three-sevenths of a given segment. Explain why this method is more difficult than the one used in Exercise **2**.
4. Construct a rhombus, given its perimeter and one angle.
5. Draw an isosceles triangle. Trisect the base. Connect the points of division with the vertex. Do these line segments trisect the vertex angle? Prove your answer.
6. Prove: A line through the midpoint of one leg of a trapezoid parallel to the bases bisects the other leg and both diagonals.

7. Prove: The perpendicular bisector of one leg of a right triangle bisects the hypotenuse.

*In the figure for Exercises **8** and **9**, $ABCD$ is a trapezoid; $AB \parallel EF \parallel DC$; and AC is a diagonal intersecting EF at O.*

8. Given: $AE = 5$, $ED = 5$, and $CF = 4$.
   a. Find CB.
   b. If $AC = 12$, find AO.

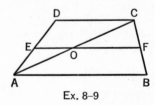

Ex. 8–9

9. Given: O is the midpoint of AC, and $AD = 10$. Find AE.

A line segment joining the midpoints of two sides of a triangle

(Do not write in this book.)

Data table:

△ABC	AB	MN	∠A	∠2
Acute scalene	?	?	?	?
Obtuse scalene	?	?	?	?
Right scalene	?	?	?	?
Isosceles acute	?	?	?	?
Isosceles obtuse	?	?	?	?
Isosceles right	?	?	?	?
Equilateral	?	?	?	?

Experiment

How is the line segment joining the midpoints of two sides of a triangle related to the third side?

Given: Any triangle ABC; M is the midpoint of CA, and N is the midpoint of CB.

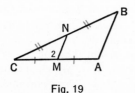

Fig. 19

Induction: Use either a dynamic triangle with an elastic thread between M and N, or construct triangles that satisfy the conditions. Measure the relevant variables such as AB, MN, $\angle A$, and $\angle 2$ of different kinds of triangles and record the measurements in a table similar to the one shown at the upper right.

Observations: (How do certain parts of $\triangle ABC$ seem to be related?)

Inductive conclusion: If a line segment joins the midpoints of two sides of a triangle, ...

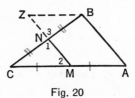

Fig. 20

Deduction: Extend MN its own length to Z. Draw BZ. Deduce the implications concerning MN and AB.

Hint: Prove $\triangle CMN \cong \triangle NBZ$, also $MA = ZB$, and $MA \parallel ZB$.

Complete Theorem 37 and write the proof.

THEOREM 37. **If a line segment joins the midpoints of two sides of a triangle, it is . . . . to the third side and . . . . .**

The converses of Theorem 37

Theorem 37 has two conclusions. Hence, to write its converses, we make two theorems of it, each having only one conclusion. We shall call one of the theorems 37-A and the other 37-B.

Theorem 37-A. If a line segment joins the midpoints of two sides of a triangle, it is parallel to the third side.

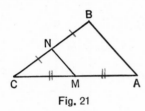

Fig. 21

In $\triangle CAB$, figure 21,
if   (s_1) M is the midpoint of CA, and
if   (s_2) N is the midpoint of CB,
then (c_1) $MN \parallel AB$.

Converses of Theorem 37-A

Converse 1. (Formed by interchanging s_1 and c_1 in Theorem 37-A.)

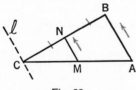

Fig. 22

In $\triangle CAB$, Figure 22,
if   (s_2) N is the midpoint of CB, and
if   (c_1) $MN \parallel AB$,
then (s_1) M is the midpoint of CA.

Converse 2. (Formed by interchanging s_2 and c_1 in Theorem 37-A.)

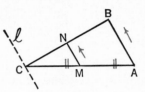

Fig. 23

In $\triangle CAB$, Figure 23,
if   (s_1) M is the midpoint of CA, and
if   (c_1) $MN \parallel AB$,
then (s_2) N is the midpoint of CB.

   To prove these converses, draw the line l through C parallel to AB, then use Theorem 36.

It is apparent that the two converses of Theorem 37-A are essentially alike. In fact, their word-statements are identical.

COROLLARY A line through the midpoint of one side of a triangle parallel to a second side passes through the midpoint of the third side.

Theorem 37-B. If a line segment joins the midpoints of two sides of a triangle, it is equal to one-half the third side.

In $\triangle CAB$, Figure 24,
if   (s_1) M is the midpoint of CA, and
if   (s_2) N is the midpoint of CB,
then (c_2) $MN = \frac{1}{2}AB$.

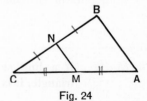

Fig. 24

Converses of Theorem 37-B

It is apparent that the two converses of Theorem 37-B yield identical word-statements. Hence, we shall consider only the converse obtained by interchanging s_1 and c_2.

In $\triangle CAB$, Figure 25,

if   (s_2) N is the midpoint of CB, and

if   (c_2) $MN = \frac{1}{2}AB$,

then (s_1) M is the midpoint of CA.

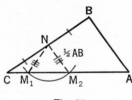

Fig. 25

Since $MN, CN,$ and $\angle C$ form a combination of parts that may produce the two triangles CM_1N and CM_2N, the converse of Theorem 37-B cannot be proved.

Exercises

1. Given: $\triangle ABC$, R is the midpoint of AB, S is the midpoint of CB, $AB = 10$, $AC = 6$, and $CB = 8$. How long is SR?

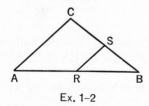

Ex. 1–2

2. Given: $\triangle ABC$, R is the midpoint of AB, $RS \parallel AC$, $CB = 6$, and $AC = 4$. How long is CS? How long is RS?

3. Find the length of the line that joins the midpoints of the 14 in. and the 18 in. sides of a triangle whose perimeter is 59 in. Show an algebraic equation.

4. If through any point of the base of an isosceles triangle lines are drawn parallel to the equal sides, how is the perimeter of the quadrilateral that is formed related to the legs of the triangle?

★**5.** Given: $\triangle ABC$; points R, S, and T are the midpoints of AB, BC, and AC, respectively.

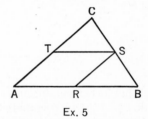

Ex. 5

In answering the following questions, do not give formal proofs, but be sure you can give reasons for your answers:

a. What can you prove about quadrilateral $ARST$?

b. What additional condition must be imposed on $\triangle ABC$ for $ARST$ to be a rectangle?

For $ARST$ to be a rectangle, is it necessary for $\triangle ABC$ to be a right triangle? Is it sufficient for $\triangle ABC$ to be a right triangle? Which one of the angles of $\triangle ABC$ must be a right angle?

c. What must be done to $\triangle ABC$ to make $ARST$ a rhombus? Is it necessary for $\triangle ABC$ to be equilateral? Is it sufficient for $\triangle ABC$ to be equilateral? Which two sides of $\triangle ABC$ must be equal?

d. How can $ARST$ be made into a square? State the necessary conditions.

⋆**6.** Given: $\triangle ABC$; R, S, and T are midpoints of AB, BC, and AC, respectively.

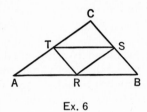

Ex. 6

a. How is $\triangle RST$ related to $\triangle ART$?

b. How is $\triangle RST$ related to $\triangle RBS$?

c. How is $\triangle RST$ related to $\triangle TSC$?

d. What other condition must be added to the given conditions for $\triangle RST$ to be equilateral? Is this condition both necessary and sufficient? Explain.

e. What must be done to $\triangle ABC$ to make $\triangle RST$ an isosceles right triangle?

f. How is the area of $\triangle RST$ related to the area of $\triangle ABC$?

⋆**7.** Write an inverse and a contrapositive of each of the following statements and prove, if possible;

a. If a line segment joins the midpoints of two sides of a triangle, it is parallel to the third side.

b. If a line segment joins the midpoints of two sides of a triangle, it is equal to one-half the third side.

_____

The median of a trapezoid

Experiment

How is the median of a trapezoid related to its bases?

Given: $BCDE$ is a trapezoid, and MN is the median.

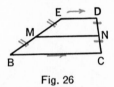

Fig. 26

Induction: Measure MN, BC, and ED. Compare the length of MN with the sum of the lengths of BC and ED. Measure $\angle B$ and $\angle NME$. What seems to be true?

Deduction: Prove your inductive conclusions by extending EN until it intersects the extension of BC at P.

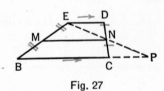

Fig. 27

Hint: Prove that N is the midpoint of EP by proving $\triangle CPN \cong \triangle NDE$.

Complete Theorem 38 and write the proof.

_____

THEOREM 38. **The median of a trapezoid is . . . . to the bases and equal to . . . . .**

The median to the hypotenuse of a right triangle

Experiment

How is the median to the hypotenuse of a right triangle related to the hypotenuse?

Given: Right $\triangle ABC$, $\angle C = 90°$, and CM is the median to AB.

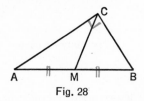
Fig. 28

Induction: Measure CM and AB. How does CM seem to be related to AB?

Deduction: You need an auxiliary line to prove your inductive conclusion. Try each of the following suggestions:

a. Through M, extend CM its own length to T. Draw BT and AT.

b. Through P, the midpoint of AC, draw MP.

c. Through M, draw a line parallel to CA and meeting CB at S.

Complete Theorem 39, and write the proof.

THEOREM 39. **The median to the hypotenuse of a right triangle . . . . .**

Exercises

1. How long is the median of a trapezoid if its bases are 7.0 inches and 15.0 inches long? What does the zero in 7.0 and 15.0 signify?

2. Given: Trapezoid $ABCD$ with diagonals AC and BD intersecting median RS at T and V, respectively.
   Prove: $TV = \frac{1}{2}(AB - DC)$.

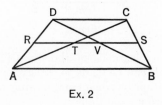
Ex. 2

3. What is the locus of the midpoint of the hypotenuse of a right triangle whose hypotenuse is fixed in length and whose legs are fixed in position?

Properties of the quadrilateral formed by joining the midpoints of the consecutive sides of a given quadrilateral

A dynamic midpoint-quadrilateral similar to the one shown below can easily be made from suitable materials. It is a convenient device for investigating the nature and properties of the figure formed by joining the consecutive midpoints of the sides of a quadrilateral.

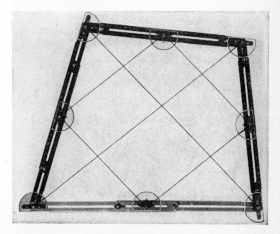

Experiment

Given: $ABCD$ is a quadrilateral, AC and BD are diagonals; $E, F, G,$ and H are the midpoints of $AB, BC, CD,$ and DA, respectively.

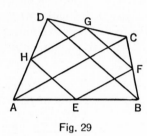

Fig. 29

1. a. How is HE related to DB? Why?

   b. How is HG related to AC? Why?

   c. How is GF related to DB? Why?

   d. How is EF related to AC? Why?

   e. How is HE related to GF? Why?

   f. How is HG related to EF? Why?

   g. What is the quadrilateral $EFGH$? Why?

2. Copy the table below and supply the answers to the questions. (Do not write in this book.)

$ABCD$ is a:	Relation of AC to BD:	$EFGH$ is a:
a. Parallelogram	?	?
b. Rectangle	?	?
c. Rhombus	?	?
d. Isosceles trapezoid	?	?
e. Square	?	?

Quadrilaterals determined by their diagonals

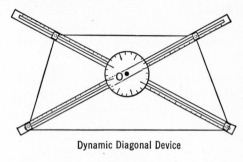

Dynamic Diagonal Device

Fig. 30

The device pictured in this figure (easily made from suitable material) is a convenient instrument for investigating how a quadrilateral is determined by its diagonals. To be effective, the diagonals should rotate about a pivotal point; and on each of the segments of the diagonals, there should be a linear scale with the zero of the scale at the pivotal point. The fixtures on the diagonals, which form the vertices and to which the elastic quadrilateral is attached, should be movable so that the diagonals can be set to satisfy different conditions.

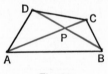

Fig. 31

The diagonals of the quadrilateral $ABCD$ can be made to satisfy any one condition or some combination of the following conditions:

1. $AC = BD$.
2. $AC \perp BD$.
3. AC and BD bisect each other.
4. AC bisects BD.
5. AC and BD are unequal.

Exercises

In each of the exercises in the table below, state what ABCD is when the diagonals are related as indicated. If the specified diagonal relationship is not sufficient to determine one of the quadrilaterals that has been defined, answer **Not determined.** *(Do not write in this book.)*

Relation of Diagonal AC to Diagonal BD	Quadrilateral $ABCD$
Example: AC bisects BD.	Not determined
1. AC and BD bisect each other.	?
2. $AC = BD$.	?
3. $AC = BD$, and AC and BD bisect each other.	?
4. $AC \perp BD$.	?
5. $AC \perp BD$, and AC and BD bisect each other.	?
6. $AC = BD$, and $AC \perp BD$.	?
7. $AC = BD$, $AC \perp BD$, and AC and BD bisect each other.	?

8. Find the lengths of the sides of the quadrilateral that is formed by joining the consecutive midpoints of a given quadrilateral whose diagonals are 36 in. and 14 in.

9. Prove that the segments joining the midpoints of the opposite sides of any quadrilateral bisect each other.

10. Given: $ABCD$ is a parallelogram, DE is an altitude meeting AB at E, $AE = 3$, and $AD = 6$. How many degrees are there in $\angle B$? Why?

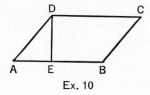

Ex. 10

11. Construct and describe the locus of the point of intersection O of the diagonals AC and BD of the parallelogram $ABCD$ if AB is fixed in length and position and the other sides are fixed in length.

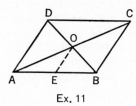

Ex. 11

12. Prove that the sum of the diagonals of a quadrilateral is equal to the perimeter of the quadrilateral that is formed by joining the consecutive midpoints of the given quadrilateral.

13. Prove that if a median to one side of a triangle is equal to one-half of the side to which it is drawn, the triangle is a right triangle.

14. Given: *ABCD* is a skew quadrilateral. ($\triangle ABD$ and $\triangle BCD$ are not in the same plane.) Points *E*, *F*, *G*, and *H* are the midpoints of *AB*, *BC*, *CD*, and *DA*, respectively.

Prove that *EFGH* is a parallelogram.

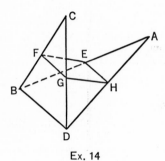

Ex. 14

Practical Applications

1. A carpenter will frequently use his square to divide a board into strips of equal width. He may do so by placing the square in two positions as shown. If he places the 0 and 24 in. divisions of the square at the edges of the board and places marks on the board at the 8 and 16 in. divisions, he can locate the points through which the two lines *a* and *b* must pass to trisect the width of the board.

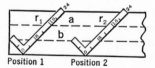

Ex. 1

a. Why will this locate the cutting lines?

b. Why is this method better than placing a ruler along the edge of the board and locating the two lines by measurement?

c. Prove that $r_1 \parallel r_2$ by drawing auxiliary lines and showing that there are two congruent triangles and a parallelogram.

d. Prove $a \parallel b$.

2. For the edges of a parallel ruler to be always parallel, how must it be constructed?

Parallel Ruler

Ex. 2

3. Perhaps you have seen an extension gate such as this one. How must the gate be constructed for *AB* to remain parallel to *CD*?

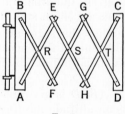

Ex. 3

4. Explain how a carpenter can check whether a rectangular window frame is properly installed by marking the midpoint of the bottom of the frame and hanging a plumb bob from the midpoint of the top of the frame.

5. A farmer wished to find the distance from A to C, but he could not measure it directly because a barn was in the way. He remembered that AC could be measured indirectly by:

a. Walking to a point B where he could see both A and C.

b. Locating E and D at definite positions on BA and BC.

Explain how he could find the length of AC.

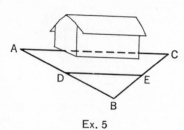

Ex. 5

6. Explain how you could divide a stick that is 12 inches long into eleven equal parts, using only a pencil and a sheet of ruled notebook paper.

7. A marking gauge is another useful carpenter's tool. By loosening the thumb screw at C, one can adjust the slider S to any position along the ruled shaft BE. A marker at B will scratch a line such as AB on the board parallel to edge DF when the slider is set and the gauge is pushed along edge DF. Why is $AB \parallel DF$?

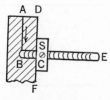

Ex. 7

8. What principle keeps the surface of the adjustable table horizontal as it is moved up or down if $LO = MN$, $LM = ON$, the surface of the table is perpendicular to ON, and the support ML is vertical?

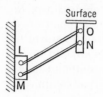

Ex. 8

9. If you have seen a lawn swing such as this one, it should not be difficult to solve this problem: Why does the floor board of the swing remain parallel to the ground as the swing moves?

Ex. 9

Puzzles   *(Optional)*

1. Magic Square

Draw a square on a piece of cardboard. Draw two perpendicular lines through the center of the square as shown in the diagram. Cut out the pieces. Then ask your friends to make a square from the four identical pieces.

Magic Square

2. Chinese Tangram

Draw a square $ABCD$ on a piece of cardboard and draw lines according to the following information:

AC is a diagonal.

E is the midpoint of AB.

F is the midpoint of BC.

G is the midpoint of AC.

H is the midpoint of GC.

I is the midpoint of EF.

J is the midpoint of AG.

Cut the cardboard along the lines, making seven pieces. You now have a geometry puzzle. How many different quadrilaterals and designs can you make with the seven pieces of the given square?

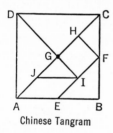

Chinese Tangram

3. The T Puzzle

Draw the T to the dimensions given. Cut along the lines indicated. Ask your friends to make a T from the four pieces.

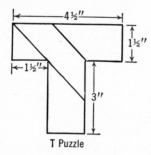

T Puzzle

4. Triangle Dissection

a. Make a scalene paper triangle WKS. R is the midpoint of WS, and M is the midpoint of KS. Make a straight cut through R and M. Can you fit the two pieces together in two different ways to form a parallelogram?

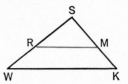

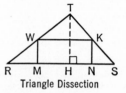

Triangle Dissection

b. Make a paper scalene triangle RST. H is the foot of the altitude TH. Fold the vertices R, S, and T to meet at H.

Show that:

The sum of the angles of a triangle is a straight angle.

$WK = \frac{1}{2}RS$, and $WK \parallel RS$.

Area of $\triangle RST$ is twice the area of rectangle $MNKW$.

5. Fallacy of the Growing Square

Make a paper square 8 units by 8 units. Cut it into four pieces as indicated in the diagram. Rearrange

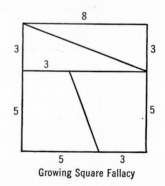

Growing Square Fallacy

the pieces to form what appears to be a rectangle 5 units by 13 units. Explain the fallacy.

6. Quadrilateral Dissection

Make a paper quadrilateral *WKRM*. *E, T, N,* and *S* are midpoints of the sides. Cut along the lines to get the four pieces 1, 2, 3, and 4. Rearrange the four pieces to form a triangle.

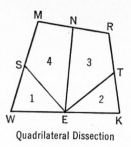

Quadrilateral Dissection

Application of Parallelograms to Vectors

Direction of a ray *(Optional)*

In mathematics, the direction of a ray is, by convention, expressed by the measure of the counter-clockwise angle between a reference line and the line of action of the ray. In navigation, mapping, and military operations, however, it is convenient to express the direction of a ray by the measure of the *clockwise* angle between the ray and a north ray used as a standard line of reference. In Figure 32, the direction of OD_1 is 47°, and the direction of OD_2 is 286°. The direction of a ray making a clockwise angle of 90° with *ON* is east. What would be the direction of a ray making an angle of 270° with *ON*? What angle would represent south? What angle would represent northeast?

Vectors *(Optional)*

A quantity involving both magnitude and direction is called a *vector* quantity. For example, in Figure 33, a 15-mile-an-hour wind blowing from 105° is a vector quantity. Since the

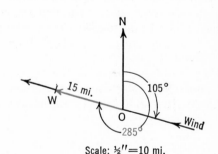

Scale: ½″=10 mi.

Fig. 33

wind is from 105°, it is blowing in the direction of 105° + 180°, or 285°. The magnitude of the wind is 15 miles an hour. The direction of the wind together with its magnitude (speed) is its velocity. The velocity of the wind can be represented geometrically by drawing the vector *OW* to represent 15 miles in the direction of 285°.

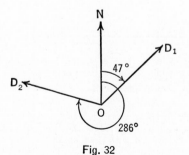

Fig. 32

Parallelogram of vector
quantities *(Optional)*

Two or more vector quantities may be acting upon an object at the same time. In Figure 34, OA represents a vector quantity of 3 units in the direction of 43°, and OB represents a vector quantity of 2 units in the direction of 97°. What is their combined effect on the object at O?

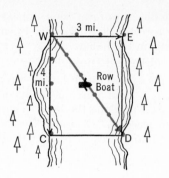

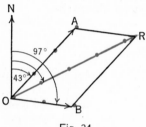

Fig. 34

It is proved in physics that the geometric sum of two vector quantities is the diagonal of the parallelogram determined by them. The vector sum of two quantities is called their resultant.

The resultant of OA and OB is the diagonal OR of the parallelogram $OBRA$. Its magnitude is the length of OR and its direction is the measure of $\angle NOR$. It is evident that vector (or geometric) addition is quite different from arithmetic and algebraic addition.

Example 1 : Suppose that a man on the west shore of a river which is flowing south and is three miles wide wants to row across the river. If the current in the river were only negligible and the man rowed straight east, he would land at E. If he rowed at the rate of 3 miles per hour, it would require just one hour to go from W to E. If, however, the current in the river were 4 miles per hour, it would carry him 4 miles south of his starting point during the hour, and he would land at D. The boat would take the diagonal path from W to D. Since $WCDE$ is a rectangle, and since $WD = \sqrt{\overline{WC}^2 + \overline{CD}^2}$,** $WD = 5$ miles. Hence, the speed of the boat, represented by the length of the resultant WD, would be 5 miles per hour.

---

* In the examples and exercises concerning vectors in this and in subsequent sections, solution by means of a scale drawing is the only method suggested. With the exception of certain special cases, solution by computation is not possible without a knowledge of trigonometry.

These topics are presented at this time to illustrate and emphasize the practical nature of the properties of parallelograms.

** Note: This formula for finding the hypotenuse of a right triangle when the legs are known is based on the Pythagorean Theorem. You are probably familiar with the formula $c^2 = a^2 + b^2$ which results from this theorem. A formal proof of this theorem will be found later in this book.

Example 2: If an airplane is headed in the direction SD, which is measured by $\angle NSD$, at 120 miles per hour, and if the wind is blowing in the direction SC, which is measured by $\angle NSC$, at 30 miles per hour, the diagram shows that the airplane will be at E at the end of one hour. The vector SD represents the heading of the airplane and its air speed in still air; the vector SC represents the direction and speed of the wind; and the resultant SE, which is the diagonal of the parallelogram $SCED$, represents the actual direction and ground speed of the airplane. Since the wind carries the airplane 30 miles in one hour in the direction the wind is blowing, the plane's direction over the ground is not the same as its heading. In the diagram, the direction of the airplane over the ground is obtained by measuring $\angle NSE$, and its ground speed is obtained by measuring SE.

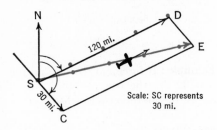

Scale: SC represents 30 mi.

Example 2 is not a practical problem because a pilot usually knows the direction he needs to fly in order to reach his destination. In a practical problem, he must determine the direction in which the airplane must be headed to allow for the effect of the wind. If the course (which is the direction the pilot wishes to fly) is known, the pilot can determine his heading from his known air speed and the speed and direction of the wind. Example 3 illustrates how this can be done.

Example 3: A pilot starting from O wishes to reach a point T which is on a course of 75°. If a wind is blowing from 190° at 30 miles per hour, and his air speed is 110 miles per hour, what must be his heading?

This problem can be solved by making a parallelogram of vector quantities as follows:

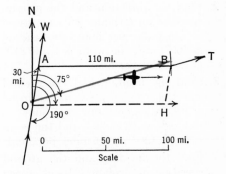

1. Let O represent the starting point on a north ray.
2. Draw OW so that $\angle NOW$ is 10°. Since the wind is blowing *from* 190°, it is blowing in the direction of 10°.
3. On OW lay off OA according to scale to represent 30 miles.
4. From O draw OT so that $\angle NOT$ is 75°. The course the pilot wishes to make good is represented by OT.

   Point A would be the position of the airplane at the end of one hour if it drifted with the wind. Now, disregarding the wind and using the engines, what is the locus of the plane when it is 110 miles from A? When it is 110 miles from A *and* on course OT?

5. With A, the end of the wind vector, as center, and a segment representing 110 miles per hour as radius, draw an arc intersecting OT at B.
6. Complete the parallelogram $OHBA$. The direction the plane needs to be headed is obtained by measuring $\angle NOH$, and the ground speed of the airplane, by measuring OB.

Exercises (*Optional*)

Make careful scale drawings and use a protractor to measure the angles.

1. Find the direction and the ground speed of an airplane if its air speed is 190 miles per hour, its heading is 30°, and the wind is from 120° at 40 miles per hour.

2. Find the direction and the ground speed of an airplane if its air speed is 150 miles per hour, its heading is 100°, and the wind is from 210° at 20 miles per hour.

3. Find the heading and the ground speed of an airplane if its air speed is 190 miles per hour, its course to be made good is 30°, and the wind is from 120° at 40 miles per hour.

4. Find the heading and the ground speed of an airplane if its air speed is 175 miles per hour, its course to be made good is 105°, and the wind is from 95° at 15 miles per hour.

Parallelogram of forces (*Optional*)

If two forces act upon an object at the same time, the forces so acting are called *components*. The *resultant* of these components is a single force which acting alone will produce the same effect as that of the combined forces. The two components and their resultant are vector quantities, that is, they have both magnitude and direction. Consider the following possibilities:

POSSIBILITY 1.

Two forces a and b act in the same direction on an object W. Their combined effect, the resultant, is equal to the sum of a and b in the direction of the components (Figure 35).

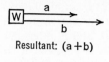

Resultant: (a + b)

Fig. 35

Example: If force a is 20 lb. and force b is 30 lb., the resultant is 50 lb.

Is the effect of a tail wind on an airplane an illustration of the vector sum of two quantities? Explain.

POSSIBILITY 2.

Two forces m and n act in opposite directions on an object R. The resultant of the forces is one single force equal to the difference of m and n in the direction of the larger force (Figure 36).

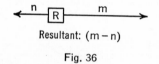

Resultant: (m − n)

Fig. 36

Example: If force m is 65 lb. and force n is 32 lb., the resultant is a force of 33 lb. in the direction of force m.

POSSIBILITY 3.

Two forces x and y act at an angle to each other on an object M. The resultant of the two forces is the diagonal of the parallelogram whose adjacent sides are the two forces.

The direction of the resultant depends upon the comparative magnitudes of the component forces and the angle between them.

Example: A force x of 40 lb. and a force y of 35 lb. are acting upon an object M so that the angle between them is 110°. $MABC$ is a scale drawing

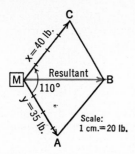

of a parallelogram in which 20 lb. is represented by 1 cm. The combined effect of the two forces is the diagonal *MB* of the parallelogram, which according to the scale is approximately 44 lb.

Resolution of forces (*Optional*)

The man shown in Figure 37 is exerting a force of 60 lb. along the handle of the lawn mower, which makes a 30° angle with the ground.

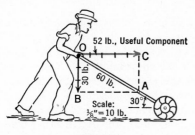

Fig. 37

Not all this force is effective in moving the mower forward. The useful horizontal component of the 60-lb. force can be found by making a scale drawing of a rectangle having as its diagonal a segment representing the magnitude and direction of the force exerted along the handle. Since the side opposite the 30° angle of a right triangle is one-half the hypotenuse, the vertical component is 30 lb. This force only pushes

the mower against the ground. The useful horizontal component of 52 lb. is obtained either by measuring *OC* or by a method of computation which you will study later.

Exercises (*Optional*)

1. Two forces of 6 lb. and 8 lb. are acting upon an object in the same direction. What is the resultant of the two forces?
2. A 12.3 lb. force and a 5.8 lb. force are acting in opposite directions upon an object. What is their resultant?
3. A force of 300 lb. is acting upon an object at *R* in the direction of *RT*, and a force of 200 lb. is acting upon the same object in the direction of *RS*. The angle between them is 60°. Use some convenient scale, such as 1 inch to 100 lb., and construct the parallelogram of forces. What is the magnitude of the resultant of the two forces?

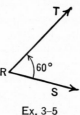

Ex. 3–5

4. If the angle between the two forces in Exercise **3** is 90°, what is the magnitude of their resultant?
5. If the angle between the two forces in Exercise **3** is 120°, what is the magnitude of their resultant?
6. If the handle of a lawn mower being pushed by a boy makes a 20° angle with the horizontal, and the boy is exerting a force of 45 lb. against the handle, what is the useful component of the force?

7. Make a scale drawing and find the components OP and OQ of the force represented by OR if a force of 1200 lb. is exerted in the direction of OR, $OP \perp OQ$, and $\angle a = 35°$.

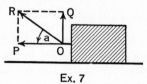

Ex. 7

8. The weight of the object B on the incline AH may be represented by the vector CW which is perpendicular to the horizontal AH'. The component of W which urges the object down the incline is the force represented by the vector CF which

is parallel to AH. The component represented by CP which is perpendicular to AH is the force pressing the object against the incline.

a. Prove that $\angle WCP = \angle a$.

b. Make a scale drawing, and find CF and CP if CW represents 800 lb. and $\angle a$ is 25°.

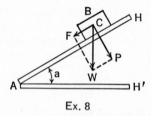

Ex. 8

Co-ordinate Geometry

Projection of a point and of a line segment (*Optional*)

The projection of a point on a line in the same plane is the point of intersection of the line and the perpendicular from the point to the line. In Figure 38, the projection of point A on line s is point A'.

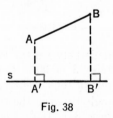

Fig. 38

The projection of a line segment upon another line in the same plane is the segment included between the projections of the end points of the segment on the given line. In Figure 38, the projection of AB on s is the segment $A'B'$.

In Figure 39, if the co-ordinates of K are (x_1, y_1), the co-ordinates of W are (x_2, y_2), $KR \perp OX$, and $WS \perp OX$, then the co-ordinates of R are $(x_1, 0)$, and the co-ordinates of S are $(x_2, 0)$. Hence, the projection of KW on the x-axis is the difference between the abscissas of W and K. In other words, $RS = x_2 - x_1$.

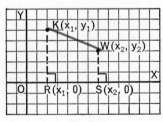

Fig. 39

What is the projection of KW on the y-axis?

Example: Find the projection of the line segment PQ, joining $P(-3, -4)$ and $Q(2, 5)$, on both the x-axis and the y-axis.

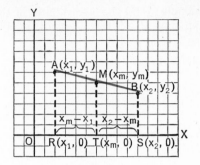

Fig. 40

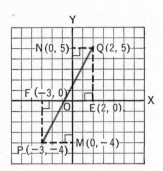

Solution: The projection of PQ on the x-axis is FE.

$FE = x_2 - x_1 = 2 - (-3) = 5.$

The projection of PQ on the y-axis is MN.

$MN = y_2 - y_1 = 5 - (-4) = 9.$

Exercises (*Optional*)

Find the projections of the segments of the following sets of points on both the x- and y-axes:

1. $A(3, 4)$ and $B(7, 9)$.

2. $C(3, 8)$ and $D(-2, -5)$.

3. $E(-3, 4)$ and $F(-6, 6)$.

4. $G(-3, -5)$ and $H(7, -7)$.

5. $I(-5, -6)$ and $J(-8, -2)$.

The co-ordinates of the midpoint of a line segment (*Optional*)

To find the abscissa of the midpoint $M(x_m, y_m)$ of a line segment AB in Figure 40, we find the abscissa of the midpoint of the projection of AB on the x-axis. If AR, MT, and BS are each perpendicular to OX, then they are parallel. Hence, T is the midpoint of RS. Why? The co-ordinates of R, T, and S are, respectively, $(x_1, 0)$, $(x_m, 0)$, and $(x_2, 0)$. Thus

$$RT = x_m - x_1,$$
$$\text{and } TS = x_2 - x_m.$$
$$\text{Since } RT = TS,$$
$$\text{then } x_m - x_1 = x_2 - x_m.$$

From this equation, $x_m = \frac{1}{2}(x_1 + x_2)$.

In a similar way, the ordinate of M can be found by finding the ordinate of the midpoint of the projection of AB on the y-axis. A second method using Figure 40 is as follows:

Since $RSBA$ is a trapezoid and TM is a median, then

$$TM = \frac{1}{2}(RA + SB). \text{ Why?}$$

Hence, $y_m = \frac{1}{2}(y_1 + y_2)$.

The co-ordinates of the midpoint of a line segment are one-half the sums of the co-ordinates of the end points.

$$x_m = \frac{x_1 + x_2}{2}$$

$$\text{and } y_m = \frac{y_1 + y_2}{2}$$

Example: Find the co-ordinates of the midpoint M of the segment joining $P(-3, -4)$ and $Q(5, 2)$.

Solution:
$$x_m = \tfrac{1}{2}(x_1 + x_2)$$
$$= \tfrac{1}{2}(-3 + 5) = 1$$
$$y_m = \tfrac{1}{2}(y_1 + y_2)$$
$$= \tfrac{1}{2}(-4 + 2) = -1$$

Hence, the midpoint of PQ is at $(1, -1)$

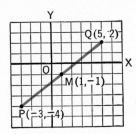

Exercises *(Optional)*

In Exercises **1-3,** *find the co-ordinates of the midpoints of the segments joining the pairs of given points.*

1. $A(3, 4)$ and $B(5, 8)$.

2. $C(4, 5)$ and $D(-7, -4)$.

3. $E(-3, -5)$ and $F(-1, 5)$.

4. Find the co-ordinates of the midpoints of the sides of the triangle whose vertices are:
$A(6, 11)$, $B(6, -11)$, and $C(-6, 5)$.

5. Find the co-ordinates of the midpoints of the sides of the quadrilateral whose vertices are $A(-4, 3)$, $B(5, 3)$, $C(6, -4)$, and $D(-6, -4)$.

The distance between two points* *(Optional)*

In order to find the distance between two points, we need the Pythagorean Theorem. It cannot be proved at this time, but we shall prove it in Chapter 13 (Theorem 77).

The Pythagorean Theorem is: The square of the hypotenuse of a right triangle is equal to the sum of the squares of the two legs. That is, $\overline{PQ}^2 = \overline{PT}^2 + \overline{TQ}^2$. It follows that $PQ = \sqrt{\overline{PT}^2 + \overline{TQ}^2}$. (Only the positive root has meaning.)

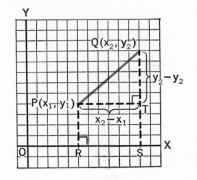

Fig. 41

To find the length of PQ, draw PR and QS perpendicular to the x-axis, and draw $PT \perp SQ$.
Now $PT = RS = x_2 - x_1$,
and $TQ = SQ - ST = y_2 - y_1$.
Therefore, $PQ = \sqrt{(x_2 - x_1)^2 + (y_2 - y_1)^2}$.

The distance d between two points is given by the formula:
$$d = \sqrt{(x_2 - x_1)^2 + (y_2 - y_1)^2}.$$

---

* Note: Although this section is out of logical sequence, there are certain advantages to be gained by using the distance formula in connection with some line segments commonly associated with triangles and quadrilaterals. For example, in some of the exercises following this section, analytical proofs of certain theorems of this chapter are suggested. At the discretion of the instructor, a study of this section may be delayed until after the proof of the Pythagorean Theorem.

Example: Find the distance between the points $P(-4, 7)$ and $Q(4, -8)$.

Solution:

$$PQ = \sqrt{(x_2 - x_1)^2 + (y_2 - y_1)^2}$$
$$= \sqrt{[4 - (-4)]^2 + (-8 - 7)^2}$$
$$= \sqrt{8^2 + (-15)^2}$$
$$= \sqrt{289}$$
$$= 17$$

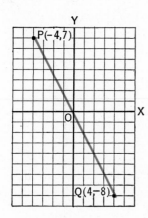

Fig. 42

Exercises (*Optional*)

1. Find the distance between the following pairs of points:

   a. $A(2, 5)$ and $B(2, 12)$
   b. $C(-3, 4)$ and $D(-3, 7)$
   c. $E(-3, -4)$ and $F(-3, -7)$
   d. $G(2, 2)$ and $H(8, 10)$
   e. $I(-4, -1)$ and $J(8, 4)$
   f. $K(-10, 7)$ and $L(-2, -8)$

2. Draw a triangle whose vertices are $A(1, -2)$, $B(5, -2)$, and $C(3, 3)$.

   a. Prove that $\triangle ABC$ is isosceles.
   b. What are the co-ordinates of the midpoint of BC?
   c. What is the length of the median to the side BC?

   d. What is the length of the side AB?
   e. What is the length of the segment joining the midpoints of AC and BC?
   f. Prove that the medians to the equal sides of $\triangle ABC$ are equal.

3. **a.** Prove that the triangle with the following vertices is a right triangle: $A(2, -2), B(-3, 3)$, and $C(-3, -2)$.
   b. Find the length of the median to the hypotenuse.

4. **a.** Prove that the quadrilateral $E(-3, -4)$, $F(5, -1)$, $G(8, 7)$, and $H(0, 4)$ is a rhombus.
   b. Find the length of the longer diagonal.

5. **a.** Draw the quadrilateral whose vertices are $A(-10, -4)$, $B(5, -1)$, $C(4, 4)$, and $D(-6, 2)$.
   b. Find the midpoints M and N of AD and BC, respectively.
   c. Prove that $MN = \frac{1}{2}(AB + CD)$.

6. **a.** Prove that the quadrilateral whose vertices are $A(-4, -1)$, $B(5, -2), C(2, 3)$, and $D(-7, 4)$ is a parallelogram.
   b. Find the length of the longer diagonal.
   c. Find the length of the segment joining the midpoints of AD and AB.
   d. Prove that the quadrilateral formed by joining the consecutive midpoints of the sides of $ABCD$ is a parallelogram.

7. **a.** Find the perimeter of the quadrilateral whose vertices are: $R(-6, -3), S(5, -4), T(3, 5)$, and $U(-4, 2)$.
   b. Find the perimeter of the quadrilateral formed by joining the consecutive midpoints of the sides of $RSTU$.

Miscellaneous:

1. If three or more parallel lines cut off equal segments on one transversal, they cut off equal segments on any transversal.

2. A line segment can be divided into any number of equal parts by using construction instruments.

3. If a line segment joins the midpoints of two sides of a triangle, it is parallel to the third side and is equal to one-half of it.

4. If a line segment bisects one side of a triangle and is parallel to a second side, it bisects the third side.

5. The median to the hypotenuse of a right triangle is equal to one-half the hypotenuse.

6. The quadrilateral $EFGH$ formed by joining the midpoints of the consecutive sides of a quadrilateral $ABCD$ is:

a. Always a parallelogram.

b. A rectangle if $AC \perp BD$.

c. A rhombus if $AC = BD$.

d. A square if $AC \perp BD$, and $AC = BD$.

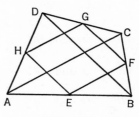

Fig. 43

Review of Chapter 8

Numerical Exercises

In Exercises **1-12**, *AC and BD are the diagonals of parallelogram ABCD. Don't judge your answers from the appearance of the figure. (Do not write in this book.)*

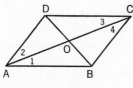

Ex. 1–12

1. If $\angle 1 = 30°$ and $\angle 2 = 45°$, then $\angle 3 = $?

2. If $\angle 1 = 30°$ and $\angle 2 = 45°$, then $\angle ADC = $?

3. If $AD = 6$ and $AB = 8$, then $BC = $?

4. If $AO = 7$ and $BO = 5$, then $OC = $?

5. If $\angle 1 = 30°$, and $\angle 4 = 40°$, then $\angle ADC = $?

6. If $\angle 1 = 30°$, $\angle AOB = 90°$, and $AB = 8$, then $OD = $?

7. If $\angle 1 = \angle 4$, and $AD = 6$, then $AB = $?

8. If $\angle 1 = \angle 4$, then $\angle AOB = $?

9. If $\angle 1 = \angle 2 = 60°$ and $AB = 8$, then $AC = $?

10. If $\angle ABC = 90°$ and $AC = 14$, then $BD = $?

11. If $\angle BAD = 90°$ and $AB = AD$, then $\angle 1 = $?

12. If $BD = AC$ and $BD \perp AC$, then $\angle 2 = $?

In Exercises **13-20**, *ABCD is a trape-zoid, AB ∥ DC, MN is the median, and DE ⊥ AB.*

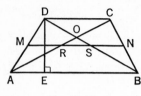

Ex. 13–20

13. If $AB = 9$ and $DC = 5$, then $MN = ?$

14. If $AB = 9$ and $DC = 5$, then $MR = ?$

15. If $AB = 9$ and $DC = 5$, then $RS = ?$

16. If $ABCD$ is isosceles and if $\angle BAD = 80°$, then $\angle DCB = ?$

17. If $AC = 8$ and $DC = 5$, then $AR = ?$

18. If $\angle BAD = 60°$ and $AD = 3$, then $AE = ?$

19. If $AC = BD$ and $\angle BAD = 50°$, then $\angle DCB = ?$

20. If $AO = OB$, $AD = 6$, and if $DC = 8$, then $BC = ?$

In Exercises **21-25**, *ABCD is a quadri-lateral, AC and BD are diagonals, and EFGH is the quadrilateral formed by joining the midpoints of the consecutive sides. Don't judge your answers on the basis of the appearance of the figure.*

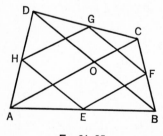

Ex. 21–25

21. If $AC = 10$ and $BD = 8$, the perimeter of $EFGH = ?$

22. If $\angle AOB = 85°$, then $\angle FEH = ?$

23. If $ABCD$ is a rhombus, then $\angle AOB = ?$

24. If $ABCD$ is an isosceles trapezoid and $BD = 6$, then $EF = ?$

25. If $AC \perp BD$ and $\angle BAD = 70°$, then $\angle FEH = ?$

Construction Exercises

1. Construct the parallelogram $ABCD$, given AB, AD, and $\angle D$.

2. Construct the square $ABCD$, given the diagonal AC.

3. Construct the rectangle $ABCD$, given AB and $\angle BAC$.

4. Construct the trapezoid $ABCD$, given the bases AB and DC, leg AD, and diagonal BD.

5. Construct the isosceles trapezoid $ABCD$, given the base AB, $\angle A$, and AD.

6. Construct the rhombus $ABCD$, given the diagonals AC and BD.

7. Find by construction two-fifths of a line segment AB.

8. Construct the locus of the point of intersection of the diagonals of a dynamic rectangle that has one side fixed in length and position.

9. Construct the locus of the mid-point of the hypotenuse of a dynamic right triangle that has its legs fixed in position (not in length) and its hypotenuse fixed in length.

10. Construct the locus of the point of intersection of the diagonals of a dynamic parallelogram that has one side fixed in length and posi-tion and the other sides fixed in length.

Symmetry

1. Construct the axes of symmetry, if any, of an isosceles trapezoid.
2. Draw the axes of symmetry, if any, of a rhombus.
3. Construct the axes of symmetry, if any, of a rectangle.
4. If a parallelogram is symmetric with respect to a point, locate it.
5. If an isosceles trapezoid is symmetric with respect to a point, locate it.

Completion Test

Write the numbers **1-7** *on your paper. After each number write the word or words that complete the corresponding statement correctly. Do not write in this book.*

1. A quadrilateral is a . . . . if its diagonals bisect each other.
2. A quadrilateral is a . . . . if its diagonals are the perpendicular bisectors of each other.
3. A quadrilateral is a . . . . if its diagonals bisect each other and are equal.
4. A quadrilateral is a . . . . if its diagonals bisect each other, are perpendicular, and are equal.
5. The sum of the interior angles of a trapezoid is . . . . .
6. If the opposite angles of a quadrilateral are equal, it is a . . . . .
7. If a line segment joins the midpoints of two sides of a triangle, it . . . . .

★Necessary and Sufficient Conditions

*In each of the following exercises, certain conditions (designated by s_1, s_2, etc.) are given about quadrilateral KARW. State whether or not the conditions are (**a**) sufficient but not necessary, (**b**) necessary but not sufficient, (**c**) necessary and sufficient, (**d**) neither necessary nor sufficient for conclusion c.*

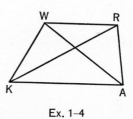

Ex. 1–4

1. s_1: $KA \parallel WR$
   s_2: $KA = WR$
   c: $KW = AR$

2. s_1: $KA \parallel WR$
   s_2: $KW = AR$
   c: $KW \parallel AR$

3. s_1: $KR = WA$
   s_2: $KR \perp WA$
   c: KR bisects WA

4. s_1: KR bisects WA
   s_2: WA bisects KR
   s_3: $WA \perp KR$
   c: $WA = KR$

One of the twentieth century's well-known architects is Frank Lloyd Wright. Notice his consciousness of geometric forms and his use of circles in this view of one of his buildings, located in Racine, Wisconsin.

Chapter 9 CIRCLES

IN THIS chapter we are going to study the simplest and most perfect figure known: the circle. We see applications of it everywhere. It appears in the complex machines used in industry. In the form of wheels, it moves the world's people and goods. It is a basic figure in art and architecture. It appears as a section of many solid figures such as the sphere, the cylinder, and the cone. Circles on the earth are important in geography, astronomy, and navigation. Without the circle and its many applications, our civilization would be as primitive as it was before the invention of the wheel.

Terms used with circles

Although we have used arcs of circles in connection with angles and in many constructions, we have not considered many of the important relationships involving circles and lines. Before we begin the study of these relationships we should review some of the facts about circles that we have already studied, and then learn some new ones.

Recall the definitions of the following:

1. Circle

2. Radius of a circle

3. Diameter of a circle

4. Arc of a circle

5. Circumference of a circle

6. Central angle of a circle

7. Equal circles

8. Concentric circles

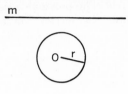

Fig. 1

Assume that the line m and the circle O have no common points (Figure 1). As they approach each other, the line m first touches the circle at one point P which we call the *point of contact* or the *point of tangency*. In that position m is a *tangent* (Figure 2).

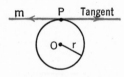

Fig. 2

As m moves nearer O it intersects the circle in two points and becomes a *secant*. The segment AB of the secant intercepted by the circle is called a *chord*. It is also referred to as the internal segment of the secant. When the secant passes through the center O, the chord is a diameter.

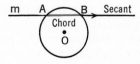

Fig. 3

259

The polygon *ABCD* has its vertices on the circle. The polygon is said to be *inscribed* in the circle. The circle is said to be *circumscribed* about the polygon.

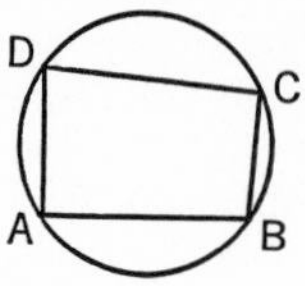

Fig. 4

If the sides of polygon *EFGH* are tangent to circle *O*, it is said to be *circumscribed* about the circle. The circle is said to be *inscribed* in the polygon.

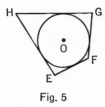

Fig. 5

POSTULATES 38. A point is within a circle if its distance from the center is less than a radius, and a point lies outside a circle if its distance from the center is greater than a radius.

39. If a point is within a circle, its distance from the center is less than a radius; and if a point lies outside a circle, its distance from the center is greater than a radius.

DEFINITIONS A *tangent to a circle* is a straight line that no matter how far extended touches the circle at only one point. The circle is also *tangent* to the line.

A *secant of a circle* is a straight line that intersects the circle in two points.

A *chord of a circle* is a straight line segment that connects two points on the circle.

A *semicircle* is an arc that is one-half of a circle.

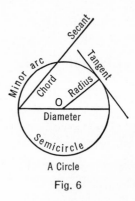

A Circle
Fig. 6

A *major arc of a circle* is an arc that is greater than a semicircle.

A *minor arc of a circle* is an arc that is less than a semicircle.

An *inscribed* polygon is a polygon whose sides are chords of a circle. The circle is then *circumscribed* about the polygon.

A *circumscribed* polygon is a polygon whose sides are tangent to a circle. The circle is then *inscribed* in the polygon.

Exercises

*In Exercises **1-6**, identify the parts of the figures that have been defined.*

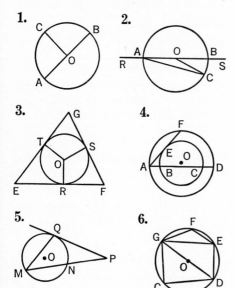

1.

2.

3.

4.

5.

6.

7. If the chord AB of circle O is equal to the radius OA, how many degrees are there in $\widehat{AB}$? Why?

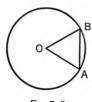

Ex. 7–8

8. If $\widehat{AB}$ of the chord AB is 60°, how is AB related to OA?

9. If a central angle of a circle is 45°, what fractional part of the circumference does it intercept?

10. How many degrees are there in the central angle of an arc 5.0 ft. long on a circle whose circumference is 60.0 ft.?

Equal arcs

A central angle is measured by its intercepted arc. Hence, $\angle S \doteq \widehat{RT}$, and $\angle O \doteq \widehat{AB}$. If the number of degrees in $\widehat{AB}$ is equal to the number of degrees in $\widehat{RT}$, then $\angle O = \angle S$.

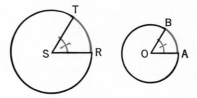

Fig. 7

Also, if $\angle O = \angle S$, then the number of degrees in $\widehat{AB}$ is equal to the number of degrees in $\widehat{RT}$. Is $\widehat{AB}$ necessarily the same length as $\widehat{RT}$?

If the radii of circles M and N are equal, then circles M and N are equal. Why? If the lengths of arcs EF and CD, measured in some linear unit, are equal, it seems reasonable to assume that $\angle M = \angle N$. Likewise, if $\angle M = \angle N$, it seems reasonable that the length of $\widehat{EF}$ is equal to the length of $\widehat{CD}$.

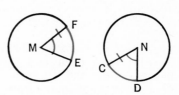

Fig. 8

POSTULATES 40. In the same circle or in equal circles if two arcs are equal, their central angles are equal.

      41. In the same circle or in equal circles if two central angles are equal, their intercepted arcs are equal.

COROLLARIES 1. If a chord is a diameter, it bisects the circle.

      2. If a chord bisects a circle, it is a diameter.

Arcs and their chords

THEOREM 40. In the same circle or in equal circles, equal arcs have equal chords.

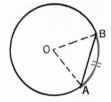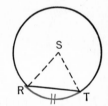

Given: Equal circles O and S; $\overset{\frown}{AB} = \overset{\frown}{RT}$.

Prove: Chord AB = chord RT.

   You write the proof.

THEOREM 41. In the same circle or in equal circles, equal chords have equal arcs.

   You write the proof.

Exercises

1. Divide a circle into six equal parts.

2. Inscribe an equilateral hexagon in a circle.

3. Prove that an equilateral hexagon inscribed in a circle is a regular hexagon.

4. Divide a circle into three equal parts.

5. Inscribe an equilateral triangle in a circle. Is an equilateral triangle regular?

6. Divide a circle into four equal arcs.

7. Inscribe an equilateral quadrilateral in a circle.

8. Prove that an equilateral quadrilateral inscribed in a circle is a square.

9. Inscribe an equilateral octagon in a circle.

10. Prove that an equilateral octagon inscribed in a circle is a regular octagon.

11. How long is the chord of a circle whose radius is 18 in. if the central angle of the arc of the chord is 60°?

12. An equilateral polygon is inscribed in a circle. Each side is a chord of an arc of 36°. How many sides has the polygon?

13. Given: Circles O and P intersect at R and S.
Deduce the relation of the line of centers OP to the common chord RS.

Ex. 13

14. Given: AB and CD are diameters of circle O.

a. Deduce the implication about $\angle DBC$.

b. What additional condition must be imposed on AB and CD to make $\angle DBC$ a square?

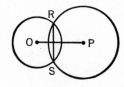

Ex. 14

15. If a circle is divided into five equal arcs, and radii are drawn to the points of division, how many degrees are there in the central angles that are formed?

16. Given: $\triangle ABC$ is inscribed in circle O; $\angle A = \angle B$.
Deduce the implications.

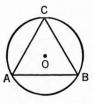

Ex. 16

17. Given: Circle O in which AB is parallel to the diameter CD, and $\overarc{BA} = 80°$.

a. What is the size of $\angle DOB$?

b. How many degrees are there in $\overarc{AC}$?

Ex. 17

18. Construct and describe the locus of the centers of circles that have a common chord.

19. Can you use this figure to prove that a diameter is longer than any other chord? If so, prove it.

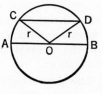

Ex. 19

20. Given: Point T on $\overarc{SR}$ is equidistant from the radii OS and OR. Deduce the implications. (Hint: Recall the locus theorem about a point equidistant from the sides of an angle.)

Ex. 20

21. If l represents the linear measure of an arc, S the number of degrees in its central angle, and C the circumference of the circle, show that $l = \dfrac{S}{360}C$. Solve the equation for S.

22. Given: AB is the diameter of circle O, and the chord CB is drawn so that $\angle ABC = 40°$.

a. Find the number of degrees in $\angle COB$.

b. Find the number of degrees in $\overarc{AC}$.

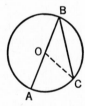

Ex. 22

23. Prove that the midpoint of an arc of a circle is equidistant from the sides of the central angle that intercepts the arc.

24. Given: The parallelogram $ABCD$ is inscribed in circle O.

a. Which arcs can you prove equal?

b. What can you prove about the diagonals AC and BD?

c. What kind of parallelogram is $ABCD$?

Ex. 24

25. In circle O, $\overarc{CD} = \frac{1}{2}\overarc{XZY}$, and Z is the midpoint of $\overarc{XY}$. Compare the length of chord CD with the length of chord XY.

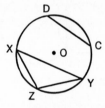

Ex. 25

26. Given: AB and CD are two equal intersecting chords in circle O. Deduce the implications.

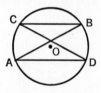

Ex. 26

27. Divide a given circle into three arcs which are to each other as 1 to 2 to 3.

28. Prove: If a rhombus is inscribed in a circle, it is a square.

29. Prove: If a parallelogram is inscribed in a circle, it is a rectangle.

A diameter and a chord

Experiment

If a diameter is perpendicular to a chord, how are the segments of the chord related? How are the intercepted arcs related?

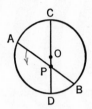

Fig. 9

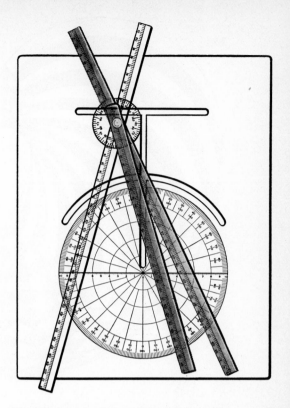

Use of a dynamic circle instrument such as this simplifies the search for important relations involving arcs of circles, chords, tangents, secants, and angles.

Induction: Let CD be the diameter of circle O, and let AB be any other chord that intersects CD at some point P. As AB rotates about P, the chord AB, its segments AP and PB, the four arcs of the circle, and the angles at P are variables.

A satisfactory device for this experiment can be made by drawing circle O and diameter CD on one piece of paper and line AB on a second piece which is semi-transparent. The figure is completed by placing the second paper over the first so that AB intersects CD.

When $AB \perp CD$, measure AP and PB. Compare $\widehat{AD}$, $\widehat{DB}$, $\widehat{BC}$, and $\widehat{CA}$.

What seems to be true?

Deduction:

Given: CD is the diameter of circle O, and chord AB is perpendicular to CD at P (Figure 10).

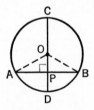

Fig. 10

Deduce the implications about AP and PB, and about the arcs AD, DB, BC, and CA.

Complete and prove Theorem 42.

THEOREM 42. **If a diameter of a circle is perpendicular to a chord, it . . . . .**

This geometric design was made by a student using a pattern of intersecting circles. Can you figure out how he did it?

Experiment

If a diameter bisects a chord that is not a diameter, how are the elements of the figure related?

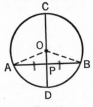

Fig. 11

Induction: Let CD be a diameter of the circle O. Rotate a chord AB until $AP = PB$. Measure the angles at P and the four arcs intercepted by the two chords. What seems to be true?

Deduction:

Given: CD is the diameter of circle O, and CD bisects chord AB.

Deduce the implications about CD and AB; $\overset{\frown}{AD}$ and $\overset{\frown}{DB}$; $\overset{\frown}{BC}$ and $\overset{\frown}{CA}$.

Complete and prove Theorem 43.

THEOREM 43. If a diameter bisects a chord that is not a diameter, it . . . . .

The perpendicular bisector of a chord

THEOREM 44. The perpendicular bisector of a chord passes through the center of the circle and bisects the major and minor arcs of the chord.

Given: Circle O in which chord SR is the perpendicular bisector of the chord AB.

Prove: $\widehat{BS} = \widehat{SA}$, $\widehat{AR} = \widehat{RB}$, and SR is a diameter.

Note: SR *appears* to be a diameter, but it is incorrect to *assume* that it is.

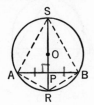

Proof

STATEMENTS	AUTHORITIES
1. SR is the perpendicular bisector of AB.	1. Why?
2. $\therefore$ SR is the locus of a point equidistant from A and B.	2. Why?
3. Draw AR, RB, BS, and SA.	3. Why possible?
4. $\therefore$ $SA = BS$, and $AR = RB$.	4. Why?
5. $\therefore$ $\widehat{SA} = \widehat{BS}$, and $\widehat{AR} = \widehat{RB}$.	5. Why?
6. $\therefore$ $\widehat{SAR} = \widehat{RBS}$.	6. Why?
7. $\therefore$ SR bisects circle O.	7. Why?
8. $\therefore$ SR is a diameter.	8. Why?

Exercises

1. Given: Circle O; diameter RS bisects chord MN; $\widehat{RM} = 120°$; $OM = 5$.

   a. $\widehat{SN} = $?   **c.** $PS = $?

   b. $\widehat{NR} = $?   **d.** $\angle SON = $?

Ex. 1

2. Given: Circle O; diameter XY is perpendicular to chord RS at N; $\widehat{RS} = 120°$; $OR = 6$.

   a. $\widehat{RY} = $?   **d.** $ON = $?

   b. $\widehat{SX} = $?   **e.** $RY = $?

   c. $\angle RON = $?   **f.** $\angle XOR = $?

Ex. 2

3. Given: Circle O; chord GH is the perpendicular bisector of chord EF; $EG = 4$, and $\stackrel{\frown}{HF} = 70°$.

a. $\stackrel{\frown}{FG} = $?   **c.** $FG = $?

b. $\stackrel{\frown}{EH} = $?   **d.** $\stackrel{\frown}{HG} = $?

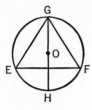

Ex. 3

4. In a circle which has a radius of $2\frac{1}{2}$ in., a chord is drawn so that its arc is 120°. How far is the chord from the center of the circle? Why?

5. In circle O, diameter AC is perpendicular to chord BD at P, and AB and AD are chords.

Deduce the implications.

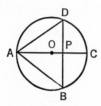

Ex. 5

6. Think of a dynamic circle and two given static points A and B.

a. How many circles can be drawn through the given points A and B?

b. What is the locus of the centers of the circles in part **a**?

7. Given the radius, construct a circle that passes through two given points. Discuss the possibilities.

8. Construct the midpoint of an arc of a circle.

9. Construct an isosceles triangle, given the base and the radius of the circumscribed circle.

10. If a point is within a given circle, construct a chord that will be bisected by the given point.

11. Prove: If two chords drawn from the end point of a radius make equal angles with the radius, the chords are equal.

12. MR is the base of an isosceles triangle inscribed in a circle. Prove that the bisector of the vertex angle passes through the center of the circle.

13. A straight line may be related to a circle in any of the following ways:

a. It may pass through the center of the circle.

b. It may be perpendicular to a chord of the circle.

c. It may bisect a chord of the circle.

d. It may bisect a minor arc of the circle.

e. It may bisect a major arc of the circle.

Taking any two of these as given conditions and the other three as conclusions to be proved, see how many different theorems you can state and prove. We have already proved three of them. Which theorems are they?

14. Prove: If a chord of a circle is prolonged equal distances in both directions and the new end points are joined to the center of the circle, the two arcs within the triangle are equal.

15. Prove: If two circles are concentric, and a chord of the larger one is drawn so that a segment of it is a chord of the smaller circle, the segments of the chord between the circles are equal.

16. A circular arch is an arc of a circle. The span of the circular arch $\overset{\frown}{BCA}$ is AB, and its altitude is DC. Construct a plan for a circular arch having a span of 96 feet and an altitude of 36 feet, using the scale 1 inch to 12 feet.

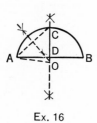

Ex. 16

17. A Gothic arch is a combination of arcs of two equal circles. Its construction is illustrated in the figure. The span of the arch is AB, its altitude is DC, and the radius of each arc is equal to OB. $AP = OB$.

Draw the plan for a Gothic arch having a span of 9 feet and an altitude of 12 feet, using the scale of 1 inch to 3 feet.

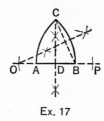

Ex. 17

Chords and their distances from the center

THEOREM 45. In the same circle or in equal circles, if two chords are equal they are equally distant from the center.

Given: Circle O, chord AB = chord RS, $OE \perp RS$, and $OF \perp AB$.

Prove: $OE = OF$.

You write the proof. (Hint: Draw OR and OA.)

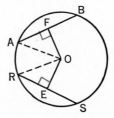

THEOREM 46. In the same circle or in equal circles, if two chords are equally distant from the center, they are equal.

You draw the figure and write the proof of Theorem 46.

Exercises

1. Given: Circle O, $AB = CB$, BD is a diameter, $\angle ABC = 60°$, and $BD = 8$. How far is AB from O?

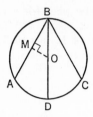

Ex. 1

2. Two equal chords intersect within a circle. A diameter is drawn through their point of intersection. Deduce the implications.

3. Prove: If the center of a circle is equidistant from the sides of an inscribed triangle, the triangle is equilateral.

4. Prove that the radius to a vertex of an inscribed equilateral pentagon bisects the angle at the vertex.

5. Show by deduction that the sides of an inscribed square are equidistant from the center of the circle.

6. If equal circles O and Q intersect in two points A and B, prove that $OAQB$ is a rhombus.

7. Construct and describe the locus of the center of a circle that cuts off equal chords from two parallel lines.

8. State and prove the converse of Exercise **3**.

9. Construct and describe the locus of the midpoint of a dynamic chord of given length in a given circle.

10. Given: Circle O in which $\angle ABC$ is an angle formed by two chords. Prove: If O is equidistant from AB

Ex. 10

and BC, then $BC = BA$, and BD bisects $\angle ABC$.

11. Prove a variation of Exercise **10** obtained by interchanging the condition, "O is equidistant from AB and BC," and the conclusion, "$BC = BA$."

12. Prove a variation of Exercise **10** obtained by interchanging the condition, "O is equidistant from AB and BC," and the conclusion, "BD bisects $\angle ABC$."

13. Prove that the opposite sides of an inscribed parallelogram are equidistant from the center of the circle.

14. Given: AB is the diameter of circle O, and chords are drawn so that $\angle A = \angle B$.

Deduce the implications.

Ex. 14

15. Given the chord MN of circle O. Construct chord RS equal and parallel to MN.

16. Prove: The diagonals of an inscribed isosceles trapezoid are equidistant from the center of the circle.

The relation of a tangent to a diameter

Think of a secant m that is perpendicular to the diameter CD. As m moves outward and P approaches C, what happens to A and B? Arcs AC and CB get smaller and smaller until finally points A, C, and B coincide. Line m is then tangent to the circle at C.

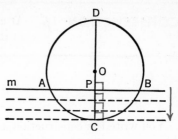

Fig. 12

THEOREM 47. **If a line is perpendicular to a diameter at one end of the diameter, it is tangent to the circle.**

Given: Line m is perpendicular to diameter EC of circle O at the point C.

Prove: Line m is tangent to circle O at C.

Plan: Show that any point on m *except* C lies outside the circle.

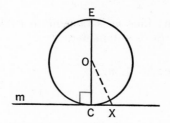

Proof

STATEMENTS	AUTHORITIES
1. Draw OX, X being any point on m other than C.	1. Two points determine a straight line.
2. $OC \perp m$.	2. Given.
3. $\therefore$ OC is the distance from O to m.	3. The length of the perpendicular from a point to a line is the distance from the point to the line.
4. $\therefore$ OX is greater than OC.	4. The distance from a point to a line is the shortest path from the point to the line.
5. $\therefore$ X lies outside the circle.	5. If the distance of a point from the center of a circle is greater than a radius, the point lies outside the circle.
6. $\therefore$ m is tangent to circle O at C.	6. If a line touches a circle in only one point, it is tangent to the circle.

CONSTRUCTION 16. **At a given point on a circle, construct a line tangent to the circle.**

You write the construction and proof.

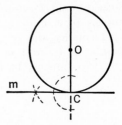

THEOREM 48. **If a line is tangent to a circle at the end of a diameter, it is perpendicular to the diameter.**

Given: Line m is tangent to circle O at C; EC is a diameter.

Prove: $EC \perp m$.

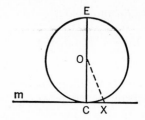

Proof

STATEMENTS	AUTHORITIES
1. Draw OX, X being any point on m other than C.	**1.** Why possible?
2. Line m is tangent to circle O at C.	**2.** Why?
3. $\therefore$ C is the only point on m which is on the circle; that is, X is outside the circle.	**3.** If a line is tangent to a circle, it touches the circle at only one point.
4. $\therefore$ OX is longer than OC.	**4.** If a point is outside a circle, its distance from the center is greater than a radius.
5. $\therefore$ OC is the distance from O to m.	**5.** The shortest path from a point to a line is the distance from the point to the line.
6. $\therefore$ $OC \perp m$.	**6.** The distance from a point to a line is the length of the perpendicular from the point to the line.

Exercises

1. What is meant by the statement, "Particles of mud fly off at a tangent from a revolving wheel"?

2. Prove that a line drawn at one end of a diameter of a circle and parallel to the tangent at the other end is tangent to the circle.

3. Prove that the tangents to a circle at the end points of one of its diameters are parallel.

4. In two concentric circles, a chord of the larger one is tangent to the smaller one. Deduce the implications.

5. Think of a dynamic circle that is tangent to a given line at a given point. Construct and describe the locus of the center of the circle.

6. Given: Line t is tangent to circle O at C, and chord $AB \parallel t$.

    Deduce the implications.

Ex. 6

7. Given: B and C are the points of contact of the tangents AB and AC; OB and OC are radii of circle O.

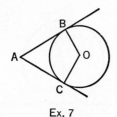

Ex. 7

a. If $\angle O = 115°$, how large is $\angle A$?

b. If $\angle A = n°$, find the size of $\angle BOC$.

8. Draw a chord of a circle and construct two tangents that are parallel to it.

9. Construct a tangent to a circle at the midpoint of an arc. Prove that the tangent is parallel to the chord of the arc.

10. Circumscribe a square about a given circle.

11. Construct triangle ABC, given $\angle A$, $\angle B$, and the radius of the inscribed circle.

12. Draw two non-parallel line segments AB and CD. With a given radius r, construct an arc of a circle tangent to AB and CD.

13. Construct and describe the locus of the center of a circle that is tangent to the sides of a given angle.

Proof by coincidence

POSTULATE 42. If two lines coincide, any point of one is a point of the other; and any property of one is a property of the other.

If CD is known to be perpendicular to AB at D, and if we can prove that FD is perpendicular to AB at D, then CD and FD coincide, and any other property of CD is a property of FD.

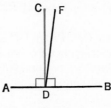

Fig. 13

A line perpendicular to a tangent of a circle at the point of contact

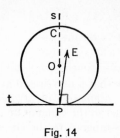

Fig. 14

It is given that the line t is tangent to circle O at P, and $EP \perp t$ at P. (See Figure 14).

Does it seem reasonable that EP should pass through the center O? To prove that it does, we shall prove that it coincides with a diameter to the point P.

Draw the secant s so that the segment CP is a diameter. By Theorem 48, $CP \perp t$ at P; hence both CP and EP are perpendicular to t at P, and the two lines coincide. Why? Hence, EP passes through O. Why?

THEOREM 49.   **If a line is perpendicular to a tangent of a circle at the point of contact, it passes through the center of the circle.**

You write the proof of Theorem 49.

A line through the center of a circle perpendicular to a tangent

---

THEOREM 50.   **If a line through the center of a circle is perpendicular to a tangent, it intersects the tangent at the point of contact.**

Given: Line t is tangent to circle O at P, and $OR \perp t$ from O meeting t at R.

Prove: OR intersects t at P.

Hint: Draw OP. Prove $OP \perp t$. Since only one perpendicular can be drawn from a point to a line, OR and OP coincide; and hence, P and R coincide.

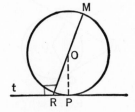

You write the proof of Theorem 50.

Tangents to a circle from an external point

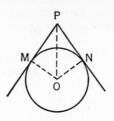

Fig. 15

DEFINITION The *length of a tangent* to a circle from an external point is the length of the segment from the external point to the point of contact.

Experiment

Given: *PM* and *PN* are tangents to circle *O* from point *P*, meeting the circle at *M* and *N*, respectively.

Induction: Use a dynamic device or line drawings to make the figures for the experiment.

A suitable dynamic device for this experiment can be made by drawing circles of different radii on one piece of paper and pairs of intersecting lines on a semi-transparent paper. Place the second over the first so that the lines of one pair are tangent to one of the circles. Repeat this with the other circles.

Measure the lengths of *PM* and *PN* in each of several different figures. What seems to be true?

Deduction: Draw *PO*, *ON*, and *OM*. Deduce the implications.

Complete and prove Theorem 51.

THEOREM 51. **If two tangents are drawn to a circle from an external point the tangents are . . . . .**

Exercises

1. Given: *ABCD* is a circumscribed quadrilateral; points *P*, *Q*, *R*, and

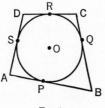

Ex. 1

S are the points of tangency; *AS* = 4.0″; *DR* = 2.5″; *RC* = 2.8″; and *BQ* = 5.0″.

a. Find the perimeter of *ABCD*.

b. Compare the sums of the lengths of the opposite sides.

2. Prove: The angle formed by two tangents to a circle from an external point is bisected by the line from the external point to the center of the circle.

3. If from the external point C, tangents are drawn to circles A and B, respectively; and if MC, which is a common tangent to the two circles, is 21 in. long, find the lengths of CL and CN.

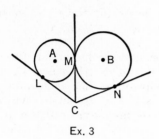

Ex. 3

4. Given: Circle O is inscribed in triangle ABC; the sides of the triangle are tangent to circle O at D, E, and F; $AB = 4''$, $BF = 2''$, and $FC = 4''$.
Find the length of AC.

Ex. 4

5. Given: BA and BC are tangents to circle O from the point B; A and C are the points of tangency; $\angle ABC = 60°$; and line OB is 22 in. long.
Find the length of AO.

Ex. 5

6. Given: AB and CB are tangents to circle O at A and C, respectively; AC is a chord; and OB is the segment from O to B, cutting chord CA at P and $\overset{\frown}{AC}$ at R. Deduce the implications.

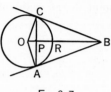

Ex. 6–7

7. In the figure for Exercise **6**, if $\angle CBA = 40°$, evaluate all the angles and arcs in the figure.

8. Prove: If a parallelogram is circumscribed about a circle, it is a rhombus.

9. Prove: A circumscribed rectangle is a square.

10. Given: AB, BC, and CD are tangents to circle O at A, E, and D, respectively; and $CD \parallel BA$. Prove the relation of BO to CO.

Ex. 10

11. Isosceles $\triangle RST$ is circumscribed about circle O; $RT = ST$; and the base RS is tangent to the circle at P.

   a. Prove that TP bisects $\angle T$.

   b. Prove that $TP \perp RS$.

   c. Prove that TP passes through O.

Indirect method of proof

In all our proofs thus far we have arranged the known facts in such a way as to lead directly to the conclusion. The plan we have been following is called the *direct method of proof*.

There is another plan, called the *indirect method of proof*, that may be used. Lawyers often use this plan in arguing a case. Suppose, for example, that Mr. X is accused of committing a crime at a certain time in Town A. If his lawyer can prove that at the specified time of the crime Mr. X was at another place, say Town B, having lunch with the Mayor, it is obviously impossible that he could have committed the crime.

Analysis of the lawyer's reasoning may be briefly stated as follows:

1. Either Mr. X is guilty or he is not.
2. If Mr. X is guilty, he was at the scene of the crime when it was committed.
3. This is impossible because he was in Town B at that time.
4. Therefore, Mr. X is not guilty.

As a second example, suppose that you turn on the switch of an electric lamp and no light comes on. Let us assume that the difficulty must be one of the following: bulb burned out, bulb unscrewed, fuse burned out, lamp not plugged into wall socket, broken wire in lamp cord, current off in the neighborhood, or faulty wiring in the house.

Suppose the wiring in the lamp fixture is faulty. How might you discover this without actually taking the lamp apart? You might use the following method:

1. Make a list of all possible conclusions, one of which must be correct.

2. Show that all the conclusions except one are false.
3. To prove a conclusion false, assume for the sake of argument that it is true; then prove directly that it contradicts a known fact.

The important thing to remember in using this method of reasoning is to be sure you have listed all possible conclusions and that you have eliminated all but one. In mathematics, it is usually quite easy to be sure that all possible conclusions have been listed. In life situations one is not always certain that all possible conclusions have been taken into account.

The following incident illustrates an incorrect application of indirect reasoning: John washed his car one evening and left it standing out all night. The next morning when he tried to start it, the motor turned over, but refused to start. John had had trouble starting his car before for three reasons:

1. The spark plugs were old and defective.
2. The gasoline tank was empty.
3. The fuel pump sometimes failed to work.

John reasoned as follows: "It can't be the spark plugs because I just got new ones yesterday. It can't be an empty gasoline tank because I got five gallons of gasoline on my way home from school. It must be the fuel pump."

Luckily he had a new fuel pump which he had not yet installed. It was only a matter of fifteen minutes' work for him to put in the new one; but, to his surprise, the car still wouldn't start. Then he called a service station. A mechanic came over, looked under the hood for a minute and said, "No wonder it wouldn't start. When you washed your car last night you sprayed water on the motor, and the plugs and distributor cap look as if they had just been dumped in the lake.''

What was wrong with John's reasoning? First, he had not listed all the possibilities for the failure of the car to start. Secondly, he had incorrectly eliminated at least one of the possibilities, the spark plugs.

Exercises

1. Mrs. Adams purchased a set of knives, forks, and spoons advertised as a stainless steel product. After using the set for several months, she found that the forks began to rust. She thereupon decided that the set was not made of stainless steel and returned it for a refund. Analyze how she reasoned indirectly.

2. Have you ever lost your pen? How can you use the indirect method of elimination of possibilities to decide where it must be?

3. One of the mathematics teachers in a city high school used indirect reasoning to convince the school custodian that a radiator valve was defective. What procedure might he have used?

4. One day Jane prepared a dessert which her mother said was excellent. A week later Jane's mother had company for dinner and prepared the dessert herself, whereupon Jane concluded that her mother hadn't really liked her dessert of the week before. Do you think the indirect reasoning used here is sound or unsound? Why?

5. Explain how a doctor often uses the indirect method to diagnose a case in which the symptoms are much like those of several different diseases.

6. Recall an experience in which you used the indirect method to solve a problem.

Indirect proof in geometry

As an example of indirect proof in geometry, we shall prove the following statement:

In the same circle or in equal circles, unequal arcs have unequal chords.

Given: Equal circles O and T in which $\overset{\frown}{AB} \neq \overset{\frown}{RS}$.

Prove: Chord $AB \neq$ chord RS.

 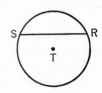

Proof

STATEMENTS	AUTHORITIES
1. Either $AB = RS$ or $AB \neq RS$.	1. These are the only possibilities.
2. If AB were equal to RS, then $\overset{\frown}{AB} = \overset{\frown}{RS}$.	2. In the same circle or in equal circles, equal chords have equal arcs.
3. But $\overset{\frown}{AB} \neq \overset{\frown}{RS}$.	3. Given.
4. ∴ $AB \neq RS$.	4. If $AB = RS$, a known fact is contradicted.

★ Indirect proof by the method of contraposition*

A very important aspect of deductive proof is the fact that a theorem can be proved by proving its contrapositive. When we do this, we are using a type of indirect proof. For example, the statement (theorem) we have just proved is the contrapositive equivalent of Theorem 41. Since we were able to prove Theorem 41 by the direct method, the proof of its contrapositive is given here only as an illustration of indirect proof. It frequently happens that a theorem cannot be proved by a direct method, but its contrapositive can be. If it can be proved both ways, the simpler of the two proofs is usually employed. We should always be alert to the fact that the contrapositive of a proved theorem needs no further proof.

★Exercises

Use the method of contraposition to prove the following statements:

1. If a line is perpendicular to one of two intersecting lines, it is not perpendicular to the other.

2. A median to a side of a scalene triangle is not an altitude.

3. If the diagonals of a parallelogram are not equal, the parallelogram is not a rectangle.

4. If two angles of a triangle are not equal, the sides opposite the angles are not equal.

5. In the same circle or in equal circles, unequal chords have unequal arcs.

Concurrency

DEFINITION *Concurrent lines* are lines that have a common point.

Bisectors of two angles of a triangle

Are the bisectors of the angles of a triangle concurrent? Can we be certain that two of the bisectors are concurrent? Construct the bisectors of the angles of different kinds of triangles. What seems to be true?

★ Proof by contraposition *(Optional)*

In $\triangle ABC$, if t_A bisects $\angle BAC$ and if t_B bisects $\angle CBA$, then the sum of $\angle 1$ and $\angle 2$ is less than 180°. Why? Hence, $\angle 1$ and $\angle 2$ are not supplementary.

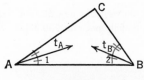

Fig. 16

The theorem "If two lines in a plane are cut by a transversal so that the interior angles on the same side of the transversal are not supplementary, the lines are not parallel" is the contrapositive of Theorem 8. Hence, t_A intersects t_B.

---

* See footnote on page 94 for an explanation of starred material.

THEOREM 52.   **The bisectors of the angles of a triangle are concurrent at a point equidistant from the sides of the triangle.**

Given: $\triangle ABC$ with t_A, t_B, and t_C the bisectors of $\angle A$, $\angle B$, and $\angle C$, respectively.

Prove: Bisectors t_A, t_B, and t_C are concurrent at a point equidistant from AB, BC, and AC.

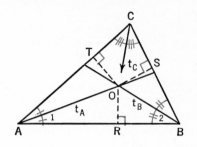

Proof

STATEMENTS	AUTHORITIES
1. Let O be the point of intersection of t_A and t_B. From O draw $OR \perp AB$, $OS \perp BC$, and $OT \perp AC$.	**1.** Why possible?
2. $\therefore OT = OR$, and $OR = OS$.	**2.** The bisector of an angle is the locus of a point . . . . .
3. $\therefore OT = OS$.	**3.** Why?
4. $\therefore O$ lies on t_C.	**4.** Any point equidistant from the sides of an angle . . . . .
5. $\therefore t_A$, t_B, and t_C are concurrent at a point equidistant from the sides of $\triangle ABC$.	**5.** Why?

This is a rear view of a new 60-foot antenna which can pick up television and telephone signals sent directly through space for 200 miles. Notice how its construction is based on a pattern of concentric circles.

A circle inscribed in a triangle

CONSTRUCTION 17. Inscribe a circle in a given triangle.

Given: △*ABC*.

Required: To inscribe a circle in △*ABC*.

Method:

1. Bisect angles *A* and *B*. Let the point of intersection be called *O*.
2. From *O* construct *OM* perpendicular to *AB*.
3. Using *OM* as radius and *O* as center, draw circle *O*.
4. Circle *O* is the required circle.

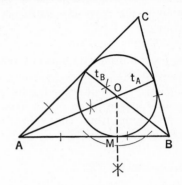

Proof

STATEMENTS	AUTHORITIES
1. t_A bisects ∠*A*, and t_B bisects ∠*B*.	1. Construction.
2. ∴ t_A and t_B intersect at some point *O*.	2. Why?
3. ∴ *O* is equidistant from *AB*, *BC*, and *AC*.	3. Why?
4. ∴ *AB*, *BC*, and *AC* are tangents to circle *O*.	4. If a line is perpendicular to a diameter (or a radius) at one end of the diameter, ...
5. ∴ Circle *O* is inscribed in △*ABC*.	5. Why?

DEFINITION The *incenter of a triangle* is the center of the inscribed circle.

Exercises

1. Construct a circle tangent to each side of a given angle *and* having its center at a given distance from a given point. Discuss the possibilities.

2. Inscribe a circle in the triangle whose sides are 3.0 in., 3.5 in., and 4.0 in.

3. The circle that is tangent to one side of a triangle and tangent to the other two sides extended is called an *escribed* circle. Construct the three escribed circles of a given triangle.

4. Construct a circle tangent to each side of a given angle *and* having its center equidistant from two given points. Discuss the possibilities.

5. Prove: If two sides of a triangle are extended beyond the base, the bisectors of the exterior angles and the bisector of the third interior angle are concurrent at a point equidistant from the sides of the triangle.

6. Prove: The bisectors of the angles of a circumscribed quadrilateral are concurrent.

7. Construct and describe the locus of points in the plane of the triangle equidistant from the sides of a triangle.

Space geometry (*Optional*)

8. Draw and describe the locus of a point in space equidistant from the sides of a triangle.

⋆ Lines respectively perpendicular to two parallel lines⋆ (*Optional*)

If there are four lines a, b, m, and n in a plane,

> if   (s_1) $a \perp b$,
> if   (s_2) $m \perp n$,
> and if (s_3) $a \parallel m$,
> then   (c) $b \parallel n$.

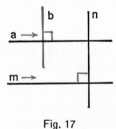

Fig. 17

The conclusion is easily proved by using these two theorems:

1. If a line is perpendicular to one of two parallel lines, it is perpendicular to the other. Hence, $n \perp a$.

2. If each of two lines is perpendicular to the same line, they are parallel. Hence, $b \parallel n$.

The theorem we have proved is: If two lines in a plane are respectively perpendicular to two parallel lines, the lines are parallel. This theorem has three contrapositives, all of which are true without further proof. Of the three, we shall consider only this one:

If there are four lines a, b, m, and n in a plane,

if   (s_1) $a \perp b$,

if   (s_2) $m \perp n$,

and if (not c) b is not parallel to n,

then   (not s_3) a is not parallel to m.

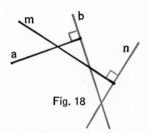

Fig. 18

If two lines in the same plane are not parallel, they must intersect. Why? Thus we have proved the next theorem, Theorem 53.

THEOREM 53.   **If two lines are respectively perpendicular to two intersecting lines, they intersect.**

⋆ If this section is omitted, accept Theorem 53 without proof.

The perpendicular bisectors of the sides of a triangle

THEOREM 54. The perpendicular bisectors of the sides of a triangle are concurrent at a point equidistant from the vertices of the triangle.

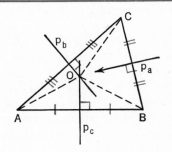

Given: $\triangle ABC$ with p_a, p_b, and p_c the perpendicular bisectors of BC, AC, and AB, respectively.

Prove: p_a, p_b, and p_c are concurrent at a point equidistant from A, B, and C.

Proof

STATEMENTS	AUTHORITIES
1. p_c is the $\perp$ bisector of AB, and p_b is the $\perp$ bisector of AC.	**1.** Given.
2. $\therefore$ p_c and p_b intersect at some point O.	**2.** Why?
3. Draw AO, BO, and CO.	**3.** Why possible?
4. $\therefore$ $AO = BO$, and $AO = CO$.	**4.** The perpendicular bisector of a line segment is the locus of a point . . . . .
5. $\therefore$ $BO = CO$.	**5.** Why?
6. $\therefore$ O lies on p_a.	**6.** The locus of a point equidistant from two given points is . . . . .
7. $\therefore$ p_a, p_b, and p_c are concurrent at a point equidistant from A, B, and C.	**7.** Why?

A circle circumscribed about a triangle.

CONSTRUCTION 18. Circumscribe a circle about a given triangle.

You write the method and prove the construction.

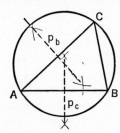

DEFINITION The *circumcenter of a triangle* is the center of the circumscribed circle.

Exercises

1. By construction, locate a point equidistant from three given points not in the same straight line.
2. By construction, locate the center of a circular arc. Do not confuse the center of an arc with its midpoint.
3. Given the end points and one other point on the arc of a circle, construct the arc.
4. Prove: The midpoint of the hypotenuse of a right triangle is the center of the circumscribed circle.
5. Circumscribe a circle about an obtuse triangle.
6. Prove: The perpendicular bisectors of the legs of a right triangle bisect the hypotenuse.
7. Construct and describe the locus of points in the plane of the triangle equidistant from the vertices of an acute triangle.
8. Construct and describe the locus of points in the plane of the triangle equidistant from the vertices of a right triangle.
9. Construct an isosceles trapezoid. Construct the perpendicular bisectors of one base and one leg. Prove that their point of intersection is the center of the circumscribed circle.
10. Prove that the perpendicular bisectors of the sides of an inscribed quadrilateral are concurrent.

Space geometry (Optional)

11. Draw and describe the locus of a point in space: (a) equidistant from the vertices of a triangle; (b) equidistant from the vertices of a rectangle.
12. Draw and describe the locus of a point in space equidistant from the points on a circle.

The altitudes of a triangle

The altitudes of a right triangle are concurrent at the vertex of the right angle. Why? Are the altitudes of any triangle concurrent?

Induction: Construct the altitudes of several acute triangles. What seems to be true? Construct the altitudes of several obtuse triangles. Do their extensions seem to be concurrent? If so, where?

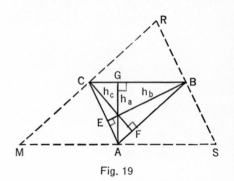

Fig. 19

Deduction: Through A, B, and C of the acute $\triangle ABC$ draw parallels to BC, AC, and AB, respectively. Use the indirect method to prove that these lines intersect to form $\triangle SRM$. Are the altitudes of $\triangle ABC$ perpendicular to the sides of $\triangle SRM$? Why?

What can you prove about the quadrilaterals $ABRC$, $ABCM$, and $ASBC$?

Are the altitudes of $\triangle ABC$ perpendicular bisectors of the sides of $\triangle SRM$? Why? Now use Theorem 54 to prove that h_a, h_b, and h_c are concurrent.

With the same pattern of reasoning as above, prove that the altitudes of an obtuse triangle, if extended, are concurrent.

You write the proof of Theorem 55.

THEOREM 55.   The altitudes of a triangle are concurrent.

DEFINITION The *orthocenter of a triangle* is the point of intersection of the altitudes of the triangle.

The medians of a triangle

Can you be certain that two medians of a triangle intersect at a point? Why?

To prove that all three medians are concurrent is more difficult. Then too, there is a relationship between the segments of the medians that is not apparent to the casual observer. Since this is such an important relationship, we shall carry out a very thorough investigation.

Experiment

If you do not have a dynamic triangle instrument, you should construct your figures very carefully and measure the segments as exactly as possible.

Given: $\triangle ABC$ in which AR and BT are medians.

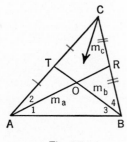

Fig. 20

Data table:

Triangle ABC	AO	OR	BO	OT
Scalene obtuse	?	?	?	?
Scalene acute	?	?	?	?
Scalene right	?	?	?	?
Etc.	?	?	?	?

Observations: Do AO and BO seem to be related in any way? How does AO seem to be related to OR? BO to OT?

Inductive conclusion: The medians of a triangle are concurrent at a point which is . . . . of the distance from each vertex to the midpoint of the opposite side.

Deduction: Let M and N be the midpoints of AO and BO, respectively. Draw MN, NR, RT, and TM. How is MN related to AB? How is TR related to AB? Then what is $MNRT$? How are the diagonals of $MNRT$ related? How is AO related to OR? How is BO related to BT?

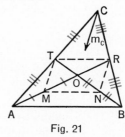

Fig. 21

Now draw a new figure containing BT and m_c extended to intersect AB at P. Using the above method, prove that m_c intersects BT at the same point that AR and BT intersect.

You write the proof of Theorem 56, which is stated on the following page.

THEOREM 56.   **The medians of a triangle are concurrent at a point which is
. . . . of the distance from each vertex to the midpoint of the
opposite side.**

DEFINITION   The *centroid of a triangle* is the point of intersection of
the medians of the triangle. (In a
physical triangle the centroid is the
center of gravity.)

Exercises

1. **a.** Prove: Any median of an equilateral triangle is also an altitude,
angle bisector, and perpendicular
bisector of a side.
   b. Prove: In an equilateral triangle,
the perpendicular bisectors of the
sides, the bisectors of the angles,
the altitudes, and the medians all
intersect at the same point.

2. **a.** Prove: The radius of the circle
circumscribed about an equilateral
triangle is two-thirds of the altitude
of the triangle.
   b. Prove: The radius of the circle
inscribed in an equilateral triangle
is one-third the altitude of the
triangle.

3. Prove: If the medians to two sides
of a triangle are equal, the triangle
is isosceles.

4. Prove: In a right triangle the
distance from the vertex of the
right angle to the point of intersection of the medians is equal to
one-third the hypotenuse. Use algebraic equations to obtain the proof.

5. Construct triangle ABC, given AB,
m_b, and m_a.

6. A machinist has a triangular plate
5.00 in. on a side through which he
wishes to drill a hole at the center
of gravity. The altitude of an equilateral triangle is 0.866 times a side.
If the plate is of uniform thickness
and composition, how far from each
vertex will the center of the hole
be located?

7. To find the center of gravity of a
physical triangle such as a triangular metal plate ABC, tie a
plumb bob at the vertex B and
suspend the triangle so that it
swings freely about point B. Trace
the line made by the plumb bob on
the triangle. Repeat this operation
at point A. The intersection G of
the two lines is the center of gravity.
Construct the medians of the triangle. Do they intersect at the
center of gravity?

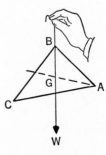

Ex. 7

The nine-point circle (*Optional*)

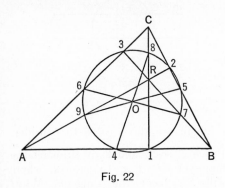

Fig. 22

An interesting construction to test your skill with the compass is the following:

1. Construct the altitudes of an acute scalene triangle ABC. R is the point of intersection of the altitudes. Points 1, 2, and 3 are the points of intersection of the altitudes and the sides.

2. Bisect the sides of the triangle. Points 4, 5, and 6 are the midpoints of the sides.

3. Points 7, 8, and 9 are the midpoints of BR, CR, and AR, respectively.

4. Draw the lines 6-7, 4-8, and 5-9. They should intersect at one point O.

5. Draw a circle with the radius O-4 and the center O. It should pass through the points 1, 2, 3, 4, 5, 6, 7, 8, and 9.

The following constructions and relationships not shown are:

6. Construct the centroid of $\triangle ABC$. Call it M.

7. Construct the circumcenter of $\triangle ABC$. Call it N.

8. $ROMN$ should be a straight line.

9. RO should be $\frac{1}{2}RN$; and MN should be $\frac{1}{3}RN$.

10. The nine-point circle should be tangent to the inscribed circle and it should be tangent to the escribed circles. (Escribed circles are circles which are tangent to one side of a triangle and to the other two extended.)

Intercepted arcs

If two lines intersect a circle, the arcs that lie between them are called *intercepted* arcs.

In circle O, $\overset{\frown}{MN}$ and $\overset{\frown}{RS}$ are the arcs intercepted by lines c and d. It is important to remember that $\overset{\frown}{SM}$ and $\overset{\frown}{NR}$ are not intercepted arcs. They are the arcs of the chords SM and RN, respectively.

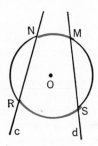

Fig. 23

In circle A, the lines e and f intercept two pairs of arcs; namely, $\overset{\frown}{PQ}$ and $\overset{\frown}{XY}$, and $\overset{\frown}{QX}$ and $\overset{\frown}{YP}$.

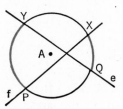

Fig. 24

Arcs of a circle intercepted by parallel lines

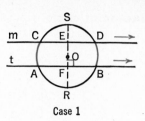

Case 1

Experiment

If two parallel lines intersect a circle, how are the intercepted arcs related?

There are three cases to consider.

Prove Cases 1 and 2 by drawing the diameter $SR \perp t$. In Case 2, where will SR meet the tangent? Why?

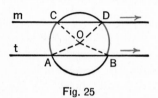

Fig. 25

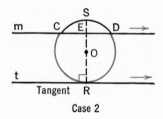

Case 2

Induction: If $m \parallel t$, and line t moves from its present position until it coincides with line m, it passes over two arcs CA and BD. How are the arcs intercepted by two parallel lines related? You can measure arcs CA and BD by measuring central angles COA and BOD, respectively. You must consider the possibility of m or t, or both m and t being tangents.

Prove Case 3 by applying Case 2 in the manner indicated by the auxiliary line n.

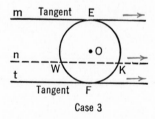

Case 3

Deduction:

Given: Circle O intersected by the parallel lines t and m.

Deduce the implications.

You write the proof of Theorem 57.

THEOREM 57.   **If two parallel lines intersect a circle, they intercept equal arcs.**

Exercises

1. Given: Circle O, $\overset{\frown}{AB} = 150°$, $AB \parallel DC$, $\overset{\frown}{CD} = 60°$, and radius $OC = 2.0$ cm.

a. How many degrees are there in $\overset{\frown}{CA}$?

b. How long is the chord CD?

c. What is the quadrilateral $ABCD$?

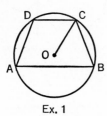

Ex. 1

2. Given: Circle O, AB is a diameter, CB and CD are chords, $CD \parallel AB$, and $\overset{\frown}{BD} = 20°$.

a. How many degrees are there in $\overset{\frown}{CA}$?

b. How many degrees are there in $\overset{\frown}{DC}$?

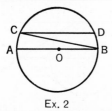

Ex. 2

3. Given: Circle O, diameters EC and DB, $AB \parallel EC$, and $\angle DBA = 43°$.

a. How many degrees are there in $\overset{\frown}{EA}$?

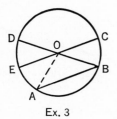

Ex. 3

b. How many degrees are there in $\overset{\frown}{DE}$?

4. Draw a figure and show why the converse of Theorem 57 is not necessarily true.

5. Prove: Two chords that are not diameters are parallel if they are each bisected by the same diameter.

6. Prove that an inscribed trapezoid is isosceles.

7. Construct and describe the locus of the midpoint of a dynamic chord of a circle that is always parallel to a given fixed line.

8. Prove that the line joining the midpoints of two parallel chords passes through the center of the circle. Hint: Draw a diameter through the midpoint of one of the chords.

9. Prove: If one pair of opposite sides of an inscribed quadrilateral are parallel, the quadrilateral is either an isosceles trapezoid or a rectangle.

10. Prove: If equal chords intersect within a circle, the quadrilateral formed by joining the consecutive end points is either an isosceles trapezoid or a rectangle.

11. Given: Points P and Q on the circle are each equidistant from the ends of chord CD.
Deduce the implications concerning PQ and any chord parallel to CD.

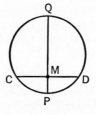

Ex. 11

Common tangents and tangent circles

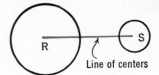

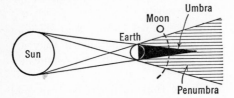

Fig. 26

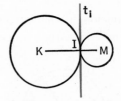

Line of centers

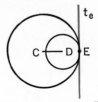

t_i

Circles tangent externally at I; common internal tangent t_i

Figure 26 illustrates why the earth's shadow consists of two parts, the *umbra*, or complete shadow, and the *penumbra*, or partial shadow. To understand the formation of these shadows, we must know that light rays are straight lines, provided the medium through which light travels is homogeneous. The boundaries of the umbra and penumbra are light rays which are tangent to both the sun and the earth.

t_e

Circles tangent internally at E; common external tangent t_e

DEFINITIONS   The *line of centers* of two circles is the line segment that joins their centers.

Tangent circles are circles tangent to the same line at the same point.

Tangent circles are *tangent externally* if they lie on opposite sides of their common tangent; they are *tangent internally* if they lie on the same side of their common tangent.

Common internal tangents to two circles are lines tangent to both circles and intersecting the line of centers of the two circles.

Common external tangents to two circles are lines tangent to both circles and not intersecting the line of centers.

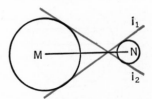

i_1

i_2

Common internal tangents i_1 and i_2

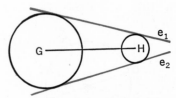

e_1

e_2

Common external tangents e_1 and e_2

Fig. 27

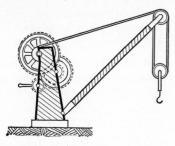

Fig. 28

The picture of the hoist illustrates some applications of tangent circles (gears) and common tangents in mechanics.

The line of centers of two tangent circles

Circles R and S are each tangent to line i at the point C and are, consequently, tangent to each other at the point C. Are they tangent externally?

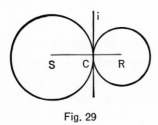

Fig. 29

How is the radius SC related to i? Why? How is the radius RC related to i? How many perpendiculars to a given line at a given point on the line can there be? What do you know now about the line SCR? How is the line of centers SR related to the point of contact C?

Circles E and F are each tangent to line e at the point A. Are the two circles tangent externally? How is EA related to e? How is FA related to e? Does the extension of EF necessarily pass through the point of contact A? Why?

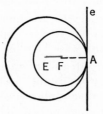

Fig. 30

COROLLARY If two circles are tangent, their line of centers, or line of centers extended, passes through their point of contact.

Exercises

1. Construct two circles so that their line of centers is greater than the sum of their radii. Draw their common internal and external tangents.
2. Construct two circles so that their line of centers is equal to the sum of their radii. Draw their common internal and external tangents.
3. Construct two circles so that their line of centers is less than the sum of their radii, but greater than the difference. Draw their common tangents.
4. Construct two circles so that their line of centers is equal to the difference of their radii. Draw their common tangents.

5. Construct two circles so that their line of centers is less than the difference of their radii, but greater than zero. Do the circles have any common tangents?

6. Construct two circles so that their line of centers is equal to zero. How are the circles related? Do they have any common tangents?

7. If two circles are tangent externally, what is the relationship of their radii and their line of centers?

8. If two circles are tangent internally, what is the relationship of their radii and their line of centers?

9. If two circles have equal radii, how are their common external tangents related?

10. Prove: If two circles have two common internal tangents, the tangent segments are equal.

11. Prove: If two circles intersect in two points, the line of centers is the perpendicular bisector of the common chord.

12. Prove: If two circles are externally tangent, their common internal tangent bisects the segments of their common external tangents.

13. Two circles are externally tangent. Prove that the two tangents to the circles from any point in the common internal tangent are equal.

14. Prove: If two unequal circles have two common external tangents, the tangent segments are equal.

15. Construct a third circle of given radius r that is tangent to each of

two given externally tangent circles. Describe the locus used in the construction.

16. Using the vertices of a scalene triangle as centers, construct three circles tangent to one another.

17. Construct a rhombus and inscribe a circle in it.

18. Given: Circles R and S are externally tangent at X. PQ is the common internal tangent, AXB is a straight line, and RB and SA are radii.

Prove: $BR \parallel SA$.

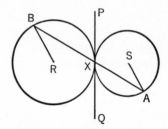

Ex. 18

The locus of a point on a rolling circle* (*Optional*)

1. The cycloid

A *cycloid* is the locus of a fixed point on a given circle as the circle rolls in its own plane, without slipping, along a straight line.

* References:
  Riddles In Mathematics, Eugene P. Northrup. D. Van Nostrand Co., Inc.
  Mathematics And The Imagination, Edward Kasner and James Newman. Simon and Schuster.
  What Is Mathematics? Courant and Robbins. Oxford University Press.
  The Mathematics Teacher, January, 1952.

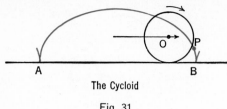

The Cycloid

Fig. 31

How to draw a cycloid

Divide circle O into six equal arcs so that $\widehat{MW} = \widehat{KM} = \widehat{HK}$, each being one-sixth of circle O.

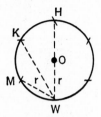

Fig. 33

There are many interesting facts about a cycloid, such as:

a. The area bounded by the arc of the cycloid APB and the straight line AB is three times the area of the rolling circle.

b. The length of the cycloid APB is four times the diameter of the rolling circle. (The length of AB is π times the diameter of the rolling circle.)

Draw the line P_0P_6 equal to the circumference of circle O. (See Figure 34.)

Divide P_0P_6 into six equal segments and call the points of division C, D, E, F, and G. If circle O is tangent to P_0P_6 at P_0, and then it rolls on P_0P_6 one-sixth of a turn, it is tangent to P_0P_6 at C and the generating point is at P_1. To locate P_1, first draw circle 1 with radius r so that it is tangent to P_0P_6 at C. With center C and radius WM draw an arc intersecting circle 1 at P_1. To locate P_2, first draw circle 2 with radius r so that it is tangent to P_0P_6 at D, and then make DP_2 equal to WK. In a similar manner P_3, P_4, and P_5 can be located. One complete turn of the circle should bring the generating point to P_6.

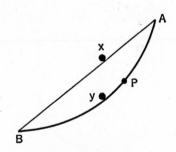

Arc BA is the path of quickest descent from A to B.

Fig. 32

c. The "path of quickest descent" between two points when one is above the other is the arc of the cycloid through the two points. In the figure, AB is a straight line and BPA is an arc of a cycloid. If the spheres x and y are released simultaneously at A, sphere y will reach point B before sphere x, even though its path is longer.

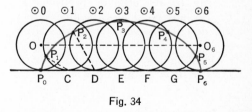

Fig. 34

To draw a cycloid more accurately, divide both P_0P_6 and the circle into a greater number of equal parts.

2. The hypocycloid

A *hypocycloid* is the locus in a plane of a fixed point on a given circle as the circle rolls inside and remains internally tangent to a given fixed circle.

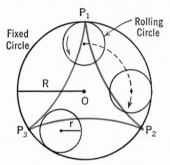

Three-cusped Hypocycloid

Fig. 35

If the moving circle describes the whole circumference of the fixed circle just once, any point P on the moving circle will return to its original position if the radius of the larger circle is an integral multiple of the radius of the smaller circle. In the figure, R is equal to $3r$, and the circumference of the fixed circle is three times the circumference of the rolling circle. Hence, any point P of the inner circle will touch the large circle three times before it returns to its original position. If $R = 2r$, any point P of the inner circle will describe a diameter of the large circle.

Draw figures of hypocycloids with $R = 2r$, $R = 3r$, and $R = 4r$.

3. The epicycloid

An *epicycloid* is the locus in a plane of a fixed point on a given circle as the circle rolls on and remains externally tangent to a given fixed circle.

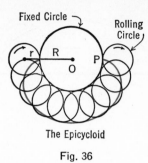

The Epicycloid

Fig. 36

In Figure 36, $R = 2r$.

Draw epicycloids with $R = 3r$, $R = 4r$, and $R = 5r$.

4. The cardioid

A *cardioid* is the locus in a plane of a fixed point on a given circle as the circle rolls on and remains externally tangent to an equal, but fixed, circle.

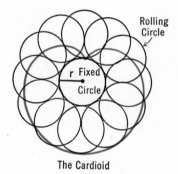

The Cardioid

Fig. 37

A cardioid is a special case of an epicycloid. The circumferences of the two circles are obviously equal; hence, if the point of contact of the rolling circle passes along one-half the circumference of the fixed circle, it will pass one-half the circumference of the moving circle.

If you roll one coin around another of the same kind, you will find that the moving coin rotates twice on its own axis as it moves once around the fixed coin. Can you explain this?

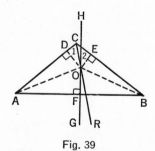

Fig. 38

Fallacy of the isosceles triangle
(*Optional*)

Can you find the fallacy in the argument below that *any* triangle is isosceles?

Given: Any $\triangle ABC$.

Prove: $\triangle ABC$ is isosceles.

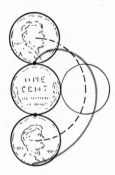

Fig. 39

Here is an outline of the proof. You complete it and write the authorities for the statements.

1. Let CR bisect $\angle C$.
2. Let GH be the perpendicular bisector of AB, intersecting AB at F.
3. Let O be the intersection of CR and GH.
4. Let OD be the perpendicular from O to AC.
   Let OE be the perpendicular from O to BC.
5. Draw OA and OB.
6. $\therefore$ $\triangle ODC \cong \triangle OEC$.
7. $\therefore$ $CD = CE$.
8. $\therefore$ $\triangle AFO \cong \triangle FBO$.
9. $\therefore$ $\triangle ADO \cong \triangle BEO$.
10. $\therefore$ $AD = BE$.
11. $\therefore$ $AC = BC$.
12. $\therefore$ $\triangle ABC$ is isosceles.

Mirrors (*Optional*)

Three kinds of mirrors are in common usage: plane, concave, and convex.

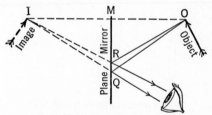

Image produced by a plane mirror

Fig. 40

Plane mirrors are most often used about the home, for they reflect an image that is undistorted and the same size as the object that is placed before them. It can be proved that the image of an object that is put before a plane mirror is as far behind the mirror as the object is in front of it, and the size of the image is equal to the size of the object. Such an image is always *virtual*, that is, although it can be seen, it is only an illusion and cannot be reflected on a screen as is possible with a real image. (See Figure 41.)

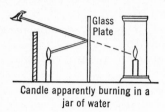

Candle apparently burning in a jar of water

Fig. 41

Figure 42 shows how three images are formed by plane mirrors at right angles. In general, if the angle between the mirrors is $x°$, there will be $\left(\frac{360}{x} - 1\right)$ images. Thus, if $x = 60°$, there will be five images.

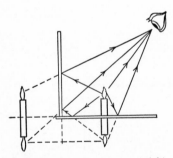

Multiple images. Two mirrors at right angles. The arrows indicate the actual paths of the rays reflected into the eye.

Fig. 42

A spherical mirror is a portion of a spherical shell. A section of a concave mirror is shown in Figure 43. The center of curvature C of the mirror is the center of the sphere of which the mirror is a portion; the radius of curvature CA is the radius of the sphere; MC is the principal axis; and

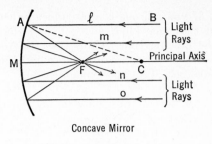

Concave Mirror

Fig. 43

F is the principal focus. Within certain limits, rays parallel to MC are reflected by the mirror through F. If CA is relatively long, F is midway between M and C, and CA bisects $\angle FAB$.

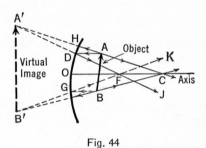

Fig. 44

If an object AB is between a concave mirror and its principal focus (Figure 44), its image $A'B'$ is virtual and magnified. For this reason concave mirrors are frequently used for shaving and cosmetic mirrors as shown in Figure 45.

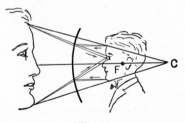

Fig. 45

Convex spherical mirrors are frequently used on cars and trucks because they form a reduced virtual image and reflect more of the rear landscape than is possible with a plane or concave mirror of the same size.

The reflection of parallel rays such as AD and BG in Figure 46 will intersect at F if they are extended through the mirror. Actually, the rays do not pass through the focal point although the backward extensions of the rays will do so. Thus, the image is virtual.

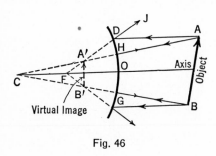

Fig. 46

The slingshot *(Optional)*

When David, the warrior and king of Biblical times, was only a youth, he used a slingshot to slay Goliath. It was essentially a leather strap that was looped with its ends held firmly in the hand. David put a stone in the loop and swung the sling in a circular manner. When the stone had gained sufficient speed, he released one end of the strap. The stone met its target and Goliath fell.

1. What was the locus of the stone as it was swung in the looped sling?
2. What was its path as it was released from the sling?
3. What relation has the first locus to the second?

Simple and compound curves
(Optional)

To make highway and railroad curves easy and safe, arcs of circles and tangent circles can be used. The transition points of the straight segments and the arcs are the points of contact of the tangents and the circles.

Figure 47 is an example of a simple curve. Draw any two intersecting lines RM and DK on your paper. For the radius CA of the curve, choose any convenient segment. What locus is used to find C? Explain how the sharpness of the curve depends upon the length of the radius and the size of $\angle ACO$.

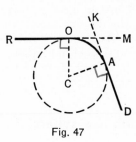

Fig. 47

A compound curve connecting two parallel roads can be made with two externally tangent circles having either equal radii or unequal radii as shown in Figure 48. Draw several examples and make certain you understand the method.

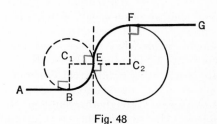

Fig. 48

The center square (*Optional*)

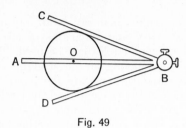

Fig. 49

The instrument shown in the illustration is called a center square. It is used by machinists to locate the center of a disk or cylindrical object. The instrument is constructed so that segment AB always bisects the angle formed by arms CB and DB. If CB and DB are tangent to cylinder O, explain why AB must pass through the center of the cylinder and how the instrument is used to locate the center.

The earth is a sphere (*Optional*)

In a plane, the locus of points at a given distance from a fixed point is a circle; in space, the locus is a sphere. Physical spheres such as baseballs, basketballs, and golf balls are common examples. A spherical container is the strongest and largest container that can be made with a given amount of material.

The earth, the very planet on which we live, closely approximates a sphere. Although we often speak of flying in a straight line between two cities, we should realize that the shortest path between two points on the earth is an arc of a *great circle*. A great circle of a sphere is the intersection of a sphere and a plane through the center of the sphere. The *axis* of the earth is the diameter between the North and South Poles. The great circle whose plane is perpendicular to the axis is called the *equator*.

Latitude and longitude (*Optional*)

For purposes of locating the position of a point on the earth and as a basis for the measurement of time, the earth is marked off with a series of imaginary circles called *meridians of longitude* and *parallels of latitude*.

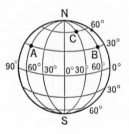

Fig. 50

Meridians of longitude are great half-circles drawn between the North and South Poles. The meridian passing through the Royal Observatory at Greenwich, England, is designated as the zero meridian.

Longitude is the number of degrees measured along the equator east or west of the zero meridian. The longitude of point A in the figure is 60° W. What is the longitude of B? of C?

Latitude is the number of degrees measured along a meridian north or south of the equator. The equator is zero latitude. All points on the earth having the same latitude lie on a *small* circle called a parallel of latitude. The latitude of point A on the figure is 30° N. What is the latitude of B? of C?

Exercises (*Optional*)

1. Define a parallel of latitude.

2. On a map or globe, find the latitude and longitude of your city; of Washington D. C.; of Ottawa; of Paris; of Tokyo.

3. What is the name of the city of latitude 49° N. and longitude 2° E.?

4. What is the latitude and longitude of New York City?

5. If you travel southeast from your present position, what effect does this have on your latitude? on your longitude?

6. Since the earth rotates through 360° every twenty-four hours, any given point on its surface moves through . . . . degrees of longitude in one hour.

7. The approximate circumference of a great circle of the earth is 25,000 miles. How many feet are there in one minute of arc? What is this unit called? How many feet are there in a land (statute) mile?

8. Point *P* is your position on the earth's surface, *PN* is the line of sight from your position to the North Star, *PO* is a plumb line, *PK*

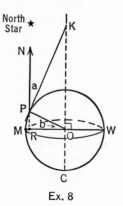

Ex. 8

is the horizontal line in the plane of *OPN*, *WM* is the diameter of the equator, and *COK* is the axis of the earth. Prove that ∠*a* is the measure of the latitude of your position. Suggestion: The number of degrees in ∠*b* is equal to the latitude of *P*. Why? *PN* and *CK* may be considered parallel because the distance from the earth to the North Star is so great.

The right circular cylinder
(*Optional*)

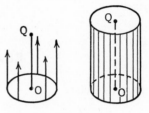

Fig. 51

A right circular cylinder can be generated by a circle as follows: Consider line segment *OQ* to be perpendicular to the plane segment enclosed by circle *O*. If plane segment *O* is dynamic and moves from *O* to *Q* so that the plane is continually perpendicular to static line *OQ*, circle *O* will trace the surface of a right circular cylinder. *OQ* is the cylinder's axis, and the circular plane segments *O* and *Q* are called its bases.

Exercises —Space Geometry (*Optional*)

1. In how many points may a straight line intersect the surface of a sphere?

2. Does the surface of a sphere have thickness? Explain.

3. Are parallels of latitude parallel? Explain.

4. Can a straight line lie entirely on the surface of a sphere? Why?

5. If a circle can intersect another in one or two points, how may two spheres intersect?

6. How may two spheres with unequal radii be tangent?

7. What is the shortest path between two points on a sphere?

8. If a plane is perpendicular to a diameter of a sphere at one end of the diameter, how is the plane related to the sphere?

9. How many lines may be tangent to a sphere at a point on its surface?

10. How many planes may be tangent to a sphere at a point on its surface?

11. If two externally tangent spheres have a point of tangency:

    a. How many common external tangent planes have they?

    b. How many common internal tangent planes have they?

12. Under what conditions will two spheres have no common internal tangent plane?

13. In space, what is the locus of a point 2″ from a line x?

14. In space, what is the locus of a point 2″ from a line segment AB?

Review of Chapter 9

Numerical Exercises

In each of these exercises, the correct answers are based on one or more geometric principles. You need not write a formal proof, but you should show how your answers were obtained.

1. Given: Chord LN ∥ chord MP, diameter $AB \perp MP$, $\overset{\frown}{PA} = 80°$, and $\overset{\frown}{LM} = 55°$.

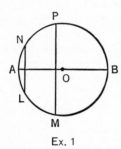

Ex. 1

Find the number of degrees in:

a. $\overset{\frown}{MB}$ **c.** $\overset{\frown}{LB}$

b. $\overset{\frown}{PL}$ **d.** $\overset{\frown}{LBN}$

2. If a square 2″ on a side is inscribed in a circle, how far are the sides of the square from the center of the circle?

3. If two tangents to a circle form a 60° angle at their point of intersection and if the chord joining their points of contact is 17″ long, find the lengths of the tangents.

4. If a 14″ radius of a circle makes a 30° angle with a chord at its end point, what is the distance of the chord from the center of the circle?

5. Given: Circle O with diameter BC and chord AC, $\angle ACB = 26°$. Find the number of degrees in $\overset{\frown}{CA}$.

Ex. 5

6. If *PM* and *PL* are tangents to circle *O* at *M* and *L*, respectively, *OP* is a line segment that is 14″ long, and ∠1 is twice as large as ∠2, find the length of *OL*.

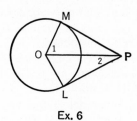

Ex. 6

7. Quadrilateral *ABCD* is circumscribed about circle *O*, the sides of *ABCD* are tangent to the circle at *E*, *F*, *G*, and *H*. If *AE* = 6, *EB* = 4, and *DC* = 8, find the sum of *AD* and *BC*.

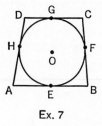

Ex. 7

8. Find the number of degrees in the major arc of a chord if the chord has the same length as the radius of the circle.

9. If the sides of a right triangle are 3, 4, and 5, what is the length of the radius of the circumscribed circle?

10. If an equilateral octagon is inscribed in circle *O*, and *XY* is one of its sides, how many degrees are there in ∠*XOY*?

Constructions

1. Construct a line parallel to a given line and tangent to a given circle.

2. From two points on a circle construct two equal and parallel chords.

3. Construct an isosceles triangle given the vertex angle and the radius of the circumscribed circle.

4. Construct a right triangle, given the radius of the inscribed circle and an acute angle.

5. Construct a triangle, given one side, an adjacent angle, and the radius of the circumscribed circle.

6. Construct a triangle, given one side, an adjacent angle, and the radius of the inscribed circle.

7. Construct a circle having a given radius passing through a given point *and* tangent to a given line.

8. Construct a circle so that it is tangent to two given parallel lines *and* so that it passes through a given point which is between the given parallel lines.

9. Construct a circle which passes through a given point *A and* is tangent to a given line *BC* at the point *B*.

10. Construct a circle tangent to the sides of a given angle *and* having its center equidistant from two given points.

Loci

Construct and describe each of the loci in Exercises **1-8**.

1. The locus of the centers of circles that have a common chord *AB*.

2. The locus of centers of circles that are tangent to line *x* at the point *P*.

3. The locus of the midpoint of a dynamic chord of fixed length in a given circle.

4. The locus of the midpoints of all chords that are parallel to a given fixed chord in a given circle.

5. The locus of points equidistant from the sides of a triangle.

6. The locus of points equidistant from the vertices of a triangle.

7. The locus of the midpoint of the hypotenuse of a right triangle if the hypotenuse is dynamic, but has a fixed length.

8. The locus of the center of a circle whose radius is d as it rolls around a fixed circle of radius r and center O.

9. **a.** Describe the loci represented by the colored lines in this figure.

   b. Discuss how many common points the loci have when OS changes length, but the radii and the distance d remain constant.

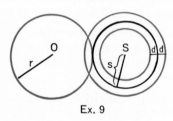

Ex. 9

10. Repeat Exercise **9** for this figure:

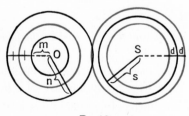

Ex. 10

True-False Test

Write the numbers **1-25** *on your paper. After each number write* **True** *if the corresponding statement is always true; write* **False** *if the statement is not necessarily true.*

1. The midpoint of a circular arc and the center of a circular arc have the same meaning.

2. The sides of a circumscribed equilateral triangle are bisected at the points of contact.

3. If two parallel chords are drawn from the ends of a diameter, the chords are equidistant from the center of the circle.

4. If a tangent makes an angle of 30° with a chord at the point of contact, the chord is equal to a radius.

5. If two chords of a circle bisect each other, both chords are diameters.

6. If two equal chords which are not diameters intersect within a circle, the quadrilateral formed by joining their consecutive end points is an isosceles trapezoid.

7. The perpendicular bisectors of the sides of an inscribed polygon are concurrent only if the polygon is regular.

8. If two equal chords intersect within a circle, the radius through the point of intersection bisects one of the sets of vertical angles formed by the chords.

9. A chord which bisects a circle and which bisects another chord is perpendicular to the chord.

10. If a line intersects a tangent to a circle at the point of contact, it passes through the center of the circle.

11. If a polygon is circumscribed about a circle, the bisectors of the angles of the polygon are concurrent.

12. Two circular arcs contain the same number of degrees if they have equal chords.

13. In the same circle the chord of an arc of $x°$ is one-half as long as the chord of an arc of $2x°$.

14. The perpendicular bisector of a chord of a circle bisects the circle.

15. The diagonals of an inscribed isosceles trapezoid are equidistant from the center of the circle.

16. If a rhombus is inscribed in a circle, it is a square.

17. The orthocenter of a circle is the locus of points equidistant from the sides of the triangle.

18. If a parallelogram is circumscribed about a circle, it is a rectangle.

19. If a line is perpendicular to a tangent to a circle, it passes through the center of the circle.

20. The lengths of two circular arcs are equal if the number of degrees in each is 40.

21. The locus of the centers of circles tangent to a given line at a given point is a line perpendicular to the given line at the given point.

22. The locus of points equidistant from the vertices of a triangle is the circumcenter of the triangle.

23. If a parallelogram is inscribed in a circle, it is a square.

24. If two circles are tangent externally, they have only one common internal tangent.

25. A trapezoid inscribed in a circle is isosceles.

Co-ordinate Geometry (*Optional*)

Find the points, if any, common to the following pairs of loci:

1. $x^2 + y^2 = 25$, and $3x + 4y = 25$
2. $x^2 + y^2 = 36$, and $x = y$
3. $x^2 + y^2 = 9$, and $x - y = 3$
4. $x^2 + y^2 = 25$, and $x + y = 7$
5. $x^2 + y^2 = 25$, and $y = x - 1$

A navigator of a ship must be able to locate his position with respect to ship lanes and to chart a course that avoids shoals and other danger spots. Here a ship's officer uses a sextant to aid in fixing his position; the angle relations of geometry will then help him in working on his charts.

THE MEASUREMENT OF ANGLES IN CIRCLES

WHEN CHORDS, secants, and tangents of a circle intersect, there is a numerical relationship between some of the angles thus formed and their intercepted arcs. In this chapter we shall identify these angles and their intercepted arcs and learn how they are related.

Angles and intercepted arcs

On paper, draw circle O and secant m intersecting the circle at C and A. On a piece of semi-transparent paper, draw line n. Place this paper over the first one. Now, by moving the transparent sheet relative to the first, each of the seven situations mentioned below can be obtained.

1. The lines may be secants (or diameters) intersecting at the center of a circle (Figure 1).

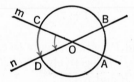

Fig. 1

If the secants m and n intersect each other at the center O and intersect the circle at points C and A, and D and B, respectively, then CO, DO, OA, and OB are radii, and they form four central angles. We know that the number of angle degrees in a central angle equals the number of arc degrees in its intercepted arc. That is, a *central angle is measured by its intercepted arc.*

You recall that the symbol for "is measured by" is: $\doteq$. Hence, $\angle COD \doteq$ $\overset{\frown}{CD}$. How is each of the other central angles measured?

2. The lines may be chords (or secants) intersecting at a point within a circle (Figure 2).

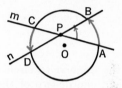

Fig. 2

If the chords DB and CA intersect at the point P within circle O, they form two pairs of vertical angles. The arcs intercepted by the vertical angles CPD and APB are $\overset{\frown}{CD}$ and $\overset{\frown}{AB}$. Which arcs are intercepted by $\angle DPA$ and its vertical angle?

3. The lines may be chords (or secants) intersecting at a point on a circle (Figure 3).

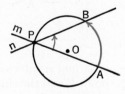

Fig. 3

If the chords PA and PB (or the secants m and n) intersect at the point P on circle O, only one of the four angles thus formed intercepts an arc. $\angle APB$ intercepts $\overset{\frown}{AB}$.

4. One line may be a tangent and the other a chord (or secant), intersecting at a point on a circle (Figure 4).

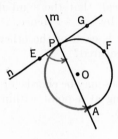

Fig. 4

If *EG* is the tangent to circle *O* at *P*, and *PA* is a chord, two of the angles thus formed intercept arcs of the circle. ∠*EPA* intercepts $\overset{\frown}{PA}$, and ∠*APG* intercepts $\overset{\frown}{AFP}$.

5. The lines may be secants intersecting at a point outside a circle (Figure 5).

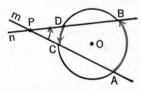

Fig. 5

If the secants *m* and *n* intersect each other at the point *P* and the circle *O* at *C* and *A*, and *D* and *B*, respectively, then only one of the angles thus formed intercepts arcs of the circle. ∠*APB* intercepts $\overset{\frown}{AB}$ and $\overset{\frown}{DC}$.

6. One line may be a tangent and the other a secant, intersecting at a point outside a circle (Figure 6).

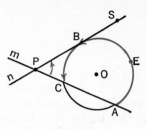

Fig. 6

If *PS* is the tangent to the circle *O* at *B*, and *PCA* is a secant, only one of the angles thus formed intercepts arcs of the circle. ∠*APS* intercepts $\overset{\frown}{AEB}$ and $\overset{\frown}{BC}$.

7. Both lines may be intersecting tangents (Figure 7).

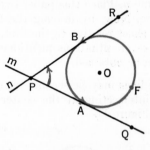

Fig. 7

If *PQ* and *PR* are tangents to circle *O* at *A* and *B*, respectively, ∠*QPR* intercepts $\overset{\frown}{AFB}$ and $\overset{\frown}{BA}$.

Exercises

1. Give the number of arc degrees in:

    a. A semicircle.

    b. One-third of a circle.

    c. The intercepted arc of a central angle of 70 angle degrees.

    d. An arc of a meridian of the earth between the equator and the North Pole.

e. An arc of a circle of latitude between two cities of the same latitude whose longitudes are 10° E. and 15° W.

2. The circumference of a circle is 50.0 inches. Find:

a. The number of arc degrees in an arc of the circle that is 12.5 in. long.

b. The number of angle degrees in the central angle of an arc that is 5.0 in. long.

c. The length of an arc of the circle intercepted by a central angle of 45°.

3. The circumference of the earth is about 25,000 miles.

a. About how many miles is an arc degree measured along the equator?

b. About how many miles is an arc degree measured along a parallel of latitude one-half the length of the equator? (This parallel will be about 60° N. or S. of the equator.)

c. About how many miles is an arc degree measured along a meridian?

d. About how many miles is 15° measured along the circle of 60° North latitude?

4. The earth rotates on its axis once in 24 hours. Explain how this fact accounts for the different time zones of the earth.

Inscribed angles

DEFINITION An *inscribed angle* is an angle formed by the intersection of two chords at a point on a circle.

We shall try to find a relationship between an inscribed angle and its intercepted arc.

Experiment

Given: Chords PA and PB intersecting at a point P on circle O forming the inscribed angle APB whose intercepted arc is AB.

Fig. 8

Induction: Either use dynamic figures or draw figures of various inscribed angles. To make a proper sampling you should experiment with acute angles, obtuse angles, and right angles. Record your data in a suitable table.

Conclusion: $\angle APB \doteq ?$

Inductive conclusion: An inscribed angle is measured by . . . . .

Deduction: There are two cases to consider:

Case 1. One side of the inscribed angle is a diameter. If we draw OB, how is the exterior angle AOB related to the opposite interior angles P and B of the isosceles triangle POB? Hence, how is $\angle P$ related to $\angle AOB$? How is $\angle AOB$ related to $\overset{\frown}{AB}$? How is $\angle P$ related to $\overset{\frown}{AB}$?

Fig. 9

You write the proof.

Case 2. Neither side of the inscribed angle is a diameter. The center of the circle may be (a) within the angle or (b) outside the angle.

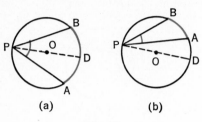

(a)   (b)

Fig. 10

In both Figure (a) and Figure (b), if we draw the diameter PD, we may use what we have proved in Case 1.

In Figure a,
$$\angle APB = \angle APD + \angle DPB.$$
In Figure b,
$$\angle APB = \angle DPB - \angle DPA.$$
In either figure, how is $\angle APB$ related to $\overarc{AB}$?

Complete and prove Theorem 58.

THEOREM 58.   An inscribed angle is measured by . . . . .

Angles inscribed in arcs

An inscribed angle is said to be inscribed in the part of the circle *not* intercepted by it.

If $\angle F$ is an inscribed angle, it is inscribed in $\overarc{AFB}$, and it intercepts $\overarc{BDA}$.

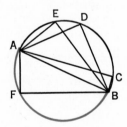

Fig. 11

If $\angle C$, $\angle D$, and $\angle E$ intercept the same arc AFB, they are inscribed in the same arc $BCDEA$. How are angles C, D, and E related?

If AB is a diameter, $\angle F$ is inscribed in the semicircle AFB, and it intercepts the semicircle BDA. If AB is a diameter, what can you conclude about angles F, C, D, and E?

If AB is a chord (not necessarily a diameter), what is the relation of $\angle F$ to $\angle E$? of $\angle F$ to $\angle C$? of $\angle F$ to $\angle D$?

How are the opposite angles of an inscribed quadrilateral related? How is $\angle FAE$ related to $\angle EBF$?

COROLLARIES   1. If two or more inscribed angles intercept the same number of arc degrees, the angles are equal; and conversely.

2. If two or more angles are inscribed in arcs of the same number of arc degrees, the angles are equal; and conversely.

3. An angle inscribed in a semicircle is a right angle.

4. The opposite angles of an inscribed quadrilateral are supplementary.

Exercises

1. Explain the difference between an inscribed angle and an angle inscribed in an arc.

2. Prove: An angle inscribed in a major arc is acute.

3. Prove: An angle inscribed in a minor arc is obtuse.

In the figures for Exercises **4-9**, *certain data are given. Find the values of the unknowns designated by* x, y, *and* z.

4.

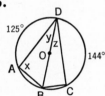

5.

6.

7.

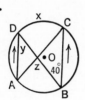

8.

9.

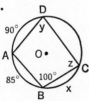

10. Given: Quadrilateral $ABCD$ inscribed in circle O; $\widehat{BC} = \widehat{DA}$.

Ex. 10

What can you prove about:

a. Chords DC and AB?

b. Quadrilateral $ABCD$?

11. Given: AC and AD are diameters of two intersecting circles R and S, and AB is their common chord.

Prove: Chords CB and DB lie in a straight line.

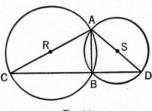

Ex. 11

12. Given: AC is a diameter of circle O, $BD \perp AC$ at D, and AB and BC are chords.

Prove: The angles of triangles ACB, ADB, and CBD are respectively equal; that is, the triangles are mutually equiangular. (Does this mean that any triangle in the figure is necessarily equiangular?)

Ex. 12

13. The vertices of a triangle inscribed in a circle divide the circle into arcs measuring 2, 3, and 5 units. How many degrees are there in each angle of the triangle?

14. $A, B, C,$ and D are points on circle O, and they are joined by chords as indicated. Prove that the three angles of $\triangle DPC$ are respectively equal to the three angles of $\triangle ABP$.

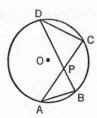

Ex. 14

15. Given: BA is tangent to circle O at A, $RS \parallel BA$, $\overset{\frown}{SA} = x°$, and $\overset{\frown}{AR} = (3x - 200°)$.

a. Find the number of degrees in $\angle R$.

b. Find the number of degrees in $\overset{\frown}{AR}$.

c. Find the number of degrees in $\angle BAR$.

d. How is $\angle BAR$ related to $\overset{\frown}{AR}$?

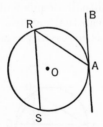

Ex. 15

16. Prove: Two triangles inscribed in a circle are congruent if two angles of one are equal to two angles of the other.

17. Prove: If two consecutive angles of an inscribed quadrilateral are equal, the quadrilateral is either an isosceles trapezoid or a rectangle.

18. Prove: If one leg of an isosceles triangle is a diameter of a circle, the circle bisects the base.

19. Given: The chords AC and BD of circle O intersect at P within the circle.

Prove: $\angle DPA \doteq \frac{1}{2}(\overset{\frown}{BC} + \overset{\frown}{DA})$.

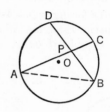

Ex. 19

20. Given: The secants PCB and PDE intersect circle O as shown.

Prove: $\angle P \doteq \frac{1}{2}(\overset{\frown}{BE} - \overset{\frown}{DC})$.

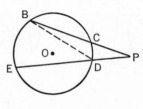

Ex. 20

21. Explain the method illustrated in the figure for constructing a line perpendicular to a given line AB at the point B without extending AB.

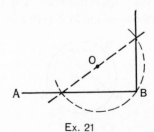

Ex. 21

A locus problem

THEOREM 59. In a plane, the locus of the vertex of the right angle of a right triangle which has a fixed hypotenuse is a circle with the hypotenuse as diameter.

Part 1. Any point on a circle is the vertex of the right angle of a right triangle having the diameter as its hypotenuse. (Being a point on a circle is sufficient for being the vertex of a right angle of a right triangle having the diameter as its hypotenuse.)

Given: Circle O, in which AB is a diameter, and $\triangle ABC$ is formed by joining any point C on the circle to A and B.

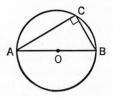

Prove: $\angle C$ is a right angle.

You write the proof.

Part 2. Any right triangle whose hypotenuse is the diameter of the circle has the vertex of its right angle on the circle. (Being a point on a circle is necessary for being the vertex of a right angle of a right triangle having the diameter as its hypotenuse.)

Given: Circle O having diameter AB, $\angle C$ is the right angle of $\triangle ABC$.

Prove: Point C lies on the circle.

Plan: If C is inside the circle as in Figure (a), AC may be extended to intersect the circle at D; if C is outside the circle as in Figure (b), AC intersects the circle at some point D. In either case, draw BD and prove that $BD \perp AC$, and hence that BD coincides with BC.

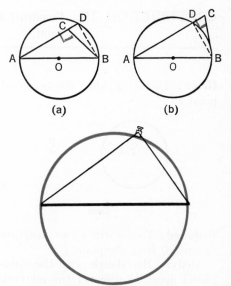

(a)   (b)

Model of the locus of the vertex of the right angle of all right triangles having a given hypotenuse.

Fig. 12

★**Note:**★ This part can also be proved by proving its contrapositive, namely, "If two of the vertices of a triangle are end points of a diameter of a circle, and the vertex of the third angle is not on the circle, then the third angle is not a right angle." To prove this would require the use of Theorems 61 and 62; however, this change of sequence could be effected without a violation of logical rigor.

*See footnote on page 94 for an explanation of starred material.

Exercises

1. Locate points that are the vertices of the right angle of a right triangle having a fixed hypotenuse *RS and* are the vertices of isosceles triangles having *RS* as base. How many points are there?

2. Locate points that are the vertices of the right angle of a right triangle having a fixed hypotenuse *MN and* are the given distance *h* from *MN*. Discuss the possibilities.

3. Locate points that are the vertices of the right angle of a right triangle having a fixed hypotenuse *QP and* are the given distance *r* from *Q*. Draw the lines from the required

points to point *P*. How are these lines related to the circle which has *Q* as center and *r* as radius?

4. A carpenter sometimes uses his steel square to determine the accuracy of a semicircular arc that has been cut in a board. Can you explain the geometric principle that is involved?

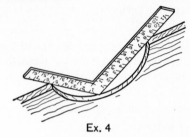

Ex. 4

Constructing tangents to a circle from an outside point

CONSTRUCTION 19. **Construct the tangents to a circle from an external point.**

Given: Circle *Q* and the external point *P*.

Given

Required: To construct two tangents to circle *Q* from the point *P*.

Analyze the sketch and the completed figure to discover the method. Notice that *QP* is the hypotenuse of two right triangles.

You write the construction and proof.

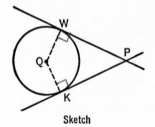

Sketch

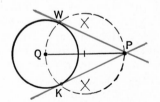

Completed Figure

Exercises

1. Construct a right triangle, given its hypotenuse and the altitude to the hypotenuse. Discuss the possibilities.

2. Construct a right triangle, given a leg and the radius of the inscribed circle. Why must the given leg be longer than twice the given radius?

3. Construct the tangents to the given circle O from the given external point P. Construct a second circle so that it is tangent to the given circle and also to the two tangents.

5. Construct the common internal tangents to two unequal circles. Hint: Construct an auxiliary circle concentric to circle R and having the radius $(r + s)$.

6. Construct a right triangle, given a leg and the radius of the circumscribed circle.

7. Construct triangle ABC, given AB, $\angle B$, and the radius of the inscribed circle.

8. Given a circle O with chord XY and any point P on the minor arc XY. Construct chords through P that will be bisected by XY. Hint: Construct the circle having OP as a diameter.

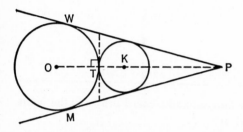

Ex. 3

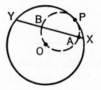

Ex. 8

4. Construct the common external tangents to two unequal circles. Hint: The radii of the two given circles R and S are r and s, respectively. The radius of the auxiliary circle having R as center is $(r - s)$. Construct SN tangent to that circle. How is TP constructed?

Next time you take a ride on a Ferris wheel, think of the number of circle and angle relationships that are at work to keep it operating properly!

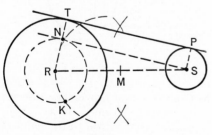

Ex. 4

An angle formed by a tangent and a chord to the point of contact

Given: *EF* is tangent to circle *O* at *P*, and *DP* is a chord.

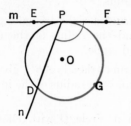

Induction

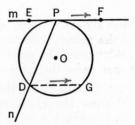

Deduction

Induction: Measure ∠*EPD*, ∠*DPF* and their intercepted arcs *PD* and *DGP*. What seems to be the relation of the angles to their intercepted arcs?

Deduction: Draw *DG* ∥ *EP*.

Complete and prove Theorem 60.

THEOREM 60. **An angle formed by a tangent and a chord drawn to the point of contact is measured by . . . . .**

Exercises

1. Given: *AB* is tangent to circle *O* at *E*; chord *CD* ∥ *AB*; $\widehat{EC}$ = 100°.

a. Find the number of degrees in ∠1.

b. Find the number of degrees in $\widehat{CD}$.

c. Find the number of degrees in ∠2.

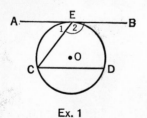

Ex. 1

2. Given: Circle *O* with *RS* and *RT* tangents at *S* and *T*, respectively; *TS* is a chord.

Deduce the implications.

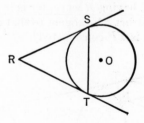

Ex. 2

3. Complete and prove: The bisector of an angle formed by a tangent and a chord drawn to the point of contact . . . . .

★**4.** State and prove an inverse of Exercise **3.**

5. Prove that a line drawn through the vertex of an inscribed isosceles triangle parallel to the base is tangent to the circle.

6. State and prove a converse of Exercise **5.**

7. Given: Circles R and S are tangent externally at P, AB is a common internal tangent, XY is a straight line through P terminated by the circles R and S.

What is the relation of $\overset{\frown}{PX}$ to $\overset{\frown}{PY}$?

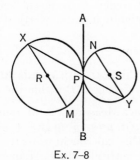

Ex. 7–8

8. In the figure for Exercise **7,** prove that the diameter through X is parallel to the diameter through Y.

9. Given: PN is tangent to circle O at B, the secant PF intersects the circle at C and F, and chord $CE \parallel PN$.

Prove: $\angle P \overset{\circ}{=} \frac{1}{2}(\overset{\frown}{FB} - \overset{\frown}{BC})$.

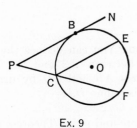

Ex. 9

10. Construct the common internal tangent to two circles that are externally tangent.

11. From certain points, tangents to each of two externally tangent circles are equal. What is the locus of these points?

12. Given: Secants PE and PF intersect circle O at B and E, and at A and F, respectively, and chord $AC \parallel BE$.

What is the relation of $\angle P$ to the arcs FE and BA?

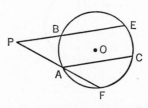

Ex. 12

13. Given: PN and PS are tangent to circle O at B and A, respectively, and chord $BC \parallel PS$.

Deduce the implications.

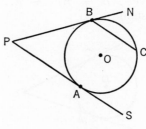

Ex. 13

14. Prove Theorem 60 by drawing the radius PO and the radius ON to the midpoint of $\overset{\frown}{PD}$. (See figure on next page.)

15. Prove Theorem 60 by drawing radius *PO* and radius *ON* ⊥ *PD* at *H*.

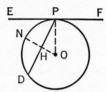

Exs. 14 and 15

16. Prove Theorem 60 by drawing the diameter *PG* and the chord *DG*.

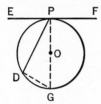

Ex. 16

17. If two static tangents to a circle from an external point are cut by a dynamic tangent to the same circle, the perimeter of the triangle thus formed is a constant.

Given: Point *P* is any point on circle *O* between *D* and *C*, the points of tangency of *ED* and *EC*, respectively.

Prove: *AB* + *BE* + *EA* is a constant.

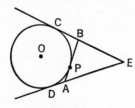

Ex. 17

18. Prove: The midpoint of the arc intercepted by the angle formed by a tangent and a chord is equidistant from the tangent and the chord.

The angle formed by two chords intersecting within a circle

In our discussion of the inscribed angle and the angle formed by a tangent and a chord, there was only one intercepted arc because the vertex of the angle was on the circle. Now if one or both of the lines are allowed to move until the point of intersection is within the circle, four angles are formed, and there are two pairs of intercepted arcs. We are now ready to study the measurement of any one of the four angles in terms of the arcs intercepted by it and its vertical angle.

Experiment

Given: Circle *O* with chords *AC* and *BD* intersecting at *P* within the circle.

Induction: Measure ∠2. Measure the intercepted arcs of angles 1 and 2. Repeat this experiment using the other pair of vertical angles. Experiment with several samples. Write a word statement of what seems to be true.

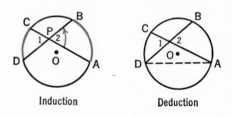

Induction   Deduction

Deduction: You can deduce the relationship between ∠2 and the intercepted arcs *AB* and *CD* by drawing the auxiliary line *DA*.

Complete and prove Theorem 61.

THEOREM 61. **If two chords intersect within a circle, each of the angles formed is measured by . . . . of the arcs intercepted by it and its vertical angle.**

Exercises

1. In circle O, arc $AD = 32°$, and arc $BC = 40°$.

Find the size of each angle at the point of intersection of the chords AB and DC.

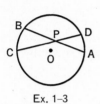

Ex. 1–3

2. In circle O, $\widehat{CA} = 192°$, $\widehat{AD} = 30°$, and $\angle APD = 36°$.

a. Find the size of $\widehat{BC}$.

b. Find the size of $\widehat{DB}$.

3. In circle O, $\widehat{AD} = 31°$, and angle $BPC = 35°$.

a. Find the size of $\widehat{BC}$.

b. What do you know about arcs DB and CA?

4. Given: Chords AB and CD of circle O are perpendicular, $\widehat{BD} = 50°$, and $\widehat{DA} = 40°$.

Find the size of arcs AC and CB.

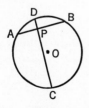

Ex. 4

5. Given: Equal chords AC and BD of circle O intersecting at P, $\widehat{BC} = 50°$, and $\widehat{CD} = 80°$.

a. Find the size of angles CPD, ADC, and DCB.

b. What is quadrilateral $ABCD$?

Ex. 5

6. Prove Theorem 61 by drawing a chord through D parallel to AC.

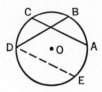

Ex. 6

7. Given: Isosceles trapezoid $ABCD$ is inscribed in circle O, diagonals AC and BD intersect at P, $AD = BA$, and $\widehat{DA} = \frac{1}{5}\widehat{BC}$.

Find the sizes of the angles at P.

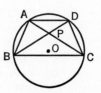

Ex. 7

8. Given: Parallel chords AE and BD are intersected by chord AC at A and P, respectively; $\overset{\frown}{CD} = \frac{1}{3}\overset{\frown}{AB}$; $\overset{\frown}{DE} = 84°$.
Find the size of $\angle CAE$.

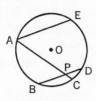

Ex. 8

9. Given: BP is a diameter of circle O; AP is a tangent; DP, CP, and BD are chords; $\angle DPA = x°$; $\overset{\frown}{BC} = (x + 40°)$; and $\overset{\frown}{CD} = (6x + 23°)$. Find the number of degrees in each of the arcs of the circle and in each of the numbered angles.

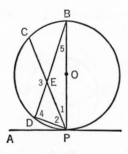

$\star$ **10.** Write a converse, an inverse, and a contrapositive of the following statements and prove each of them if possible:

a. If an angle is an inscribed angle, it is measured by one-half its intercepted arc.

b. If an angle is formed by a tangent and a chord, it is measured by one-half its intercepted arc.

c. If an angle is formed by two intersecting chords, it is measured by one-half the sum of its intercepted arcs.

Angles formed by lines meeting outside a circle

When two lines meet outside a circle, there are three cases to be considered. In each case the lines intercept two arcs. The proofs that the measure of the angle formed by the two lines depends upon the measure of their intercepted arcs are so similar that we will treat them together.

Experiment

Case 1. Both lines are secants of a circle.

Given: Circle O cut by secants PDB and PCA.

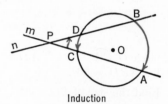

Induction

Induction: Measure $\angle APB$, $\overset{\frown}{AB}$, and $\overset{\frown}{DC}$. For a proper sampling, repeat the experiment several times.
What seems to be true?

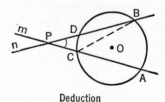

Deduction

Deduction: Draw either CB or AD.
$\angle ACB = \angle P + \angle DBC$. Why?
Hence, $\angle P = \angle ACB - \angle DBC$.
Finally, $\angle P = \frac{1}{2}(\overset{\frown}{AB} - \overset{\frown}{DC})$.
Why?

Case 2. One line is a tangent, and the other is a secant of a circle.

Case 3. Both lines are tangents to a circle.

Given: Circle *O*, *PB* is tangent to circle *O* at *B*, and *PCA* is a secant.

Given: Circle *O* with *PB* tangent at *B*, and *PA* tangent at *A*.

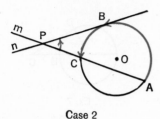

Case 2

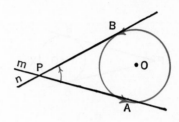

Case 3

Induction: Perform an experiment similar to the one for Case 1.

Deduction: Draw *CB* or *AB*, and proceed as in Case 1.

Complete and prove Theorem 62.

THEOREM 62. **The angle formed by two secants, or by a secant and a tangent, or by two tangents intersecting outside a circle, is measured by . . . . .**

Exercises

1. In this figure, secants *PC* and *PB* intersect circle *O* at *D* and *C*, and at *A* and *B*, respectively.

a. If $\widehat{BC} = 100°$, and $\widehat{DA} = 40°$, find $\angle P$.

b. If $\widehat{BC} = 100°$, and $\angle P = 20°$, find $\widehat{DA}$.

2. In this figure, *PR* is tangent to circle *O* at *C*, and the secant *PB* intersects the circle at *A* and *B*.

a. If $\widehat{BC} = 110°$, and $\widehat{CA} = 60°$, find $\angle P$.

b. If $\widehat{CA} = 50°$, and $\angle P = 20°$, find $\widehat{BC}$.

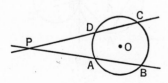

Ex. 1

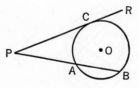

Ex. 2

3. In this figure, PB and PA are tangents to circle O at B and A, respectively.

   a. If $\overset{\frown}{AXB} = 200°$, find $\angle P$.
   b. If $\angle P = 20°$, find $\overset{\frown}{BA}$.

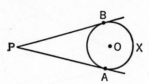

Ex. 3

4. If chord LM is drawn to the points of tangency of tangents a and b so that $\triangle LMP$ is equilateral, find $\overset{\frown}{MXL}$.

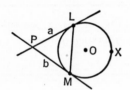

Ex. 4

5. Prove: A common internal tangent of two equal circles bisects the line of centers.

6. Given: Circle O with secants PAB and PDC.

   Prove: There are two pairs of triangles having their angles respectively equal.

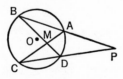

Ex. 6

7. Given: AB is the diameter of circle O, OB is extended its own length to C, and CD is tangent to circle O at D.

   Find the size of $\angle C$.

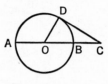

Ex. 7

8. Given: Circles R and S are tangent internally at T; TC and TD are chords of circle R that intersect circle S at A and B, respectively. What can you prove about AB and CD?

Ex. 8

9. Given: Two circles R and S are tangent externally at P. Through P two line segments are drawn terminating in the circles as indicated.

   What can you prove about AD and BC?

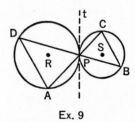

Ex. 9

★10. Prove Part 2 of Theorem 59 by the method of contrapositives.

11. Given: Tangent *LB* and secant *MB* are intersected by chords *LM* and *LN* so that ∠*MLN* is twice ∠*M*, and ∠*MLN* is the complement of ∠*M*.

Find the size of ∠*LBN*.

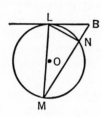

Ex. 11

12. If a tangent and a secant intersect to form an 18° angle, and the lines intercept two arcs on a circle so that one of them is four-thirds the other, find the number of degrees in each of the arcs.

13. Given: *PA* and *PB* are tangents to circle *O* at *A* and *B*, respectively; *OA* and *OE* are radii; *PCE* is a secant; *BA* and *EC* are chords;

$\widehat{AC} = x°$; $\widehat{CB} = \left(\dfrac{x}{2} - 20°\right)$;

$\widehat{BE} = (x + 15°)$; and $\widehat{EA} = 140°$.

Find the number of degrees in each of the following:

a. ∠*PAB*   **d.** ∠*EFA*

b. ∠*BPA*   **e.** ∠*BAO*

c. ∠*BPE*   **f.** ∠*OEC*

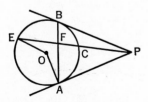

Ex. 13

14. Given: *EFP* and *HGP* are secants; chords *EG* and *HF* intersect at *D*; ∠*P* = 28°; ∠*HDE* = 84°.

Find the number of degrees in arcs *x* and *y*. Show equations.

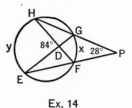

Ex. 14

Positive and negative arcs

(*Optional*)

In our study of algebra we learned the meaning of signed, or directed, numbers. We also learned how to find their algebraic sum. For example, the algebraic sum of +6 and −4 is +2.

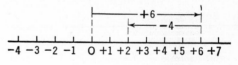

Fig. 13

In geometry we define positive and negative angles. A positive angle is generated by the counterclockwise rotation of a line about a point; a negative angle is generated by the clockwise rotation of a line about a point. In Figure 14, ∠*AOB* is a positive angle, and ∠*RST* is a negative angle.

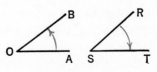

Fig. 14

We shall now define positive and negative arcs on the same basis as positive and negative angles. That is, counterclockwise arcs are positive, and clockwise arcs are negative.

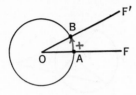

Fig. 15

In Figure 15, as OF rotates in a positive direction about point O to OF', it generates the positive angle AOB. At the same time, point A generates the positive arc AB.

In naming an angle of rotation, we read the initial side first and the terminal side last, keeping the name of the vertex as the middle letter. In this system the intercepted arc is named by the first and last letters of the name of the angle.

As the positive angle P is generated, in Figure 16, point A on the initial side of $\angle P$ generates the positive arc AB; and the point D, also on the initial side of $\angle P$, generates the negative arc DC.

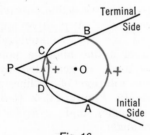

Fig. 16

We should remember that the minor $\overarc{CD}$ and minor $\overarc{DC}$ are numerically equal but they have opposite algebraic signs. In fact, $\overarc{CD}$ is positive, and $\overarc{DC}$ is negative.

The concept of positive and negative angles and arcs is not important in plane geometry because we are primarily interested in the size of angles and arcs and not in their direction. The direction of angles, however, is important in the study of trigonometry. Moreover, it leads us to an interesting generalization of the theorems concerning angles and the arcs they intercept on a circle. In the next topic, we shall see how the theorems relating angles and their intercepted arcs can be combined into one theorem.

Principle of continuity (*Optional*)

In Figure 17, m and n are two straight lines intersecting at the center of circle O. Since $\angle x$ is a central angle, $\angle x \doteq \overarc{AB}$. If we consider the arcs intercepted by $\angle x$ and $\angle COD$, the angle vertical to it, then
$$\angle x \doteq \tfrac{1}{2}(\overarc{AB} + \overarc{CD}).$$
Arcs AB and CD are positive.

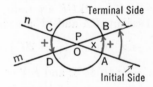

Fig. 17

In Figure 18, the point of intersection of m and n has moved from O to P. $\angle x$ is no longer a central angle, but we have proved that $\angle x \doteq \tfrac{1}{2}(\overarc{AB} + \overarc{CD})$. Arcs AB and CD are positive.

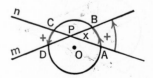

Fig. 18

If we allow P to move toward a point on the circle, $\overset{\frown}{CD}$ becomes smaller and smaller until finally, when P reaches the circle as in Figure 19, the number of degrees in $\overset{\frown}{CD}$ has become zero. However, $\angle x$ is still measured by $\frac{1}{2}(\overset{\frown}{AB} + \overset{\frown}{CD})$.

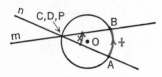

Fig. 19

If m rotates about P until it is tangent to the circle, as in Figure 20, $\angle x$ becomes an angle formed by a tangent and a chord, and

$$\angle x \doteq \tfrac{1}{2}(\overset{\frown}{AB} + \overset{\frown}{CD}).$$

Note that the number of degrees in $\overset{\frown}{CD}$ is zero.

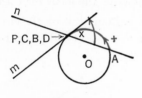

Fig. 20

As point P moves outside the circle, PA is still the initial side of $\angle x$. Hence, as the positive angle x is generated, point A generates the positive arc AB, and point C generates the negative arc CD.

Since $\angle x \doteq \tfrac{1}{2}(\overset{\frown}{AB} - \overset{\frown}{DC})$,
then $\angle x \doteq \tfrac{1}{2}(\overset{\frown}{AB} + \overset{\frown}{CD})$.

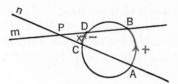

Fig. 21

The same principle applies to lines m and n when one is a tangent and the other is a secant (Figure 22) and when both m and n are tangents (Figure 23). In each case, $\angle x \doteq \tfrac{1}{2}(\overset{\frown}{AB} + \overset{\frown}{CD})$.

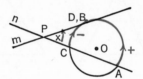

Fig. 22

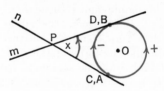

Fig. 23

At each stage of the process illustrated in Figures 17-23, $\angle x$ is measured by one-half the algebraic sum of its intercepted arcs.

GENERAL THEOREM   **An angle between two lines which intersect a circle is measured by one-half the *algebraic* sum of the intercepted arcs.**

Exercises (*Optional*)

The following exercises further illustrate the principle of continuity:

1. In each of these figures, $AB \parallel CD$, R is the midpoint of AC, and S is the midpoint of BD. In each figure prove that $RS = \frac{1}{2}(AB + CD)$.

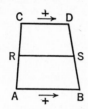

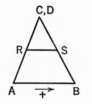

Ex. 1

2. A dynamic line l through a given point P intersects the circle O of radius r at A and B. Construct and describe the locus of the midpoints M and N of the segments PA and PB, respectively, as l rotates about point P.

There are four cases to consider:

Case 1. The given point P is at the center of the given circle.

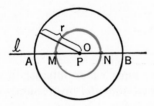

Ex. 2 Case 1

What is the locus of M and N, the midpoints of PA and PB, respectively, as line l rotates about point P?

Case 2. Point P is within circle O.

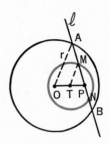

Ex. 2 Case 2

Draw OP and name its midpoint T. Draw MT and AO. Since M and T are the midpoints of two sides of $\triangle OPA$, $MT = \frac{1}{2}AO$. Why? Similarly, $TN = \frac{1}{2}OB$; therefore, the midpoints of the segments PA and PB are each the distance $\frac{1}{2}r$ from the midpoint T of OP.

Describe the locus for Case 2.

Case 3. Point P is on the circle.

In this case B and P (or A and P) coincide.

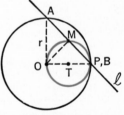

Ex. 2 Case 3

Construct and describe the locus of the midpoint M of PA, as l rotates about P.

Case 4. Point P is outside the circle.

Construct and describe the locus of the midpoints M and N of PA and PB, respectively, as line l rotates about point P.

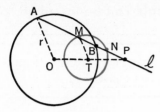

Ex. 2 Case 4

Can you describe the loci of all four cases in one single statement? In all four cases the center of the locus is the midpoint of OP, and the radius of the locus is $\frac{1}{2}r$.

3. Construct and describe the locus of the midpoint M of the chord AB of circle O cut from line l which rotates about a given point P.

Case 1. Point P is at the center of the circle.

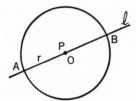

Ex. 3 Case 1

Point P is the midpoint of all chords of circle O through point P. The locus might be described as a circle with OP as diameter.

Case 2. Point P is within the circle. Draw OM. Why is $OM \perp AB$?

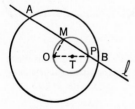

Ex. 3 Case 2

In general, if the midpoints of the chords through the point P are joined to the center of the circle, these segments make right angles with the chords.

What is the locus of the midpoints of the chords through point P?

How does the description of the locus of Case 2 compare with the locus of Case 1?

Case 3. Point P is on the circle. In this case, B and P (or A and P) coincide.

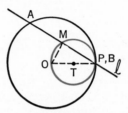

Ex. 3 Case 3

Describe the locus of M, and compare it with the description of the locus in Case 2.

Case 4. Point P is outside the circle.

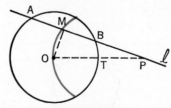

Ex. 3 Case 4

In this case the locus is only an arc. Why? How does its description compare with those of the other three cases?

In all four cases, the center of the locus is the midpoint of OP, and the radius of the locus is $\frac{1}{2}OP$; hence, as point P moves away from the center, the radius of the locus gets longer.

Constructing an arc in which a given angle can be inscribed

CONSTRUCTION 20. Upon a given segment as chord, construct an arc in which a given angle can be inscribed.

Given: Angle A and chord XY.

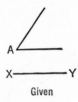

Given

Required: To construct an arc on XY as chord such that $\angle A$ can be inscribed in it.

Analysis: Since $\angle A$ and $\angle BXY$ are both measured by $\frac{1}{2}\widehat{XY}$, they must be equal; hence, begin by constructing an angle equal to $\angle A$ in the position shown by $\angle BXY$ in the sketch below.

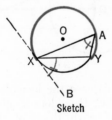

Sketch

Point O is the intersection of two loci:

a. The locus of the center of a circle tangent to a given line at a given point.

b. The locus of the center of a circle passing through the ends of a given line segment.

You make the construction and write the proof.

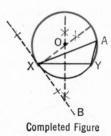

Completed Figure

Complete this statement: The locus of the vertex of a triangle having a given fixed side and a given angle opposite it is . . . . . .

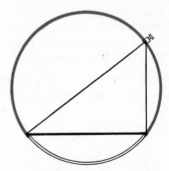

Model of the locus of the vertex of a triangle having a given base and a given vertex angle.

Fig. 24

Exercises

1. Upon a given chord AB construct an arc in which a 45° angle can be inscribed.

2. Upon a given chord RS construct an arc in which a 60° angle can be inscribed.

3. Upon a given chord EF construct an arc in which a 90° angle can be inscribed.

4. Upon a given chord PQ construct an arc in which a given obtuse angle can be inscribed.

5. Construct $\triangle ABC$, given $\angle C$, side c, and h_c.

6. Construct $\triangle RST$, given $\angle T$, RS, and m_t.

The three-point problem (*Optional*)

How can a knowledge of geometry be used by the navigator of a ship to locate his position so as to avoid dangerous shoals?

If the navigator of the ship in the figure below can measure angles L_3PL_2 and L_2PL_1 with his transit, and if he has a chart showing the position of lighthouses L_1, L_2, and L_3, he can easily make a scale drawing as explained below and from it find his distance from each of the lighthouses.

With a three-arm protractor as shown in Figure 25 on the following page, a navigator can easily fix his position on a chart. The arms of the protractor, a, b, and c are set to the angles L_3PL_2 and L_2PL_1. The protractor is then moved about until the

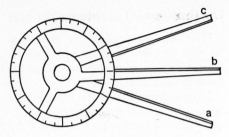

Three-arm Protractor

Fig. 25

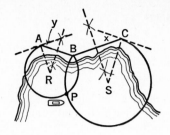

Fig. 27

arms a, b, and c pass through the points L_3, L_2, and L_1, respectively. Through the opening in the center of the protractor the position P of the boat may be marked on the chart.

A geometric construction (*Optional*)

A navigator at point P wishes to locate his unknown position with reference to three visible landmarks, A, B, and C, whose positions can be identified on his chart. He is able to measure angles x and y with a transit. (See Figure 26.) How can the navigator find how far he is from A, B, or C?

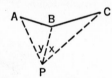

Fig. 26

Point P can be located as follows:
1. Locate A, B, and C on a scale drawing. (See Figure 27.)
2. Upon BC as a chord construct the arc of the circle in which $\angle x$ can be inscribed.
3. Upon AB as a chord construct the arc of the circle in which $\angle y$ can be inscribed.
4. The two arcs intersect at points B and P. The navigator's position is point P. Why?

Exercises (*Optional*)

1. Find the position of point P if $\angle CBA = 135°$, $\angle x = 38°$, $\angle y = 29°$, $AB = 2.9$ mi., and $BC = 4.7$ mi. The scale 1 cm. to 1 mi. is a convenient scale to use. How far is P from A, B, and C?

2. Find the position of point P if $\angle CBA = 122°$, $\angle x = 26°$, $\angle y = 19°$, $AB = 8$ mi., and $BC = 18$ mi. The scale $\frac{1}{4}$ in. to 1 mi. is a convenient scale to use. How far is P from A, B, and C?

Construction of triangles
(*Optional*)

Every construction is based on the location of points that satisfy two conditions simultaneously; that is, every construction is based on one or more loci.

We shall now construct triangles for which we are given certain combinations of sides, angles, medians, angle bisectors, and altitudes. Often more than one triangle can result from the given parts. Sometimes these triangles are congruent, and sometimes they are not. In every construction all possibilities should be considered.

Example 1: Construct $\triangle ABC$, given a, c, and h_a.

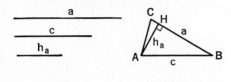

Given   Sketch

Questions on the construction:

1. Describe the circle locus through points A and B.
2. Points H_1 and H_2 are intersections of two loci. Explain.
3. Points C_1 and C_2 are intersections of two loci. Explain.

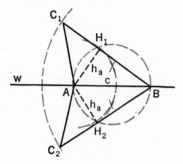

Completed Figure

4. How many triangles can be made from these three given parts? Are the triangles congruent?
5. Can you do this construction another way? (Hint: On a working line w, construct $h_a \perp w$. Find point A, then C, etc.)

Example 2: Construct $\triangle ABC$, given a, m_c, and h_c.

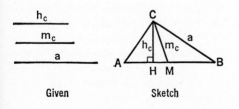

Given   Sketch

Comments and questions on the construction:

1. The construction was begun at point H.
2. Why must m_c be equal to or longer than h_c? Why must a be longer than h_c?

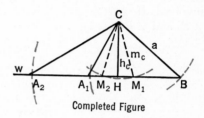

Completed Figure

3. There are two points M_1 and M_2. Why?
4. There are two points A_1 and A_2. Why?
5. There are two triangles, namely, $\triangle A_1BC$ and $\triangle A_2BC$. Why?
6. Are the triangles A_1BC and A_2BC congruent?
7. For the given parts to determine only one triangle, h_c must be equal to m_c. Why?

Exercises (*Optional*)

Construct $\triangle ABC$, given the following combinations of parts:

1. $\angle B$, t_B, and h_b.
2. h_a, m_a, and $\angle B$.
3. b, h_b, and c.
4. t_A, c, and $\angle B$.
5. b, h_a, and c.
6. $\angle A$, $\angle C$, and t_C.
7. t_A, h_b, and c.
8. b, m_a, and $\angle C$.
9. $\angle C$, $\angle A$, and h_c.
10. h_a, m_a, and c.

Marine safety

Two buoys are frequently placed at positions L and M to warn sailors of treacherous waters. A captain can avoid the danger area by keeping his ship R on a course so that $\angle LRM$ is either equal to or less than a specified size. Explain the geometric principle involved. If $\angle R = 42°$, explain why $\angle R'$ and $\angle R''$ are each less than 42°.

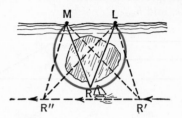

Fig. 28

Review of Chapter 10

Constructions

1. Construct a right triangle, given the radius of the circumscribed circle and one leg.

2. Construct a right triangle, given the radius of the circumscribed circle and an acute angle.

3. Through a given point on a given circle, construct a chord at a given distance from the center.

4. Construct a right triangle, given the hypotenuse and the altitude upon the hypotenuse. When is no solution possible?

5. Construct a circle which is tangent to a given line x *and* is also tangent to a given circle O at a given point A.

6. Through a given point on a circle, construct a chord which shall be bisected by another given chord. Hint: Draw the radius to the given point; and on it, as diameter, describe a circle, etc. When is the solution impossible?

7. Construct the locus of points of contact of tangents drawn from a given point to a series of concentric circles.

Completion Test

*Write the numbers **1-9** on your paper. After each number write the expression that correctly completes the corresponding statement. (Do not write in this book.)*

1. In a circle whose radius is 6 in., if an inscribed angle between a diameter and a chord intercepts an arc of 60°, the chord is . . . . in. from the center of the circle.

2. An angle inscribed in a semicircle is . . . . .

3. If a quadrilateral is inscribed in a circle, its opposite angles are . . . . .

4. An angle inscribed in a minor arc is . . . . .

5. Angles inscribed in the same arc are . . . . .

6. If an angle between two tangents is 20°, the intercepted arcs are . . . . and . . . . .

7. If a right triangle is inscribed in a circle, its hypotenuse is . . . . .

8. If an inscribed angle intercepts a major arc, it is . . . . .

9. If two intersecting chords intercept non-adjacent arcs of 45° and 139°, an angle between the chords is . . . . .

True-False-Sometimes Test

Write the numbers **1-10** *on your paper. Opposite each number write* **True** *if the corresponding statement is always true; write* **False** *if the corresponding statement is always false; write* **Sometimes** *if the statement is sometimes true.*

1. If the opposite angles of a quadrilateral are supplementary, a circle may be circumscribed about it.

2. If a tangent to a circle intersects a vertex of an inscribed triangle, it forms an angle with one of the sides which is equal to one of the angles of the triangle.

3. An inscribed angle is measured by one-half the arc in which it is inscribed.

4. If one side of an inscribed triangle is a diameter of a circle, two of the angles of the triangle are complementary.

5. The bisector of an inscribed angle formed by two equal chords passes through the center of the circle.

6. The construction of a tangent to a circle from an external point is based on the principle that an angle inscribed in a semicircle is a right angle.

7. An angle inscribed in a major arc is obtuse.

8. If a circle is circumscribed about a hexagon, the length of the radius is equal to the length of one of the sides of the hexagon.

9. If a triangle has one fixed side and the number of degrees in the opposite angle is constant, the locus of the vertex of that angle is an arc of a circle of which the given side is a chord.

10. An inscribed angle that intercepts a minor arc is acute.

Numerical Exercises

1. In the adjoining figure, PC and PB are secants of circle O; AC, BD, and BC are chords; $\angle BDC = 50°$; $\overset{\frown}{DA} = 30°$; and $\overset{\frown}{CD} = 90°$. Find the number of degrees in each of the numbered angles.

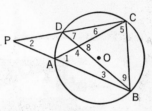

Ex. 1

2. In the figure, DC and DA are tangents to circle O at C and A, respectively; AB is a diameter; FC and FA are secants intersecting the circle at G and C, and E and A, respectively; $\overset{\frown}{EA} = 86°$; $\overset{\frown}{GE} = 56°$, and $\overset{\frown}{AC} = 110°$. Find the number of degrees in each of the numbered angles.

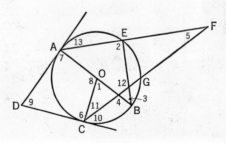

Ex. 2

This laboratory technician started out with an *inequality* when he put the two standard weights on one tray of his very accurate balance. Now he is adding minute amounts of the substance he is weighing out to the other tray in order to make the two sides balance. Then he will have an *equality*.

INEQUALITIES

I<small>N</small> our work so far, we have been thinking about equal line segments, equal angles, and equal arcs in connection with triangles, quadrilaterals, and circles. We know that it is impossible to draw or construct two quantities that are exactly equal. It is only in theory that two line segments, angles, or arcs are equal. From a practical viewpoint, we deal with inequalities more often than we deal with equalities.

In this chapter we are going to consider such problems as the following:

1. If two sides of a triangle are unequal, how are the opposite angles related?

2. If a median is drawn to the base of a scalene triangle, can we predict the order of inequality of the angles at its foot?

3. If two chords of a circle are unequal, are their intercepted arcs unequal in the same order?

4. If two chords of a circle are unequal, are they unequally distant from the center? If so, which one is nearer the center?

5. If certain pairs of parts of two triangles are equal, and another pair of parts are unequal, what can we predict about the remaining pairs of parts?

Symbols of inequality

The symbol for "is greater than" is $>$; the symbol for "is less than" is $<$; the symbol for "is not equal to" is $\neq$.

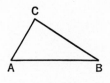

Fig. 1

In $\triangle ABC$, $\angle A \neq \angle B$; in other words, $\angle A > \angle B$ or $\angle B < \angle A$. In the last two expressions, note that the symbol points to the smaller quantity.

Order of inequalities

When two inequalities are given, they are in the *same order* if the symbols point in the same direction and in the *opposite order* if the symbols point in opposite directions.

Illustrative examples:

Same order:

1. $7 > 5$ **2.** $a < b$
$\quad\,\, 6 > 4$ $x < y$

Opposite order:

1. $9 > 7$ **2.** $a > b$
$\quad\,\, 6 < 8$ $m < n$

Exercises

State the results of the following operations, supplying the correct symbols in each case. Do not write in this book.

1. Add:

a. $8 > 7$	**b.** $8 = 8$	**c.** $8 > 7$
$4 = 4$	$4 < 5$	$4 > 3$
?	?	?

2. Subtract the lower line from the upper in each case:

a. $8 > 7$ **b.** $8 = 8$ **c.** $10 = 10$
$\dfrac{4 = 4}{?}$ $\dfrac{4 < 5}{?}$ $\dfrac{3 > 2}{?}$

3. Multiply:

a. $5 > 4$ **b.** $8 > 6$ **c.** $4 = 4$
$\dfrac{2 = 2}{?}$ $\dfrac{3 > 2}{?}$ $\dfrac{7 < 9}{?}$

4. Divide the upper line by the lower line in each case:

a. $6 > 4$ **b.** $10 = 10$ **c.** $10 = 10$
$\dfrac{2 = 2}{?}$ $\dfrac{2 < 5}{?}$ $\dfrac{5 > 2}{?}$

Axioms of inequality

The inequality axioms we need for this course are listed on page 334. Although some of the inequality axioms apply to both positive and negative numbers (or quantities), they are stated here for *positive* quantities only. It should be noted that some of these axioms are not true for negative numbers (or quantities).

AXIOMS

1. Addition Axioms

a. If equals are added to unequals, the sums are unequal in the same order.

b. If unequals are added to unequals in the same order, the sums are unequal in the same order.

2. Subtraction Axioms

a. If equals are subtracted from unequals, the differences are unequal in the same order.

b. If unequals are subtracted from equals, the differences are unequal in the opposite order.

3. A given quantity when compared with another of the same kind is equal to, greater than, or less than the other quantity.

4. Multiplication Axioms

a. If unequals are multiplied by equals, the products are unequal in the same order.

b. If unequals are multiplied by unequals in the same order, the products are unequal in that order.

5. Division Axioms

a. If unequals are divided by equals, the quotients are unequal in the same order.

b. If equals are divided by unequals, the quotients are unequal in the opposite order.

6. If three quantities are so related that the first is greater than the second, and the second is greater than the third, then the first is greater than the third.

Exercises

In Exercises **1-12**, *replace the question marks by the correct inequality symbols and identify the axioms on which your answers are based. Do not write in this book.*

1. If $\qquad a > b$
and $\qquad k = k$
then $\quad a + k \ ? \ b + k$

2. If $\qquad a < b$
and $\qquad x = y$
then $\quad a - x \ ? \ b - y$

3. If $\quad\quad\quad x > y$
and $\quad\quad\quad a > b$
then $\quad\quad\overline{xa \ ? \ yb}$

4. If $\quad\quad\quad x = y$
and $\quad\quad\quad m < n$
then $\quad\quad\dfrac{x}{m} \ ? \ \dfrac{y}{n}$

5. If $\quad\quad\quad a > b$
and $\quad\quad\quad x > y$
then $\quad a + x \ ? \ b + y$

6. If $\quad\quad\quad a < b$
and $\quad\quad\quad s = t$
then $\quad\quad\overline{as \ ? \ bt}$

7. If $\quad\quad\quad x = y$
and $\quad\quad\quad m < n$
then $\quad x - m \ ? \ y - n$

8. If $\quad\quad\quad x > y$
and $\quad\quad\quad m = n$
then $\quad\quad\dfrac{x}{m} \ ? \ \dfrac{y}{n}$

9. If $\quad\quad\quad a < b$
and $\quad\quad\quad x = y$
then $\quad a + x \ ? \ b + y$

10. If $\quad\quad\quad k = k$
and $\quad\quad\quad m < n$
then $\quad k - m \ ? \ k - n$

11. If $a > b$ and $b > c$, then $a \ ? \ c$.

12. If $m \neq y$ and m is not $> y$, then $m \ ? \ y$.

*Answer the questions in Exercises **13-22** and choose the correct axiom as an authority. If it is impossible to answer the question, write **No Answer.***

13. John has more money than Frank, and Frank has more money than Sam. How do John's and Sam's amounts compare?

14. Jim has more money than Ann. They spend equal amounts. How do their amounts then compare?

15. Firm B made more money than Firm A. They both agreed to give 10% of their earnings to their employees. Which firm gave the greater amount? Which firm had the greater amount left?

16. Jim has more money than Sam, and Frank has more money than Harry.

a. How does the sum of Jim's and Frank's amounts compare with the sum of Sam's and Harry's?
b. How does the sum of Jim's and Sam's amounts compare with the sum of Frank's and Harry's?

17. Mary has less money than James. How will their amounts compare if Mary spends more money than James?

18. John had saved more money than Frank. They earned unequal amounts which they added to their savings. How do their savings now compare?

19. If Mary and Jane each have equal weekly allowances, and Mary spends more than Jane, who has the greater amount left?

20. If Sam has a greater weekly allowance than Harry, and the allowance of each is doubled, how do their allowances then compare?

21. Jane is older than Mary. Six years ago who was older?

22. Mary's earnings per week are more than Harry's, but Mary spends more each week than Harry. Who has the greater amount left?

*In Exercises **23-30**, supply the correct inequality symbol to complete each statement and give the correct axiom as an authority.*

23. If $CA < CB + AB$
    and $CB = DB,$
    then $CA \ ? \ DB + AB.$

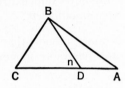

Ex. 23–24

24. If $\angle n > \angle A$
    and $\angle n = \angle C,$
    then $\angle C \ ? \ \angle A.$

25. If $\angle 1 < \angle 4$
    and $\angle 3 < \angle 5,$
    then $\angle MPO \ ? \ \angle ONM.$

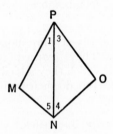

Ex. 25–29

26. If $\angle 1 > \angle 4$
    and $\angle 3 = \angle 5,$
    then $\angle MPO \ ? \ \angle ONM.$

27. If $\angle MPO = 2\angle 1$
         $\angle ONM = 2\angle 5,$
    and $\angle 1 < \angle 5,$
    then $\angle MPO \ ? \ \angle ONM.$

28. If $\angle MPO > \angle ONM$
    and $\angle 1 = \angle 4,$
    then $\angle 3 \ ? \ \angle 5.$

29. If $\angle MPO = \angle ONM$
    and $\angle 1 > \angle 4,$
    then $\angle 3 \ ? \ \angle 5.$

30. If $\angle a + \angle x = 90°$
        $\angle b + \angle y = 90°,$
    and $\angle a > \angle b,$
    then $\angle x \ ? \ \angle y.$

31. Complete and prove: Complements of unequal angles are unequal in the . . . . order.

32. Complete and prove: Supplements of unequal angles are . . . . .

33. Prove: Each side of a triangle is greater than the difference of the other two sides.

34. Prove: The sum of the diagonals of a quadrilateral is less than the perimeter of the quadrilateral.

35. If D is a point inside $\triangle ABC$, prove that $AD + DB < AC + CB$. Hint: Prolong AD to meet BC at E.

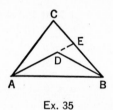

Ex. 35

36. Addition, subtraction, multiplication, and division involving two pairs of positive unequals do not always give results that can be stated in the form of a general axiom.

Investigate the difference and quotient of $a > b$ and $x > y$. If you have difficulty, substitute small numbers for the letters. Illustrative example:

Subtract:

$12 > 8$	$12 > 8$	$12 > 8$
$9 > 7$	$9 > 5$	$9 > 2$
$3 > 1$	$3 = 3$	$3 < 6$

Can we draw a conclusion about unequals subtracted from unequals in the same order?

An exterior angle of a triangle

In Figure 2, $\angle EBC$ is an exterior angle of $\triangle ABC$. If $BD \parallel AC$, then $\angle A = \angle 1$, and $\angle C = \angle 2$. Why?

Also, $\angle EBC = \angle 1 + \angle 2.$
Why?

Therefore, $\angle EBC > \angle 1$, and
$$\angle EBC > \angle 2. \text{ Why?}$$

Thus, $\angle EBC > \angle A,$
and $\angle EBC > \angle C.$ Why?

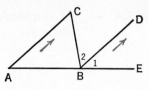

Fig. 2

You write the proof of Theorem 63.

THEOREM 63. **An exterior angle of a triangle is greater than either remote interior angle.**

Exercises

1. Given: $\triangle ABC$ in which CD bisects $\angle ACB$.

Deduce the relation between $\angle 2$ and $\angle 1$.

2. Given: $\triangle ABC$ in which $DC = AC$.

Deduce the relation between $\angle A$ and $\angle B$.

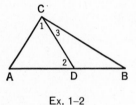

Ex. 1–2

A triangle with two unequal sides

Induction: Make a number of triangles in which $AC < BC$. Measure $\angle A$ and $\angle B$. Are they always unequal? Can you predict the order of inequality of angles opposite unequal sides of a triangle?

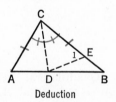

Deduction

Hint: 1. On CB mark off $CE = AC$.
2. Draw CD bisecting $\angle ACB$.
3. Draw DE.
4. Which triangles are congruent?
5. How is $\angle 1$ related to $\angle A$? to $\angle B$?

Induction

Deduction: $\triangle ABC$ with $AC < BC$.

Deduce the implications.

You write the complete proof of Theorem 64, which is stated on the next page.

THEOREM 64. **If two sides of a triangle are unequal, the angles opposite them are . . . . . in the . . . . . order.**

Exercises

1. The three sides of a triangle are 10, 12, and 9. Name the three angles in the order of their size.

2. Can a triangle be constructed with the sides equal to any three segments chosen at random? Explain the restrictions.

3. Given: $ABCD$ is a parallelogram, $AB > BC$.

Deduce the relation of $\angle 1$ to $\angle 2$.

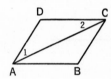

Ex. 3

4. Given: Quadrilateral $ABCD$ in which AC is a diagonal, $AB > BC$, and $AD > DC$. How is $\angle BAD$ related to $\angle DCB$?

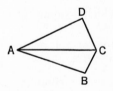

Ex. 4

*Write the numbers **5-7** on your paper. After each number write the expression that correctly completes the corresponding statement.*

5. In $\triangle ABC$, if $a > b > c$, the largest angle of the triangle is . . . . .

6. In $\triangle ABC$, if $AB = 10.0$ inches and $BC = 6.0$ inches, then AC must be greater than . . . . inches.

7. If $\angle m$ is the supplement of $\angle n$, $\angle x$ is the supplement of $\angle y$, and $\angle n < \angle x$, then . . . . .

8. Prove Theorem 64 by making $CE = AC$ and drawing AE.

9. Prove: In a parallelogram which is not a rhombus, the diagonals do not bisect the angles.

10. Prove: The sum of the diagonals of a quadrilateral is less than the sum of the four segments drawn from any point within the quadrilateral, other than the point of intersection of the diagonals, to the four vertices.

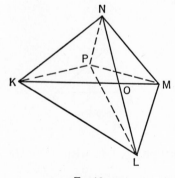

Ex. 10

A triangle with two unequal angles

THEOREM 65. If two angles of a triangle are unequal, the sides opposite these angles are unequal in the same order.

Given: $\triangle ABC$ in which $\angle B > \angle A$.

Prove: $AC > BC$.

Plan: Use the indirect method of proof.

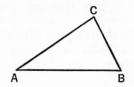

Proof

STATEMENTS	AUTHORITIES
1. $AC = BC$, $AC < BC$, or $AC > BC$.	1. Why?
2. If $AC = BC$, then $\angle A = \angle B$.	2. Why?
3. $\angle A \neq \angle B$.	3. Why?
4. If $AC < BC$, then $\angle B < \angle A$.	4. Why?
5. $\angle B$ is not $< \angle A$.	5. Why?
6. $\therefore AC > BC$.	6. Why?

Exercises

1. In acute $\triangle ABC$, $\angle A = 65°$, and $\angle B = 75°$. Which side of the triangle is the shortest? Which side is the longest? Why?

2. In $\triangle ABC$, if $\angle A > \angle B > \angle C$, name the sides in order beginning with the longest.

3. Prove: The hypotenuse of a right triangle is greater than either of the legs.

4. Given: $\triangle CAB$, D is a point on CA, and $\angle BDC$ is acute.
   Prove: $BA > BD$.

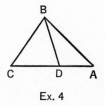

Ex. 4

5. Prove: The length of the perpendicular from a point to a line is the shortest path from the point to the line.

6. Prove: The perimeter of pentagon $ABCDE$ is greater than the perimeter of triangle ACE.

7. Prove Theorem 65 by constructing $\angle DBA = \angle A$.

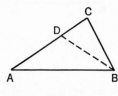

Ex. 7

8. In $\triangle ABC$, $AC > BC$, AO bisects $\angle A$, and BO bisects $\angle B$. Prove that $AO > BO$.

9. Prove: If a line is drawn from the vertex C of an isosceles $\triangle ABC$ to any point D on the base, then $CD < CA$.

10. If two oblique segments are drawn from a point on a perpendicular to a line so that they cut off on the line unequal distances from the foot of the perpendicular, they are unequal; and the segment cutting off the greater distance is the greater.

11. If two unequal oblique segments are drawn from a point on a perpendicular to a line, the greater segment cuts off the greater distance from the foot of the perpendicular.

12. Prove: The perimeter of a triangle is greater than the sum of its three altitudes.

Inequalities in triangles

We know that the combination of two sides and the included angle of a triangle determines the third side of the triangle; likewise a triangle having three sides of fixed length has its angles fixed in size.

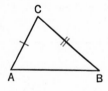

Fig. 3

Experiment

Suppose we keep AC and BC of the dynamic triangle ABC constant and allow $\angle C$ to vary. What happens to AB as $\angle C$ becomes larger? What happens to AB as $\angle C$ becomes smaller? (See Figure 4.)

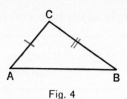

Fig. 4

Let us repeat the experiment. This time, however, we shall keep AC and BC constant and vary the length of AB. How is $\angle C$ affected by a change in the length of AB (Figure 5)?

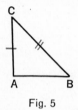

Fig. 5

POSTULATES 43. If two triangles have two sides of one respectively equal to two sides of the other, but the included angles are unequal, the third sides are unequal in the same order.

44. If two triangles have two sides of one respectively equal to two sides of the other, but the third sides are unequal, the angles opposite the third sides are unequal in the same order.

Exercises

1. Given: CD is a median of $\triangle ABC$, and $BC > AC$.
   What can you prove about $\angle BDC$? How?

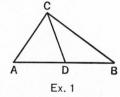

Ex. 1

2. Given: Quadrilateral $ABCD$, AC is a diagonal, $AD = AB$, and DC is greater than BC.
Deduce the implications.

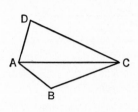

Ex. 2

3. Given: $\triangle ABC$ is isosceles, D is a point on the base AB, and CD is drawn so that $\angle 2 > \angle 1$.
Deduce the implications.

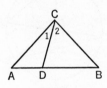

Ex. 3

4. Given: AC and BD are the diagonals of the parallelogram $ABCD$, and $AB > BC$.
What can you prove about angles 1 and 2? How?

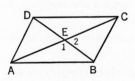

Ex. 4

5. Given: Circle O with $\angle 1 > \angle 2$; angles 1 and 2 are central angles. How is AB related to DC? Why?

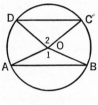

Ex. 5

6. Given: $\triangle ABC$ with $AB > AC$, D is on AC, E is on AB, and $CD = EB$.
Prove: $DB > CE$.

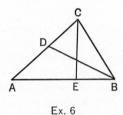

Ex. 6

7. If, in the dynamic $\triangle ABC$, median CD rotates counter-clockwise about D, and AB and CD have a constant length, describe the relationship of AC and BC: (**a**) when $\angle 1$ is acute, (**b**) when $\angle 1$ is a right angle, (**c**) when $\angle 1$ is obtuse.

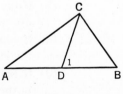

Ex. 7

Copy the numbers **8-17** *on your paper. If a statement is always true, write* **True;** *if a statement is not necessarily true, write* **False.** *In Exercises* **8-12**, *TM is a median to side RS in* $\triangle RST$.

In Exercises **13-17**, *MS and RT are diagonals of parallelogram MRST.*

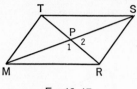

Ex. 13–17

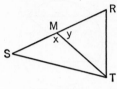

Ex. 8–12

8. If $\angle x < \angle y$, then $RT > ST$.

9. If $\angle R > \angle S$, then $\angle y$ is obtuse.

10. If $\angle x$ is acute, then $\angle S > \angle R$.

11. If $\angle R < \angle S$, then $\angle y < \angle x$.

12. If $\angle x = \angle y$, then $RT > ST$.

13. If $\angle RMT > \angle SRM$, then $MS > RT$.

14. If $\angle 1$ is acute, then $MR < RS$.

15. If $\angle 1 = \angle 2$, then $MR < RS$.

16. If $MS < RT$, then $\angle RMT > \angle SRM$.

17. If $MR < RS$, then $\angle 1 < \angle 2$.

Unequal central angles, arcs, and chords

In the same circle or in equal circles, equal central angles intercept equal arcs, and equal arcs have equal chords. Now we shall see how these quantities are related if the central angles, arcs, or chords are unequal.

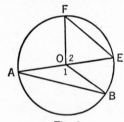

Fig. 6

In circle O, $\angle 1 \doteq \overset{\frown}{AB}$, and $\angle 2 \doteq \overset{\frown}{EF}$. Why?

If $\angle 1 > \angle 2$, then $\overset{\frown}{AB} > \overset{\frown}{EF}$. Why? Conversely, if $\overset{\frown}{AB} > \overset{\frown}{EF}$, then $\angle 1 > \angle 2$. Why?

Also, if $\overset{\frown}{AB} > \overset{\frown}{EF}$, then $AB > EF$. Why? Conversely, if $AB > EF$, then $\overset{\frown}{AB} > \overset{\frown}{EF}$. Why?

THEOREM 66.   **In the same circle or in equal circles:**

> **(a) If two central angles are unequal, their arcs are unequal in the same order;**
>
> **(b) If the arcs of two central angles are unequal, the angles are unequal in the same order;**
>
> **(c) If two minor arcs are unequal, their chords are unequal in the same order;**
>
> **(d) If two chords are unequal, their minor arcs are unequal in the same order.**

Unequal chords and their distances from the center

In the same circle or in equal circles, equal chords are equidistant from the center. We shall now consider two *unequal* chords and their distances from the center of the circle.

THEOREM 67.   In the same circle or in equal circles, the longer of two unequal chords is nearer the center.

Given: Equal circles O and R in which $AB > ST$, $OM \perp AB$, and $RN \perp ST$.

Prove: $RN > OM$.

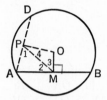 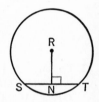

Proof

STATEMENTS	AUTHORITIES
1. At A in circle O, construct chord $AD =$ chord ST and in the position indicated.	1. Why possible?
2. Draw $OP \perp AD$.	2. Why possible?
3. Draw MP.	3. Why possible?
4. $AB > ST$.	4. Why?
5. $\therefore AB > AD$.	5. Why?
6. $OM \perp AB$.	6. Why?
7. $\therefore AB$ and AD are bisected at M and P, respectively.	7. Why?

Continue, by proving $AM > AP$, $\angle 1 > \angle 2$, $\angle 4 < \angle 3$, $OP > OM$, $OP = RN$, and finally, $RN > OM$.

THEOREM 68.   In the same circle or in equal circles, if two chords are unequally distant from the center, the chord nearer the center is the longer.

You draw the figure and write the complete proof.

Hint: Use the indirect method of proof.

Exercises

1. Given: Circle O, $\overset{\frown}{ABD} > \overset{\frown}{BDC}$, $OM \perp AB$, and $ON \perp CD$. Prove how ON is related to OM.

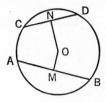

Ex. 1

2. Given: $\triangle ABC$ is inscribed in circle O, $OM \perp AB$, $ON \perp BC$, $OP \perp AC$, and $ON > OM > OP$.
   a. How are chords AB, BC, and AC related? Why?
   b. How are arcs AB, BC, and CA related? Why?
   c. How are the angles A, B, and C related? Why?

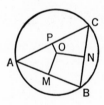

Ex. 2

3. A rectangle $ABCD$ is inscribed in a circle, and $\angle ABD < 45°$. Compare the length of AB with the length of AD.

4. Choose the phrase that correctly completes this statement: In the same circle, the length of the chord of an arc of $n°$ is .... of the length of an arc of $2n°$. **(a)** *one-half,* **(b)** *greater than one-half,* or **(c)** *less than one-half.*

5. Prove: If the chord AB, which is not a diameter, bisects the chord CD, then AB is nearer the center than CD.

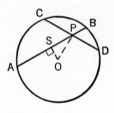

Ex. 5

6. If one of the sides of a central angle rotates in a clockwise direction and the other side remains static, describe: **(a)** the change in the length of the chord of the arc of the angle, and **(b)** the change in the distance the chord of the arc of the angle is from the center.

Review of Chapter 11

General Questions

1. Prove: The shortest chord that can be drawn through a given point within a circle is perpendicular to the radius at that point. Hint: Draw any other chord through the point, and draw a perpendicular to the auxiliary chord from the center.

2. In a given circle how does the chord of an arc of 60° compare in length with the chord of an arc of 180°? Explain.

3. A right triangle ABC is inscribed in circle O, $\angle C$ is the right angle, and $\angle A < \angle B$. Prove which leg is nearer the center of the circle. How far is the hypotenuse from the center of the circle?

4. Prove: If a square and a regular hexagon are inscribed in the same circle, the side of the square is nearer the center of the circle.

5. Given: SR is the perpendicular bisector of AB.

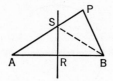

Ex. 5

Complete:

a. If P is on the extension of AS, then $PA \ldots . PB$.

b. If P is between A and S, then $PA \ldots . PB$.

c. If P is the same point as S, then $PA \ldots . PB$.

What locus theorem can be used to justify your answers?

6. Given: $\triangle ABC$, AO bisects $\angle CAB$, BO bisects $\angle CBA$, and $AO < BO$. Deduce the relationship between AC and BC.

Ex. 6

7. Given: Quadrilateral $ABCD$ in which $AB = AD$, $BC = DC$, and $AD > DC$. Prove: $\angle BAD < \angle DCB$.

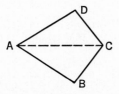

Ex. 7

8. Given: $ABCD$ is a quadrilateral, $AD = BC$, and $AC > BD$. Prove: $\angle CBA > \angle BAD$.

Ex. 8

9. Given: $ABCD$ is a parallelogram, and $\angle CBA$ is obtuse. Deduce the relationship between AC and BD.

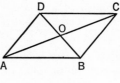

Ex. 9

10. The path of a ray of light from B as reflected to A by the mirror MN makes $\angle x = \angle y$.

Prove that the ray takes the shortest path from B to the mirror MN to A.

Hint: Let Q be any point on MN other than P, and prove that $BP + PA < QA + BQ$.

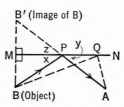

Ex. 10

Completion Test

Write the numbers **1-20** *on your paper. After each number write the expression that correctly completes the corresponding statement. Do not write in this book.*

1. In $\triangle ABC$, if $AB = 10.0$ in. and $BC = 6.0$ in., then AC must be less than . . . . in.

2. Angle ABC is inscribed in circle O, and $AB > CB$. The chord nearer the center is . . . . .

3. The diagonals AC and BD of the parallelogram $ABCD$ intersect at O. If $\angle AOB$ is obtuse, AB is . . . . than AD.

4. The altitude CD of the scalene triangle ABC is . . . . than the median CM.

5. Two angles of a triangle are 75° and 60°. The smallest exterior angle is . . . . .

6. If $\angle a$ is the complement of $\angle b$, $\angle m$ is the complement of $\angle n$, and $\angle a < \angle m$, then $\angle b$ is . . . . than $\angle n$.

7. The shortest chord through point A within circle O is the chord that is . . . . .

8. In $\triangle ABC$, if $\angle A = 60°$ and $\angle B = 50°$, the longest side of the triangle is . . . . .

9. If the diagonals of a parallelogram are unequal, the parallelogram is not a . . . . .

10. If CM is the median to the side AB of $\triangle ABC$, and if $AC < BC$, then angle . . . . is obtuse.

11. Triangle ABC is inscribed in circle O; AB is the diameter and $\angle CBA = 47°$. The longer leg of the triangle is . . . . .

12. If $\angle A$ of the parallelogram $ABCD$ is obtuse, diagonal AC is . . . . than diagonal BD.

In Exercises **13-17**, *circle O has a diameter 8.0 inches long, a chord PA makes a 30° angle with OP, and a chord PB makes a 60° angle with OP.*

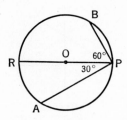

Ex. 13–17

13. The length of PB is . . . . than the length of PA.

14. The length of $\overset{\frown}{PB}$ is . . . . than the length of $\overset{\frown}{AP}$.

15. Chord PA is . . . . the center than PB.

16. Chord PB is . . . . inches long.

17. Chord PA is . . . . inches from the center O.

18. If the median NO of $\triangle LMN$ is not an altitude, LN . . . . MN.

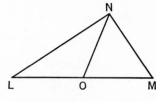

Ex. 18–20

19. If NO is a median of $\triangle LMN$, and if $LN > MN$, then $\angle NOL$ . . . . $\angle MON$.

20. If NO is a median of $\triangle LMN$, and if $\angle NOL > \angle MON$, then $\angle MLN$ . . . . $\angle NML$.

True-False Test

Copy the numbers **1-15** *on your paper. If a statement is always true, write* **True;** *if a statement is not necessarily true, write* **False.**

In the figure for Exercises **1-10,** *EG is the diagonal of quadrilateral EFGH.*

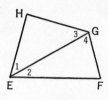

Ex. 1–10

1. If $\angle 1 = \angle 3$,
and $\angle 2 > \angle 4$,
then $\angle FEH < \angle HGF$.

2. If $\angle 1 > \angle 3$,
and $\angle 2 > \angle 4$,
then $\angle FEH > \angle HGF$.

3. If $\angle FEH = \angle HGF$,
and $\angle 1 < \angle 4$,
then $\angle 2 > \angle 3$.

4. If $\angle FEH > \angle HGF$,
and $\angle 1 = \angle 3$,
then $\angle 2 > \angle 4$.

5. If $\angle FEH > \angle HGF$,
then $\frac{1}{2} \angle FEH < \frac{1}{2} \angle HGF$.

6. If $\angle 1 = \angle 4$,
then $2\angle 1 > 2\angle 4$.

7. If $\angle 1 > \angle 3$,
and $\angle 3 > \angle 4$,
then $\angle 4 < \angle 1$.

8. If $\angle HEF = \angle 1 + \angle 2$,
and $\angle 1 = \angle 3$,
then $\angle HEF = \angle 3 + \angle 1$.

9. If $\angle 1 > \angle 2$,
and $\angle 3 > \angle 4$,
then $\angle H > \angle F$.

10. If $HG > EH$,
and $FG > EF$,
then $\angle HGF < \angle FEH$.

In Exercises **11-15,** *AB and BC are chords of circle O. OE ⊥ AB at E, OD ⊥ BC at D, and BF is a diameter.*

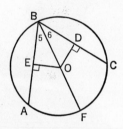

Ex. 11–15

11. If $AB < BC$, then $DB > EB$.

12. If $OD > OE$, then $\angle 6 < \angle 5$.

13. If $\overset{\frown}{BA} < \overset{\frown}{CB}$, then $OE < OD$.

14. If $BD > BE$, then $\overset{\frown}{CB} > \overset{\frown}{BA}$.

15. If $\angle 5 > \angle 6$, then $\overset{\frown}{BA} < \overset{\frown}{CB}$.

The principles of ratio and proportion are being applied when a photographer enlarges a picture. The enlargement has the same shape as the original negative. The ratio of the lengths of the corresponding segments of the negative and the enlargement can be controlled by adjustments on the enlarger.

Chapter 12 PROPORTION AND PROPORTIONAL LINE SEGMENTS

WE FREQUENTLY compare quantities of the same kind by means of ratios. Such expressions as "a batting average of .278," "an interest rate of 5%," or "a vote of 7 to 3" are common in everyday language.

The ratio of one number to another number is the quotient, or indicated quotient, of the first number by the second. The ratio of 3 to 8 may be written $3:8$, or $\frac{3}{8}$, or 0.375, or $\frac{375}{1000}$, or $\frac{37.5}{100}$, or 37.5%. The ratio of $2a$ inches to b feet is $\frac{2a(\text{in.})}{12b(\text{in.})} = \frac{a}{6b}$, or $a:6b$.

To measure a quantity means to compare it with some accepted unit of measure. A segment six inches long is six times as long as the unit of measure called an inch. The inch is the unit of measure, and six is the numerical measure, or simply the measure.

The ratio of one quantity to another quantity of the same kind is the quotient obtained by dividing the measure of the first quantity by the measure of the second if both measures are expressed in terms of a common unit.

The first term of a ratio is called the *antecedent*; the second term is called the *consequent*. Because a ratio is often written as a fraction, the names numerator and denominator are also used.

Rules governing the use of ratios

1. A ratio is a fraction, and all the rules governing fractions may be used in working with ratios.

2. If quantities to be compared by ratio are of the same kind, they must be expressed in the same unit of measure. For example, the ratio of one-half a right angle to one-third a straight angle is found by changing the latter to right angles and expressing the relationship as the fraction

$$\frac{\frac{1}{2}}{\frac{1}{3} \times 2} = \frac{\frac{1}{2}}{\frac{2}{3}} = \frac{3}{4}.$$

Sometimes we compare unlike quantities by ratio. For example, we are familiar with such statements as "40 miles per hour" and "3 pounds for a quarter."

3. The quotient should be reduced to its lowest terms.

4. The ratio of two geometric quantities of the same kind, such as segments, arcs, or angles, is the quotient of their numerical measures when expressed in terms of the same unit of measure. Thus, if a segment AB is 3 feet long and another segment RS is 15 inches long, the ratio of AB to RS is $\frac{36}{15}$ or $\frac{12}{5}$.

Exercises

1. Write as fractions the ratios of each of the following pairs of quantities and reduce to lowest terms:

    a. 8 to 24

    b. $4x$ to $5x$

    c. $6x^2$ to $12xy$

    d. 5 degrees to 30 minutes

    e. 2 in. to 2 ft.

    f. 4 votes to 6 votes

    g. $x^2 - 2x + 1$ to $x - 1$

    h. $a^2 - b^2$ to $a - b$

    i. 800 lb. to 2 tons

    j. $15x^2$ to $45x + 3$

    k. $2a - 2b$ to $a - b$

    l. $a^2 - b^2$ to $a + b$

2. If a line segment AB is 21 inches long, and point C is placed on it so that AC is 7 inches, what is the ratio of the shorter segment to the longer segment? What is the ratio of CB to AB?

3. What is the ratio of the perimeter of a regular hexagon to one of its sides?

4. What is the ratio of the sum of the interior angles of a quadrilateral to the sum of the interior angles of a pentagon?

5. Two quantities are in the ratio of 4 to 5. If $4x$ represents the first quantity, what represents the second?

6. Segment AB is 12 inches long. It is divided at the point P so that AP is to PB as 1 is to 3. How long is AP?

7. Draw a line dividing a straight angle into two parts having the ratio of 7 to 13.

8. Mary is 6 years old and Jane is 11 years old. Divide $48.28 between them in the ratio of their ages.

9. John is 10 years old and his sister Mary is 15. What is the ratio of their present ages? What will be the ratio of their ages in 5 years? What was the ratio of their ages 5 years ago?

10. Two complementary angles are in the ratio of 2 to 3. How many degrees are there in each angle?

11. The ratio of two supplementary angles is 3 to 5. How many degrees are there in each angle?

12. The angles of a triangle are to each other as 1 to 2 to 3. How large is each angle?

13. Find the lengths of two line segments whose difference is 15 units and whose ratio is $3:8$.

14. The sum of two segments is 16 in. and their difference is 4 in. What is their ratio?

15. The sides of a triangle whose perimeter is 36 in. are in the ratio of $5:6:7$. Find the shortest side of the triangle.

16. In the accompanying figure, $AB = 5y$, and $AC = 5x$.

    a. What is the ratio of AD to DB?

    b. What is the ratio of AE to EC?

    c. How are the ratios in **a** and **b** related?

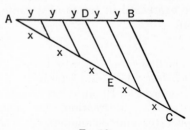

Ex. 16

d. Can you find the numerical value of the ratio of AB to AC? Explain your answer.

17. Divide 178 into two parts x and y so that the ratio of x to y is 3 to 8. Solve it first by using an equation in one unknown and then by using two equations in two unknowns.

18. Water weighs 62.4 pounds per cubic foot. The specific gravity of marble is 2.61; that is, marble weighs 2.61 times as much as water, volume for volume. What is the weight of a cubic foot of marble?

19. Find, correct to the nearest minute, the angles of an isosceles triangle if the ratio of the vertex angle to one of the base angles is $2:3$.

20. If the areas of two squares are in the ratio of 2 to 5, the smaller is what percent of the larger?

The square root of a number

Some of the work that follows involves the square roots of numbers. A table of square roots of numbers from 1 to 300 is given on page 429. For those who have forgotten how to work with square roots, a brief review is given.

A. *The square root of a number is one of two equal factors of that number.*

Examples:

1. $\sqrt{25} = \sqrt{5 \times 5} = 5$

2. $\sqrt{1437.5} = \sqrt{37.9 \times 37.9} = 37.9$
to the nearest tenth.

The method for finding the square root of a number which is not in a table of square roots is illustrated in the next example.

3. Find the square root of 2868.4 to the nearest tenth.

$$
\begin{array}{r}
5\ \ 3.\ 5\ \ 5 \\
\sqrt{28\ 68.40\ 00} \\
25 \\
\end{array}
$$

103	3 68
	3 09

1,065	59 40
	53 25

10,705	6 15 00
	5 35 25

The square root of 2868.4 to the nearest tenth is 53.6.

B. *The square of a product is the product of the squares of the factors.*

Examples:

1. $(2x)^2 = 2^2 \cdot x^2 = 4x^2$

2. $(2\sqrt{3})^2 = 2^2(\sqrt{3})^2 = 4 \times 3 = 12$

C. *The square of a quotient is the square of the numerator divided by the square of the denominator.*

Examples:

1. $\left(\dfrac{2\sqrt{3}}{3}\right)^2 = \dfrac{2^2(\sqrt{3})^2}{3^2} = \dfrac{4 \times 3}{9} = \dfrac{4}{3}$

2. $\left(\dfrac{\sqrt{2}}{\sqrt{3}}\right)^2 = \dfrac{2}{3}$

D. *The square root of a product is the product of the square roots of the factors.*

Examples:

1. $\sqrt{xy} = \sqrt{x} \cdot \sqrt{y}$

2. $\sqrt{9 \times 4} = \sqrt{9} \times \sqrt{4} = 3 \times 2 = 6$

3. $\sqrt{18} = \sqrt{9 \times 2} = \sqrt{9} \times \sqrt{2} = 3\sqrt{2}$

If 18 is an exact number, the exact answer is $3\sqrt{2}$; the approximate answer to the nearest thousandth is $3 \times 1.414 = 4.242$.

4. $\sqrt{45} = \sqrt{9 \times 5} = \sqrt{9} \times \sqrt{5} = 3\sqrt{5}$. If 45 is an exact number, and if $\sqrt{5} = 2.236$ to the nearest thousandth, what is $3\sqrt{5}$ to the nearest hundredth?

5. $\sqrt{252} = \sqrt{4 \times 9 \times 7} = \sqrt{4} \times \sqrt{9} \times \sqrt{7} = 6\sqrt{7}$. If 252 is an approximate number, and if $\sqrt{252} = 15.875$ to the nearest thousandth, then $\sqrt{252} = 15.9$ to the nearest tenth.

E. *The square root of a fraction is the square root of the numerator divided by the square root of the denominator.*

Examples:

1. $\sqrt{\dfrac{3}{4}} = \dfrac{\sqrt{3}}{\sqrt{4}} = \dfrac{\sqrt{3}}{2}$

2. $\sqrt{\dfrac{4}{3}} = \sqrt{\dfrac{4}{3} \times \dfrac{3}{3}} = \dfrac{\sqrt{4} \times \sqrt{3}}{\sqrt{9}} = \dfrac{2}{3}\sqrt{3}$

Note: To express $\sqrt{\dfrac{4}{3}}$ as $\dfrac{2}{\sqrt{3}}$ is correct, but it is not convenient because $\dfrac{2}{1.732}$ is difficult to evaluate, whereas $\frac{2}{3} \times 1.732$ is much simpler. It is always desirable to express the denominator of an irrational fraction as a rational number.

AXIOM   Like powers and like roots of equals are equal.

Equations of the form $x^2 = a$

Example:
If $x^2 = 48$, $x = $?
$$x^2 = 48$$
$$x = \pm\sqrt{48} = \pm\sqrt{16} \times \sqrt{3}$$
$$= \pm 4 \times 1.732$$
$$= \pm 6.928 \text{ to the nearest thousandth.}$$

In geometry we do not often deal with negative line segments, and so the negative root is generally discarded. The answer is left as $4\sqrt{3}$ if the data of the problem are exact; otherwise as many significant digits of 6.928 are kept as the accuracy of the data allows.

Exercises

1. Find the square roots of each of the following numbers to the nearest tenth, assuming the numbers to be exact.

a. 27	**g.** 143
b. 128	**h.** 400
c. $\frac{2}{9}$	**i.** 40
d. $\frac{4}{5}$	**j.** 4
e. $\frac{3}{2}$	**k.** 0.4
f. 132	**l.** 0.04

2. Simplify the following:

a. $\sqrt{\frac{5}{8}}$	**f.** $\dfrac{2b}{\sqrt{3}}$
b. $\sqrt{\frac{2}{3}}$	**g.** $\sqrt{\dfrac{4b^2}{3}}$
c. $\sqrt{\frac{4}{3}}$	**h.** $\sqrt{32}$
d. $\dfrac{14}{\sqrt{2}}$	**i.** $\sqrt{\dfrac{3b^2}{2}}$
e. $\dfrac{32}{\sqrt{3}}$	**j.** $\sqrt{108}$

3. Solve the following equations for x (the answers may be left in simplified radical form):

a. $x^2 = 40$ **b.** $3x^2 = 4$

c. $2x^2 = 27$

d. $49 = x^2 + 25$

e. $x^2 + 4 = 36$

f. $x^2 + 81 = (2x)^2$

g. $x^2 + \left(\dfrac{x}{2}\right)^2 = 36$

h. $36 - x^2 = 25$

i. $x^2 + x^2 = a^2$

j. $4x^2 = x^2 + a^2$

The meaning of proportion

The statement $\frac{2}{3} = \frac{4}{6}$ is a proportion. It may be read, "2 is to 3 as 4 is to 6." It may be written also as $2 : 3 = 4 : 6$.

All house plans are drawn to scale, which is another way of saying that corresponding segments of the plan and house are proportional. For example, if an architect draws a plan to the scale $\frac{1}{2}$ inch to 1 foot and makes a room plan 6 inches by 7 inches, the carpenter will make the room 12 feet by 14 feet. Verify this.

A proportion is a statement that two ratios are equal.

If the ratios $\dfrac{a}{b}$ and $\dfrac{c}{d}$ are equal, $\dfrac{a}{b} = \dfrac{c}{d}$ is a proportion. Every proportion contains four terms. It would be meaningless to say that two numbers are proportional to each other; two numbers can only be proportional to two other numbers.

It is not necessary that all four terms of a proportion be measured in the same unit. For example, if 1 cubic foot of water weighs 62.4 pounds, we can find the weight of 3 cubic feet of water by writing the relation

$$\frac{1(\text{cu. ft.})}{3(\text{cu. ft.})} = \frac{62.4(\text{lb.})}{x(\text{lb.})}$$

The proportion is: $\dfrac{1}{3} = \dfrac{62.4}{x}$.

Terms of a proportion

In the proportion $a : b = c : d$

$$\text{or } \frac{a}{b} = \frac{c}{d},$$

a is called the *first term*; b is the *second term*; c is the *third term*; and d is the *fourth term* of the proportion. The first and third terms are numerators, and the second and fourth terms are denominators of the fractions.

The first and fourth terms, a and d, are called *extremes*; the second and third terms, b and c, are called *means*.

In the special case where the means are equal, as $\dfrac{a}{m} = \dfrac{m}{c}$ (or, $a : m = m : c$),

m is the *mean proportional* between a and c.

In the proportion $r : s = x : y$

$$\text{or } \frac{r}{s} = \frac{x}{y},$$

y is the *fourth proportional* to r, s, and x in that order.

Rules governing the use of a proportion

Since proportions are equations, all axioms applying to equations may be used. For example, to clear a proportion of fractions, we may multiply both members of the equation by the lowest common denominator.

A proportion is a special case of a fractional equation since it has only one fraction on each side of the equal sign. Consequently, it has special properties not common to a general fractional equation. We shall now derive those properties.

Fundamental properties of

a proportion

A. *In any proportion the product of the extremes is equal to the product of the means.*

If $\dfrac{a}{b} = \dfrac{c}{d}$, the lowest common denominator is bd. Then $bd \cdot \dfrac{a}{b} = bd \cdot \dfrac{c}{d}$ or $ad = bc$.

B. *If the product of one pair of numbers is equal to the product of another pair of numbers, either pair may be made the means and the other pair the extremes of a proportion.*

1. If $ad = bc$, we may divide both members of the equation by bd.
   Therefore, $\dfrac{ad}{bd} = \dfrac{bc}{bd}$ or $\dfrac{a}{b} = \dfrac{c}{d}$.

2. If $ad = bc$, by what must we divide both members of the equation to get $\dfrac{a}{c} = \dfrac{b}{d}$?

3. If $ad = bc$, by what must we divide both members of the equation to get $\dfrac{b}{a} = \dfrac{d}{c}$?

It should be obvious that we divide both ad and bc by the product of the two denominators of the proportion that we seek to write. Thus, to get $\dfrac{d}{b} = \dfrac{c}{a}$ from $ad = bc$, we divide both ad and bc by ab.

We should also note that when we write a proportion from $ad = bc$, if a is the first term, d must be the fourth term; if b is the first term, c must be the fourth term, etc. In any case a check is possible by using Property A.

C. *In a proportion, the terms are in proportion by alternation and also by inversion.*

If (a) $\dfrac{m}{n} = \dfrac{x}{y}$, then (b) $\dfrac{m}{x} = \dfrac{n}{y}$,

(c) $\dfrac{n}{m} = \dfrac{y}{x}$, and (d) $\dfrac{n}{y} = \dfrac{m}{x}$.

When we simplify (a) we get $my = nx$; when we simplify (b), (c), and (d), we get $my = nx$. Thus if (a) is a proportion, (b), (c), and (d) are proportions.

Proportion (b) is formed from (a) by interchanging n and x; the ratios of (c) are the reciprocals of the ratios of (a); and (d) is formed from (c) by interchanging m and y.

D. *If the numerators of a proportion are equal, the denominators are equal, and conversely.*

If $\dfrac{a}{x} = \dfrac{a}{y}$, then $ax = ay$, or $x = y$.
In general, if $\dfrac{a}{b} = \dfrac{c}{d}$ and $a = c$, then $b = d$.

E. *If three terms of one proportion are equal, respectively, to the corresponding terms of another proportion, the remaining terms are equal.*

If $\dfrac{2}{3} = \dfrac{c}{4}$ and $\dfrac{2}{3} = \dfrac{x}{4}$, then $c = x$.

In general, if $\dfrac{a}{b} = \dfrac{c}{d}, \dfrac{x}{y} = \dfrac{w}{z}, a = x$, $b = y$, and $c = w$, then $d = z$.

F. *In a series of equal ratios, the sum of the numerators is to the sum of the denominators as any numerator is to its denominator.*

If $\dfrac{a}{b} = \dfrac{c}{d} = \dfrac{e}{f}$, we can equate each ratio to k, which is a convenient symbol for the value of any one of the ratios.

Then $\dfrac{a}{b} = k$, $\dfrac{c}{d} = k$, and $\dfrac{e}{f} = k$. Thus $a = bk$, $c = dk$, and $e = fk$. Why? Adding, $a + c + e = k(b + d + f)$. Why?

Thus, $\dfrac{a + c + e}{b + d + f} = k = \dfrac{a}{b} = \dfrac{c}{d} = \dfrac{e}{f}$.

Why?

G. *In a proportion, the terms are in proportion by addition or subtraction.*

1. If $\dfrac{a}{b} = \dfrac{c}{d}$, then $\dfrac{a}{b} + 1 = \dfrac{c}{d} + 1$. Why?

   Thus $\dfrac{a + b}{b} = \dfrac{c + d}{d}$. Explain.

2. Explain how $\dfrac{a - b}{b} = \dfrac{c - d}{d}$ is obtained from $\dfrac{a}{b} = \dfrac{c}{d}$.

H. *The mean proportional between any two numbers is the square root of their product.*

   If $\dfrac{a}{b} = \dfrac{b}{c}$, then $b^2 = ac$. Why?

   Thus, $b = \pm \sqrt{ac}$. Why?

   Of course, the positive value of $\sqrt{ac}$ is used when b is necessarily a positive number or quantity.

Exercises

1. **a.** Is $\dfrac{a}{b} = \dfrac{c}{d}$ a proportion when $a = 3$, $b = 5$, $c = 6$, and $d = 9$?

   b. Since $\dfrac{3}{4} = \dfrac{6}{8}$, then $\dfrac{3}{?} = \dfrac{4}{?}$.

   c. Since $\dfrac{3}{4} = \dfrac{6}{8}$, then $\dfrac{?}{3} = \dfrac{?}{6}$.

   d. Since $\dfrac{3}{4} = \dfrac{6}{8}$, then $\dfrac{?}{3} = \dfrac{?}{4}$.

2. If $ax = bc$, then $\dfrac{a}{c} = \dfrac{?}{?}$.

3. If $ax = mn$, then $x = ?$

4. If $\dfrac{a}{x} = \dfrac{b}{y}$, and $\dfrac{a}{z} = \dfrac{b}{y}$, then $x = ?$

5. Write the following equations as proportions in which x is the fourth proportional:

   a. $ab = cx$

   b. $ax = bd$

   c. $xa = mn$

6. Write the four proportions that can be made from the equation $mn = rs$ by using Property B.

7. Write the other three proportions that can be made from $\dfrac{x}{y} = \dfrac{r}{s}$ by using Property C.

8. Solve the following proportions for x:

   a. $\dfrac{4}{x} = \dfrac{5}{7}$

   b. $\dfrac{7}{8} = \dfrac{2x}{3}$

   c. $\dfrac{x}{7a} = \dfrac{3b}{5}$

   d. $\dfrac{4a}{3x} = \dfrac{2}{9c}$

   e. $\dfrac{6ab}{x} = \dfrac{3ab}{2}$

   f. $\dfrac{x + 3}{x - 5} = \dfrac{1}{5}$

   g. $\dfrac{a + b}{c} = \dfrac{x + d}{x}$

   h. $\dfrac{a - b}{b} = \dfrac{a - x}{x}$

   i. $\dfrac{x^2 - x}{3} = \dfrac{2}{1}$

9. Find the mean proportional between the following pairs of numbers:

    a. 9 and 16   **c.** a and b

    b. 3 and 27   **d.** $3a$ and $12a$

10. a. If $\dfrac{r}{a} = \dfrac{m}{n} = \dfrac{x}{y}$, then

$$\frac{r + m + x}{?} = \frac{m}{?}.$$

    b. If $\dfrac{r}{s} = \dfrac{m}{n}$, then $\dfrac{r + s}{?} = \dfrac{?}{n}$.

    c. If $\dfrac{r}{s} = \dfrac{m}{n}$, then $\dfrac{r - s}{s} = \dfrac{?}{?}$.

11. Find the ratio of x to y if:

    a. $6x = 11y$

    b. $mx = ny$

    c. $(a + b)x = (r + s)y$

    d. $ax + bx = cy + dy$

    e. $ax + by = mx + ny - ex$

    f. $\dfrac{5x - 3y}{7x - 4y} = \dfrac{3}{5}$

    g. $\frac{2}{3}x = \frac{7}{8}y$

12. Write proportions using the letters a, b, c, and x which when solved for x will give the following:

    a. $x = \dfrac{bc}{a}$

    b. $x = \dfrac{ac}{b}$

    c. $x = \dfrac{ab}{c}$

    d. $x = \dfrac{ab}{2c}$

    e. $x = \dfrac{(a + b)b}{c}$

    f. $x = \dfrac{2ab}{3c}$

13. Write proportions using the letters a, b, and x which when solved for x will give:

    a. $x = \dfrac{a^2}{b}$

    b. $x = \dfrac{b^2}{a}$

    c. $x = \dfrac{a(a + b)}{b}$

    d. $x = \dfrac{2ab}{a + b}$

    e. $x = \sqrt{ab}$

    f. $x = \sqrt{\dfrac{ab}{2}}$

14. Separate 286 into three parts in the ratio $6 : 7 : 9$.

15. Show how to get the following proportions from $\dfrac{a}{b} = \dfrac{c}{d}$:

    a. $\dfrac{a - c}{c} = \dfrac{b - d}{d}$

    b. $\dfrac{a + c}{c} = \dfrac{b + d}{d}$

    c. $\dfrac{a + c}{b + d} = \dfrac{c}{d}$

    d. $\dfrac{a - c}{a + c} = \dfrac{b - d}{b + d}$

Direct variation

Although two fixed quantities are not proportional, two variables might be proportional. The length s of a side of a dynamic square is a variable, and thus the perimeter p of the square is also a variable; for example, p is doubled when s is doubled; p is divided by one-third when s is divided by one-third; or, in general, p is multiplied or divided by n as s is multiplied or divided by n. Although both p and s are variables, the ratio of p to s is always the same; that is, their ratio is a constant.

If we consider two squares whose sides are s_1 and s_2 and whose perimeters are p_1 and p_2, respectively, then

$\dfrac{p_1}{s_1} = k$ and $\dfrac{p_2}{s_2} = k$. Thus

$\dfrac{p_1}{s_1} = \dfrac{p_2}{s_2}$ or $\dfrac{p_1}{p_2} = \dfrac{s_1}{s_2}$.

We can express this in words by saying that the perimeters of two squares are directly proportional to their sides. The *constant of variation* k in this example is 4. In some problems of direct variation, k can be found from known or given values of the variables; sometimes it is given; and sometimes it is found experimentally.

If the ratio of two variables is a constant, one variable is said to vary directly as the other; or the two variables are directly proportional.

Example 1. At a fixed price per article the cost varies as the number of articles bought.

Let c_1 be the cost in dollars of n_1 articles and c_2 be the cost in dollars of n_2 articles.

Then, $\dfrac{c_1}{n_1} = k$, and $\dfrac{c_2}{n_2} = k$. The constant of variation k in each instance is the fixed price of one article.

Hence, $\dfrac{c_1}{n_1} = \dfrac{c_2}{n_2}$ or $\dfrac{c_1}{c_2} = \dfrac{n_1}{n_2}$. Why?

If $c_1 = \$5.00$ when $n_1 = 10$, find c_2 when $n_2 = 12$.

Solution: $\dfrac{5.00}{c_2} = \dfrac{10}{12}$

$10c_2 = 12 \times 5.00$

$c_2 = \dfrac{12 \times 5.00}{10} = 6.$

The cost of n_2 articles is $6.00.

(Note: Since $c_1 = \$5.00$, when $n = 10$, $k = 50\cancel{c}$ per article.)

Example 2. If the speed of an automobile is uniform, the distance varies directly as the speed, the time being fixed.

Let d_1 be the distance in miles when the speed is s_1 miles per hour and d_2 be the distance in miles when the speed is s_2 miles per hour.

Then $\dfrac{d_1}{s_1} = k$ and $\dfrac{d_2}{s_2} = k$. The constant variation k in each instance is the fixed time since $\dfrac{\text{distance}}{\text{uniform speed}} = \text{time}$.

Hence, $\dfrac{d_1}{s_1} = \dfrac{d_2}{s_2}$ or $\dfrac{d_1}{d_2} = \dfrac{s_1}{s_2}$. Why?

If $d_1 = 60.0$ miles when $s_1 = 45.0$ miles per hour, and $d_2 = 50.0$ miles, find s_2.

Solution: $\dfrac{60}{50} = \dfrac{45}{s_2}$

$60s_2 = 50 \times 45$

$s_2 = \dfrac{50 \times 45}{60} = 37.5.$

The speed is 37.5 miles per hour.

(Note: Since $d_1 = 60.0$ miles when $s_1 = 45$ miles per hour, then $k = \frac{4}{3}$ hour.)

Example 3. If y varies directly as x, what is the effect on y when x is multiplied by 7?

Solution: $\dfrac{y_1}{x_1} = k$ and $\dfrac{y_2}{x_2} = k$.

Hence, $\dfrac{y_1}{x_1} = \dfrac{y_2}{x_2}$ or $\dfrac{y_1}{y_2} = \dfrac{x_1}{x_2}$.

Substituting: $\dfrac{y_1}{y_2} = \dfrac{x_1}{7x_1}$.

Simplifying: $\dfrac{y_1}{y_2} = \dfrac{1}{7}$.

Solving for y_2: $y_2 = 7y_1$. Hence, when x is multiplied by 7, y is multiplied by 7.

In a similar way, you find the effect on y when x is divided by 3.

Inverse variation

If two children of unequal weights are riding on a seesaw, the heavier child is closer to the pivotal point when the seesaw is in balance. In fact, if we represent the weights of the children by w_1 and w_2 and their respective distances from the pivotal point by d_1 and d_2, then $w_1d_1 = w_2d_2$. This pair of products can be expressed as the proportion:

$$\frac{w_1}{w_2} = \frac{d_2}{d_1}.$$

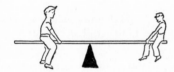

Fig. 1

A proportion of this type is an inverse proportion and the variables are said to be inversely proportional. When one variable is multiplied by 2, the other variable is divided by 2; when one variable is divided by three, the other variable is multiplied by three; in general, when one variable is multiplied by n, the other variable is divided by n.

If the product of two variables is a constant, then one variable varies inversely as the other; or the variables are inversely proportional.

Example 1. If the temperature of a gas does not change and the amount of gas is kept the same, its volume is inversely proportional to the external pressure. That is, the product of the pressure and the volume is a constant.

Let v_1 be the volume of a gas and p_1 be the pressure. Then $v_1p_1 = k$ when k is the constant of variation.

Similarly, $v_2p_2 = k$.

Thus, $v_1p_1 = v_2p_2$.

Hence, $\dfrac{v_1}{v_2} = \dfrac{p_2}{p_1}$.

What is the effect on the volume if the pressure becomes 5 times as great?

Substituting: $\dfrac{v_1}{v_2} = \dfrac{5p_1}{p_1}$.

Simplifying: $\dfrac{v_1}{v_2} = \dfrac{5}{1}$.

Solving for v_2: $v_2 = \dfrac{1}{5}v_1$.

In a similar way, you find the effect on the pressure if the gas is compressed into half the space.

Example 2. If the area of a rectangle is constant, the length varies inversely as its width.

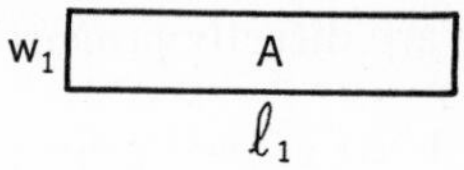

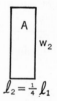

Fig. 2

Hence, $l_1w_1 = l_2w_2$ or $\dfrac{l_1}{l_2} = \dfrac{w_2}{w_1}$.

If the area of a rectangle is constant, find the effect on w if l is divided by 4.

Fig. 3

Solution: $\dfrac{l_1}{\frac{1}{4}l_1} = \dfrac{w_2}{w_1}$, or $\dfrac{4}{1} = \dfrac{w_2}{w_1}$.

Hence, $w_2 = 4w_1$.

In a similar way, you find the effect on l if w is multiplied by 4.

Exercises

In each of the following exercises write a proportion to show the relation between the variables:

1. The weight of an object varies directly as its volume if its composition is constant.

2. The length of a shadow at a given time varies directly as the height of the object.

3. The income of a person who works for a given amount per hour is directly proportional to the number of hours he works.

4. The distance a motorist drives at a constant rate is directly proportional to the time he drives.

5. The number of slices to be cut from a loaf of bread varies inversely as the thickness of the slice.

6. The time required to move from one point to another is inversely proportional to the rate of motion.

7. Air pressure is inversely proportional to altitude.

8. The amount of money invested to yield a given return varies inversely as the rate of interest.

9. The distance required to stop a car varies directly as the square of the speed.

10. The area of a circle is directly proportional to the square of the radius.

Graphical representation of direct variation (*Optional*)

If the ratio $\dfrac{y}{x}$ of the variables y and x is constant, that is, if $\dfrac{y}{x} = k$, then $y = kx$. Hence, this equation expresses direct variation of y and x. In your opinion, is the locus (graph) of this relationship a straight line, a circle, or some other curve? If you do not already know the correct answer, you may learn it from this example:

Suppose a boy is riding a bicycle at a constant rate of 6 miles per hour. Let d be the number of miles he travels in t hours. Then $d = 6t$. (In words, the formula is: distance = rate $\times$ time.)

Table of values:

t	1	2	3	$\frac{1}{2}$	0
d	6	12	18	3	0

The graph of $d = 6t$ is a straight line through the origin of the set of axes on which t represents the time in hours and d represents the distance in miles. In this example, negative values of t have no meaning, so the graph is drawn only for positive values of the variables.

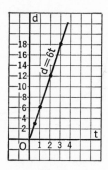

Fig. 4

How would the graph of $d = 8t$ differ from the graph of $d = 6t$? How would they be alike?

How would the graph of $d = t$ differ from the graph of $d = 6t$? How would they be alike?

Explain the nature of the graph of $y = kx$ and the effect on the graph of different values of the constant of variation k.

Graphical representation of inverse variation (*Optional*)

If the product of two variables x and y is constant, then $xy = k$. This equation expresses inverse variation of x and y. The constant k is the constant of variation. To learn the nature of the locus (graph) of this relationship, we shall use the following example:

The time required for a boy to travel 8 miles on a bicycle varies inversely with his rate. If t is the number of hours he rides and r is his rate in miles per hour, then $rt = 8$.

Table of values:

r	1	2	4	8	12
t	8	4	2	1	$\frac{2}{3}$

The graph of $rt = 8$ is a curve called a hyperbola.

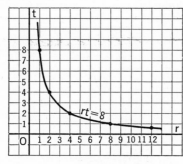

Fig. 5

Although a hyperbola has two branches, the branch shown above was obtained by taking only positive values of r.

How would the graph of $rt = 12$ differ from the graph of $rt = 8$? How would they be alike?

Explain the nature of the graph of $xy = k$ and the effect on the graph of different values of the constant of variation k.

Proportional line segments

Two line segments are said to be divided proportionally when a proportion can be formed with the numbers representing the lengths of the parts.

In this figure, $\dfrac{AP}{PB} = \dfrac{2u}{3u} = \dfrac{2}{3}$

and $\dfrac{RS}{ST} = \dfrac{2x}{3x} = \dfrac{2}{3}$.

Therefore, $\dfrac{AP}{PB} = \dfrac{RS}{ST}$.

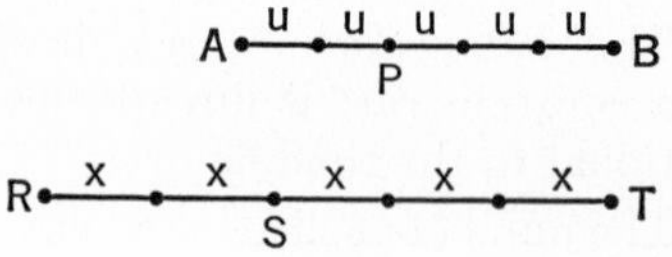

Fig. 6

Thus, AB and RT are divided proportionally because the measures of the segments of one have the same ratio as the measures of the corresponding segments of the other.

Commensurable and incommensurable quantities

Two quantities of the same kind are commensurable if there is a common unit of measure that is contained in each of them an integral number of times. Thus 3 feet and 2 inches are commensurable because 2 inches is a common unit of measures; 2 inches and $1\frac{1}{4}$ inches are commensurable because $\frac{1}{4}$ inch is contained 8 times in 2 inches and 5 times in $1\frac{1}{4}$ inches.

Two quantities of the same kind are incommensurable when there is no common unit of measure which is contained in each of them an integral number of times. There is, for example, no common unit which can be used to measure the circumference C and the diameter d of a circle. As you learned in arithmetic, the circumference is π times the diameter. The value of π cannot be represented as the ratio of two integers; therefore, no matter how far the decimal is carried, there is no common unit which is contained a whole number of times in both C and d. Other numbers such as 2 and $\sqrt{2}$ are incommensurable.

Note: In this text we prove certain theorems for the commensurable case only and assume them true for the incommensurable case. The proof of the incommensurable case involves methods which are beyond the scope of this course.

Exercises

1. Name the largest common unit of measure which is contained an integral number of times in each of the following pairs of quantities:
   a. 4 feet and 3 yards
   b. 8.32 cm. and 2.30 cm.
   c. $\frac{1}{4}$ foot and $\frac{1}{3}$ foot
   d. 4.32 feet and 2.20 inches
2. Find a common unit of measure of:
   a. 2.3 mi. and 4.3 yd.
   b. $2\frac{1}{2}$ m. and $3\frac{1}{4}$ cm.
3. Given: $\triangle ABC$ in which $\dfrac{CD}{DA} = \dfrac{CE}{EB}$.

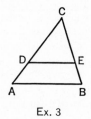

Ex. 3

Complete the following proportions:

a. $\dfrac{CD}{CE} = \dfrac{?}{?}$

b. $\dfrac{DA}{CD} = \dfrac{?}{?}$

c. $\dfrac{CD + DA}{DA} = \dfrac{?}{?}$

  or $\dfrac{CA}{DA} = \dfrac{?}{?}$

d. $\dfrac{CA - CD}{CD} = \dfrac{?}{?}$

  or $\dfrac{DA}{CD} = \dfrac{?}{?}$

Proportional line segments in triangles

Given: $\triangle MRY$ with $DE \parallel MY$; the unit d is contained four times in DR and three times in MD.

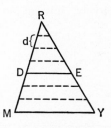

Fig. 7

What is the numerical ratio of DR to MD?

If the dashed lines are parallel to DE, they are parallel to each other. Why?

Are the seven segments of RY equal to each other? Why? Are they equal to d? Why? Are DR, MD, ER, and YE proportional? Why?

THEOREM 69. If a line is parallel to one side of a triangle and intersects the other two sides, it divides these sides proportionally.

Given: $\triangle ABC$ with $DE \parallel AB$.

Prove: $\dfrac{CD}{DA} = \dfrac{CE}{EB}$.

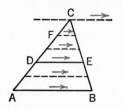

Proof

STATEMENTS	AUTHORITIES
1. Select a unit CF which can be contained in CD and DA an integral number of times. Let CF be contained m times in CD (in this case 3 times), and in DA, n times (in this case 2 times).	1. Since CD and AD are commensurable, we may assume CF as the common unit.
2. $\therefore \dfrac{CD}{DA} = \dfrac{m}{n}$.	2. Why?
3. Through C and the points of division, draw lines $\parallel AB$.	3. Why possible?
4. These lines divide CE and EB, respectively, into m and n equal parts.	4. Why?
5. $\therefore \dfrac{CE}{EB} = \dfrac{m}{n}$.	5. Why?
6. $\therefore \dfrac{CD}{DA} = \dfrac{CE}{EB}$.	6. Why?

COROLLARY 1. If a line is parallel to one side of a triangle and intersects the other two sides, it divides these sides so that either side is to one of its segments as the other side is to its corresponding segment.

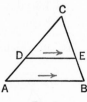

Fig. 8

From $\dfrac{CD}{DA} = \dfrac{CE}{EB}$ show that $\dfrac{CA}{DA} = \dfrac{CB}{EB}$.

From $\dfrac{CD}{DA} = \dfrac{CE}{EB}$ show that $\dfrac{DA}{CD} = \dfrac{EB}{CE}$ and then prove that $\dfrac{CA}{CD} = \dfrac{CB}{CE}$.

COROLLARY 2. Three or more parallel lines intercept proportional segments on transversals.

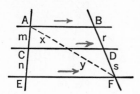

Fig. 9

Suggestions:

Draw AF.

Then $\dfrac{m}{n} = \dfrac{x}{y}$. Why?

Also $\dfrac{r}{s} = \dfrac{x}{y}$. Why?

You complete the proof.

Exercises

In Exercises 1-5, M and N are points on RS and RT of $\triangle RST$ and $MN \parallel ST$.

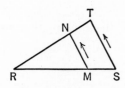

Ex. 1–5

1. If $RM = 12.0$ in., $MS = 5.0$ in., and $RN = 8.0$ in., find NT.
2. If $RS = 9.0$ in., $MS = 3.0$ in., and $RT = 5.0$ in., find NT.
3. If $RS = 8.0$ in., $MS = 4.0$ in., and $RN = 3.0$ in., find NT.
4. If $RM = MS$, and $RT = 3.5$ in., find NT.
5. If $RM = MS$, and $NT = 2.0$ in., find RN.

In Exercises 6-8, parallels l, s, and t are cut by transversals n and m.

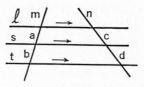

Ex. 6–8

6. If $a = 4$, $b = 6$, and $c = 5$, find d.
7. If $a + b = 12$, $a = 4$, and $c = 3$, find d.
8. If $a + b = 10$, $c + d = 8$, and $a = 4$, find d.
9. In a given triangle two sides are 15 inches and 20 inches. A line parallel to the third side cuts the 15-inch side into segments having the ratio $2:3$. Find the segments of the 20-inch side.
10. If $m = 3\frac{1}{4}$ in., $n = 2\frac{1}{8}$ in., and $r = 1\frac{1}{2}$ in., find BC.

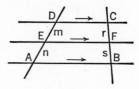

Ex. 10–11

11. If $m = a + b$, $n = a$, and $r = a^2 - b^2$, find s.
12. Construct and describe the locus of midpoints of line segments drawn from a given point to a given line.
13. The non-parallel sides of a trapezoid are 8.0 in. and 13.0 in., respectively. A line parallel to the base divides the 8.0-in. side in the ratio of 1 to 3. Find the segments of the 13.0-in. side.

Constructing the fourth proportional

Suppose we wish to find a point E on AX so that $\dfrac{AB}{BC} = \dfrac{AD}{DE}$. Can you construct a line through C which will determine the point E?

If three line segments AB, BC, and AD are given, can you construct the fourth proportional DE so that

$$\frac{AB}{BC} = \frac{AD}{DE}?$$

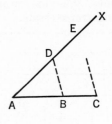

Fig. 10

CONSTRUCTION 21. **Construct the fourth proportional to three given line segments.**

Given: The segments a, b, and c.

a _____

b ____

c _____

Given

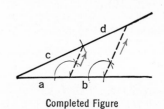

Completed Figure

Required: To construct d so that $\dfrac{a}{b} = \dfrac{c}{d}$.

You do the construction and write the proof.

Exercises

1. a. Compute x in the proportion $\dfrac{2(\text{in.})}{1(\text{in.})} = \dfrac{3(\text{in.})}{x(\text{in.})}$.

b. Construct the fourth proportional to the given segments 2 in., 1 in., and 3 in.

c. Does your construction answer agree with the algebraic answer?

2. Given: $\dfrac{2}{x} = \dfrac{3}{5}$. **(a)** Find x by algebra. **(b)** Find x by construction.

Hint: To construct x you must first transform the given proportion to a correct one that has x as the fourth term. Why?

If a, b, and c are given line segments, construct x so that:

3. $x = \dfrac{ab}{c}$

4. $x = \dfrac{ac}{b}$

5. $x = \dfrac{bc}{a}$

6. $x = \dfrac{a^2}{b}$

7. $x = \dfrac{2ab}{c}$

8. $x = \dfrac{ab}{a + c}$

Dividing a line into parts proportional to given segments

CONSTRUCTION 22. Divide a given line segment into parts proportional to two or more given line segments.

Given: Segment AB and segments r, s, and t.

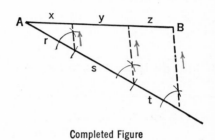

r

s

t

Given

Completed Figure

Required: Divide AB into three segments x, y, and z proportional to r, s, and t. That is, construct x, y, and z so that $\dfrac{x}{r} = \dfrac{y}{s} = \dfrac{z}{t}$.

You do the construction and write the proof.

The draftsman shown here is using an instrument called a pantograph to fill in the details on a scale drawing of an aerial map. The design of a pantograph is based on the principles of ratio and proportion.

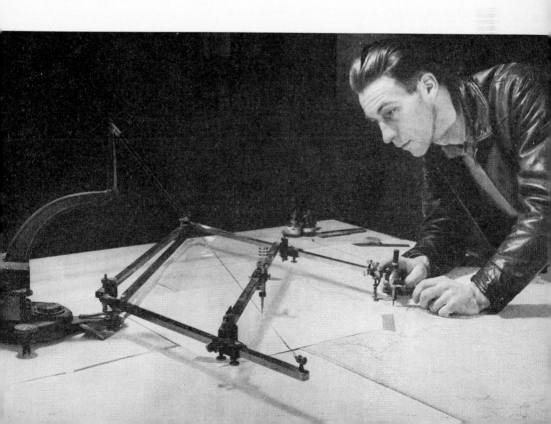

Exercises

1. Divide a given segment MN into parts r, s, and t proportional to three given segments a, b, and c.

2. Divide a given segment into parts proportional to 1, 2, and 3.

3. Trisect a given line segment RS.

4. Divide one side of a triangle into segments proportional to the other two sides.

5. Given the perimeter of a triangle, construct the triangle so that its sides are proportional to 2, 3, and 4.

A line dividing two sides of a triangle proportionally

THEOREM 70. **If a line divides two sides of a triangle proportionally, it is parallel to the third side.**

Given: DE intersects AC and BC in the $\triangle ABC$ so that $\dfrac{CD}{DA} = \dfrac{CE}{EB}$.

Prove: $DE \parallel AB$.

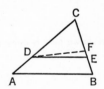

Plan: Through D draw $DF \parallel AB$ and prove that DF coincides with DE.

Proof

STATEMENTS	AUTHORITIES
1. Through D draw $DF \parallel AB$.	1. Why possible?
2. $\therefore \dfrac{CA}{DA} = \dfrac{CB}{FB}$.	2. Why?
3. $\dfrac{CD}{DA} = \dfrac{CE}{EB}$.	3. Why?
4. $\therefore \dfrac{CA}{DA} = \dfrac{CB}{EB}$.	4. Why?
5. $\therefore FB = EB$.	5. Why?
6. $\therefore F$ and E coincide.	6. Why?
7. $\therefore DF$ and DE coincide.	7. Why?
8. $\therefore DE \parallel AB$.	8. Why?

Exercises

In Exercises **1-5**, *use the figure for Theorem 70. Explain your answers.*

1. In $\triangle ABC$, if $AC = 15.0$ in., $AD = 5.0$ in., $BC = 21.0$ in., and $BE = 7.0$ in., is $DE \parallel AB$?

2. In $\triangle ABC$, if $AD:DC = 2:3$ and $BC:EC = 5:2$, is $DE \parallel AB$?

3. In $\triangle ABC$, if $AD = \frac{1}{4}AC$ and $BE = \frac{1}{3}EC$, is $DE \parallel AB$?

4. In $\triangle ABC$, if $\dfrac{AD}{DC} = \dfrac{BE}{EC}$, is $DE \parallel AB$?

5. In $\triangle ABC$, if $\dfrac{AC}{DC} = \dfrac{BC}{EC}$, is $DE \parallel AB$?

6. In $\triangle ABC$, if $AD = \frac{3}{4}DC$, $BC = 10.0''$, and $DE \parallel AB$, find BE.

7. If a line is drawn through the point of intersection of the medians of a triangle and parallel to one side, what is the ratio of the segments into which it divides the other two sides? Prove.

Internal and external division of a line segment

A line segment is divided *internally* into two segments if the point of division lies on the line segment. In Figure 11, X divides AB internally into two segments AX and XB so that $AX:XB = 2:3$. The sum of the two segments AX and XB is equal to the given segment AB.

A •——u——•—u—•—u—•—u——• B
　　　　　　X

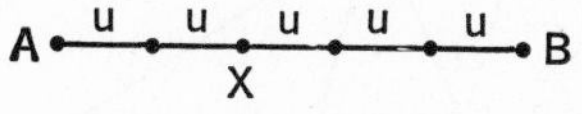

Fig. 11

A line segment is divided *externally* into two segments if the point of division lies on the line segment extended. In Figure 12, X divides AB externally into two segments AX and XB so that $AX:XB = 2:5$. The difference of the two segments AX and XB is equal to the given segment AB.

X •——u——•—u—•—u—•—u——• B
　　　　　A

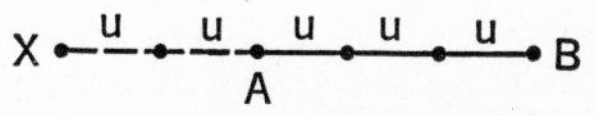

Fig. 12

Exercises

1. Draw a triangle ABC so that AB is any convenient length, AC is 3 units, and BC is 4 of the same units. Then $AC:BC = 3:4$.

Divide AB internally at the point X so that $AX:XB = AC:BC$.

Then $\dfrac{AX}{XB} = \dfrac{3}{?}$ and $\dfrac{AX}{AB} = \dfrac{3}{?}$.

Bisect $\angle C$. Does t_C seem to pass through X?

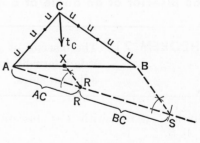

Ex. 1

If $AB = 2.8$ cm., how long is AX?

Hint: $\dfrac{AX}{AB} = \dfrac{AR}{AS}$.

2. Given: $\triangle ABC$, CD bisects $\angle ACB$, $AR \parallel CD$, and BC extended meets AR at R.

Prove: **a.** $\dfrac{AD}{DB} = \dfrac{RC}{CB}$

    b. $\angle 1 = \angle 2$

    c. $\dfrac{AD}{DB} = \dfrac{AC}{CB}$

Refer to Exercise **1.** Should t_C have passed through the point X?

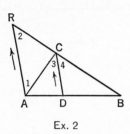

Ex. 2

3. Draw $\triangle ABC$ so that $AC : BC = 2 : 5$. Construct the point X on AB so that $AX : XB = 2 : 5$. AB is now divided externally into segments AX and XB whose ratio is $2 : 5$. Extend BC to P. Bisect $\angle PCA$. Does the bisector seem to intersect AB extended at X? (See figure for Exercise **3.**)

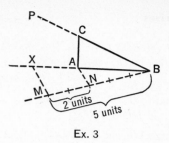

Ex. 3

4. Given: $\triangle ABC$, CD bisects the exterior $\angle PCA$ meeting BA extended at D, and $AR \parallel CD$.

a. Prove $\dfrac{AD}{DB} = \dfrac{RC}{CB}$

b. Prove $\angle 3 = \angle 4$

c. How are AD and DB related to AC and CB?

Refer to Exercise **3** above. Should the bisector of $\angle PCA$ have intersected AB extended at X?

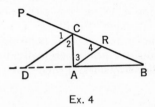

Ex. 4

The bisector of an angle of a triangle

THEOREM 71. **The bisector of an angle of a triangle divides the opposite side internally into segments which are proportional to the adjacent sides.**

Given: $\triangle ABC$ with CD bisecting $\angle ACB$.

Prove: $\dfrac{AD}{DB} = \dfrac{AC}{CB}$.

Hint: From A draw $AE \parallel DC$ and let it meet BC extended at E.

You write the proof.

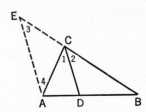

THEOREM 72. **If the bisector of an exterior angle of a triangle meets the**
(*Optional*). **extension of the opposite side, it divides that side exter-**
nally into segments which are proportional to the adjacent
sides.

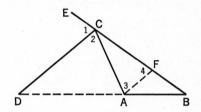

Given: CD bisects exterior $\angle ECA$ of
$\triangle ABC$; CD intersects BA extended
at D.

Prove: $\dfrac{AD}{DB} = \dfrac{AC}{BC}$.

Hint: From A draw $AF \parallel DC$.

You write the proof.

Exercises

1. If the bisector of an angle of a
   triangle bisects the opposite side,
   what is the ratio of the other two
   sides of the triangle?

2. The sides of a triangle are 9, 12,
   and 14. Find the segments formed
   by the bisector of the largest angle
   where it meets the opposite side.

3. In the figure for Theorem 71, find
   AD if $DB = 6$, $AC = 8$, and
   $BC = 10$.

4. In the figure for Theorem 71, find
   AC if AD is $\frac{2}{5}$ of AB and $BC = 9$.

5. The sides of a triangle are 6, 7,
   and 10. Find the segments into
   which the longest side is divided
   externally by the bisector of the
   opposite exterior angle.

6. In the figure for Theorem 72, if
   $AC = 10$, $CB = 12$, and $DA = 18$,
   find AB.

Review of Chapter 12

True-False Test

Write the numbers **1-20** *on your paper.*
If a statement is always true, write **True**;
if a statement is not necessarily true,
write **False**.

1. All equations are proportions.

2. If $\dfrac{a}{b} = \dfrac{c}{d}$, then $\dfrac{d}{b} = \dfrac{a}{c}$.

3. If the second and third terms of a
   proportion are equal, either term

is the square root of the product of
the first and fourth terms.

4. The ratio $\dfrac{2x^2}{14x^2 + 3y}$ is equal to
   $\dfrac{1}{7 + 3y}$.

5. In $\triangle ABC$ if P divides AC so that
   $\dfrac{AP}{PC} = \dfrac{2}{3}$ and Q divides BC so that
   $\dfrac{CQ}{QB} = \dfrac{2}{3}$, then $PQ \parallel AB$. (Assume
   internal division.)

In Exercises **6-10**, *ABC is a triangle and* $ED \parallel BC$.

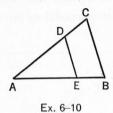

Ex. 6–10

6. If $AE = EB$, then $AD = \frac{1}{2}AC$.

7. If $AB = 8$, $EB = 3$, and $AD = 6$, then $DC = 2\frac{1}{4}$.

8. If $AE = 4$, $EB = 3$, and $AD = 5$, then $DC = 3\frac{3}{4}$.

9. If $AE = \frac{3}{5}AB$, then $\frac{AD}{DC} = \frac{3}{2}$.

10. If $AE = \frac{3}{5}AB$, then $DC = \frac{3}{5}AC$.

11. The fourth proportional to $2a$, $3a$, and $4a$ is $6a$.

12. If $x = \frac{rs}{t}$, then $\frac{r}{t} = \frac{x}{s}$.

13. All proportions are equations.

14. The extremes of the proportion $\frac{3}{4} = \frac{6}{x}$ are 4 and x.

15. The ratio $\frac{x}{y}$ is equal to $\frac{x+a}{y+a}$.

16. If $\frac{a}{b} = \frac{b}{c}$, then b is the mean proportional between a and c.

17. If the second and the fourth terms of a proportion are equal, the first and third terms are equal.

18. If $\frac{x}{y} = \frac{a}{b}$, then $xa = yb$.

19. If $mn = rs$, then $\frac{m}{n} = \frac{r}{s}$.

20. If $\frac{m}{n} = \frac{r}{s}$, then $\frac{m-n}{m+n} = \frac{r-s}{r+s}$.

Completion Test

Write the numbers **1-14** *on your paper. After each number write the expression that correctly completes the statement. Do not write in this book.*

1. The fourth proportional to 5, 7, and 15 is . . . . .

2. If $rs = cd$, then $\frac{r}{?} = \frac{?}{?}$.

3. If $\frac{x+4}{5} = \frac{7}{5}$, then $x = $ . . . . .

4. A common unit of measure of 3.000 inches and 10.732 inches is . . . . .

5. If the sides of a triangle whose perimeter is 45 inches are in the ratio $2:3:4$, then the longest side is . . . . .

6. If $DE \parallel AC$, $\frac{AD}{DB} = \frac{2}{3}$, and $CE = 2.8$ inches, then $BE = $ . . . . .

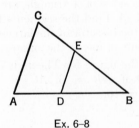

Ex. 6–8

7. If $DE \parallel AC$, $AD = 3.0$ inches, $DB = 4.0$ inches, and $BC = 8.0$ inches, then $BE = $ . . . . .

8. If $\frac{AD}{DB} = \frac{3}{4}$ and $\frac{CE}{CB} = \frac{3}{7}$, then . . .

9. The mean proportional between $9a$ and $4a$ is . . . . .

10. If $\frac{a}{b} = \frac{r}{s}$, then $\frac{?}{?} = \frac{a}{r}$.

11. If $2x - \frac{3}{4} = \frac{4}{3}$, then $x = $ . . . . .

12. If CD bisects $\angle ACB$ of $\triangle ABC$, $\dfrac{AC}{BC} = \dfrac{3}{2}$, and $AD = 4.00$ in., then $DB = \ldots$

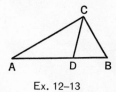

Ex. 12–13

13. If CD bisects $\angle ACB$ of $\triangle ABC$, $\dfrac{AC}{BC} = \dfrac{3}{2}$, and $AD = 3.00$ in., then $AB = \ldots$

14. A motorist touring Canada stopped at a filling station and had 10 Imperial gallons of gasoline put into the fuel tank of his car. If the ratio of the U. S. gallon to the Imperial gallon is 4 to 5, $\ldots$ U. S. gallons of gasoline were put into the tank.

Constructions

1. Construct and describe the locus of the midpoints of the segments drawn from one vertex of a triangle to the opposite side.

2. Divide the given segment AB into two parts m and n so that $\dfrac{m}{n} = \dfrac{2}{3}$.

3. Divide the given segment RS into three parts x, y, and z so that $\dfrac{x}{a} = \dfrac{y}{b} = \dfrac{z}{c}$ if a, b, and c are given line segments.

4. Construct x, given the segments r, s, and t if $\dfrac{t}{r} = \dfrac{s}{x}$.

5. Construct $x = \dfrac{mn}{c}$ if m, n, and c are given line segments.

6. Divide the side AB of $\triangle ABC$ into two parts AP and PB so that $\dfrac{AP}{PB} = \dfrac{AC}{BC}$.

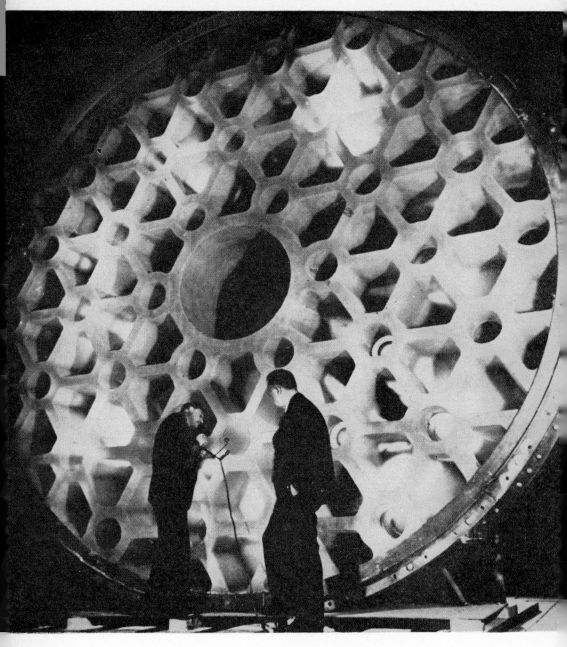

This 200-inch disc for the telescope of Mt. Palomar Observatory in California is the largest piece of glass ever made. A honeycomb of similar six-sided polygons and circles helped to cool the glass uniformly after it was poured.

Chapter 13 SIMILAR POLYGONS

W_{HEN} YOU look at an object through binoculars you see a magnified image of the object. The object and the image have the same shape. Two figures that have the same shape are said to be *similar*. (A highway map is supposed to be similar to the portion of territory of which it is a small-scale reproduction.)

This is the symbol for "is similar to": $\sim$.

Figures with the same shape

Do you think $ABCD \sim EFGH$? They are both equilateral and equiangular; their corresponding sides are proportional, and their corresponding angles are equal.

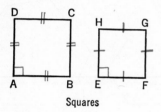

Squares

Fig. 1

Do $RSTU$ and $XYZW$ appear to be similar? Both of them are equilateral; hence, their corresponding sides are proportional. Are the corresponding angles of two rhombuses necessarily equal?

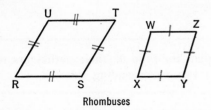

Rhombuses

Fig. 2

$EFGH$ is a 2 x 5 rectangle, and $RSTU$ is a 2 x 3 rectangle. Are their corresponding angles equal? Are their corresponding sides proportional? Do the rectangles have the same shape?

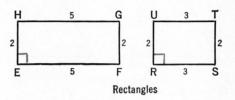

Rectangles

Fig. 3

Are the corresponding sides of $MNOP$ and $XYZW$ proportional? Are the corresponding angles equal? Are the parallelograms similar? Are any two parallelograms similar?

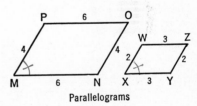

Parallelograms

Fig. 4

Obviously, the shape of a polygon is not determined by its sides alone, otherwise any two rhombuses would be similar; nor is the shape of a polygon determined by its angles alone, otherwise any two rectangles would be similar.

The corresponding angles of quadrilaterals $ABCD$ and $EFGH$ are equal, and the corresponding sides are proportional. That is: (a) $\angle A = \angle E$, $\angle B = \angle F$, $\angle C = \angle G$, and $\angle D = \angle H$; also (b) $\dfrac{AB}{EF} = \dfrac{BC}{FG} = \dfrac{CD}{GH} = \dfrac{DA}{HE}$.

Quadrilateral $ABCD$ is similar to quadrilateral $EFGH$.

DEFINITION *Similar polygons* are polygons in which the corresponding angles are equal and the corresponding sides are proportional.

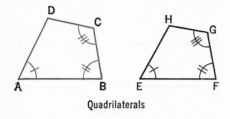

Quadrilaterals

Fig. 5

Corresponding sides of polygons are proportional if the ratio of the corresponding sides is constant. In Figure 5, $\dfrac{AB}{EF} = r$, where r is the constant of variation. The ratio of any two corresponding sides of two similar polygons is a constant called the *ratio of similitude* of the polygons.

The ratio of perimeters of similar polygons

In Figure 6, if polygon I is similar to polygon II, then $\dfrac{a'}{a} = \dfrac{b'}{b} = \dfrac{c'}{c} = \dfrac{d'}{d} = \ldots = \dfrac{n'}{n} = r$, where r is the ratio of similitude; that is, r is the constant of variation.

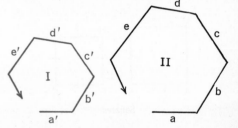

Fig. 6

Therefore, $a' = ar$, $b' = br$, $\ldots$, $n' = nr$. Why?

Therefore, $a' + b' + \ldots + n' = ar + br + \ldots + nr$. Why?
$$= r(a + b + \ldots + n).\text{ Why?}$$

Hence, $\dfrac{a' + b' + \ldots + n'}{a + b + \ldots + n} = r$. Why?

But, $a' + b' + \ldots + n'$ is the perimeter p' of I, and $a + b + \ldots + n$ is the perimeter p of II.

Hence, $\dfrac{p'}{p} = r = \dfrac{a'}{a} = \dfrac{b'}{b} = \ldots = \dfrac{n'}{n}$.

THEOREM 73. **If two polygons are similar, the ratio of their perimeters is equal to the ratio of any two corresponding sides.**

Theorem 73 may be stated this way: If two polygons are similar, their perimeters are directly proportional to any two corresponding sides.

Exercises

1. a. Are two congruent figures similar? Explain.

b. Are two similar figures necessarily congruent? Explain.

2. Can a quadrilateral be similar to a triangle? Explain.

3. a. Are two equiangular polygons necessarily similar? Explain.

b. Are two equilateral polygons necessarily similar? Explain.

c. Are two regular polygons necessarily similar? Explain.

4. Explain why the following figures are, or are not, similar:

a. Any two right triangles

b. Any two isosceles triangles

c. Any two equilateral triangles

d. Any two equiangular triangles

5. Two isosceles triangles are similar. The base of the smaller is 3.6 cm. The ratio of similitude is 3 to 4. Find: (**a**) The base of the larger, (**b**) the ratio of their perimeters.

6. The legs of a right triangle are 5.8 inches and 7.0 inches. The shorter leg of a similar triangle is 17.4 inches. Find: (**a**) the other leg of the second triangle, (**b**) the ratio of the hypotenuses.

7. Two triangles are similar and the sides of one are 3.0 inches, 4.0 inches, and 6.0 inches. The longest side of the second triangle is 5.0 inches.

a. Find the other two sides of the second triangle.

b. What is the ratio of similitude?

c. Find the perimeter of the smaller triangle.

The Pentagon Building in Arlington, Virginia, is one of the most famous buildings of the nation's capital. A second pentagon forms an inner court. Is it similar to the pentagon forming the outer perimeter of the building?

8. Two triangles are similar and the sides of the larger are 3.0 inches, 5.0 inches, and 6.2 inches. The ratio of similitude is 3 to 2. Find the perimeter of the smaller triangle.

9. Triangles ABC and RST are similar. $\angle A = \angle R = 75°$, $\angle B = \angle S$, $\angle C = 65°$, $AB = 2.4$ inches, and $\dfrac{AB}{RS} = \dfrac{3}{4}$. Find (**a**) $\angle S$, (**b**) RS, (**c**) the ratio of the perimeters.

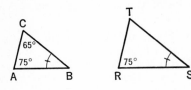

Ex. 9

10. The sides of one polygon are 4, 7, 6, 8, and 15. The longest side of a similar polygon is 20. Find its perimeter. Do you need to find the remaining sides of the larger polygon to find its perimeter?

11. The sides of a pentagon are 3, 4, 5, 6, and 7. Find the sides of a similar pentagon if its perimeter is 50.

12. The ratio of similitude of two similar quadrilaterals is 4 to 5. The perimeter of the smaller quadrilateral is 24 inches. What is the perimeter of the larger quadrilateral?

Proportion in scale drawings

You are familiar with plans for houses or other buildings. Such plans are drawn to some scale such as $\frac{1}{4}$ inch to 1 foot. This scale means that $\frac{1}{4}$ inch on the drawing represents 1 foot for the corresponding part of the building. The ratio of $\frac{1}{4}$ inch to 1 foot can be expressed as the fraction $\frac{1}{48}$. This fraction is the ratio of similitude of the plan and the building because they are similar.

In our work we shall refer to a scale such as $\frac{1}{4}$ inch to 1 foot as a *conventional scale*, and the corresponding fraction, $\frac{1}{48}$, as the *fractional scale*, or *representative fraction*.

What is the scale used in the house plan in Figure 7?

Find several different types of maps and plans. Notice the scales to which they are drawn.

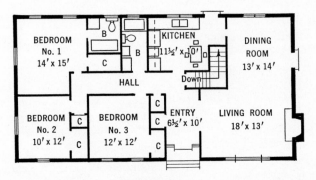

Fig. 7

Exercises

1. On a house plan which shows a living room to be 18′ x 12′, the width of the living room measures $\frac{3}{4}$ inch.

a. What is the ratio of the scale width to the actual width of the room? Suggestion:
$$\frac{\text{Scale width in inches:}}{\text{Actual width in inches}} = \frac{?}{?}.$$
b. To what fractional scale is the plan drawn?

c. To what conventional scale is the plan drawn? Suggestion: If $\frac{3}{4}$ inch represents 12 feet, then . . . . inch represents 1 foot?

d. What is the ratio of similitude of the plan and the house?

2. If the scale of a house plan is $\frac{1}{16}$ inch to 1 foot, what distance on the plan represents 14′ 6″?

3. If the scale of a building plan is $\frac{1}{96}$, find the outside perimeter of the building which measures $\frac{35}{16}''$ x $\frac{31}{16}''$ on its plan.

4. On a road map the distance between two towns measures $3\frac{5}{8}$ inches. The scale of the map is 1 inch to 8 miles. How far apart are the towns? Show several solutions and explain why you think one solution is better than another.

5. In making a drawing to the scale $\frac{1}{192}$, what length should be used to represent 64 feet?

6. (**a**) Convert the scale $\frac{1}{8}$ inch to 1 foot to a fractional scale. (**b**) Convert the scale 1 inch to 1 mile to a fractional scale.

7. Convert the fractional scale $\frac{1}{120}$ to a conventional scale.

8. Make a scale drawing of your classroom or some room in your house.

Two triangles with two angles respectively equal

Induction : Draw or make two triangles ABC and RST so that $\angle A = \angle R$, and $\angle B = \angle S$. Measure all three sides of each triangle. What is the ratio of AB to RS? BC to ST? AC to RT?

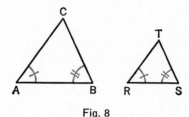

Fig. 8

Repeat the experiment with different kinds of triangles. Do the given conditions seem to be sufficient to make the triangles similar?

POSTULATE 45. If two triangles have two angles of one equal, respectively, to two angles of the other, the triangles are similar.

Since angles A and B of $\triangle ABC$ are respectively equal to angles R and S of $\triangle RST$, the third angles C and T are equal. Although we do not need this third pair of equal angles to prove the triangles similar, we use them when we identify AB and RS as corresponding sides of the triangles.

COROLLARIES 1. If two right triangles have an acute angle of one equal to an acute angle of the other, the triangles are similar.

2. If two triangles are similar to a third triangle, they are similar to each other.

Exercises

1. Prove: The line joining the midpoints of two sides of a triangle cuts off a triangle similar to the given triangle.

2. Prove: If a line is parallel to one side of a triangle, it cuts off a triangle similar to the given triangle.

3. Draw $\triangle ABC$ on your paper. On a given segment RS which corresponds to AB, construct $\triangle RST$ similar to $\triangle ABC$.

4. Draw $\triangle RST$ on your paper. On the segment $R'S'$ which corresponds to RS and is twice as long as RS, construct $\triangle R'S'T'$ similar to $\triangle RST$.

   Compare the lengths of RT and $R'T'$; of ST and $S'T'$. Compare $\angle T$ with $\angle T'$.

5. Draw $\triangle WKM$ on your paper. On the segment $W'K'$ which corresponds to WK and is one-half as long as WK, construct $\triangle W'K'M'$ similar to $\triangle WKM$.

   Compare the lengths of WM and $W'M'$; of KM and $K'M'$. Compare $\angle M$ with $\angle M'$.

6. Draw $\triangle EFG$ on your paper. On the segment $E'F'$ which corresponds to EF and is two-thirds as long as EF, construct $\triangle E'F'G'$ similar to $\triangle EFG$.

   Compare the lengths of EG and $E'G'$; of FG and $F'G'$.

7. Draw $\triangle MNO$ on your paper. On the segment $M'N'$ which corresponds to MN and is three-halves MN, construct $\triangle M'N'O'$ similar to $\triangle MNO$.

   Compare the lengths of MO and $M'O'$; of NO and $N'O'$.

8. Construct a triangle similar to a given triangle so that the ratio of similitude of the given triangle to the required triangle is 3 to 4.

Corresponding sides of similar triangles

From the definition we know that the corresponding sides of similar triangles are proportional. That is, the ratio of two corresponding sides is equal to the ratio of any other two corresponding sides. Corresponding sides are sides opposite pairs of equal angles. (See Figure 9.)

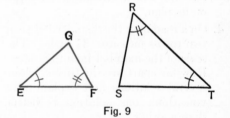

Fig. 9

A very good way to match the corresponding sides in the three ratios is shown below. Notice that the triangles in Figure 9 are not in corresponding positions.

$$\frac{FG \text{ (opposite } \angle E)}{? \text{ (opposite } \angle T)} = \frac{EG \text{ (opposite } \angle F)}{? \text{ (opposite } \angle R)} = \frac{EF \text{ (opposite } \angle G)}{? \text{ (opposite } \angle S)}$$

$$\frac{FG}{RS} = \frac{EG}{ST} = \frac{EF}{RT}.$$

When you select pairs of corresponding sides, it is helpful but not necessary to write the names of the angles opposite them as has been done above.

The following examples illustrate the different meanings of the proportions involving corresponding sides of similar triangles.

Example 1. Equal Quotients

Given: AC and BD are diagonals of quadrilateral $ABCD$, $\angle 2 = \angle 5$ and $\angle 3 = \angle 6$.

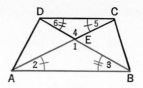

Fig. 10

How are the segments of the diagonals related?

1. $\triangle ABE \sim \triangle ECD$. Why?

2. $\therefore \dfrac{AB \text{ (opp. } \angle 1)}{DC \text{ (opp. } \angle 4)} = \dfrac{BE \text{ (opp. } \angle 2)}{ED \text{ (opp. } \angle 5)} = \dfrac{AE \text{ (opp. } \angle 3)}{EC \text{ (opp. } \angle 6)}$. Why?

The segments in which we are interested are in the last two ratios, namely $\dfrac{BE}{ED} = \dfrac{AE}{EC}$. Thus, the quotient of the segments of one diagonal is equal to the quotient of the segments of the other. That is, the segments of the diagonals are directly proportional.

Example 2. Equal Products

Given: AC and BD are diagonals of quadrilateral $ABCD$ in which $\angle 2 = \angle 6$, and $\angle 3 = \angle 5$.

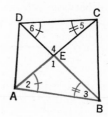

Fig. 11

How are the segments of the diagonals related?

1. $\triangle ABE \sim \triangle ECD$. Why?

2. $\therefore \dfrac{BE \text{ (opp. } \angle 2)}{EC \text{ (opp. } \angle 6)} = \dfrac{AE \text{ (opp. } \angle 3)}{ED \text{ (opp. } \angle 5)} = \dfrac{AB \text{ (opp. } \angle 1)}{DC \text{ (opp. } \angle 4)}$. Why?

Since the first two ratios contain the segments of the diagonals, we discard the last ratio and use $\dfrac{BE}{EC} = \dfrac{AE}{ED}$.

3. $\therefore BE \times ED = EC \times AE$. Why?

Since the product of the segments of one diagonal is equal to the product of the segments of the other, the segments of the diagonals are inversely proportional.

Notice the resemblance of the quadrilaterals in Examples 1 and 2. Their sides and angles are named the same way, but the segments of their diagonals are not proportional in the same manner. In Example 1, the ratio of the segments of AC is equal to the ratio of the segments of BD; in Example 2, the product of the segments of AC is equal to the product of the segments of BD.

Example 3. Mean Proportional Between Two Segments

Given: $\triangle ABC$, H is a point on AB,
$\angle A = \angle 2$, and $\angle 1 = \angle B$.

How is CH related to AH and HB?

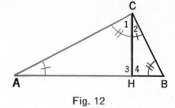

Fig. 12

1. $\triangle AHC \sim \triangle HBC$. Why?

2. $\therefore \dfrac{AH \text{ (opp. } \angle ?)}{HC \text{ (opp. } \angle ?)} = \dfrac{AC \text{ (opp. } \angle ?)}{? \text{ (opp. } \angle ?)} = \dfrac{HC \text{ (opp. } \angle ?)}{HB \text{ (opp. } \angle ?)}$. Why?

Since the first and last ratios contain the segments in which we are interested,
we discard the second ratio and use $\dfrac{AH}{HC} = \dfrac{HC}{HB}$.

3. $\therefore \overline{HC}^2 = AH \times HB$. Why?

It can be seen from either Statement 2 or Statement 3 that HC is the mean
proportional between AH and HB.

Exercises

1. Given: AB and CD intersect at P
and $AC \parallel BD$.
a. Prove $\triangle APC \sim \triangle PDB$.
b. Complete the following equations: (1) $\dfrac{AP}{?} = \dfrac{PC}{?}$,
    (2) $AP \times PD = ? \times ?$

Ex. 1

2. A flagpole casts a shadow 130 feet
long when a 30-foot telephone pole
casts a shadow 115 feet long. How
high is the flagpole? Show the
proportion.

3. Given: $\triangle ABC$, D and E are points
on AC and BC, respectively, and
$\angle 1 = \angle 2$.
a. Prove $\triangle ABC \sim \triangle DEC$.
b. Complete the following:
    (1) $\dfrac{AB}{?} = \dfrac{BC}{?} = \dfrac{AC}{?}$.
    (2) $AB \times DC = ? \times ?$

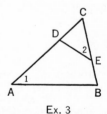

Ex. 3

4. Prove: Two isosceles triangles are
similar if their vertex angles are
equal.

5. Given: $\triangle RDM$, Q and P are points on RD and DM, respectively, and $PQ \parallel RM$.

a. Complete: $\dfrac{RD}{?} = \dfrac{DM}{?} = \dfrac{MR}{?}$.

b. If $MD = 3.0$ inches, $PD = 1.4$ inches, and $RM = 3.8$ inches, then $PQ = ?$

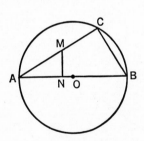

Ex. 5

6. Given: $\triangle ABC$ is inscribed in circle O, AB is a diameter, M is on AC, and $MN \perp AB$ at N.

a. Prove: $\triangle ANM \sim \triangle ABC$.

b. Complete: $\dfrac{AN}{?} = \dfrac{NM}{?} = \dfrac{?}{?}$.

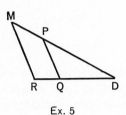

Ex. 6

7. Prove: If two triangles are similar, the ratio of any two corresponding altitudes is equal to the ratio of any two corresponding sides.

8. Given: MN is a common internal tangent of circles O and R meeting the circles at A and B, respectively; OR is the line of centers; and $OA = \frac{3}{2}RB$. How is AP related to PB? Why?

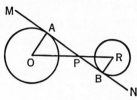

Ex. 8

9. Two circles are externally tangent at the point P. AB and CD are lines through P and terminated by the circles. Prove that the four chords are proportional.

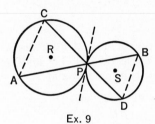

Ex. 9

10. Given: $\triangle ABC$ is inscribed in circle O, AB is a diameter, and CH is the altitude to AB from C.
Complete and prove:

a. $\triangle ABC \sim \triangle AHC$.

b. $\overline{AC}^2 = ? \times ?$

c. $\triangle ABC \sim \triangle HBC$.

d. $\overline{BC}^2 = ? \times ?$

e. $\triangle AHC \sim \triangle HBC$.

f. $\overline{HC}^2 = ? \times ?$.

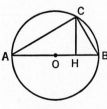

Ex. 10

11. Given: AB is tangent to circle O at A, BCD is a secant, and AC and AD are chords.

Complete and prove:

a. $\triangle ABD \sim \triangle$?

b. $\dfrac{AC}{AD} = \dfrac{?}{?} = \dfrac{?}{?}$

c. $\overline{AB}^2 = \,? \times \,?$

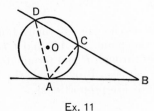

Ex. 11

12. Given: ABC and EDC are secants to circle O, and AD and BE are chords intersecting at P.

Complete and prove:

a. $\triangle ABP \sim \triangle$?

b. $AP \times PD = \,? \times \,?$

c. $\triangle ACD \sim \triangle$?

d. $AC \times CB = \,? \times \,?$

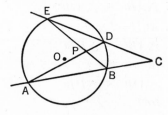

Ex. 12

13. Given: $\triangle ABC$ with altitudes AE and CD intersecting at F.

Complete and prove:

a. $\dfrac{AF}{CF} = \dfrac{?}{?} = \dfrac{?}{?}$.

b. $\dfrac{AE}{?} = \dfrac{AB}{?} = \dfrac{?}{?}$.

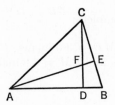

Ex. 13

Two triangles with an angle of one equal to an angle of the other and the including sides proportional

Induction: Make two triangles ABC and RST so that $\angle C = \angle T$ and so that $\dfrac{AC}{RT} = \dfrac{BC}{ST}$. This can be done by making RT some fractional part of AC, and ST the same fractional part of BC. For example, make $RT = \frac{2}{3} AC$, and $ST = \frac{2}{3} BC$. Compare $\angle A$ with $\angle R$, and $\angle B$ with $\angle S$. Repeat the experiment with different kinds of triangles. Do the pairs of triangles in each trial seem to be similar?

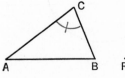

Fig. 13

POSTULATE 46. If two triangles have an angle of one equal to an angle of the other and the including sides proportional, the triangles are similar.

Exercises

1. Given: $\triangle ABC$ with DE drawn so that $\dfrac{AD}{AB} = \dfrac{AE}{AC}$.

Prove: $\triangle ADE \sim \triangle ABC$.

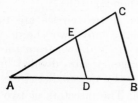

Ex. 1–2

2. If $\dfrac{AD}{DB} = \dfrac{3}{2}$, $\dfrac{AE}{EC} = \dfrac{3}{2}$, and $BC = 2.8$ cm., find DE.

3. Prove: If two triangles are similar, corresponding medians have the same ratio as any two corresponding sides.

4. Proportional dividers are convenient drafting instruments. An adjustment screw at P keeps $AP = PC$, and $DP = PB$. The arms AB and CD can be set so that they are divided proportionally at P in any desired ratio.

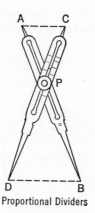

Proportional Dividers

Ex. 4

a. What should be the ratio of the segments of the arms in order that DB shall be $1\frac{1}{2}$ times AC?

b. If you wished to enlarge a plan in the ratio 7 to 3, how would you adjust the dividers?

5. Make proportional dividers out of strips of cardboard about 10 inches long and $\frac{1}{2}$ inch wide. Punch holes in the cardboard in order to get ratios such as 1 to 2, 1 to 3, 1 to 4, 2 to 3, 2 to 5, etc.

Two triangles with their sides respectively proportional

Induction: Draw any triangle ABC. Construct $\triangle RST$ so that $RS = \frac{3}{4}AB$, $ST = \frac{3}{4}BC$, and $RT = \frac{3}{4}AC$.

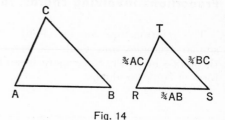

Fig. 14

Measure all the angles of both triangles. Are the corresponding angles equal?

Repeat the experiment several times using different ratios each time. Do the triangles seem to be similar?

POSTULATE 47. If the corresponding sides of two triangles are proportional, the triangles are similar.

Exercises

1. If $\triangle ABC$ is to be similar to $\triangle RST$, and if ST and RT correspond to BC and AC, respectively, how long must ST and RT be if $AB = 9$, $BC = 10$, $AC = 15$, and $RS = 6$?

2. Given the perimeter, construct a triangle similar to a given triangle.

3. If $\triangle ABC \sim \triangle RST$, the sides of $\triangle ABC$ are 3, 5, and 7, and the perimeter of $\triangle RST$ is 60, how long are the sides of $\triangle RST$? Use sides as in Exercise **1**.

4. Prove: The diagonals of a trapezoid divide each other proportionally.

5. Prove: If the diagonals of a quadrilateral divide each other proportionally, the quadrilateral is a trapezoid.

6. Prove: If two triangles are similar, the radii of the inscribed circles have the same ratio as any two corresponding sides.

7. Prove: If two triangles are similar, the radii of the circumscribed circles have the same ratio as any two corresponding sides.

8. Prove: If two circles are tangent internally, any two chords of the larger circle drawn from the point of tangency are divided proportionally by the smaller circle.

9. Prove: The bisectors of two corresponding angles of two similar triangles have the same ratio as any pair of corresponding sides.

10. Prove: Corresponding angle bisectors of similar triangles are proportional.

Proportions involving chords, tangents, and secants

The relationships among chords, tangents, and secants are obtained from similar triangles and might be stated as proportions. The statements of the theorems, however, have more meaning if the conclusions are expressed in the form of equal products.

THEOREM 74. **If two chords intersect within a circle, the product of the segments of one chord is equal to the product of the segments of the other.**

Given: Circle O with chords AB and CD intersecting at P.

Prove: $AP \times PB = CP \times PD$.

Suggestions: Draw AC and BD.

Prove $\triangle APC \sim \triangle PDB$.

You write the proof.

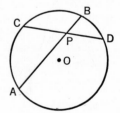

It is important to remember that we agreed to refer to the segment CP as the *tangent* to circle O from P to the point of tangency C. Also, for convenience, we speak of PA as the *whole secant* from the point P to A. Segment PB is called the *external segment* of the secant, and the chord BA is the *internal segment* of the secant (*Figure 15*).

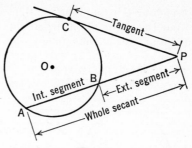

Fig. 15

THEOREM 75. If a tangent and a secant are drawn to a circle from an external point, the tangent is the mean proportional between the whole secant and its external segment.

Given: PC is a tangent to circle O at C, and PBA is a secant from point P meeting the circle at B and A. (See figure opposite).

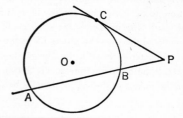

Prove: a. $\dfrac{AP}{CP} = \dfrac{CP}{BP}$

b. $\overline{CP}^2 = AP \times BP$

c. $CP = \sqrt{AP \times BP}$

Suggestion: Draw BC and AC.

You write the proof.

COROLLARY If two secants are drawn to a circle from an external point, the product of one secant and its external segment is equal to the product of the other secant and its external segment.

You draw the figure and write the proof of the corollary.

Exercises

1. If $AP = 10.0$ cm., $PB = 8.0$ cm., and $CP = 5.2$ cm., find PD.

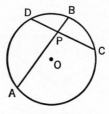

Ex. 1–3

2. If $AP = PB$, $CP = 2.0$ inches, and $AB = 8.0$ inches, find DP.

3. If AB is a diameter perpendicular to CD, $CD = 6.0$ inches, and $PB = 4.0$ inches, find AP.

4. A chord 8.0 inches long is 3.0 inches from the midpoint of its arc. Find the diameter of the circle.

5. If tangent $PC = 6.0$ inches, and $PB = 3.0$ inches, find PA.

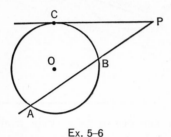

Ex. 5–6

6. If $PB = 2$ and $BA = 6$, find PC.

7. A point W is 4 inches from a circle whose diameter is 5 inches. Find the length of the tangent from W to the circle.

8. A point M is 4 feet from a circle. The length of the tangent from M is 10 feet. Find the diameter of the circle.

9. Theorem 75 may be used to determine the distance to the horizon from a point above the earth. If the observer is at the point P, let h represent the distance above the earth in feet, and x represent the distance to the horizon in miles. Assume that the diameter AB of the earth is 7960 miles.

If we assume that the earth is spherical, that rays of light are straight lines, and that there are no obstructions to our view, then our line of sight as we look toward the horizon from the point P is tangent to the earth. The horizon is the small circle of the earth that forms the apparent boundary between the earth and the sky. The distance x to the horizon is related to the elevation h of the observer and to the diameter d of the earth. This relation is based on the geometry of the similar triangles APT and BPT. If the complete sphere were shown, we would see that B (the intersection of PB and TB) would lie on the surface of the sphere directly below A.

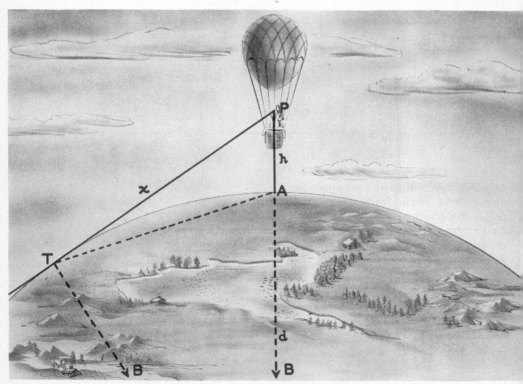

Converting h feet to miles, h feet is $\dfrac{h}{5280}$ miles.

$$PT = \sqrt{PB \times PA}$$

$$x = \sqrt{\left(7960 + \frac{h}{5280}\right)\frac{h}{5280}}$$

$$x = \sqrt{\frac{7960}{5280}h + \frac{h^2}{(5280)^2}}$$

We may disregard $\dfrac{h^2}{(5280)^2}$ for small values of h.

Hence, $x = \sqrt{\dfrac{199}{132}h} = \sqrt{1.5h}$

where h is measured in feet and x is measured in miles.

a. How far away is the horizon from a point 5 feet above the surface of the earth?

b. Find the decimal value of $\dfrac{5^2}{(5280)^2}$ and explain why the fraction may be disregarded in the formula.

c. How far away is the horizon from a point 267 feet above the surface of the earth?

Inverse variation (*Optional*)

Theorems 74 and 75 and the corollary to Theorem 75 illustrate both an interesting continuity and the principle of inverse variation.

If AB rotates about the fixed point P within circle O, PA gets shorter as PB gets longer (Figure 16). Any two positions of the chord could be considered as two chords intersecting within the circle, so the product of the segments of the chord is a constant. That is, $PA \times PB = k = PA' \times PB'$; hence, the two variables PA and PB are inversely proportional.

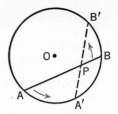

Fig. 16

For what position of P within the circle is $PA \times PB$ a maximum? (Do an experiment to find out.) As the point P approaches the circle, does the product of the two segments of the chord increase or decrease? When the point P is on the circle, one of the segments of the chord is zero. What is the product of the two segments?

When the point P is outside the circle (Figure 17), the product of the segments is also a constant for any fixed position of P; thus

$$PD \times PC = k_1 = PB \times PA.$$

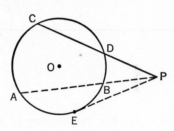

Fig. 17

When the secant rotates to the position of the tangent,

$$PE \times PE \text{ or } \overline{PE}^2 = k_1.$$

Theorems 74 and 75 and the corollary to Theorem 75 can be combined into one theorem as follows:

If a line through a given point intersects a circle, the product of the two segments from the point to the circle is a constant.

Quadratic equations (*Optional*)

Since some problems in geometry involve the solution of quadratic equations, it may be timely to review the principal methods.

If the quadratic expression $ax^2 + bx + c$ is equal to zero, where a, b, and c are real numbers and a is not equal to zero, the resulting equation is called a quadratic equation. There are three algebraic methods commonly used to solve such quadratic equations: *factoring, completing the square,* and using the *quadratic formula.* We shall briefly review the methods of factoring and using the formula.

1. The factoring method

To solve a quadratic equation by factoring, we use the principle that if the product of two or more factors equals zero, then at least one of these factors equals zero.

Example: Chord EF of the circle is divided into segments 9.0 inches long and 4.0 inches long by chord CD which is 15.0 inches long. How long are the segments of CD?

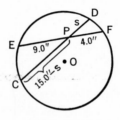

Fig. 18

Solution: Let s be the number of inches in the length of PD, and $15 - s$ be the number of inches in the length of CP.

a. $EP \times PF = PD \times CP$.   Why?

b. $9 \times 4 = s(15 - s)$

c. $s^2 - 15s + 36 = 0$

d. $(s - 12)(s - 3) = 0$

e.   If $s - 12 = 0$ If $s - 3 = 0$

          then $s = 12$ then $s = 3$

        and $15 - s = 3$ and $15 - s = 12$

     Check: $9 \times 4 = 3 \times 12$.

Hence, the segments of CD are 3.0 inches and 12.0 inches long.

2. The formula method

A formula for solving a quadratic equation is obtained by solving the general equation $ax^2 + bx + c = 0$ by completing the square. The solution is as follows:

$$x^2 + \frac{b}{a}x + \frac{b^2}{4a^2} = -\frac{c}{a} + \frac{b^2}{4a^2} \text{ or } \frac{b^2 - 4ac}{4a^2}$$

$$\left(x + \frac{b}{2a}\right)^2 = \frac{b^2 - 4ac}{(2a)^2}$$

$$x + \frac{b}{2a} = \frac{\pm\sqrt{b^2 - 4ac}}{2a}$$

$$\therefore x = \frac{-b \pm \sqrt{b^2 - 4ac}}{2a}$$

Example: A tangent PX touching circle O at T and a secant PY intersecting circle O at B and A are drawn from point P. If PT is 3.00 inches long, and BA is 2.00 inches long, find the length of PB.

Solution: Let e be the number of inches in the length of PB. Then PA is $e + 2$ inches long.

a. $PB \times PA = \overline{PT^2}$. Why?

b. $e(e + 2) = 3^2$

c. $e^2 + 2e - 9 = 0$

d. $e = \dfrac{-2 \pm \sqrt{4 + 36}}{2}$

$= \dfrac{-2 \pm 2\sqrt{10}}{2}$

$= -1 \pm \sqrt{10}$

$= -1 \pm 3.16$

$e_1 = 2.16$

$e_2 = -4.16$

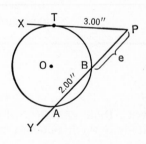

Fig. 19

The equation has two roots; that is, there are two values of e that satisfy the equation in Step **b**; however, the negative value has no meaning in this problem.

The answer, 2.16, is rounded to agree with the given data and, hence, is not an exact root of the equation. Thus when 2.16 is substituted in Step **b** to check, $2.16(2.16 + 2)$ is not exactly 9; however, to the nearest hundredth, PB is 2.16 inches long.

Exercises (*Optional*)

1. Two chords intersect within a circle. The segments of one chord are 10 inches and 2 inches long. The length of the second chord is 9 inches. Find the length of its segments.

2. Two chords intersect within a circle. The segments of one are each 4 inches long and the length of the other is 10 inches. Find the segments of the 10-inch chord.

3. A tangent and a secant are drawn to a circle from an external point. The tangent is 4 inches long; the internal segment of the secant is 6 inches long. Find the external segment of the secant.

4. If a tangent to a circle from a point is 6.00″ long and the internal segment of a secant from the same point is 4.00″ long, find the length of the secant.

Proportions in a right triangle with the altitude to the hypotenuse

THEOREM 76. **If the altitude is drawn to the hypotenuse of a right triangle,**

(a) the altitude is the mean proportional between the segments of the hypotenuse,

(b) each leg is the mean proportional between the whole hypotenuse and the segment adjacent to that leg.

Given: Right $\triangle ABC$ with CH the altitude to the hypotenuse AB.

Prove: 1. $\dfrac{m}{h_c} = \dfrac{h_c}{n}$ or $h_c^2 = mn$

2. $\dfrac{c}{b} = \dfrac{b}{m}$ or $b^2 = cm$

also

$\dfrac{c}{a} = \dfrac{a}{n}$ or $a^2 = cn$

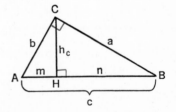

Suggestions:

1. Prove $\triangle AHC \sim \triangle HBC$.

2. Prove $\triangle ABC \sim \triangle AHC$.

Also prove $\triangle ABC \sim \triangle HBC$.

You write the proof.

COROLLARY If a perpendicular is drawn to a diameter from a point on a circle, it is the mean proportional between the segments of the diameter.

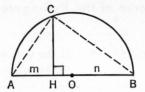

You write the proof of the Corollary. (Hint: In Figure 20, since $\angle ACB$ is inscribed in a semicircle, what is true?)

Fig. 20

The Pythagorean Theorem

THEOREM 77.   In a right triangle, the square of the hypotenuse is equal to the sum of the squares of the legs.

Given: Right $\triangle ABC$ with the right angle at C.
Prove: $c^2 = a^2 + b^2$.
Suggestions: From C draw $CH \perp AB$. Show that $a^2 = cn$, $b^2 = cm$, $a^2 + b^2 = c(n + m)$, etc.

You write the proof.

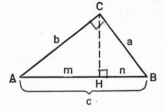

The square *constructed* on the hypotenuse of a right triangle is equal to the sum of the squares *constructed* on the legs. That is, $c^2 = a^2 + b^2$.

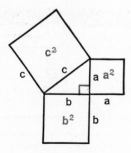

Fig. 21

COROLLARY   In a right triangle, the square of either leg is equal to the square of the hypotenuse minus the square of the other leg.

If c is the hypotenuse of the right triangle ABC, then $c^2 = a^2 + b^2$.

Hence, $a^2 = c^2 - b^2$, and $b^2 = c^2 - a^2$.

Thus, the square constructed on either leg of a right triangle equals the difference of the squares constructed on the hypotenuse and the other leg.

Converse of the Pythagorean Theorem

THEOREM 78.   **If the sum of the squares of two sides of a triangle is equal to the square of the third side, the triangle is a right triangle.**

Given: $\triangle ZYX$ in which $y^2 = x^2 + z^2$.

Prove: $\triangle ZYX$ is a right triangle with a right angle at Y.

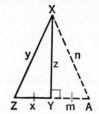

Proof

STATEMENTS	AUTHORITIES
1. Draw $YA \perp YX$, and make $YA = ZY$.	1. Why possible?
2. $\therefore n^2 = m^2 + z^2$.	2. Why?
3. $m = x$.	3. Why?
4. $\therefore n^2 = x^2 + z^2$.	4. Why?
5. $y^2 = x^2 + z^2$.	5. Why?
6. $\therefore n^2 = y^2$.	6. Why?
7. $\therefore n = y$.	7. Why?
8. $\therefore \triangle ZYX \cong \triangle YAX$.	8. Why?
9. $\therefore \angle XYZ = \angle AYX$.	9. Why?
10. $\therefore \angle XYZ = 90°$.	10. Why?
11. $\therefore \triangle ZYX$ is a right triangle.	11. Why?

Historical note

Certain combinations of integers such as 3, 4, and 5; 5, 12, and 13; 8, 15, and 17 are sides of right triangles. About 2000 B.C., the Egyptians knew that a right triangle could be formed by stretching around three pegs a cord measured off into 3, 4, and 5 units. The surveyors of those days were known as "rope stretchers."

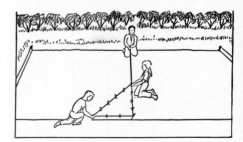

Modern Rope Stretchers

Fig. 22

Pythagorean triads

Sides of triangles that are whole numbers which satisfy $c^2 = a^2 + b^2$ are called Pythagorean triads. If u and v are relatively prime numbers, with u greater than v, then the numbers $u^2 + v^2$, $2uv$, and $u^2 - v^2$ constitute a Pythagorean triad.

Example:

Let $u = 5$ and $v = 2$. Then $u^2 + v^2 = 29$, $2uv = 20$, and $u^2 - v^2 = 21$. $(29)^2 = (20)^2 + (21)^2$. Hence, 29, 20, and 21 is a Pythagorean triad.

Exercises

1. Show that $(u^2 + v^2)^2 = (2uv)^2 + (u^2 - v^2)^2$.

2. Find the Pythagorean triads for which
   a. $u = 2$ and $v = 1$
   b. $u = 3$ and $v = 2$
   c. $u = 4$ and $v = 3$
   d. $u = 4$ and $v = 1$

3. Find the Pythagorean triad which has 37 for the longest side.

The relation between the hypotenuse and the side opposite the 60° angle of a 30°, 60°, 90° triangle

We have previously proved that the leg opposite the 30° angle of a 30°, 60° right triangle is one-half the hypotenuse. Using this fact and the Pythagorean Theorem, we can prove a relation between the hypotenuse and the leg opposite the 60° angle.

Since, $a^2 + b^2 = c^2$ and $b = \dfrac{c}{2}$, then

$$a^2 + \frac{c^2}{4} = c^2.$$

or $$a^2 = \frac{3c^2}{4}.$$

Hence, $$a = \frac{c}{2}\sqrt{3}$$

Show that $a = b\sqrt{3}$.

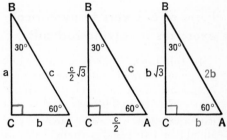

Fig. 23

In the table below, two sides of a 30°, 60°, 90° triangle are expressed in terms of the third side.

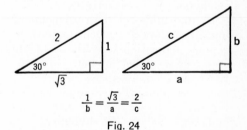

$$\frac{1}{b} = \frac{\sqrt{3}}{a} = \frac{2}{c}$$

Fig. 24

c (Hypotenuse)	b (Opp. 30° $\angle$)	a (Opp. 60° $\angle$)
c	$\dfrac{c}{2}$	$\dfrac{c}{2}\sqrt{3}$
$2b$	b	$b\sqrt{3}$
$\dfrac{2a}{\sqrt{3}} = \dfrac{2a\sqrt{3}}{3}$	$\dfrac{a}{\sqrt{3}} = \dfrac{a\sqrt{3}}{3}$	a

COROLLARIES 1. In a 30°, 60°, 90° triangle, the side opposite the 60° angle is equal to the side opposite the 30° angle multiplied by $\sqrt{3}$.

2. In a 30°, 60°, 90° triangle, the side opposite the 30° angle is equal to the side opposite the 60° angle divided by $\sqrt{3}$.

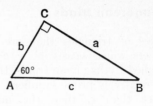

Ex. 1–8

4. If $c = 8.00$ feet, find a and b.

5. If $b = 6$, find a and c.

6. If $b = 5.0$ cm., find a and c.

7. If $a = 9$, find b and c.

8. If $a = 4.00$ inches, find b and c.

Form of answers to numerical exercises involving radicals

In this book, numerical data which are given without specifying the units of measurement are intended to represent exact data. The answers to such exercises should be exact; hence, they should be expressed in radical form if irrational numbers are involved. For example, if the hypotenuse of a 30°, 60°, 90° triangle is 6, then the longer leg is exactly $3\sqrt{3}$. Again, if the legs of a right triangle are 8 and 4, then the hypotenuse is exactly $4\sqrt{5}$.

If the units of measurement of numerical data are given, or if there is some indication that the data are approximate, the answers may be rounded to agree with the accuracy of the given data. For example, if the legs of a right triangle are 3.00 inches and 2.00 inches, the hypotenuse is $\sqrt{(3.00)^2 + (2.00)^2}$ or 3.61 inches.

The relation between the hypotenuse and the legs of an isosceles right triangle

Since $a^2 + b^2 = c^2$, and $a = b$,

Then $a^2 + a^2 = c^2$, or $2a^2 = c^2$.

Hence, $a^2 = \dfrac{c^2}{2}$,

Thus, $a = \dfrac{c}{\sqrt{2}}$ or $a = \dfrac{c}{2}\sqrt{2}$.

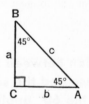

Exercises

In these exercises use a 30°, 60°, 90° $\triangle ABC$ as shown at the top of the next column:

1. Show that $b = \dfrac{a}{\sqrt{3}}$ or $b = \dfrac{a\sqrt{3}}{3}$.

2. Show that $c = \dfrac{2a}{\sqrt{3}}$ or $c = \dfrac{2a\sqrt{3}}{3}$.

3. If $c = 12$, find a and b.

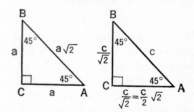

Fig. 25

In the table below, two sides of an isosceles right triangle are expressed in terms of the third side. Each time the third side is shown by the colored letter.

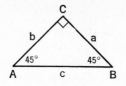

Ex. 1–5

3. If $b = 7.000$ feet, find c.

4. If $c = 10$, find b.

5. If $c = 9.0$ inches, find b.

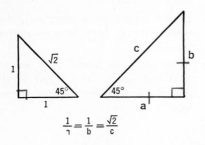

$$\frac{1}{1} = \frac{1}{b} = \frac{\sqrt{2}}{c}$$

Fig. 26

c (Hypot.)	b (Leg)	a (Leg)
c	$\dfrac{c}{\sqrt{2}} = \dfrac{c\sqrt{2}}{2}$	$\dfrac{c}{\sqrt{2}} = \dfrac{c\sqrt{2}}{2}$
$b\sqrt{2}$	b	b
$a\sqrt{2}$	a	a

COROLLARIES 1. In an isosceles right triangle, either leg is equal to the hypotenuse divided by $\sqrt{2}$.

2. In an isosceles right triangle, the hypotenuse is equal to either leg multiplied by $\sqrt{2}$.

Exercises

In these exercises, use an isosceles right triangle ABC as shown above at right:

1. Show that $c = a\sqrt{2}$.

2. If $b = 6$, find c.

The altitude of an equilateral triangle

If $\triangle ABC$ is an equilateral triangle, and CH is the altitude to AB, then $\triangle HBC$ is a 30°, 60°, 90° triangle.

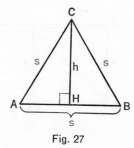

Fig. 27

If each side of $\triangle ABC$ is s, and h is an altitude, show that $h = \dfrac{s}{2}\sqrt{3}$.

COROLLARY The altitude of an equilateral triangle with side s is equal to $\dfrac{s}{2}\sqrt{3}$.

Exercises

1. Find the altitude of an equilateral triangle whose side is 12.

2. Find the altitude of an equilateral triangle whose side is 9.0 inches.

3. If the altitude of an equilateral triangle is h, and each side is s, prove that $s = \dfrac{2h\sqrt{3}}{3}$.

4. If the altitude of an equilateral triangle is 12, find the length of one of its sides.

5. If the altitude of an equilateral triangle is 9.00 feet, find the length of one of its sides.

The diagonal of a square

The diagonal of the square $ABCD$ is AC. Triangle ABC is an isosceles right triangle. If each side of the square is s, how long is AC?

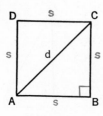

Fig. 28

COROLLARY **The diagonal of a square with side s is equal to $s\sqrt{2}$.**

Exercises

1. If the length of a side of a square is 8, find the length of one of its diagonals.

2. If the length of a side of a square is 5.00 inches, find the length of one of its diagonals.

3. If the length of a diagonal of a square is 6.00 inches, how long is one of its sides?

4. If the length of a diagonal of a square is 12, how long is one of its sides?

5. A baseball diamond is a square 90.0 feet on a side. What is the distance from home plate to second base?

Exercises on Right Triangles

1. Which of the following combinations of numbers could be sides of right triangles? (If they are not right triangles, can you tell whether they are acute or obtuse?)

  a. 3, 4, and 5

  b. 6, 8, and 9

  c. 6, 8, and 10

  d. 6, 8, and 11

  e. 5, 12, and 15

  f. 5, 12, and 13

  g. 8, 15, and 17

  h. 7, 24, and 25

  i. 1, $\sqrt{3}$, and 2

  j. 1, 1, and $\sqrt{2}$

2. Prove: The altitude to the hypotenuse of a right triangle is equal to the product of the legs divided by the hypotenuse. Hint: Prove $\triangle AHC \sim \triangle ABC$, etc.

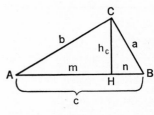

Ex. 2–3

3. Using the statement just proved in Exercise **2**:

　a. Find h_c if $a = 3.0$ inches and $b = 4.0$ inches.

　b. Find h_c if $a = 5.0$ inches and $c = 13.0$ inches.

　c. Find h_c if $\angle A = 30°$ and $AB = 6$.

　d. Find h_c if $\angle A = 45°$ and $AB = 6$.

　e. Find h_c if $\angle A = 60°$ and $AB = 6$.

4. Find the altitude to the base of an isosceles triangle if the base is 48 and the legs are each 25.

5. The bottom of a 16-foot ladder leaning against a house is 5 feet from the house. How high on the house does the ladder reach?

6. The side of a rhombus is 12, and one angle is 60°. Find the diagonals of the rhombus.

7. One angle of a rhombus is 120°. The shorter diagonal of the rhombus is 12. Find the other diagonal and the side of the rhombus.

8. $ABCD$ is a trapezoid, $AB \parallel DC$, $DC = 10$, $AD = 12$, $\angle A = 30°$, and $\angle B = 45°$. (**a**) Find AB; (**b**) find the perimeter of $ABCD$.

6. 6.0 inches. What is the length of the tangent from the point to the circle?

11. If the diameters of two concentric circles are 20.0 inches and 16.0 inches, find the length of the chord of the larger circle which is tangent to the smaller circle.

12. The centers of two circles with radii of 7.0 cm. and 15.0 cm. are 17.0 cm. apart. Find the length of the common external tangent.

13. AB is the diameter of the semicircle BCA, and $CH \perp AB$ at H. Find:

　a. CH if $AH = 4$ and $HB = 16$.

　b. CH if $AH = a$ and $HB = b$.

　c. CH if $AH = 2a$ and $HB = a$.

　d. CH if $AH = \dfrac{a}{2}$ and $HB = a$.

14. Construct an isosceles right triangle with each leg equal to one unit. By repeatedly constructing right triangles upon the hypotenuse of previous triangles as illustrated, a segment equal to the square root of any integer may be found.

　Construct a segment equal to $\sqrt{5}$.

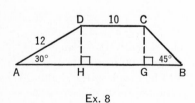

Ex. 8

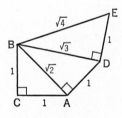

Ex. 14

9. If a chord 24.0 inches long is 5.0 inches from the center, what is the radius of the circle?

10. A point is 10.0 inches from the center of a circle whose radius is

15. The legs of an isosceles right triangle are each 6. Find the radius of the circumscribed circle.

16. The sides of an equilateral triangle are 12.

 a. Find the radius of the inscribed circle.

 b. Find the radius of the circumscribed circle.

17. The sides of a regular hexagon are 12.

 a. Find the radius of the circumscribed circle.

 b. Find the radius of the inscribed circle.

18. The sides of a square are 8.

 a. Find the radius of the inscribed circle.

 b. Find the radius of the circumscribed circle.

19. Prove: If an altitude is drawn to the hypotenuse of a right triangle, the segments of the hypotenuse are proportional to the squares of the legs.

20. The centers of two circles whose radii are 6.0 inches and 3.0 inches are 12.0 inches apart. Find the length of the common internal tangent.

21. The centers of two circles whose radii are 4.0 inches and 3.0 inches are 5.0 inches apart. Find the length of their common chord.

22. In circle O, the diameter CD is perpendicular to the chord AB at E, $OD = 13$, and $OE = 5$. Find: **(a)** AB; **(b)** AC; **(c)** AD.

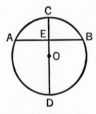

Ex. 22

23. Two parallel chords of a circle on the same side of the center are 6 and 8 inches long. The radius of the circle is 5 inches. How far apart are the chords?

24. Prove: The product of the diagonals of an inscribed quadrilateral is equal to the sum of the products of the opposite sides. Hint: Draw DE so that $\angle ADE = \angle BDC$. Then prove $\triangle ADE \sim \triangle CDB$ and $\triangle ADB \sim \triangle EDC$.

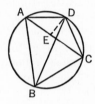

Ex. 24

25. If C is the vertex of the right angle of the right triangle ABC, CH is the altitude to AB, $CH = 6$, and $AB = 13$, find AH.

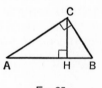

Ex. 25

26. The base of the circular arch of a bridge is 60 feet wide and the arch is 14 feet high in the middle. What is the radius of the arc of the arch?

Ex. 26

27. In the figure for Exercise **25**, if $AH = 6$ and $BC = 4$, find BH.

28. The strongest beam that can be cut from a round log has a cross section which may be constructed as follows: Draw a diameter WK and trisect it at H and E. Draw $ME \perp WK$ at E and $HR \perp WK$ at H. Draw WR, RK, KM, and MW. If WK is 12, find WR and RK.

Ex. 28

29. The Maltese Cross in the figure is made of five equal squares. Cut it into the fewest possible number of pieces which can be arranged to form a single square. Hint: If the area of the cross is 5 units of area, the side of the required square is $\sqrt{5}$ units of length. Prove that

the four pieces made by the two cuts indicated by the dashed lines will form the required square.

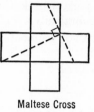

Maltese Cross

Ex. 29

30. The pitch of a common gable roof is the ratio of the rise to the span. The span is equal to twice the run of the rafter. Find the pitch of a roof whose rise is 6 feet and whose span is 30 feet. If the overhang is 1 foot, what is the length of the rafter?

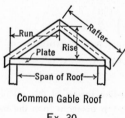

Common Gable Roof

Ex. 30

The mean proportional between two line segments

CONSTRUCTION 23. Construct the mean proportional between two given line segments.

Given: Line segments a and b.

Given

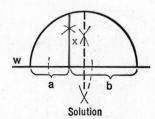

Solution

Required: To construct x so that $\dfrac{a}{x} = \dfrac{x}{b}$.

You do the construction and write the proof.

Exercises

1. Construct the mean proportional between segments 1 inch and 4 inches long. Check the construction algebraically.

2. Given two segments c and d, construct:
   a. $x = \sqrt{cd}$.
   b. $x = \sqrt{2cd}$.
   c. $x = \sqrt{\dfrac{cd}{2}}$.

3. Given the segment c, construct:
   a. $x = \sqrt{2c^2}$ or $\sqrt{2c \cdot c}$.
   b. $x = c\sqrt{3}$ or $\sqrt{3c^2}$.

4. Find $\sqrt{6}$ geometrically.

5. Given the segments a and c, construct $x = \sqrt{\dfrac{a^2}{c}}$.

6. Given the segment a, construct $x = \sqrt{\dfrac{a^2}{2}}$.

7. Given two segments a and b, construct $c = \sqrt{a^2 + b^2}$.

8. Given two segments c and a with $c > a$, construct $b = \sqrt{c^2 - a^2}$.

9. Construct a right triangle, given a leg and the altitude upon the hypotenuse. Describe the loci used in the construction.

10. Construct a right triangle, given the hypotenuse and the altitude upon the hypotenuse. Describe the loci used in the construction.

11. Construct a circle passing through two given points and tangent to a given line. Hint: Base the construction on Theorem 75.

12. Inscribe a square in a semicircle. Hint: Solve for r in terms of s.

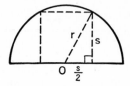

Ex. 12

The pagoda-like towers of this oil refinery unit under construction have an octagonal shape. The sides of the top octagons form the bases of eight isosceles triangles which have a common vertex. Notice the many similar polygons used in the construction.

Similar polygons

THEOREM 79. If two polygons are similar, they can be separated into the same number of triangles similar each to each and in corresponding positions.

Given: Similar polygons $ABCDE$ and $A'B'C'D'E'$, the corresponding vertices being A and A', B and B', etc.

Prove: $ABCDE$ and $A'B'C'D'E'$ can be separated into the same number of similar triangles and in corresponding positions.

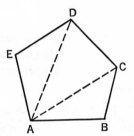

Suggestion: Draw AC, AD, $A'C'$, and $A'D'$. Prove $\triangle ABC \sim \triangle A'B'C'$, $\triangle ADC \sim \triangle A'D'C'$, etc., by proving in each pair of triangles that the sides including the equal angles are proportional.

You write the proof.

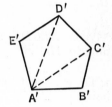

Polygons composed of triangles similar each to each

The three triangles composing each of the four pentagons in Figure 29 are similar each to each. That is, the triangles labeled A are similar, the triangles labeled B are similar, and the triangles labeled C are similar; but they are not in corresponding positions. Do any of the pentagons seem to be similar?

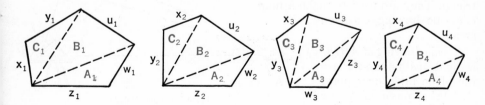

Fig. 29

The three triangles composing each of the two pentagons in Figure 30 are similar each to each and they are in corresponding positions. Are the pentagons similar?

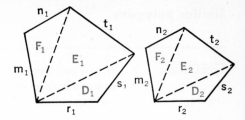

Fig. 30

THEOREM 80. **If two polygons are composed of the same number of triangles similar each to each in corresponding positions, the polygons are similar.**

CONSTRUCTION 24. **Upon a given line segment corresponding to one side of a given polygon, construct a polygon similar to the given polygon.**

Given: Polygon $ABCDE$ and $A'B'$ corresponding to AB.

Required: To construct on $A'B'$ a polygon similar to $ABCDE$.

You do the construction and write the proof.

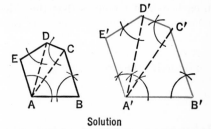

Solution

Plane table and alidade (*Optional*)

An *alidade* is essentially a straight-edge. As an added refinement for more precise work, sights are attached to it. A *plane table* is a drawing board on a tripod. They are used to make a map or a scale drawing of a given area.

A scale drawing of $ABDC$ is made as follows: Place the plane table over point A. On a piece of paper tacked to it, designate point A'.

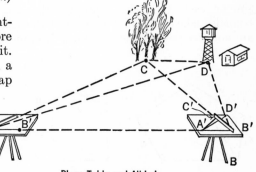

Plane Table and Alidade

Fig. 31

Place the alidade in line with C and draw a line along its edge. Repeat this procedure for points D and B. The length of $A'B'$ represents the measured distance between A and B.

Next move the plane table to position B. The line $A'B'$ previously drawn is placed directly over AB and in line with it. Sight along the alidade as before and draw lines to intersect those previously drawn from A'. Points C' and D' are now determined, and $A'B'D'C'$ is a scale drawing of $ABDC$.

After the lines in the drawing are measured, the actual distances can be computed by means of proportions.

Explain how this instrument might be used by forest rangers in fire towers to locate forest fires.

Exercises (*Optional*)

1. On a given line segment as side, construct a hexagon similar to a given hexagon.

2. Construct a quadrilateral similar to a given quadrilateral so that the ratio of similitude of the given figure to the required figure is 3 to 4.

3. Given the perimeter of quadrilateral $EFGH$, construct $EFGH$ similar to any given quadrilateral $ABCD$.

4. Given a diagonal, construct a rectangle similar to a given rectangle.

45° angle mirror (*Optional*)

A 45° angle mirror is an instrument for constructing and checking right angles. It consists of two mirrors held at 45° in a supporting frame, as shown in Figure 32. Use the laws of the mirror and Figure 32 to prove that a ray of light from X is reflected by the angle mirror to Y so that $IX \perp IY$.

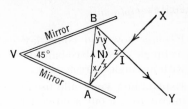

Fig. 32

If the mirror is held so the line of sight from the observer at E (Figure 33) passes along the front edge of the mirror to some fixed point such as F, and the point F appears to coincide with the image of the point T, then $FE \perp ET$.

The mirror can be used to measure the height of the pole FT if EH, which is perpendicular to FT, and FH can be measured.

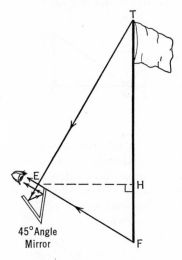

Fig. 33

Since $\angle FET = 90°$, and $EH \perp FT$, then $\triangle FEH \sim \triangle EHT$. Why?

Hence, $\dfrac{HT}{EH} = \dfrac{EH}{FH}$, or $HT = \dfrac{\overline{EH}^2}{FH}$.

Therefore, $FT = \dfrac{\overline{EH}^2}{FH} + FH$.

Exercises (*Optional*)

1. Explain how you could lay out a rectangle, or a baseball diamond, with an angle mirror.
2. Explain how you could use an angle mirror to lay out a circle having a given diameter.

Practical Applications of Similar Triangles

1. The height of an object can be measured by means of a mirror M placed in a horizontal position on the ground as shown in the figure. If the observer's eye E is 5′ 6″ above the ground, OM is 5′ 0″, and MA is 30′ 6″, how high above the ground is the top of the flagpole?

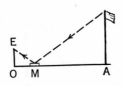

Ex. 1

2. A boy 5′ 6″ tall measures his shadow and finds it to be 6′ 0″ long. At the same time, a tree he wishes to measure casts a shadow 50′ 0″ long. How high is the tree?

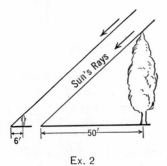

Ex. 2

3. The principle of a box camera in taking a picture is illustrated in the figure below. The rays of light from the object AB pass through the opening L and form an inverted image $A'B'$ on the film.

   How far from a 30′ tree must L be placed to produce a 4″ image on the film if the film is 8″ behind L?

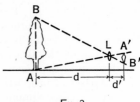

Ex. 3

4. The pantograph is an instrument for enlarging or reducing maps and drawings to scale. The bars must be arranged so that PBP' is a straight line and $\triangle PBA \sim \triangle PP'D$.

   Explain how the bars must be arranged so that the ratio of similitude of M' to M is 3 to 1.

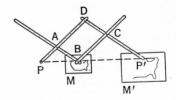

Ex. 4

5. Heavy loads that could not otherwise be raised to a desired height can be pushed into position along an inclined plane. The vector BC, representing the weight of a 250-pound desk, is perpendicular to the floor RS as a result of the attraction of gravity. The vector BA, representing the downward force of the desk along the plane, is parallel to

TS. The vector AC, representing the force perpendicular to the incline, forms with BC and BA the right triangle ABC.

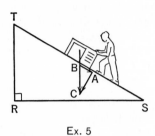

Ex. 5

a. Prove: $\triangle ABC \sim \triangle RST$.

b. Prove: $\dfrac{AB}{TR} = \dfrac{BC}{TS}$.

c. If $TR = 10$ feet, $TS = 25$ feet, and BC represents 250 lb., how many pounds does BA represent?

d. If the length of TS is increased, but TR and BC remain constant, how is the force represented by BA affected?

6. This picture shows a simple device which you can make to find the approximate height of an object. $\angle PMA$ is a right angle. The bars XA and AM are hinged at A so that XA can rotate to coincide with the line of sight AC. If $AM = 12.0$ inches, $MP = 6.0$ inches, and $AB = 60$ feet, find BC.

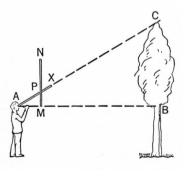

Ex. 6

7. A carpenter's square can be used to find indirectly the distance across a pond. Place the square as indicated on top of a pole whose height will conveniently allow one to sight along BC to position P across the pond. Fix the position of the square and sight along BE to Q on the ground. If $QA = 1$ foot and $BA = 5$ feet, find AP. State the principal theorem involved in this problem.

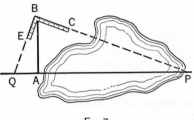

Ex. 7

8. Show how the inaccessible distance from R to T can be measured indirectly if the lengths of RY and TY can be measured directly, and if a line corresponding to XQ is appropriately located and measured.

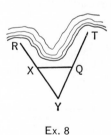

Ex. 8

9. Make a scale drawing of a baseball diamond showing the location of the pitcher's mound in relation to the bases and home plate.

On a sheet of paper of standard size, what is a convenient scale to use?

Co-ordinate Geometry

The linear equation (*Optional*)

An equation like $2x - 3y - 4 = 0$ may be written in several different forms such as:

1. $2x - 3y = 4.$
2. $2x = 3y + 4$
3. $y = \frac{2}{3}x - \frac{4}{3}$

Equation 3 has the general form $y = mx + b$, where m and b are constants and the unknowns x and y have the exponent 1. You have learned that such an equation is called a linear equation and that the locus (or graph) of a linear equation is a straight line.

The slope of a straight line

(*Optional*)

The *slope* or steepness of the line EB with reference to EH depends upon the relative lengths of the legs HB and EH of the right triangle EHB. That is, the slope of EB is the ratio of HB to EH. A road grade of 3% means that its slope is 3%; that is, its slope $=$

$$\frac{3 \text{ feet vertical rise}}{100 \text{ feet horizontal distance}}.$$

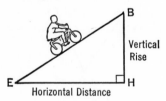

Fig. 34

In a co-ordinate system, direction is indicated by positive and negative signs. When we find the slope of a line on a graph we take into account both direction and distance. Although we do not think of the slope of a hill or a roof

as being either positive or negative, the slope of a straight-line graph may be positive or negative, depending upon the angle it makes with the x-axis.

Example 1. Find the slope of line WF in Figure 35.

Solution: **a.** Start at any convenient point D on WF and go horizontally to the right any number of units to E. DE is $+3$ units.

b. From E go vertically up to the line at B. EB is $+2$ units.

c. The slope of WF is $\dfrac{EB}{DE} = \dfrac{+2}{+3} = \dfrac{2}{3}$.

Proceed from B to D and verify that the slope of WF is $\dfrac{-2}{-3} = \dfrac{2}{3}$.

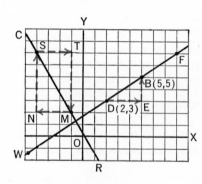

Fig. 35

Example 2. Find the slope of the line RC in Figure 35.

Solution: **a.** Start at any convenient point M on RC and go horizontally to the left any number of units to N. MN is -3 units.

b. From N, go vertically up to the line at S. NS is $+5$ units.

c. The slope of RC is

$$\frac{NS}{MN} = \frac{+5}{-3} = -\frac{5}{3}.$$

The slope of RC is also

$$\frac{TM}{ST} = \frac{-5}{+3} = -\frac{5}{3}.$$

Example 3. Find the slope of the graph of $y = 2x - 4$ in Figure 36.

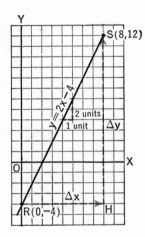

Fig. 36

Solution: Think of the line RS as the path of a point whose ordinate is always 4 units less than twice its abscissa. As the point moves, both its ordinate and its abscissa change. In fact, as the point moves 1 unit to the right it also moves 2 units upward. If the point moves downward, for every change of -1 unit in the value of x, there is a corresponding change of -2 units in the value of y. That is, for every change of 1 unit in the value of x, there is a corresponding change of 2 units in the value of y. Hence, the

$$\text{slope of } RS = \frac{\text{change in the value of } y}{\text{change in the value of } x}$$

$$= \frac{2}{1} \text{ or } 2.$$

The symbol for "change in the value of" is the Greek capital letter, delta, written Δ. The ratio of Δy to Δx is the slope of the line. Thus if the value of y (the ordinate) increases twice as fast as the value of x (the abscissa) increases, the slope of the line is 2. The slope of RS is $\frac{HS}{RH} = \frac{\Delta y}{\Delta x} = \frac{+16}{+8} = \frac{2}{1}.$

Notice that the slope of the line whose equation is $y = 2x - 4$ is equal to the coefficient of x.

Example 4. Find the slope of the graph of $y = -\frac{2}{5}x + 4$ in Figure 37.

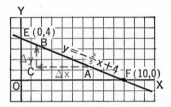

Fig. 37

Solution: In this equation, the value of y increases as the value of x decreases; the value of y decreases as the value of x increases. This means that the line has a negative slope. If a point moves along the line from F to E, FO is -10 units, and OE is $+4$ units. If a point moves along the line from E to F, EO is -4 units, and OF is $+10$ units. The slope of FE is $\frac{OE}{FO} = \frac{+4}{-10} = -\frac{2}{5}.$

Notice that the slope of the line whose equation is $y = -\frac{2}{5}x + 4$ is the coefficient of x.

Since the triangles OFE and CAB are similar, then $\frac{OE}{FO} = \frac{\Delta y}{\Delta x}$. Notice that Δx is negative in relation to Δy. Thus, $\frac{\Delta y}{\Delta x} = -\frac{2}{5}.$

Example 5. Find the slope of the graph of $y = 5$ in Figure 38.

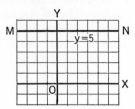

Fig. 38

Solution: MN is the locus of the equation $y = 5$. MN is parallel to the x-axis. As a point on it moves, there is no change in the value of the ordinate y although the abscissa x does change. Hence, $\dfrac{\Delta y}{\Delta x} = \dfrac{0}{\Delta x} = 0$. That is, the slope of MN is zero. The equation $y = 5$ is equivalent to the equation $y = 0x + 5$. Notice that the coefficient of x and the slope are both zero.

Example 6. Find the slope of a line parallel to the y-axis in Figure 39.

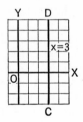

Fig. 39

Solution: The line CD is parallel to the y-axis and its equation is $x = 3$. As a point on it moves, the value of x remains constant and hence Δx is zero.

Since $\dfrac{\Delta y}{0}$ has no meaning, for we cannot divide by zero, the slope of a line parallel to the y-axis is not expressible.

The slope of a line through two given points (*Optional*)

If $G(x_1, y_1)$ and $H(x_2, y_2)$ are two points on a line GH, $\Delta y = y_2 - y_1$, and
$$\Delta x = x_2 - x_1.$$

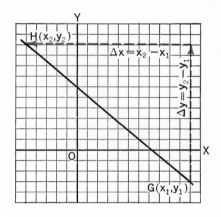

Fig. 40

Hence, the slope of GH is
$$\frac{\Delta y}{\Delta x} = \frac{y_2 - y_1}{x_2 - x_1}.$$

Example: Find the slope of the line through $G(11, -3)$ and $H(-5, 10)$.

Solution:

Slope of $GH =$
$$\frac{\Delta y}{\Delta x} = \frac{y_2 - y_1}{x_2 - x_1}$$
$$= \frac{10 - (-3)}{-5 - 11}$$
$$= -\frac{13}{16}.$$

Verify that $\dfrac{y_1 - y_2}{x_1 - x_2} = -\dfrac{13}{16}.$

Exercises (*Optional*)

Plot the points given in each exercise and find the slope of the line determined by them.

1. $C(2, 3)$ and $D(6, 7)$.

2. $E(3, 4)$ and $F(2, 7)$.

3. $G(4, -2)$ and $H(-5, 6)$.

4. $I(-4, -2)$ and $J(-5, -6)$.

5. $K(4, -2)$ and $L(5, -6)$.

6. $M(-6, 2)$ and $N(6, -2)$.

7. $P(-4, 6)$ and $Q(-4, -2)$.

8. $R(-6, 3)$ and $S(5, 3)$.

Slope-y-intercept form of a linear equation (*Optional*)

If the graph of a linear equation is not parallel to the y-axis, then it crosses the axis at some point. The distance on the y-axis from the origin to the point where the graph crosses the y-axis is called the *y-intercept*.

The equation $y = \frac{2}{3}x + 2$ is of the form $y = mx + b$ where m is the coefficient of x $(m = \frac{2}{3})$ and b is the constant term $(b = 2)$.

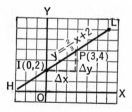

Fig. 41

The line HL is the graph of the equation $y = \frac{2}{3}x + 2$. Notice that the value of y is 2 when the value of x is 0. That is, HL crosses the y-axis at the point $(0, 2)$; hence, b is the y-intercept of the graph.

If $y = mx + b$, then $y = b$ when $x = 0$; hence, the y-intercept is the constant term b.

The line HL passes through the two points $I(0, 2)$ and $P(3, 4)$; hence, its slope is $\dfrac{\Delta y}{\Delta x} = \dfrac{y_2 - y_1}{x_2 - x_1} = \dfrac{2 - 4}{0 - 3} = \dfrac{2}{3}$.

In the equation $y = \frac{2}{3}x + 2$, $m = \frac{2}{3}$; hence, if $y = mx + b$, the coefficient of x is the slope of the line.

A linear equation of the form $y = mx + b$ is said to be written in the slope-y-intercept form.

The coefficient of x in the equation of the form $y = mx + b$ is the slope of the line; that is, m is the slope.

The constant term in the equation $y = mx + b$ is the y-intercept of the line; that is, b is the y-intercept.

Example 1. Draw the locus (graph) of the equation $5x + 2y = 6$.

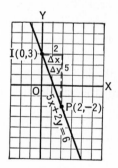

Fig. 42

Solution: The slope-y-intercept form of the equation is $y = -\frac{5}{2}x + 3$. The coefficient of x is $-\frac{5}{2}$; hence the slope m of the line is $-\frac{5}{2}$; that is, the ordinate decreases 5 units as the abscissa increases 2 units. Since $b = 3$, the y-intercept b is 3. Locate $I(0, 3)$, then go to the right 2 units and down 5 units to the point P. The points P and I determine the required line.

Example 2. Write the equation of the straight line which has the slope $\frac{3}{4}$ and the y-intercept -3.

Solution: Since $m = \frac{3}{4}$ and $b = -3$, the equation $y = mx + b$ becomes $y = \frac{3}{4}x - 3$.

Exercises (*Optional*)

1. Give the slope and the y-intercept of the graph (locus) of each of the following:
   a. $y = \frac{3}{5}x + 3$
   b. $y = -\frac{3}{2}x + 4$
   c. $y = 3$
   d. $y = -x + 5$
   e. $y = x - 3$
   f. $y = -2x - 4$

2. Draw the graphs (loci) of the following equations on the same set of axes:
   a. $y = 3x + 3$
   b. $y = \frac{3}{2}x + 3$
   c. $y = -\frac{3}{2}x + 3$
   d. $y = x + 3$
   e. $y = -x + 3$
   f. $y = 0x + 3$

3. How are the graphs in Exercise **2** related? Explain.

4. Draw the graphs of the following equations on the same set of axes:
   a. $y = \frac{3}{4}x + 1$
   b. $y = \frac{3}{4}x + 3$
   c. $y = \frac{3}{4}x - 4$
   d. $y = \frac{3}{4}x$

5. How are the graphs of Exercise **4** related? Explain.

6. Write the equation of the straight line having the indicated slope and y-intercept.
   a. $m = 2, b = 3$
   b. $m = 0, b = -4$
   c. $m = 1, b = 0$

d. $m = -1, b = 0$
e. $m = \frac{5}{2}, b = 4$
f. $m = -\frac{2}{5}, b = 3$

7. Draw the lines represented by (a) $y = 0$, and (b) $x = 0$. What is another name for each of these lines?

The equation of a line that has a given slope and passes through a given point (*Optional*)

Suppose we know that a straight line has a slope of -2 and that it passes through the point $P(-1, 4)$. That is, we know that the value of m is -2, and we also know that when the value of x is -1, the value of y is 4. To find the value of b, we substitute these values for m, x, and y in the equation $y = mx + b$, and solve for b.

Since $y = mx + b$
$4 = (-2)(-1) + b$
$4 = 2 + b$
$2 = b$

Hence $y = -2x + 2$.

Remember: If, and only if, a point is on a line, (then) its co-ordinates satisfy the equation of the line.

The equation of a line that passes through two given points (*Optional*)

If a line passes through the points $A(2, 5)$ and $B(-3, 3)$, then
$$m = \frac{y_2 - y_1}{x_2 - x_1} = \frac{5 - 3}{2 - (-3)} = \frac{2}{5}.$$

Verify that $\dfrac{3-5}{-3-2} = m = \dfrac{\Delta y}{\Delta x}$.

To find b, substitute $\tfrac{2}{5}$ for m, and the co-ordinates of either A or B for x and y in the equation $y = mx + b$, and solve for b.

Since $y = mx + b$
$$5 = \tfrac{2}{5}(2) + b$$
$$5 = \tfrac{4}{5} + b$$
$$25 = 4 + 5b$$
$$\tfrac{21}{5} = b$$

Hence, $y = \tfrac{2}{5}x + \tfrac{21}{5}$.

Exercises (Optional)

Write the equation of the straight line which has the given slope m and passes through the point whose co-ordinates are given.

1. $m = 2$, $A(3, 4)$
2. $m = 3$, $B(-3, -4)$
3. $m = -3$, $C(-3, 5)$
4. $m = 3$, $D(3, -2)$
5. $m = 0$, $I(0, -3)$
6. $m = \tfrac{4}{3}$, $E(-1, 2)$
7. $m = -\tfrac{3}{4}$, $F(0, 0)$
8. $m = \tfrac{2}{3}$, $G(0, 6)$
9. $m = -\tfrac{3}{2}$, $H(-4, 0)$

Write the equation of the straight line which passes through the two points whose co-ordinates are given.

10. $A(0, 0)$ and $B(5, 5)$
11. $C(0, 0)$ and $D(-5, 5)$
12. $E(1, 6)$ and $H(8, -4)$
13. $G(2, 3)$ and $H(8, -4)$
14. $I(0, -4)$ and $J(-4, -4)$
15. $K(0, 4)$ and $L(-4, -4)$
16. Show that $y - y_1 = m(x - x_1)$ is the equation of a straight line that has the slope m and passes through the point $P(x_1, y_1)$.

This equation is called the point-slope form of a linear equation.

17. Show that $y - y_1 = \dfrac{y_2 - y_1}{x_2 - x_1}(x - x_1)$ is the equation of a straight line that passes through the two points $P(x_1, y_1)$ and $Q(x_2, y_2)$.

This equation is called the two-point form of a linear equation.

The slopes of parallel lines
(*Optional*)

Let a and b represent any two parallel lines whose slopes are m_1 and m_2, respectively.

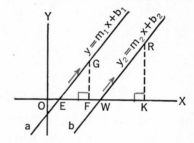

Fig. 43

Since $a \parallel b$, $\angle FEG = \angle KWR$. Why?
Then $\triangle EFG \sim \triangle WKR$. Why?

Hence, $\dfrac{FG}{EF} = \dfrac{KR}{WK}$. Why?

But $\dfrac{FG}{EF} = m_1$, and $\dfrac{KR}{WK} = m_2$. Why?

Since FG, EF, KR, and WK represent positive segments, both m_1 and m_2 are positive. Hence, $m_1 = m_2$.

You prove that if $m_1 = m_2$, then $a \parallel b$.

If two lines are parallel, their slopes are equal.

If the slopes of two lines are equal, the lines are parallel.

The slopes of perpendicular lines (*Optional*)

Let m_1 and m_2 be the slopes of two perpendicular lines a and b, respectively. Then $m_1 = \dfrac{HM}{WH} = \dfrac{+h}{+c}$ since both HM and WH are positive. Explain.

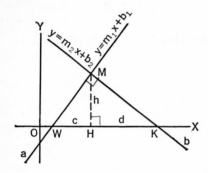

Fig. 44

Also, $m_2 = \dfrac{HM}{KH} = \dfrac{+h}{-d}$ since HM is positive and KH is negative. Explain.

Now $\triangle WHM \sim \triangle HKM$. Why?

Then $\dfrac{c}{h} = \dfrac{h}{d}$. Why?

Therefore, $\dfrac{1}{m_1} = -m_2$. Why?

Or, $m_1 \cdot m_2 = -1$.

The proof of the converse, *if* $m_1 \cdot m_2 = -1$, then $a \perp b$, is easily accomplished after certain trigonometric relationships have been learned. For the present we shall postulate it.

If two lines are perpendicular, the product of their slopes is -1; that is, the slope of a line is the negative reciprocal of the slope of any line perpendicular to it.

If the product of the slopes of two lines is -1, the lines are perpendicular.

Some of the exercises below require the use of the formula for finding the distance between two points. See Chapter 8.

1. Write the equation of the line that passes through the origin and is parallel to the line $4x - 3y + 8 = 0$.

2. Write the equation of the line that passes through the origin and is perpendicular to the line having the equation $4x - 3y + 8 = 0$.

3. Write the equation of the line that passes through $P(3, 4)$ and is parallel to the locus of $y = \frac{1}{2}x - 3$.

4. Write the equation of the line that passes through $P(3, 4)$ and is perpendicular to the locus of $y = \frac{1}{2}x - 3$.

5. The vertices of a triangle are $A(2, 5)$, $B(7, 2)$, and $C(-1, -6)$.
   a. Write the equation of the line through A and B.
   b. Write the equation of the line through C perpendicular to AB.
   c. Write the equation of the line through C parallel to AB.
   d. Write the equation of the perpendicular bisector of AB.
   e. Write the equation of the line through C and the midpoint of AB.

6. Identify the quadrilaterals having the following sets of vertices:
   a. $A(0, -3)$, $B(2, 0)$, $C(0, 3)$, and $D(-2, 0)$.
   b. $E(-5, 2)$, $F(2, 2)$, $G(3, 5)$, and $H(-3, 5)$.
   c. $I(-2, 1)$, $J(3, 3)$, $K(3, 6)$, and $L(-2, 4)$.
   d. $X(-1, 4)$, $M(4, -2)$, $R(5, 2)$, and $Y(-2, 0)$.
   e. $C(-4, -1)$, $F(7, 0)$, $J(1, 5)$, and $D(2, -6)$.
   f. $M(-3, -1)$, $N(5, 3)$, $P(4, -1)$, and $Q(0, -3)$.

7. The vertices of a triangle are $A(-4, -2)$, $B(4, 2)$, and $C(-2, 4)$.

a. Prove that triangle ABC is isosceles.

b. Prove that a line segment joining the midpoints of any two sides is parallel to the third side and equal to one-half of it.

8. Show that $R(3, 1)$, $S(5, 5)$, and $T(9, -2)$ are the vertices of a right triangle.

9. Verify by co-ordinate geometry that the median to the hypotenuse is half the hypotenuse.

10. The vertices of a triangle are $A(1, -2)$, $B(5, -2)$, and $C(3, 3)$.

a. Write the equation of the altitude from C to AB.

b. Find the co-ordinates of the point of intersection of AB and the altitude from C to AB.

c. Find the length of the altitude from C to AB.

d. Write the equation of the median from C to AB.

e. Find the length of the median from C to AB.

f. Write the equation of the perpendicular bisector of AB.

g. Prove that $\triangle ABC$ is isosceles.

h. Repeat parts (**a**) through (**f**) for the altitude and median from B to AC.

11. The vertices of a quadrilateral are $A(-1, 3)$, $B(-2, -1)$, $C(2, -2)$, and $D(3, 2)$. Show that

a. $AD \parallel BC$

b. $AD \perp DC$

c. $AC \perp BD$

d. $AC = BD$

e. The point of intersection of AC and BD is equidistant from A, B, C, and D.

12. The co-ordinates of the vertices of $\triangle ABC$ are $A(-6, -8)$, $B(6, 4)$, and $C(-6, 10)$.

a. Write the equations of the sides of $\triangle ABC$.

b. Find the length of each side of $\triangle ABC$.

c. Find the co-ordinates of the midpoints E, F, and G of the sides AB, BC, and AC of $\triangle ABC$.

d. Write the equations of the medians AF, CE, and BG.

e. Write the equations of the altitudes CH, AI, and BJ.

f. Find the co-ordinates of H, I, and J, the feet of the altitudes.

g. Find the co-ordinates of the centroid M.

h. Find the co-ordinates of the orthocenter N.

i. Find the lengths of BM and MG.

j. Write the equations of the perpendicular bisectors of the sides of $\triangle ABC$.

k. Find the co-ordinates of the circumcenter P.

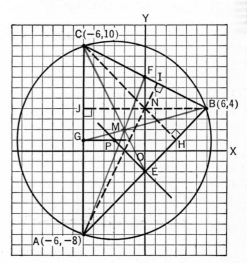

Ex. 12

13. In Exercise **12**,

   a. Find the radius of the circumscribed circle.

   b. Write the equation of the circumscribed circle.

14. The vertices of a triangle are $E(-3, -4)$, $F(2, 3)$, and $G(-4, 5)$.

   a. Find the co-ordinates of the point of intersection of the medians.

   b. Prove that the medians intersect at a point which is two-thirds of the distance from a vertex to the midpoint of the opposite side.

   c. Find the co-ordinates of the point of intersection of the altitudes.

15. **a.** Prove that the triangle formed by joining $A(0, 0)$, $B(6, 0)$, and $C(3, 3\sqrt{3})$ is an equilateral triangle.

   b. Find the co-ordinates of the center of the circumscribed circle.

   c. Write the equation of the circumscribed circle.

16. Prove that the diagonals of the quadrilateral $A(0, 0)$, $B(8, 0)$, $C(12, 4)$, and $D(4, 4)$ bisect each other.

Exercises—Space Geometry *(Optional)*

1. The figure shown here is a rectangular box. All the faces and bases are rectangles.

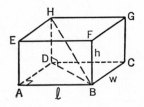

Ex. 1

   a. Express DB in terms of l and w.

   b. Express HB in terms of l, w, and h.

   c. If $l = 3$, $w = 4$, and $h = 12$, find HB.

2. Find the diagonal of a cube whose edge is 6.

3. Prove that the diagonals of a cube are not perpendicular.

4. Prove that a diagonal of a cube is equal to the edge of the cube multiplied by $\sqrt{3}$.

5. The base of this pyramid is a square. The altitude VH intersects the base $ABCD$ at the point of intersection of the diagonals AC and BD, VE and HE are both $\perp BC$ at E. If $AB = 6$, and $VH = 8$, find AC, VC, and VE.

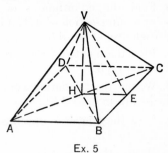

Ex. 5

6. The base of the pyramid V-ABC is the triangle ABC; the plane of $\triangle A'B'C'$ is parallel to the plane of $\triangle ABC$; VH is perpendicular to the plane of $\triangle ABC$; AV and VH determine a plane that intersects the planes of $\triangle ABC$ and $\triangle A'B'C'$ in the lines AH and $A'H'$, respectively.

Assume these statements:

(1) If two parallel planes are cut by a third plane, the lines of intersection are parallel.

(2) If a line is perpendicular to one of two parallel planes, it is perpendicular to the other.

Prove:

(a) $A'B' \parallel AB$, $\quad B'C' \parallel BC$,
$A'C' \parallel AC$, and $A'H' \parallel AH$.

(b) VH' is perpendicular to the plane of $\triangle A'B'C'$.

(c) $\dfrac{VH'}{VH} = \dfrac{VA'}{VA} = \dfrac{VB'}{VB} = \dfrac{VC'}{VC}$.

(d) $\triangle A'B'C' \sim \triangle ABC$.

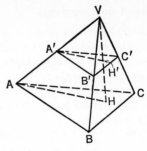

Ex. 6

Chapter Summary

Polygons are similar if:

1. Their corresponding angles are equal and their corresponding sides are proportional.

2. They are composed of the same number of triangles similar each to each in corresponding positions.

If polygons are similar:

1. Their corresponding angles are equal and their corresponding sides are proportional.

2. The ratio of their perimeters is equal to the ratio of any two corresponding sides.

3. They can be separated into the same number of triangles similar each to each.

Triangles are similar if:

1. Two angles of one are equal to two angles of the other.

2. They are right triangles, and an acute angle of one is equal to an acute angle of the other.

3. An angle of one is equal to an angle of the other, and the including sides are proportional.

4. Their corresponding sides are proportional.

5. They are similar to another triangle.

6. They are corresponding triangles of similar polygons.

7. They are right triangles, and one of them is formed by the altitude to the hypotenuse of the other.

8. They are formed by the altitude on the hypotenuse of a right triangle.

Mean proportionals

1. If a tangent and a secant are drawn to a circle from an external point, the tangent is the mean proportional between the secant and its external segment.

2. The altitude to the hypotenuse of a right triangle is the mean proportional between the segments into which it divides the hypotenuse.

3. If the altitude is drawn to the hypotenuse of a right triangle, either leg is the mean proportional between the whole hypotenuse and the segment of the hypotenuse that is adjacent to the leg.

4. Any perpendicular to a diameter from a point on a circle is the mean proportional between the segments of the diameter.

Products of line segments

1. If two chords intersect within a circle, the product of the segments of one is equal to the product of the segments of the other.
2. If two secants are drawn to a circle from an external point, the product of the whole secant and its external segment is equal to the product of the other secant and its external segment.

The Pythagorean Theorem and its converse

1. If a triangle is a right triangle, the square of the hypotenuse is equal to the sum of the squares of the legs.
2. If the sum of the squares of two sides of a triangle is equal to the square of the third side, the triangle is a right triangle.

Review of Chapter 13

Numerical Exercises

1. A tower casts a shadow 110 feet long at the same time a yardstick held vertically casts a shadow 16.0 inches long. How high is the tower?
2. The sides of a triangle are 5, 6, and 8. Find the corresponding sides of a similar triangle whose perimeter is 57.
3. The ratio of similitude of two similar triangles is 3 to 8. If an altitude of the smaller triangle is 9, find the corresponding altitude of the larger triangle.
4. A segment parallel to the 6.0-inch side of a scalene triangle divides each of the other two sides into parts in the ratio 1 to 2. Find the length of the segment. Why are there two possible answers?
5. Find the side of an equilateral triangle whose altitude is 8.
6. Find the side of a square whose diagonal is 10.

7. Find the length of a chord of a circle which is perpendicular to a diameter and which divides the diameter into segments of 9.0 inches and 3.0 inches.
8. Construct the mean proportional between two adjacent sides of a rectangle.
9. Find $\sqrt{3}$ geometrically.
10. Draw a quadrilateral on your paper. Construct a quadrilateral similar to it if the ratio of similitude is 3 to 2.

Completion Test

Copy the numbers **1-10** *on your paper. After the numbers, write the word or words which will complete the following statements correctly. Do not write in this book:*

1. If two triangles are similar, corresponding angles are . . . . .
2. If two triangles are similar, corresponding sides are . . . . .
3. If two triangles are similar, corresponding altitudes and correspond-

ing medians are . . . . to any two corresponding sides.

4. If two polygons are similar, their perimeters have the same ratio as any two . . . . sides.

5. The length of each leg of an isosceles right triangle is equal to the length of the hypotenuse divided by . . . . .

6. If the sizes of the angles of a triangle are proportional to 1, 2, and 3, the sides opposite the angles are proportional to . . . . , ... , and . . . . .

7. The length of the leg opposite the 60° angle of a 30°, 60°, 90° triangle is equal to the length of the leg opposite the 30° angle . . . . by the $\sqrt{3}$.

8. The length of the hypotenuse of a 30°, 60°, 90° triangle is the length of the leg opposite the 60° angle multiplied by . . . . .

9. If the sides of a triangle are proportional to 1, 1, and $\sqrt{2}$, the triangle is . . . . .

10. If $\triangle ABP \sim \triangle CDP$, and if $AP = \frac{4}{3}PC$, then $DC = \ldots . AB$.

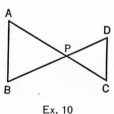

Ex. 10

True-False Test

Copy the numbers of these statements on your paper. If a statement is true, write **True** *after its number; if a statement is not necessarily true, write* **False** *after its number. Do not write in this book.*

1. All rhombuses are similar.

2. If the hypotenuse of a right triangle is 13 and one leg is 5, the other leg is 12.

3. If the corresponding angles of two quadrilaterals are equal, the corresponding sides are proportional.

4. The altitude to the hypotenuse of a right triangle is the mean proportional between the segments into which it divides the hypotenuse.

5. Corresponding medians and corresponding altitudes of similar triangles are proportional.

6. In triangles ABC and RST, if $\frac{a}{b} = \frac{r}{s}$ and $\angle C = \angle T$, $\triangle ABC \sim \triangle RST$.

7. The conventional scale $\frac{1}{8}''$ to $1'$ corresponds to the fractional scale $\frac{1}{48}$.

8. If a drawing is made to the scale $\frac{1}{4}''$ to $1'$, then $\frac{5}{8}''$ represents $2'\,6''$.

9. If chords are drawn through a given point within a circle, the product of the segments of any chord is a constant.

10. If secants are drawn through a given point outside a circle, the product of any secant and its external segment is a constant.

These surveyors are communicating by telephone with the men at the survey point they are observing. The trigonometric ratios studied in this chapter are indispensable to the surveyor when making his drawings and calculations.

Chapter 14 NUMERICAL TRIGONOMETRY

(Optional)

IT IS FREQUENTLY impossible to obtain by direct measurement the height of an object or the distance between two points. Methods for indirect measurement, based on the constant ratios of the sides of similar triangles, have been devised. The branch of mathematics in which these methods are studied is called *trigonometry*. Trigonometry is a word derived from two Greek words meaning "triangle measurement."

In this course we shall consider only the most elementary concepts of trigonometry. We shall learn how to solve a right triangle; that is, given certain parts of a right triangle, in addition to the right angle, we shall learn how to find the remaining parts.

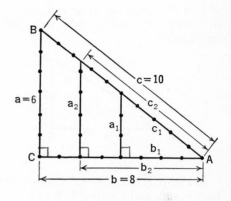

Fig. 1

In Figure 1, $\angle A$ is approximately

$$37°, \quad \frac{a}{b} = \frac{3}{4}, \quad \frac{a}{c} = \frac{3}{5}, \quad \text{and} \frac{b}{c} = \frac{4}{5}.$$

Trigonometric ratios

In Figure 1, the three right triangles are similar. Why? Hence,

$$\frac{a_1}{b_1} = \frac{a_2}{b_2} = \frac{a}{b}. \text{ Why?}$$

$$\frac{a_1}{c_1} = \frac{a_2}{c_2} = \frac{a}{c}. \text{ Why?}$$

$$\frac{b_1}{c_1} = \frac{b_2}{c_2} = \frac{b}{c}. \text{ Why?}$$

Therefore, the ratio of a to b, the ratio of a to c, and the ratio of b to c are constants for the given $\angle A$. The value of each of these constants depends upon the size of $\angle A$; that is, as the angle changes in size, the values of the ratios also change.

In Figure 2, $\angle A$ is approximately

$$22° 40', \frac{a}{b} = \frac{5}{12}, \frac{a}{c} = \frac{5}{13}, \text{ and} \frac{b}{c} = \frac{12}{13}.$$

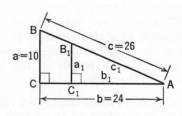

Fig. 2

What is the value of $\frac{a_1}{b_1}$? of $\frac{a_1}{c_1}$? of $\frac{b_1}{c_1}$?

Do these ratios give you the actual lengths of the sides of $\triangle AB_1C_1$?

419

In Figure 3, if $\angle A$ = 30°, and a = 5, then c = 10, and b = $5\sqrt{3}$. Why?

What is the ratio of a to b? of a to c? of b to c? Would the same ratios exist in larger or smaller 30°, 60°, 90° triangles?

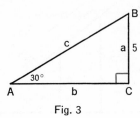

Fig. 3

In Figure 4, if $\angle A$ = 45°, and a = 6, then b = 6, and c = $6\sqrt{2}$. Why?

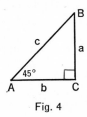

Fig. 4

What is the ratio of a to b? of a to c? of b to c?

Does the size of the isosceles right triangle affect the value of these ratios?

DEFINITIONS The *tangent* of an acute angle of a right triangle is the ratio of the length of the leg opposite the angle to the length of the leg adjacent to the angle.

The *sine* of an acute angle of a right triangle is the ratio of the length of the leg opposite the angle to the length of the hypotenuse of the triangle.

The *cosine* of an acute angle of a right triangle is the ratio of the length of the leg adjacent to the angle to the length of the hypotenuse of the triangle.

Using the notation shown in Figure 5, we can abbreviate each of these ratios as follows:

1. $\tan A = \dfrac{\text{opposite leg}}{\text{adjacent leg}} = \dfrac{a}{b}$.

   Similarly, $\tan B = \dfrac{b}{a}$.

2. $\sin A = \dfrac{\text{opposite leg}}{\text{hypotenuse}} = \dfrac{a}{c}$.

   Similarly, $\sin B = \dfrac{b}{c}$.

3. $\cos A = \dfrac{\text{adjacent leg}}{\text{hypotenuse}} = \dfrac{b}{c}$.

   Similarly, $\cos B = \dfrac{a}{c}$.

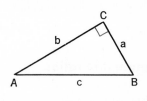

Fig. 5

The approximate values of the trigonometric ratios may be found by scale drawings. By the methods of higher mathematics, the values of the trigonometric ratios of any angle can be computed to any desired degree of accuracy, and they are available in tables.

Since the ratio of one side of a right triangle to another depends upon the size of the acute angle, these ratios are functions of the angle; hence the tangent, sine, and cosine of an angle of a right triangle are called *trigonometric functions*.

Using the table of trigonometric functions

The values of the sine, cosine, and tangent of angles from 0° to 90° can be found directly from the table on page 423. To find any required function, locate the angle in the column headed "Angle," and read the function desired in the proper column.

Example:
$$\sin 20° = 0.3420$$
$$\cos 27° = 0.8910$$
$$\tan 84° = 9.5144$$

The table can also be used to find the angle when the sine, cosine, or tangent of the angle is known. For example, if $\sin x = 0.8387$, we locate this value in the column headed *sin* and find the corresponding angle to be 57°.

When the exact value is not in the table we shall, for the purpose of this course, use the angle whose function is nearest to our given value. For example, if $\tan y = 1.0837$, we observe that this is between 1.0724 and 1.1106, but nearer 1.0724; hence, angle y is 47° to the nearest degree.

Exercises

1. Using the 4-place table of values of trigonometric ratios, find the value of each of the following:

   a. sin 39° **f.** tan 30°
   b. cos 43° **g.** sin 63°
   c. tan 79° **h.** cos 27°
   d. sin 30° **i.** tan 45°
   e. cos 60° **j.** cos 87°

2. Using the 4-place table of values of trigonometric ratios, find the number of degrees in $\angle A$ to the nearest 1°, when:

   a. sin $A = 0.6010$
   b. cos $A = 0.8036$
   c. tan $A = 0.7536$

d. sin $A = 0.8700$
e. cos $A = 0.8700$
f. tan $A = 0.5700$
g. sin $A = 0.7131$
h. cos $A = 0.7131$
i. tan $A = 9.8776$

Increasing and decreasing functions

We observe from the table that as an angle *increases* from 0° to 90°, its sine *increases* from 0 to 1. Notice that the sine of 30° is 0.5000 and that the sine of 45° is 0.7071; hence the increase in the sine function is *not* proportional to the increase in the angle.

The tangent function is also an increasing function. As the angle *increases* from 0° to 90°, the tangent of the angle *increases* from 0 to a very large number.

The cosine function is a decreasing function. As the angle *increases* from 0° to 90°, the cosine of the angle *decreases* from 1 to 0.

This geologist is using a plane table and alidade, similar to the one described on page 402, in mapping territory where oil is probably to be found. A leveling device on the top of the instrument shows when the table is ready for taking measurements.

Interpolation

In order to find values of functions of angles not listed in the table, we use a method called *interpolation*. The method is based on the assumption that a change in a function is proportional to a change in the angle. While this is not strictly correct, the method is sufficiently correct for *very small* changes in the angle.

Example 1. Find the sine of 16° 30′.

$$60' \begin{bmatrix} 30' \begin{bmatrix} \sin\ 16°\ \ 0' = 0.2756 \\ \sin\ 16°\ 30' = ? \end{bmatrix} ? \\ \sin\ 17°\ \ 0' = 0.2924 \end{bmatrix}$$

Tabular difference $= 0.0168$.
(0.2924–0.2756)

Since 16° 30′ is $\frac{30}{60}$ of the way between 16° and 17°, and since the sine of an angle is an *increasing* function, we *add* $\frac{30}{60}$, or $\frac{1}{2}$, of 0.0168 to 0.2756; hence, sin 16° 30′ = 0.2756 + 0.0084 = 0.2840.

Example 2. Find cos 63° 42′.

$$60' \begin{bmatrix} 42' \begin{bmatrix} \cos\ 63°\ \ 0' = 0.4540 \\ \cos\ 63°\ 42' = ? \end{bmatrix} ? \\ \cos\ 64°\ \ 0' = 0.4384 \end{bmatrix}$$

Tabular difference $= 0.0156$.
(0.4540–0.4384)

Since 63° 42′ is $\frac{42}{60}$ of the way between 63° and 64°, and since the cosine of an angle is a *decreasing* function, we *subtract* $\frac{42}{60}$ or $\frac{7}{10}$ of 0.0156 from 0.4540; hence cos 63° 42′ = 0.4540 − 0.0109 = 0.4431.

When we need to find the angle whose function is given, we use another form of interpolation if we wish to find the angle with more accuracy than the nearest degree.

Example 3. If tan B = 1.2444, find $\angle B$ to the nearest 10′.

$$60' \begin{bmatrix} ? \begin{bmatrix} \tan\ 51°\ 0' = 1.2349 \\ \tan\ B\ \ \ \ = 1.2444 \end{bmatrix} \begin{matrix} \text{Actual diff.} = \\ 0.0095 \end{matrix} \\ \tan\ 52°\ 0' = 1.2799 \end{bmatrix}$$

Tabular diff. = 0.0450.
(1.2799–1.2349)

$\frac{0.0095}{0.0450}$, or $\frac{19}{90}$, of 60′ is added to 51° 0′. Why?

$\therefore\ \angle B = 51°\ 10'$.

Exercises

1. Find the values of the functions of the following angles:
   a. sin 46° 40′
   b. cos 27° 30′
   c. tan 30° 10′
   d. sin 75° 20′
   e. cos 68° 50′
   f. tan 80° 50′

2. Find the number of degrees in each angle to the nearest 10′:
   a. sin $A = 0.9930$
   b. cos $B = 0.2950$
   c. tan $x = 1.7321$
   d. sin $A = 0.4100$
   e. cos $A = 0.1422$
   f. tan $A = 0.2967$

Table of Trigonometric Ratios

Angle	Sin	Cos	Tan	Angle	Sin	Cos	Tan
1°	.0175	.9998	.0175	46°	.7193	.6947	1.0355
2°	.0349	.9994	.0349	47°	.7314	.6820	1.0724
3°	.0523	.9986	.0524	48°	.7431	.6691	1.1106
4°	.0698	.9976	.0699	49°	.7547	.6561	1.1504
5°	.0872	.9962	.0875	50°	.7660	.6428	1.1918
6°	.1045	.9945	.1051	51°	.7771	.6293	1.2349
7°	.1219	.9925	.1228	52°	.7880	.6157	1.2799
8°	.1392	.9903	.1405	53°	.7986	.6018	1.3270
9°	.1564	.9877	.1584	54°	.8090	.5878	1.3764
10°	.1736	.9848	.1763	55°	.8192	.5736	1.4281
11°	.1908	.9816	.1944	56°	.8290	.5592	1.4826
12°	.2079	.9781	.2126	57°	.8387	.5446	1.5399
13°	.2250	.9744	.2309	58°	.8480	.5299	1.6003
14°	.2419	.9703	.2493	59°	.8572	.5150	1.6643
15°	.2588	.9659	.2679	60°	.8660	.5000	1.7321
16°	.2756	.9613	.2867	61°	.8746	.4848	1.8040
17°	.2924	.9563	.3057	62°	.8829	.4695	1.8807
18°	.3090	.9511	.3249	63°	.8910	.4540	1.9626
19°	.3256	.9455	.3443	64°	.8988	.4384	2.0503
20°	.3420	.9397	.3640	65°	.9063	.4226	2.1445
21°	.3584	.9336	.3839	66°	.9135	.4067	2.2460
22°	.3746	.9272	.4040	67°	.9205	.3907	2.3559
23°	.3907	.9205	.4245	68°	.9272	.3746	2.4751
24°	.4067	.9135	.4452	69°	.9336	.3584	2.6051
25°	.4226	.9063	.4663	70°	.9397	.3420	2.7475
26°	.4384	.8988	.4877	71°	.9455	.3256	2.9042
27°	.4540	.8910	.5095	72°	.9511	.3090	3.0777
28°	.4695	.8829	.5317	73°	.9563	.2924	3.2709
29°	.4848	.8746	.5543	74°	.9613	.2756	3.4874
30°	.5000	.8660	.5774	75°	.9659	.2588	3.7321
31°	.5150	.8572	.6009	76°	.9703	.2419	4.0108
32°	.5299	.8480	.6249	77°	.9744	.2250	4.3315
33°	.5446	.8387	.6494	78°	.9781	.2079	4.7046
34°	.5592	.8290	.6745	79°	.9816	.1908	5.1446
35°	.5736	.8192	.7002	80°	.9848	.1736	5.6713
36°	.5878	.8090	.7265	81°	.9877	.1564	6.3138
37°	.6018	.7986	.7536	82°	.9903	.1392	7.1154
38°	.6157	.7880	.7813	83°	.9925	.1219	8.1443
39°	.6293	.7771	.8098	84°	.9945	.1045	9.5144
40°	.6428	.7660	.8391	85°	.9962	.0872	11.4301
41°	.6561	.7547	.8693	86°	.9976	.0698	14.3007
42°	.6691	.7431	.9004	87°	.9986	.0523	19.0811
43°	.6820	.7314	.9325	88°	.9994	.0349	28.6363
44°	.6947	.7193	.9657	89°	.9998	.0175	57.2900
45°	.7071	.7071	1.0000	90°	1.0000	.0000	

Problems solved by trigonometric functions

We can find the other sides and angles of a right triangle if we know:
1. One acute angle and one side.
2. Any two sides.

Example 1. Given: Right $\triangle ABC$, $\angle A = 25°$, $a = 3.5$ inches.
To find: $\angle B$, b, and c.

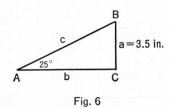

Fig. 6

Solution:
a. To find $\angle B$
$$\angle B = 90° - \angle A$$
$$= 90° - 25°$$
$$= 65°$$

b. To find b
$$\tan A = \frac{a}{b}$$
$$\tan 25° = \frac{3.5}{b}$$
$$\therefore \quad b = \frac{3.5}{\tan 25°}$$
$$= \frac{3.5}{0.4663}$$
$$= 7.5 \text{ inches.}$$

c. Side b may also be found as follows:
$$\tan B = \frac{b}{a}$$
$$\tan 65° = \frac{b}{3.5}$$
$$\therefore \quad b = 3.5 \times \tan 65°$$
$$b = 3.5 \times 2.1445$$
$$= 7.5 \text{ inches.}$$

d. To find c
$$\sin A = \frac{a}{c}$$
$$\sin 25° = \frac{3.5}{c}$$
$$\therefore \quad c = \frac{3.5}{\sin 25°}$$
$$= \frac{3.5}{0.4226}$$
$$= 8.3 \text{ inches.}$$

Note: The values of b and c are rounded off to two digits because a was given to only two digits. (See Chapter 6: "Computation with Approximate Data.")

Example 2. Given: Right $\triangle ABC$, $a = 23.50$ feet, and $b = 18.00$ feet.

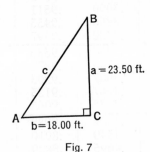

Fig. 7

To find: $\angle A$, $\angle B$, and c.

Solution:
a. To find $\angle A$
$$\tan A = \frac{a}{b}$$
$$= \frac{23.50}{18.00}$$
$$= 1.3056$$
$$\therefore \quad \angle A = 52° \, 30' \text{ (to the nearest 10').}$$

b. To find $\angle B$
$\angle B$ is the complement of $\angle A$.
Hence, $\angle B = 37° \, 30'$.

c. To find side c

$$c^2 = a^2 + b^2$$
$$c^2 = 876.25$$
$$c = \sqrt{876.25}$$
$$= 29.61 \text{ feet.}$$

Check the value of c by using either the formula $\sin A = \dfrac{a}{c}$ or the formula $\cos A = \dfrac{b}{c}$. We used the Pythagorean Theorem to find c in order not to carry on a possible error made in finding the number of degrees in $\angle A$.

Example 3. In a circle of radius 4.000 cm., find the length of a chord of an arc of $50° 0'$, and the distance the chord is from the center.

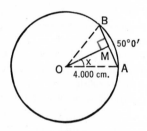

Fig. 8

Solution:

Draw $OM \perp AB$.
Then $AM = MB$, and $\angle x = 25° 0'$. Why?

a. $\qquad \sin x = \dfrac{AM}{OA}$

$$\sin 25° = \dfrac{AM}{4}$$

$$\therefore AM = 4 \times 0.4226.$$
$$= 1.690 \text{ cm.}$$

Now how do you find AB?

b. $\qquad \cos x = \dfrac{OM}{OA}$

$$\cos 25° = \dfrac{OM}{4}$$

$$\therefore OM = 4 \times 0.9063$$
$$= 3.625 \text{ cm.}$$

Example 4. In $\triangle ABC$, $AC = 4.00$ inches, and $\angle A = 36°$. Find the altitude to the side AB.

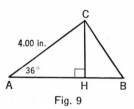

Fig. 9

Solution: $\quad \sin A = \dfrac{CH}{AC}$

$$\sin 36° = \dfrac{CH}{4}$$

$$\therefore CH = 4 \times 0.5878$$
$$= 2.35 \text{ inches.}$$

Here you see a close-up of the surveyor's transit. It is a precision instrument having a vertical protractor for measuring vertical angles and a horizontal protractor for measuring horizontal angles. A plumb bob attached to the center of the transit head is suspended directly over the survey point. The high-power telescope enables the operator to sight accurately at long distances.

Exercises

In Exercises **1-6**, *∠C is the right angle of the right triangle ABC; certain other parts of △ABC are given. You are to find the remaining parts. Do not write in this book.*

	∠A	∠B	a	b	c
1.	?	?	8	15	?
2.	32° 0′	?	12.4 in.	?	?
3.	57° 10′	?	?	28.6 in.	?
4.	?	?	8.7 ft.	18.1 ft.	?
5.	?	?	47.2 yd.	?	64.3 yd.
6.	42° 40′	?	?	?	10.0 ft.

7. A ladder standing against a house makes an angle of 70° with the ground. If the ladder is 30.0 feet long, how far up on the house does it reach?

8. How long a wire is needed to brace a 22.0 ft. vertical pole if the brace is to make an angle of 75° with the ground?

9. A tree 54.0 ft. high casts a shadow 28.4 feet long. What angle do the sun's rays make with the ground at that time?

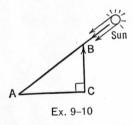

Ex. 9–10

10. At a time when the sun's rays make an angle of 28° with the horizontal, the length of the shadow of a flagpole is 48.8 ft. How high is the flagpole?

11. Two sides of a rectangle are 8.61 inches and 6.32 inches long. Find the angle made by a diagonal and the shorter side.

Find the length of a diagonal.

12. A ship sails on a course 36° west of north for a distance of 26 miles. How far is the ship west, and how far is it north of its original position?

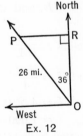

Ex. 12

13. Find the base and altitude of an isosceles triangle if each base angle is 50°, and each of its equal legs is 9.00 inches long.

14. In △ABC, ∠A = 48°, and AC = 6.28 cm. How long is the altitude to the side AB?

15. A man pushes on a lawnmower handle with a force of 50.0 pounds. The handle makes a 32° angle with the ground. Find the component of the force parallel to the ground. (Find the number of pounds force represented by AC.)

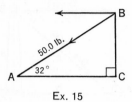

Ex. 15

16. Find the base and the altitude of an isosceles triangle if its vertex angle is 70°, and its equal sides are each 6.00 inches long.

17. If the radius of a circle is 6.50 inches, how far from the center is a chord whose arc is 72°? How long is the chord of the arc?

18. If the radius of a circle is 8.00 cm., how far from the center is a chord of an arc of 45°? How long is the chord of the arc?

19. On a circular track an arc of 40° has a chord of 500 feet. Find the radius of the curve.

20. In the right triangle ABC, show that $\sin A = \cos B$.

21. In the right triangle ABC show that $\tan A = \dfrac{\sin A}{\cos A}$.

22. In the right triangle ABC, show that $(\sin A)^2 + (\cos A)^2 = 1$.

23. The sides of the 30°, 60° right triangle and the sides of the isosceles right triangle are related in such a way that we can find the sine, cosine, and tangent ratios of 30°, 60°, and 45° without using a table. Copy and complete the following table by referring to the figure. *Do not write in this book.*

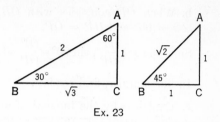

Ex. 23

Ratio	Angle		
	30°	60°	45°
sine	$\frac{1}{2}$	?	?
cosine	$\dfrac{\sqrt{3}}{2}$	?	?
tangent	$\dfrac{1}{\sqrt{3}} = \dfrac{\sqrt{3}}{3}$	?	?

24. Let OP be the radius of a circle, and let x be the number of degrees in the angle formed by OP and OA as OP rotates from the initial position OA to the terminal position OB:

Ex. 24

a. When OP coincides with OA, $\angle x = 0°$ and $HP = 0$.

Since $\sin x = \dfrac{HP}{OP}$, $\sin 0° = \dfrac{0}{OP} = 0$.

In like manner, find $\cos 0°$ and $\tan 0°$.

b. When OP coincides with OB, $\angle x = 90°$ and $HP = OP$.

Since $\sin x = \dfrac{HP}{OP}$, $\sin 90° = \dfrac{OP}{OP} = 1$.

In like manner, find $\cos 90°$.

c. Explain why the tangent of an angle increases very rapidly as the number of degrees in the angle approaches 90°. Copy and complete the table. *Do not write in this book.*

Ratio	Angle	
	0°	90°
sine	0	1
cosine	?	?
tangent	?	?

Angles of elevation and depression

When an observer is looking up at an object above him, the angle between his line of sight and the horizontal is called the *angle of elevation* (Figure 10).

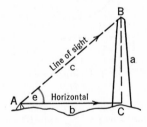

$\angle e$ is the angle of elevation.

Fig. 10

When an observer is looking down at an object below him, the angle between his line of sight and the horizontal is called the *angle of depression.* (Figure 11).

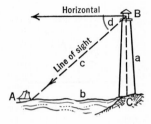

$\angle d$ is the angle of depression.

Fig. 11

Exercises

1. From the top of a lighthouse 125.4 feet above the water level, the angle of depression of a sailboat is 36° 40'. Find the distance from the base of the lighthouse to the sailboat.

2. At a time when the angle of elevation of the sun is 54° 40', a building casts a shadow 86.8 feet long. How high is the building?

3. The Empire State Building in New York City is 1250 feet high. Find, to the nearest degree, the angle of elevation of the top of the building from a position 600 feet from the building on the street level.

4. The Washington Monument is 555 feet high. Find, to the nearest 10 minutes, the angle of depression of a point on the ground 729 feet from its foot.

5. Find, to the nearest degree, the angle of elevation of a road that rises 7.0 feet for every 100 feet of horizontal distance.

Table of Square Roots of Numbers   1–300

N	$\sqrt{N}$	N	$\sqrt{N}$	N	$\sqrt{N}$	N	$\sqrt{N}$	N	$\sqrt{N}$	N	$\sqrt{N}$
1	1.000	51	7.141	101	10.050	151	12.288	201	14.177	251	15.843
2	1.414	52	7.211	102	10.100	152	12.329	202	14.213	252	15.875
3	1.732	53	7.280	103	10.149	153	12.369	203	14.248	253	15.906
4	2.000	54	7.348	104	10.198	154	12.410	204	14.283	254	15.937
5	2.236	55	7.416	105	10.247	155	12.450	205	14.318	255	15.969
6	2.449	56	7.483	106	10.296	156	12.490	206	14.353	256	16.000
7	2.646	57	7.550	107	10.344	157	12.530	207	14.388	257	16.031
8	2.828	58	7.616	108	10.392	158	12.570	208	14.422	258	16.062
9	3.000	59	7.681	109	10.440	159	12.610	209	14.457	259	16.093
10	3.162	60	7.746	110	10.488	160	12.649	210	14.491	260	16.124
11	3.317	61	7.810	111	10.536	161	12.689	211	14.526	261	16.155
12	3.464	62	7.874	112	10.583	162	12.728	212	14.560	262	16.186
13	3.606	63	7.937	113	10.630	163	12.767	213	14.594	263	16.217
14	3.742	64	8.000	114	10.677	164	12.806	214	14.629	264	16.248
15	3.873	65	8.062	115	10.724	165	12.845	215	14.663	265	16.279
16	4.000	66	8.124	116	10.770	166	12.884	216	14.697	266	16.310
17	4.123	67	8.185	117	10.817	167	12.923	217	14.731	267	16.340
18	4.243	68	8.246	118	10.863	168	12.962	218	14.765	268	16.371
19	4.359	69	8.307	119	10.909	169	13.000	219	14.799	269	16.401
20	4.472	70	8.367	120	10.955	170	13.038	220	14.832	270	16.432
21	4.583	71	8.426	121	11.000	171	13.077	221	14.866	271	16.462
22	4.690	72	8.485	122	11.045	172	13.115	222	14.890	272	16.492
23	4.796	73	8.544	123	11.091	173	13.153	223	14.933	273	16.523
24	4.899	74	8.602	124	11.136	174	13.191	224	14.967	274	16.553
25	5.000	75	8.660	125	11.180	175	13.229	225	15.000	275	16.583
26	5.099	76	8.718	126	11.225	176	13.267	226	15.033	276	16.613
27	5.196	77	8.775	127	11.269	177	13.304	227	15.067	277	16.643
28	5.292	78	8.832	128	11.314	178	13.342	228	15.100	278	16.673
29	5.385	79	8.888	129	11.358	179	13.379	229	15.133	279	16.703
30	5.477	80	8.944	130	11.402	180	13.416	230	15.166	280	16.733
31	5.568	81	9.000	131	11.446	181	13.454	231	15.199	281	16.763
32	5.657	82	9.055	132	11.489	182	13.491	232	15.232	282	16.793
33	5.745	83	9.110	133	11.533	183	13.528	233	15.264	283	16.823
34	5.831	84	9.165	134	11.576	184	13.565	234	15.297	284	16.852
35	5.916	85	9.220	135	11.619	185	13.602	235	15.330	285	16.882
36	6.000	86	9.274	136	11.662	186	13.638	236	15.362	286	16.912
37	6.083	87	9.327	137	11.705	187	13.675	237	15.395	287	16.941
38	6.164	88	9.381	138	11.747	188	13.711	238	15.427	288	16.971
39	6.245	89	9.434	139	11.790	189	13.748	239	15.460	289	17.000
40	6.325	90	9.487	140	11.832	190	13.784	240	15.492	290	17.029
41	6.403	91	9.539	141	11.874	191	13.820	241	15.524	291	17.059
42	6.481	92	9.592	142	11.916	192	13.856	242	15.556	292	17.088
43	6.557	93	9.644	143	11.958	193	13.892	243	15.588	293	17.117
44	6.633	94	9.695	144	12.000	194	13.928	244	15.620	294	17.146
45	6.708	95	9.741	145	12.042	195	13.964	245	15.652	295	17.176
46	6.782	96	9.798	146	12.083	196	14.000	246	15.684	296	17.205
47	6.856	97	9.849	147	12.124	197	14.036	247	15.716	297	17.234
48	6.928	98	9.899	148	12.166	198	14.071	248	15.748	298	17.263
49	7.000	99	9.950	149	12.207	199	14.107	249	15.780	299	17.292
50	7.071	100	10.000	150	12.247	200	14.142	250	15.811	300	17.321

6. An observer on the roof of a building 156 feet high finds the angles of depression of the top and bottom of a lower building to be 30° and 45°, respectively. Find the height of the lower building.

7. A vertical beam SP of a searchlight S at an airport illuminates a cloud at the point P. An observer at the point Q, 100 feet from S and in the same horizontal plane, measures the angle of elevation of the point P and finds it to be 82°. How high is the cloud?

Hypsometer

A hypsometer is a very convenient and easily constructed instrument with which the height of an object and the sine, cosine, and tangent of an angle of elevation can be found. It consists of a sheet of graph paper fastened to a backing which can be mounted on a pole. The hypsometer has peep sights along its upper edge and a plumb line fastened to the upper right hand corner. The side SC of the graph chart is 100 units, and the units on GC are the same length as those on SC.

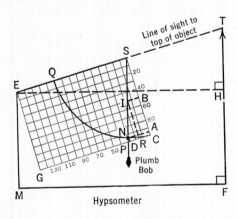

Hypsometer

Fig. 12

To find the height of an object, proceed as follows: Line up the top of an object through the sights of the hypsometer. From the figure it is apparent that

$$\triangle PCS \sim \triangle IBS \sim \triangle EHT;$$

hence, $\dfrac{HT}{EH} = \dfrac{PC}{SC}$ or $HT = EH \times \dfrac{PC}{SC}$.

If the hypsometer is placed so that EH is 100 feet, and SC is 100 units, then the number of feet in HT is equal to the number of units in PC.

Also, $\dfrac{HT}{EH} = \dfrac{IB}{SB}$, or $HT = EH \times \dfrac{IB}{SB}$.

If SB is numerically equal to EH, the number of feet in HT is equal to the number of units in IB, which is equal to the number of units in RC. That is, the length of HT can be found by reading the chart. To find the total height of the object, the length of FH or ME must be added to HT.

The angle of elevation of the top of the object is $\angle E$. If a quadrant of a circle with center S and radius SC is drawn on the chart, the tangent, sine, and cosine of $\angle E$ can be read from the chart.

Since $\angle E = \angle S$,

$$\tan E = \tan S = \frac{PC}{SC} = \frac{PC}{100}.$$

$$\sin E = \sin S = \frac{NA}{NS} = \frac{DC}{100}.$$

$$\cos E = \cos S = \frac{AS}{NS} = \frac{AS}{100}.$$

(In this figure, $PC = 30$; hence $\tan S = 0.3$. The number of degrees in $\angle S$ or $\angle E$ can be found from a table of trigonometric ratios. If $\widehat{QC}$ is calibrated in degrees, $\angle S \stackrel{\circ}{=} \widehat{NC}$.)

Review of Chapter 14

Numerical Exercises

1. Find the length of the diagonals of a rhombus if one side is 8.2 cm. long and one angle is 45°.

2. The diagonals of a rhombus are 8.0 inches and 9.2 inches long. Find the length of each side and the size of each angle of the rhombus.

3. Find the length of the chord of an arc of 36° in a circle of radius 10.0 inches.

4. The angle between two tangents from a point to a circle is 46°. What is the length of one of the tangents if the radius of the circle is 3.6 cm.?

5. A man 6′ 2″ tall casts a shadow 4′ 8″ long. Find the angle of elevation of the sun.

True-False Test

*Copy the numbers 1-20 on your paper. After each number write **True** if the corresponding statement is always true; write **False** if the corresponding statement is not necessarily true. Use tables where necessary.*

1. If $\angle R$ is a right angle of $\triangle RST$, $\sin \angle R = \dfrac{r}{s}$.

2. As an angle increases from 0° to 90°, the numerical value of the cosine increases from 0 to 1.

3. The tangent of 30° is $\dfrac{1}{\sqrt{3}}$.

4. The sine of 60° is $\dfrac{\sqrt{3}}{2}$.

5. Cos 60° = 2 cos 30°.

6. As an angle increases from 0° to 90°, the numerical value of the sine increases from 0 to 1.

7. If $\angle C$ is the right angle of $\triangle ABC$, tan A is the reciprocal of tan B.

8. If $\angle A$ is the complement of $\angle B$, sin A = sin B.

9. If $\cos x = \dfrac{m}{n}$, then $\tan x = \dfrac{\sqrt{n^2 - m^2}}{n}$.

10. In circle C of radius r, the length of the chord MN, whose central angle is $\angle C$, is $r(\cos C)$.

11. Sin 30° = $\frac{1}{2}$ sin 60°.

12. The sine of one acute angle of an isosceles right triangle is equal to the sine of the other acute angle.

13. If tan $x = 1$, and if x is acute, then $x = 45°$.

14. If sin $y = \frac{1}{2}$, and y is acute, then $y = 45°$.

15. The cosine of 60° is $\sqrt{3}$.

16. Sin 30° + sin 60° = sin 90°.

17. Sin 30° = cos 60°.

18. If A and B are acute angles of a right triangle, sin A = cos B.

19. $(\sin 30°)^2 + (\cos 30°)^2 = 1$.

20. The altitude h_t of $\triangle RST$ may be found from the formula $h_t = s \cdot \sin R$.

Here a geometry student uses pieces of felt which stick to the special blackboard, in order to prove one of the important and useful area relationships which you will study in this chapter.

TO MEASURE the area of a surface means to find how many times the given surface contains another surface of the same kind which has been selected as a unit. For this purpose we must have some convenient units of measurement. A *unit of area* is a surface enclosed by a square whose side is some unit of length. Thus a square whose side is one inch is a unit of area called a *square inch*. A square foot, a square centimeter, a square mile, and a square yard are some of the other common units of area.

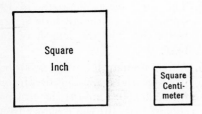

Fig. 1

DEFINITION A *unit of area* is a square whose side is a unit of length.

The area of a polygon

We use the expression, "area of a polygon," when we really mean the area of the surface within the polygon. When we say that the area of a polygon is 20 square centimeters we mean that the surface within the polygon is 20 times as large as a square that is 1 centimeter on a side.

DEFINITION The *area of a polygon* is the number of square units in the plane surface bounded by the polygon.

Equal areas

Figures that have the same area are equal or equivalent. Are equal figures necessarily congruent? Are congruent figures necessarily equal? Do equal figures necessarily have the same shape?

The areas of these figures are approximately equal.

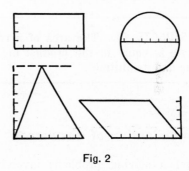

Fig. 2

The area of a rectangle

The area of the rectangle $ABCD$ is 20 unit squares since there are 4 rows each containing 5 unit squares.

Fig. 3

In general, if some linear unit u is contained b times in the base of a rectangle, and the same unit u is contained h times in the altitude of the rectangle, the area of the rectangle is given by the algebraic formula $A = bh$. In the formula, A stands for the measure of the area of the rectangle, and bh indicates the product of the measures of the base and the altitude.

It is beyond the scope of this book to prove that this same formula applies to a rectangle whose base and altitude have no common unit of measure. For example, we shall assume that the area of a rectangle 6.0 inches by $2\sqrt{3}$ inches is $12\sqrt{3}$ square inches.

POSTULATE 48. The area of a rectangle is equal to the product of its base and its altitude.

Denomination of answers

When solving problems involving denominate numbers, it is important to state not only the numerical answer, but also the name of the unit of measure of the answer. For example, $6 per square foot is not the same quantity as 6 square feet, or 6 feet, or 6.

Exercises

In Exercises **1** *and* **2**, *find the area in square yards of the plot of ground represented by the figures.*

1.

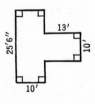

Ex. 1

2.

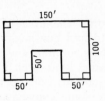

Ex. 2

3. Find the cost of sodding a rectangular plot which is 30.0 feet wide and 46.0 feet long at $1.25 a square yard.

4. If carpet costs $7.25 a square yard, find the cost of carpeting a floor 15 feet by 24 feet.

5. The area of a rectangle is 192 square feet. If the altitude is 12.0 feet long, find the length of the base.

6. A rectangular lot with a 50-foot frontage and a 230-foot depth sold for $5000.00. Find (**a**) the cost per square foot, (**b**) the cost per front foot, and (**c**) the cost per acre (1 acre = 43,560 square feet).

7. How many blocks of linoleum, each 10.0 inches square, will it take to cover a rectangular floor 9 feet 10 inches wide and 10 feet 8 inches long? Remember to allow for waste.

8. The outside dimensions of a rectangular picture frame are 8.0 inches by 10.0 inches. The inside dimensions are 7.0 inches by 9.0 inches. Find the area of the frame.

9. Find the cost of a rectangular farm that is 60.0 rods wide and 108.0 rods long at $350.00 an acre. (1 acre = 160 square rods.)

10. Find the area of a square whose diagonal is 20.0 feet.

11. A square field contains 5.0 acres. How many rods long is a side of the square?

12. The altitude of a rectangle is 5 times its base, and the area of the rectangle is 720. Find the base of the rectangle.

13. A cement walk 3.0 feet wide is placed around the outside of a rectangular garden plot that is 20.0 feet by 30.0 feet. Find the cost of the walk at $6.25 a square yard.

14. Derive the formula for the area of a square in terms of its diagonal.

15. How many square inches are there in the total surface of a cube that is 6.0 inches on an edge?

16. If the area of a rectangle is $a^2 - b^2$, and its base is $a + b$, what is its altitude?

17. Prove geometrically:
$$(a + b)^2 = a^2 + 2ab + b^2.$$

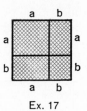

Ex. 17

18. Prove geometrically:
$$(a - b)^2 = a^2 - 2ab + b^2.$$

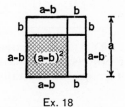

Ex. 18

The ratio of the areas of two rectangles

The most effective way to compare the areas of two rectangles is to find the ratio of their areas. If A_1, b_1, and h_1 represent the area, base, and altitude, respectively, of rectangle $EFGH$; and if A_2, b_2, and h_2 represent the area, base, and altitude, respectively, of rectangle $RSTU$, then

$$A_1 = b_1 h_1$$
and $$A_2 = b_2 h_2.$$

To compare the areas of $EFGH$ and $RSTU$, we divide each member of one equation by the corresponding member of the other.

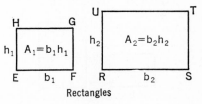

Rectangles

Hence, $\dfrac{A_1}{A_2} = \dfrac{b_1 h_1}{b_2 h_2}$ or $\dfrac{A_1}{A_2} = \dfrac{b_1}{b_2} \times \dfrac{h_1}{h_2}$.

Fig. 4

THEOREM 81. **The ratio of the areas of two rectangles is equal to the ratio of the products of their bases and altitudes.**

Other ways of stating Theorem 81: (1) The areas of two rectangles are directly proportional to the products of their bases and altitudes. (2) The area of a rectangle varies directly as the product of its base and altitude.

Rectangles having equal altitudes

If the altitudes of the two rectangles whose areas are A_1 and A_2 are equal, then $\dfrac{A_1}{A_2} = \dfrac{b_1 h}{b_2 h}$ or $\dfrac{A_1}{A_2} = \dfrac{b_1}{b_2}$.

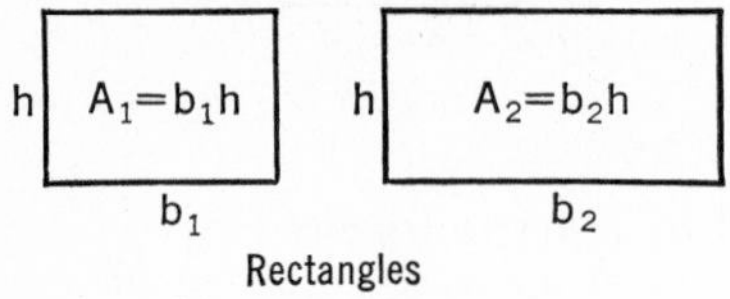

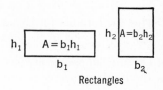

Rectangles

Fig. 5

COROLLARY 1. The ratio of the areas of two rectangles having equal altitudes is equal to the ratio of their bases.

State Corollary 1 in two other ways.

Rectangles having equal bases

If the bases of the two rectangles whose areas are A_1 and A_2 are equal, then $\dfrac{A_1}{A_2} = \dfrac{b h_1}{b h_2}$ or $\dfrac{A_1}{A_2} = \dfrac{h_1}{h_2}$.

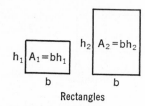

Rectangles

Fig. 6

COROLLARY 2. The ratio of the areas of two rectangles having equal bases is equal to the ratio of their altitudes.

State Corollary 2 in two other ways.

Rectangles having equal areas

If the areas of the two rectangles are equal, then $\dfrac{A_1}{A_2} = \dfrac{b_1 h_1}{b_2 h_2}$ or $1 = \dfrac{b_1 h_1}{b_2 h_2}$.

Hence, $b_1 h_1 = b_2 h_2$. Why?

Or $\dfrac{b_1}{b_2} = \dfrac{h_2}{h_1}$. Why?

Rectangles

Fig. 7

If the area of a rectangle is to remain constant when the base is multiplied by some number n, the altitude must be divided by n, and vice versa.

COROLLARY 3. If two rectangles have equal areas, their bases and altitudes are inversely proportional.

Another way of stating Corollary 3: If two rectangles have equal areas, the ratio of their bases is equal to the reciprocal of the ratio of their altitudes.

Exercises

1. The base of one rectangle is 6.0 inches long and its altitude is 4.2 inches long; the base of another rectangle is 8.0 inches long, and its altitude is 3.6 inches long. Compare their areas.

2. State the effect on the area of a rectangle if both the base and the altitude are multiplied by 4.

3. Does the area of a rectangle remain the same if its base is increased by 2 units, and its altitude is diminished by 2 units? Verify your answer algebraically.

4. If the area of a rectangle remains constant, state the effect on the base if:

   a. The altitude is multiplied by 2

   b. The altitude is divided by 3

   c. The altitude is multiplied by $\frac{2}{3}$

   d. The altitude is divided by $\frac{3}{4}$

   e. The altitude is increased by 25%.

5. State the effect on the area of a rectangle if the base is divided by 4 and the altitude is multiplied by 4.

6. Compare the areas of two rectangles which have equal altitudes if their bases are in the ratio 2 to 3.

7. State the effect on the area of a rectangle if the base is increased by 25% and the altitude is decreased by 25%.

8. Compare the areas of two rectangles if their altitudes are in the ratio 2 to 3 and their bases are in the ratio 3 to 4.

The area of a parallelogram

$ABCD$ is a parallelogram. If we choose AB for its base, then DE and CF are equal altitudes.

  Prove that $EFCD$ is a rectangle.

  Prove that $\triangle AED \cong \triangle BFC$.

  Can you prove that parallelogram $ABCD$ is equal to rectangle $EFCD$?

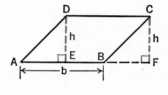

Fig. 8

THEOREM 82.   The area of a parallelogram is equal to the product of its base and its altitude.

COROLLARIES 1. The ratio of the areas of two parallelograms is equal to the ratio of the products of their bases and altitudes.

      2. Parallelograms having equal bases and equal altitudes are equal in area.

      3. The ratio of the areas of two parallelograms having equal altitudes is equal to the ratio of their bases.

      4. The ratio of the areas of two parallelograms having equal bases is equal to the ratio of their altitudes.

      5. If two parallelograms have equal areas, their bases and altitudes are inversely proportional.

Exercises

Find the areas of the parallelograms in Exercises **1-3:**

1.

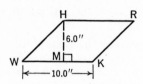

2.

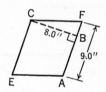

3.

4. The area of a parallelogram is 293.0 square feet, and its altitude is 21.0 feet long. Find the length of its base.

5. Two parallelograms have bases 10.0 inches and 15.0 inches long. Their altitudes are 6.0 inches and 9.0 inches long. Find the ratio of their areas.

6. Two parallelograms have equal bases. The lengths of their altitudes are 6.0 inches and 8.0 inches. If the area of the smaller parallelogram is 18.0 square inches, what is the area of the larger?

7. Two parallelograms have equal areas. If the ratio of their altitudes is $\frac{4}{3}$, what is the ratio of their bases?

8. Find the side of a square if its area is equal to the area of a parallelogram whose base is 8.0 inches and whose altitude is 6.0 inches.

9. If the areas of two parallelograms are in the ratio $\frac{2}{3}$, and their altitudes are in the ratio $\frac{3}{4}$, what is the ratio of their bases?

10. If two parallelograms are similar and the ratio of their bases is 3 to 2, what is the ratio of their altitudes? their areas?

11. The base of a parallelogram is fixed in length and position. If the area of the parallelogram remains constant, what is the locus of the side opposite the base?

12. Construct a parallelogram *ABCD*. On a given segment *RS* corresponding to *AB*, construct a parallelogram *RSTU* similar to *ABCD*.

Find the areas and perimeters of the parallelograms in Exercises **13-18.**

13.

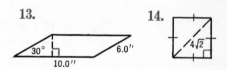

14.

15.

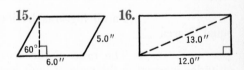

16.

17.

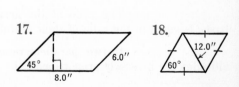

18.

19. If the corresponding sides of two similar parallelograms are in the ratio m to n, what is the ratio of their areas?

20. If each side of a parallelogram is multiplied by n and its angles remain the same, is its area multiplied by n^2? Explain.

21. A rectangle is inscribed in a circle whose diameter is 17.0 inches long. If the width of the rectangle is 8.0 inches, find its area.

22. Find the area of a parallelogram if its base is $(x + 2)$ and its altitude is $(2x - 3)$.

23. The area of a rectangle is 432 square feet. If its base is 18.0 feet long, find the length of a diagonal.

24. If the areas of two similar parallelograms are in the ratio m to n and their bases are in the ratio x to y, what is the ratio of their altitudes?

The area of a triangle

Through the vertices T and S of $\triangle RST$, lines are drawn parallel to RS and RT, respectively. These lines meet at common point E. Why?

Can you prove that $RSET$ is a parallelogram? Is $\triangle RST \cong \triangle SET$? Why? Is the area of $\triangle RST$ one-half the area of parallelogram $RSET$? Why?

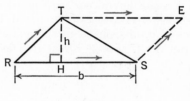

Fig. 9

THEOREM 83. **The area of a triangle is equal to one-half the product of its base and its altitude.**

The ratio of the areas of two triangles

If the areas of two triangles are A_1 and A_2, then $A_1 = \frac{1}{2}b_1h_1$ and

$$A_2 = \frac{1}{2}b_2h_2.$$

Hence, $\dfrac{A_1}{A_2} = \dfrac{\frac{1}{2}b_1h_1}{\frac{1}{2}b_2h_2}$. Why?

$$\frac{A_1}{A_2} = \frac{b_1h_1}{b_2h_2}.$$

$$= \frac{b_1}{b_2} \times \frac{h_1}{h_2}.$$

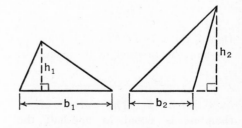

Fig. 10

COROLLARIES 1. The areas of two triangles have the same ratio as the products of their bases and altitudes.

2. Two triangles having equal bases have the same ratio as their altitudes.

3. Two triangles having equal altitudes have the same ratio as their bases.

4. If the areas of two triangles are equal, their bases and altitudes are inversely proportional.

The area of a quadrilateral with perpendicular diagonals

If a quadrilateral has perpendicular diagonals, its area can be found in terms of its diagonals. In the quadrilateral $EFGH$, $EG \perp FH$ at P. Then,

$A_{\triangle EFH} = \frac{1}{2}EP \times FH$ and

$A_{\triangle FGH} = \frac{1}{2}PG \times FH$. Why?

$A_{EFGH} = \frac{1}{2}FH(EP + PG)$

$= \frac{1}{2}FH \times EG$. Why?

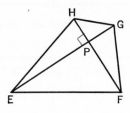

Fig. 11

Hence, the area of $EFGH$ is equal to one-half the product of its diagonals.

COROLLARY 5. The area of a rhombus is equal to one-half the product of its diagonals.

The area of an equilateral triangle

If each side of $\triangle MNO$ is s, and h is an altitude, then the area of $\triangle MNO$ is $\frac{1}{2}hs$. Why? But, $h = \frac{1}{2}s\sqrt{3}$. Why?

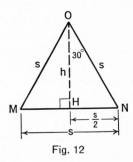

Fig. 12

$$\therefore \quad A = \frac{1}{2}(\frac{1}{2}s\sqrt{3})\cdot s = \frac{s^2}{4}\sqrt{3}.$$

COROLLARY 6. The area of an equilateral triangle having a side s is $\frac{s^2}{4}\sqrt{3}$.

Exercises

Find the unknown quantity in Exercises 1-5 if A is the area, b is the base, and h is the altitude of a triangle. Do not write in this book.

	A	b	h
1.	?	8	10
2.	?	6.2 in.	4.3 in.
3.	?	$3\sqrt{3}$	$2\sqrt{3}$
4.	24 sq. in.	?	6.8 in.
5.	$4\sqrt{3}$	4	?

6. The lengths of the diagonals of a rhombus are 9.0 feet and 12.0 feet. Find the area of the rhombus.

7. Each side of a rhombus is 13.0 inches long, and one diagonal is 10.0 inches long. Find the area of the rhombus.

8. If the area of a rhombus is 96.0 square inches and one diagonal is 12.0 inches long, find the length of the other diagonal.

9. Find the area of an equilateral triangle whose side is 7.

10. If the area of an equilateral triangle is $18\sqrt{3}$, find the length of one of its sides.

11. Find the area of an equilateral triangle whose perimeter is 15.0 cm.

12. What is the locus of the vertex of a triangle if its area is constant and its base is fixed in length and position?

13. If the diagonal of a square is d, prove that the area of the square is $\frac{1}{2}d^2$.

14. Prove that a median of a triangle bisects the area of a triangle. (In a homogeneous physical triangle, this means that the triangle should balance on a knife-edge placed under any median. The triangle should also balance on a point placed under the intersection of the medians. Explain.)

15. Construct a rectangle equal to a given triangle if the base of the rectangle is equal to the base of the triangle.

16. Find the area of an equilateral triangle whose altitude is $6\sqrt{3}$.

17. Find the altitude of an equilateral triangle whose area is $9\sqrt{3}$.

18. Find the area of an equilateral triangle whose altitude is 6.

19. Find the altitude of an equilateral triangle whose area is 15.

20. Find the area of an isosceles triangle if its base is b and the other two sides are each a.

21. Find the side of an equilateral triangle whose area is $25\sqrt{3}$.

22. Find the side of an equilateral triangle whose area is 96.0 square inches.

23. The hypotenuse of an isosceles right triangle is $6\sqrt{2}$. Find the area of the triangle.

24. The hypotenuse of a 30°, 60°, 90° triangle is 12.0 cm. Find the area of the triangle.

25. The side of an equilateral triangle is 10.0 inches. What is the side of an equilateral triangle with twice the area? with three times the area? with four times the area?

26. The hypotenuse of a right triangle is 29.0 inches and one leg is 20.0 inches. Find the area of the triangle.

27. The area of a 30°, 60°, 90° triangle is 173.2 square inches. Find the length of each of its sides.

28. Find the area of a square if its diagonal is $3\sqrt{2}$.

29. The sum of the diagonals of a rhombus is 69.0 inches and one of its diagonals is 21.0 inches shorter than the other. Find the area of the rhombus.

30. Prove: The product of the legs of a right triangle is equal to the product of the hypotenuse and the altitude upon it.

Hero's formula for finding the area of a triangle (*Optional*)

About 2000 years ago, Hero, a mathematician of Alexandria, derived the following formula for finding the area of a triangle:

$$A = \sqrt{s(s - a)(s - b)(s - c)}$$

where a, b, and c are the three sides, $s = \frac{1}{2}(a + b + c)$, and A is the area of the triangle.

Example: Find the area of a triangle whose sides are 4.0 inches, 5.0 inches, and 7.0 inches long.

Solution:
$$s = \frac{1}{2}(4 + 5 + 7) = 8$$
$$A = \sqrt{8(8-4)(8-5)(8-7)}$$
$$= \sqrt{8 \times 4 \times 3 \times 1}$$
$$= \sqrt{96}$$
$$= 4\sqrt{6} \text{ or } 9.8$$

The area of the triangle is 9.8 square inches. (See square root table on page 429.)

The length of an altitude of a triangle in terms of its sides (*Optional*)

If the sides of a triangle are a, b, and c, the length of the altitude h_b can be found as shown at the top of the next column.

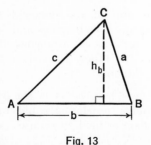

Fig. 13

Since $A_{\triangle ABC} = \frac{1}{2}bh_b$ and

$$A_{\triangle ABC} = \sqrt{s(s - a)(s - b)(s - c)},$$

then $\frac{1}{2}bh_b = \sqrt{s(s-a)(s-b)(s-c)}.$

Hence $h_b = \dfrac{2\sqrt{s(s-a)(s-b)(s-c)}}{b}$

Exercises (*Optional*)

*In Exercises **1-4**, using Hero's formula, find the area of each of the triangles with the three given sides.*

1. 5.0″, 12.0″, and 13.0″. Could the area have been found in an easier way?
2. 9.6 cm., 6.4 cm., and 8.0 cm.
3. 7.2″, 8.3″, and 9.0″.
4. 12.0′, 13.0′, and 14.4′.
5. Find the length of the altitude to the longest side of each of the triangles in Exercises **1-4**.
6. Use Hero's formula to find the area of an equilateral triangle of side 9. Compare the answer with the one you get by using $A = \dfrac{s^2\sqrt{3}}{4}$.

The length of a median of a triangle in terms of its sides (*Optional*)

It can be proved that the formula for the length of the median m_c of $\triangle ABC$ is:

$$m_c = \frac{1}{2}\sqrt{2(a^2 + b^2) - c^2}.$$

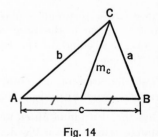

Fig. 14

Exercises (*Optional*)

1. Find the length of the median to the longest side of the triangle whose sides are 7, 24, and 25 by using the median formula. Can you find the answer an easier way?
2. Find the length of the median to the shortest side of a triangle whose sides are 8, 10, and 12.
3. Find the length of the median to the shortest side of the triangle whose sides are 7.0 inches, 8.0 inches, and 9.2 inches.
4. Find the lengths of the medians to the equal sides of the triangle whose sides are 6, 6, and 8.
5. Use the median formula to find the length of the median to one side of an equilateral triangle whose side is 6. Can this be done an easier way?

The length of the bisector of an angle of a triangle (*Optional*)

It can be proved that the formula for finding the length of the bisector t_A of $\triangle ABC$ is:

$$t_A = \frac{2}{b+c}\sqrt{bcs\ (s-a)} \ \text{ if } s = \tfrac{1}{2}(a+b+c).$$

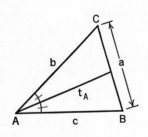

Fig. 15

Exercises (*Optional*)

1. Find the length of the bisector of the largest angle of a triangle whose sides are 21, 22, and 11.
2. Find t_C if $a = 6.0$ inches, $b = 8.0$ inches, and $c = 10.0$ inches.
3. Find the length of the bisector of the vertex angle of an isosceles triangle whose sides are 13, 13, and 24.
4. Find the length of the bisector of one of the angles of an equilateral triangle whose side is 9.
5. Find the length of the bisector of the right angle of the triangle whose sides are 7, 24, and 25.

The area of a trapezoid

The area of the trapezoid $ABCD$ is equal to the area of $\triangle ABD +$ the area of $\triangle BCD$. Why?

Hence $A_{ABCD} = \tfrac{1}{2}b_1h + \tfrac{1}{2}b_2h.$
$$= \tfrac{1}{2}h(b_1 + b_2).$$

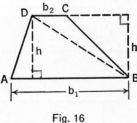

Fig. 16

THEOREM 84. **The area of a trapezoid is equal to one-half the product of its altitude and the sum of its bases.**

Exercises

1. Prove: The area of a trapezoid is equal to the product of its altitude and its median.

2. Given the trapezoid as indicated. Find (a) h, (b) AB, and (c) area of $ABCD$.

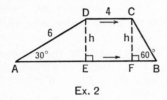

Ex. 2

3. Given the trapezoid as indicated. Find: (a) h, (b) MR, and (c) area of $MRSK$.

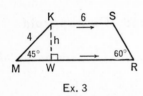

Ex. 3

In the trapezoids in Exercises 4-6, find the unknown quantities. Do not write in this book.

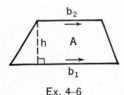

Ex. 4–6

	b_1	b_2	h	Area
4.	12.4"	8.6"	3.2"	?
5.	10	14	?	144
6.	28	?	17	425

7. A railroad embankment is 36 feet wide at the top, 60 feet wide at the bottom, and 15 feet high. Find the area of a right section of the embankment in square yards. (A right section is the trapezoid formed by a plane perpendicular to the edges of the embankment.)

8. Find the area of the trapezoid cut off by a line segment joining the midpoints of two sides of an equilateral triangle of side s.

9. Prove: Any trapezoid is bisected by a line joining the midpoints of its bases.

Continuity of area formulas

The area formula for a trapezoid can be used to find the areas of certain other polygons. Show that the area of each of the figures below is $\frac{1}{2}h(b_1 + b_2)$.

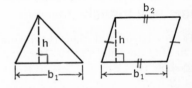

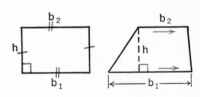

Fig. 17

Areas by trigonometry (*Optional*)

We have used the trigonometric functions of angles to find parts of right triangles when certain other parts of the triangles were known. With certain data we can apply the same principles in problems in which we are to find the area of such polygons as triangles, parallelograms, and trapezoids.

Exercises (*Optional*)

1. In $\triangle WKR$, $WK = 3.650''$, $WR = 2.850''$, and $\angle W = 55° 10'$. Find the area of $\triangle WKR$.
2. Prove: The area of $\triangle ABC = \frac{1}{2}bc \sin A$.
3. Find the area of a rhombus if the length of the shorter diagonal is $6.8''$, and one of the angles is $46°$.
4. In parallelogram $MWKR$, $\angle M = 50°$, $MW = 6.0''$, and $MR = 3.5''$. Find the area of $MWKR$.
5. Show that the area of parallelogram $RSTU = RU \times RS \sin R$.
6. In trapezoid $RMCK$, $\angle R = 63°$, $h = 40.0'$, $MC = 95.0'$, and $\angle K = 68°$.
   a. Find the length of RK.
   b. Find the area of $RMCK$.
   c. Find the perimeter of $RMCK$.

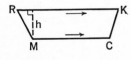

Ex. 6

7. Prove that the area of the isosceles trapezoid $AFST$ is $\dfrac{b_2{}^2 - b_1{}^2}{4} \tan A$.

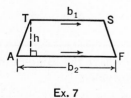

Ex. 7

Areas by co-ordinate geometry (*Optional*)

If we know the co-ordinates of the vertices of certain polygons, we can find the lengths of their sides, the equations of their sides, the equations of their altitudes, and the lengths of their altitudes. From these data we can find the areas of the polygons.

Exercises (*Optional*)

1. If the vertices of triangle ABC are $A(-3, -4)$, $B(8, -2)$, and $C(-5, 5)$, find its area.
2. If the vertices of a quadrilateral are $E(-3, -4)$, $F(5, -1)$, $G(8, 7)$, and $H(0, 4)$, find its area.
3. If the vertices of a quadrilateral are $A(-10, -4)$, $B(5, -1)$, $C(4, 4)$, and $D(-6, 2)$, find its area.
4. If the vertices of a quadrilateral are $R(-4, -1)$, $S(5, -2)$, $T(2, 3)$, and $U(-7, 4)$, find its area.
5. If the vertices of a quadrilateral are $G(-8, -2)$, $H(-3, -7)$, $E(2, -2)$, and $F(-3, 3)$, find its area.
6. The vertices of a triangle are $W(-6, -4)$, $K(4, 2)$, and $R(-3, 4)$. Find the area of $\triangle WRK$ by subtracting the areas of right triangles WEK, KMR, and WRS from the area of the rectangle $WEMS$.

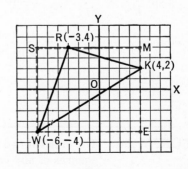

Ex. 6

Areas of similar triangles

In Figure 18, $\triangle M_1 B_1 C_1 \sim \triangle M_2 B_2 C_2$, c_1 and c_2 are corresponding sides, h_1 and h_2 are the corresponding altitudes to those sides, and A_1 and A_2 are their areas.

Since $\quad A_1 = \frac{1}{2} c_1 h_1$ and $A_2 = \frac{1}{2} c_2 h_2$,

then $\quad \dfrac{A_1}{A_2} = \dfrac{c_1}{c_2} \times \dfrac{h_1}{h_2}$. Why?

However, $\dfrac{c_1}{c_2} = \dfrac{h_1}{h_2}$. Why?

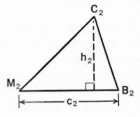

Hence, $\quad \dfrac{A_1}{A_2} = \dfrac{c_1}{c_2} \times \dfrac{c_1}{c_2} = \dfrac{c_1{}^2}{c_2{}^2} = \left(\dfrac{c_1}{c_2}\right)^2$.

Fig. 18

THEOREM 85. The areas of two similar triangles have the same ratio as the squares of any two corresponding sides.

Areas of similar polygons

If polygon $ABC \ldots$ is similar to polygon $RST \ldots$, then $\triangle ABC \sim \triangle RST$, $\triangle ACD \sim \triangle RTU \ldots$, etc. Why?

Fig. 19

Hence, $\dfrac{\text{Area of } \triangle ABC}{\text{Area of } \triangle RST} = \dfrac{\overline{AB}^2}{\overline{RS}^2}$,

$\dfrac{\text{Area of } \triangle ACD}{\text{Area of } \triangle RTU} = \dfrac{\overline{CD}^2}{\overline{TU}^2}$, etc. Why?

Also, $\dfrac{\overline{AB}^2}{\overline{RS}^2} = \dfrac{\overline{BC}^2}{\overline{ST}^2} = \dfrac{\overline{CD}^2}{\overline{TU}^2}$, etc. Why?

Therefore, $\dfrac{\text{Area of } \triangle ABC}{\text{Area of } \triangle RST} = \dfrac{\text{Area of } \triangle ACD}{\text{Area of } \triangle RTU} = $ etc. Why?

Hence, $\dfrac{\text{Area of polygon } ABC \ldots}{\text{Area of polygon } RST \ldots} = \dfrac{\overline{AB}^2}{\overline{RS}^2} = $ etc. Why?

THEOREM 86. The areas of two similar polygons have the same ratio as the squares of any two corresponding sides.

Example 1. If two corresponding sides of two similar polygons are 24.0 in. and 15.0 in., and the area of the larger is 56.0 sq. in., what is the area of the smaller polygon?

Solution:

$$\frac{A_1}{A_2} = \frac{s_1{}^2}{s_2{}^2}$$

$$\frac{A_1}{56} = \frac{15^2}{24^2} = \left(\frac{15}{24}\right)^2 = \left(\frac{5}{8}\right)^2 = \frac{25}{64}$$

$$A_1 = \frac{56 \times 25}{64} = \frac{7 \times 25}{8} = 21.9$$

The area of the smaller polygon is 21.9 sq. in.

Example 2. If the areas of two similar triangles are 75 and 25, and a side of the smaller triangle is 15, find the corresponding side of the larger.

Solution:

$$\frac{A_1}{A_2} = \frac{s_1{}^2}{s_2{}^2}$$

$$\frac{75}{25} = \frac{s_1{}^2}{15^2}$$

$$\sqrt{\frac{75}{25}} = \frac{s_1}{15}$$

$$\frac{\sqrt{3}}{1} = \frac{s_1}{15}$$

$$s_1 = 15\sqrt{3}$$

Exercises

1. The corresponding sides of two similar polygons are in the ratio 2 to 3.

   What is the ratio of their perimeters? their areas?

2. The sides of a triangle are twice as long as the sides of another similar triangle.

   Find the ratio of their areas.

3. The area of a triangle is 16 times that of a similar one.

   a. Find the ratio of two corresponding sides.

   b. Find the ratio of two corresponding altitudes.

   c. Find the ratio of two corresponding medians.

4. The area of a polygon is one-fourth that of a similar one.

   Find the ratio of two corresponding sides.

5. The areas of two similar polygons are in the ratio 2 to 3.

   What is the ratio of their corresponding sides?

6. The three sides of a triangle are 8″, 10″, and 14″. A second triangle is similar to the first and has 4 times its area.

   Find the sides of the second triangle.

7. The areas of similar polygons are 400 square feet and 144 square feet.

   What is the ratio of their corresponding sides?

8. If the sides of a square are doubled, by what number is the area of the square multiplied?

9. If the ratio of the areas of two equilateral triangles is 1 to 2, what is the ratio of their sides?

10. By what number must the side of a square be multiplied to triple its area?

11. If pentagon $ABCDE$ is similar to pentagon $MNOPQ$ and if each side of $ABCDE$ is $\sqrt{5}$ times as long as the sides of $MNOPQ$, how does the area of $ABCDE$ compare with the area of $MNOPQ$?

12. Complete: To double the area of a square, multiply each side by . . .

13. Complete: Doubling the length of each side of a square multiplies its area by . . . . .

Constructions based upon fourth proportional

Many interesting constructions depend upon the use of the fourth proportional to find the unknown values.

Example: Construct a rectangle with one side given, and equal to a given triangle.

Given: $\triangle RST$ and the side b_2 of a rectangle.

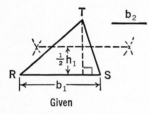

Given

Required: To construct a rectangle on b_2 equal in area to $\triangle RST$.

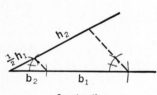

Construction

Analysis: Since $A_\triangle = \frac{1}{2}b_1h_1$,
$$A_{\text{rect.}} = b_2h_2,$$
$$\text{and } A_\triangle = A_{\text{rect.}}$$
$$\text{then } \tfrac{1}{2}b_1h_1 = b_2h_2.$$

Hence, $\dfrac{b_2}{b_1} = \dfrac{\frac{1}{2}h_1}{h_2}$. Why?

Required Rectangle

Note: The proportion $\dfrac{b_2}{\frac{1}{2}b_1} = \dfrac{h_1}{h_2}$ may also be used. Why is it important to make h_2 the fourth proportional?

Exercises

1. Upon a given side construct a rectangle equal to a given parallelogram.
2. Upon a given side construct a triangle equal to a given parallelogram. May the triangle have any shape you please to make it?
3. Upon a given side construct a right triangle equal to a given square.
4. Upon a given leg construct a right triangle equal to a given triangle.
5. Upon a given side construct a triangle similar to a given triangle.
6. Construct an isosceles triangle on a given line segment as base and equal to a given triangle.
7. Construct a parallelogram upon a given side and with a given angle so that the parallelogram is equal to a given triangle.
8. Construct triangle DEF with the given segment DE as base and with the given angle D so that it is equal to a given parallelogram.
9. Upon a given side construct a parallelogram similar to a given parallelogram.

Constructions based upon mean proportional

By constructing the mean proportional between certain given segments, we are able to construct a square equal in area to certain polygons. We are also able to construct figures similar to given figures with some number k times their area.

Example 1: Construct a square equal to a given triangle.

Given: $\triangle RST$.

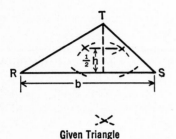

Given Triangle

Required: To construct a square equal to $\triangle RST$.

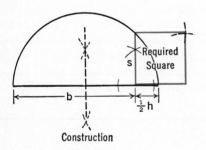

Construction

Analysis: Since $A_\triangle = \frac{1}{2}bh$,

$$A_{\text{sq.}} = s^2,$$

and $A_\triangle = A_{\text{sq.}}$,

then $\frac{1}{2}bh = s^2$.

Hence, $\dfrac{b}{s} = \dfrac{s}{\frac{1}{2}h}$.

The side of the square, therefore, is the mean proportional between which two line segments?

Example 2: Construct a rectangle similar to a given rectangle and twice as large.

Given: A rectangle whose area is R_1.

b_1
Given Rectangle R_1

Required: To construct a rectangle R_2 similar to the given rectangle R_1, and twice as large.

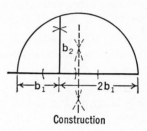

Construction

Analysis: $\dfrac{R_1}{R_2} = \dfrac{b_1{}^2}{b_2{}^2}$, and $R_2 = 2R_1$.

Hence, $\dfrac{R_1}{R_2} = \dfrac{1}{2}$ and $\dfrac{1}{2} = \dfrac{b_1{}^2}{b_2{}^2}$.

Therefore, $b_2{}^2 = 2b_1{}^2$.

or $b_2{}^2 = 2b_1 \times b_1$.

Hence, $\dfrac{2b_1}{b_2} = \dfrac{b_2}{b_1}$.

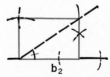

Required Rectangle R_2

The side of the required rectangle is the mean proportional between what two segments? In this case, notice that $b_2 = b_1\sqrt{2}$. That is, the side of the required rectangle is the $\sqrt{2}$ times the side of the given rectangle.

Exercises

1. Construct a square equal to a given rectangle.

2. Construct a square equal to a given parallelogram.

3. Construct a square equal to a given right triangle.

4. Construct a square equal to twice a given square.

5. Construct a triangle similar to a given triangle and twice as large.

6. Construct a parallelogram similar to a given parallelogram and twice as large.

7. Construct a square having four-ninths of the area of a given square.

8. Construct a square equal to one-half a given square.

9. Construct a square equal to three-fifths a given square.

10. Construct a triangle similar to a given triangle and one-half as large.

11. Construct a trapezoid similar to a given trapezoid and two-thirds as large.

12. Construct two similar pentagons so that their areas are in the ratio 3 to 4.

13. Construct a square equal to four times a given triangle.

14. Construct a line parallel to the base of a given triangle dividing the triangle into two parts which have the ratio 4 : 5.

Construction of a triangle equal to a given polygon

CONSTRUCTION 25   **To construct a triangle equal to a given polygon.** (*Optional*).

Given: Polygon *ABCDE*. (We are using a pentagon in this construction.)

Required: To construct a triangle equal to *ABCDE*.

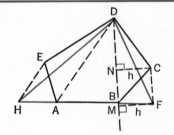

Method:

1. Draw diagonal *BD*.
2. Construct *CF* ∥ *BD*.
3. Extend *AB* to meet *CF* at *F*.
4. Draw *DF*.
5. Similarly, construct *HD*.

Proof: You write the proof.

Suggestions: Triangles *BCD* and *BFD* have the same base *BD* and equal altitudes, *CN* and *FM*. Why? The area

of △*BCD* is equal to the area of △*BFD*. Why? Hence, △*BCD* may be replaced by △*BFD*. Why? Thus the number of sides of polygon *ABCDE* is reduced by one.

Note: Polygon *ABCDE* was transformed into △*HFD*; hence, the statement of Construction 25 may have been written, "To transform a given polygon into an equivalent triangle."

Exercises (*Optional*)

1. Construct a triangle equal to a given quadrilateral.

2. Construct a triangle equal to a given trapezoid.

3. Construct a square equal to a given quadrilateral.
   Hint: First transform the given quadrilateral into a triangle with the same area.

4. Construct a triangle equal to a given hexagon.

5. Construct a square equal to a given pentagon.

6. Construct a square equal to twice a given parallelogram.

7. Construct a square equal to three times a given quadrilateral.

8. Construct a square equal to two-thirds the area of a given quadrilateral.

9. Construct a square equal to three-halves the area of a given quadrilateral.

10. Draw a triangle ABC. Construct the line DE parallel to AB so that the area of $\triangle DEC$ is $\frac{1}{3}$ of the area of $\triangle ABC$.

11. Draw a triangle ABC. Construct the line DE parallel to AB so that the area of $\triangle DEC$ is $\frac{2}{3}$ of the area of the trapezoid $ABED$.

Euclid's proof of the Pythagorean Theorem (*Optional*)

Perhaps the most important theorem in geometry is the Pythagorean Theorem which we proved by an algebraic method in Chapter 13. The first proof of the theorem is attributed to Pythagoras about 525 B.C., but his complete proof is not known. There have been many different proofs for this theorem, but perhaps the most interesting one is Euclid's proof. He proved that the area of a square constructed on the hypotenuse of a right triangle is equal to the sum of the areas of the two squares constructed on the legs. The outline of the proof follows (see Figure 20):

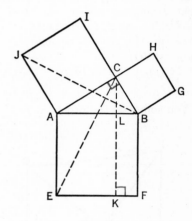

Fig. 20

1. Draw $CK \perp EF$.

2. Now prove
   square $ACIJ$ = rectangle $EKLA$.
   To do this, draw BJ and CE.

3. Square $ACIJ$ = $2\triangle ABJ$. (They both have the base AJ and equal altitudes.)

4. Similarly,
   rectangle $EKLA$ = $2 \triangle ECA$.

5. $\triangle ECA \cong \triangle ABJ$. Why?

6. Square $ACIJ$ = rectangle $EKLA$. Why?

7. Similarly, prove
   square $BGHC$ = rectangle $KFBL$
   by drawing lines AG and CF.

8. The sum of the two rectangles is the square $EFBA$.

9. Square $EFBA$ = square $ACIJ$ + square $BGHC$.

President Garfield's proof of the Pythagorean Theorem (*Optional*)

President Garfield placed two identical right triangles as shown in Figure 21. They form a trapezoid whose altitude is $a + b$ and whose bases are a and b. It can be proved that the trapezoid $MNOP$ consists of three right triangles; hence, the area of $MNOP$ is equal to the sum of the areas of the three triangles.

Area $MNOP$

$= \triangle MRP + \triangle ROP + \triangle RNO.$

$\frac{1}{2}(a + b)(a + b) = \frac{1}{2}ab + \frac{1}{2}c^2 + \frac{1}{2}ab.$

You complete the proof.

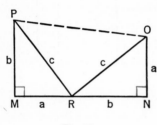

Fig. 21

Exercises (*Optional*)

1. Prove that $c^2 = a^2 + b^2$ by a method suggested by each of the figures below:

(a)   **(b)**

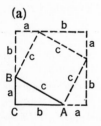   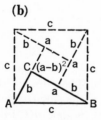

Ex. 1

2. If BC is tangent to circle A at C, and BR is a secant through A, prove that $c^2 = a^2 + b^2$.

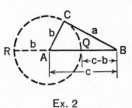

Ex. 2

3. Construct a square of area C equal to the sum of two given squares of area A and B, respectively.

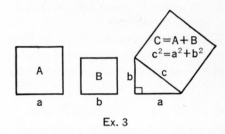

Ex. 3

4. Construct a square of area A equal to the difference of two given squares of area C and B, respectively.

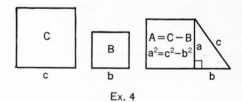

Ex. 4

5. Construct a square equal to the sum of three given squares.

6. Construct a square equal to three times a given square.

7. Construct a square equal to five times a given square.

8. Construct a triangle that is similar to and equal to the sum of two given similar triangles.

Given: $\triangle A \sim \triangle B$.

Construct: $\triangle C = \triangle A + \triangle B$, and $\triangle C \sim \triangle A$ (or $\triangle C \sim \triangle B$).

Hint: $\dfrac{\triangle B}{\triangle C} = \dfrac{b^2}{c^2}$ and $\dfrac{\triangle A}{\triangle C} = \dfrac{a^2}{c^2}$. Why?

$\therefore \dfrac{\triangle B + \triangle A}{\triangle C} = \dfrac{b^2 + a^2}{c^2} = 1$. Why?

$\therefore \triangle B + \triangle A = \triangle C$.

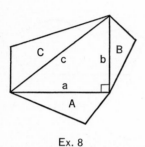

Ex. 8

9. Construct a polygon that is similar to and equal to the sum of two given similar polygons.

10. Construct a polygon that is similar to and equal to the difference of two given similar polygons.

11. Construct a triangle equal to the sum of any two given triangles.

12. Divide a parallelogram into three equal parts by straight lines through one vertex.

13. Divide a given trapezoid into two equal parts by a straight line perpendicular to the bases.

Areas of irregular polygons
(*Optional*)

If an irregular polygon can be divided into triangles, parallelograms, and trapezoids, its area can be found. For example, the polygon RST. . . . can be divided into polygons whose areas can be measured by first drawing RU and then the perpendiculars to

RU as illustrated in Figure 22. Of course, the lengths of certain segments must be measured.

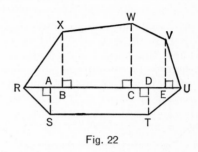

Fig. 22

Draw a polygon similar to RST. . . . on your paper and find its area.

Areas of figures by the offset method (*Optional*)

To find the approximate area of $ABCD$, divide AB into a number of equal segments each d units long. Construct perpendiculars to AB at the points of division as indicated in the diagram. Each resulting figure is approximately a trapezoid.

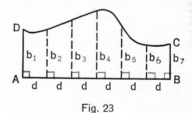

Fig. 23

The area of $ABCD = \frac{1}{2}d\,(b_1 + b_2) + \frac{1}{2}d(b_2 + b_3) + \ldots + \frac{1}{2}d(b_6 + b_7)$. Why?

Show that area of $ABCD$ is

$$d\left[\frac{b_1 + b_7}{2} + b_2 + b_3 + b_4 + b_5 + b_6\right].$$

Explain how a closer approximation to the actual area of $ABCD$ can be obtained by dividing AB into a greater number of equal parts.

Exercises (*Optional*)

1. An engineer measured the depth of water at five points 90.0 feet apart at a place where the river was 540.0 feet wide. To find the flow of the water in the river, it is necessary to know the rate of the current and the area of the right section of the river. Find the area of the right section of the river from the data.

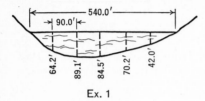

Ex. 1

2. Find the approximate number of square feet in the plot of ground represented by *EMKW*.

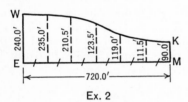

Ex. 2

3. The approximate right section of a valley to be filled with dirt is represented by *ARSK*. If *AM* = 15.0', *MN* = 82.5', *NK* = 25.0', *MR* = 25.5', and *NS* = 45.0', and the valley to be filled is 972.0' long, how many cubic yards of dirt will be required to fill it?

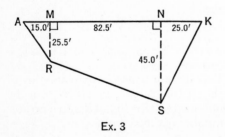

Ex. 3

Areas of irregular figures by counting unit squares (*Optional*)

The approximate area of an irregular figure may be found as follows:
1. Trace the given figure on graph paper or draw the figure to scale on graph paper.

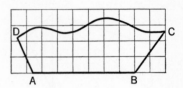

Fig. 24

2. Count the number of unit squares in the figure as follows:

   a. Count the number of whole squares which lie entirely within the figure.

   b. Count as a whole square any square of which more than half lies within the figure.

   c. Count as a half square any square which is half within the figure.

   d. Do not count any square of which more than half lies outside the figure.

Areas of irregular figures by a planimeter (*Optional*)

An instrument called a polar planimeter is designed and calibrated to automatically compute the area of a figure. The operator merely guides a tracer point around the boundary of the figure. The area is read on the dials.

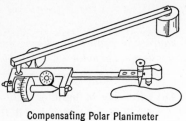

Compensating Polar Planimeter

Fig. 25

You can make a simple planimeter out of some wire and two wheels from a toy. A bent wire *AEFB* is fastened to the middle of the axle of the wheels as illustrated. To find the area of figure *X*, place the point *A* of the planimeter on some marked point on the boundary of *X* and the other end *B* outside *X*. Mark the position of *B*. Move the point *A* around the boundary of *X* until you return to the starting point. Mark the new position of *B*. Measure the distance between the original position of *B* and the final position of *B*. The product of that distance and the distance between *A* and *B* of the planimeter should give the area of *X*. Try it!

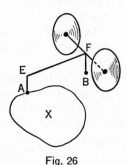

Fig. 26

The person operating a commercial planimeter must follow very carefully the directions provided by the manufacturer. It is a precision instrument, but for good results the operator must be very skillful.

Space geometry *(Optional)*

The pyramid of light rays *S-ABCD* from a source *S* is cut by a plane *MWRK* which is parallel to the plane *ABCD*. Let d_1 be the distance of *ABCD* from *S*, and d_2 be the distance of *MWRK* from *S*.

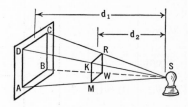

Fig. 27

Can you prove these conclusions?

1. $\dfrac{SC}{SR} = \dfrac{SD}{SK} = \dfrac{SA}{SM} = \dfrac{SB}{SW} = \dfrac{d_1}{d_2}$.

2. $\dfrac{CD}{RK} = \dfrac{DA}{KM} = \dfrac{AB}{MW} = \dfrac{BC}{WR} = \dfrac{d_1}{d_2}$.

3. $ABCD \sim MWRK$.

4. $\dfrac{\text{Area of } ABCD}{\text{Area of } MWRK} = \dfrac{d_1{}^2}{d_2{}^2}$.

The verbal statement of (4) is, "The area of a section of a pyramid which is parallel to the base of the pyramid varies directly as the square of the distance from the vertex of the pyramid."

It can be proved in physics that the intensity of light on a screen varies inversely as the square of the distance from the source. That is,

$$\frac{\text{Intensity of light on } ABCD}{\text{Intensity of light on } MWRK} = \frac{d_2{}^2}{d_1{}^2}.$$

Exercises (*Optional*)

Make a table like the one below. Draw a large figure like Figure **27**. *Then, using the data in the table, write the correct answers to the questions. Do not write in this book.*

	d_1	d_2	$\dfrac{SA}{SM}$	$\dfrac{AD}{MK}$	$\dfrac{\text{Area of } ABCD}{\text{Area of } MWRK}$	$\dfrac{\text{Intensity of light on } ABCD}{\text{Intensity of light on } MWRK}$
1.	6″	2″	?	?	?	?
2.	4′	1′	?	?	?	?
3.	8 cm.	5 cm.	?	?	?	?
4.	50 yd.	10 yd.	?	?	?	?
5.	2 mi.	2 yd.	?	?	?	?

Review of Chapter 15

True-False Test

Copy the numbers **1-14** *on your paper. After each number write* **True** *if the corresponding statement is always true; write* **False** *if the corresponding statement is not necessarily true.*

1. Two congruent triangles are equal.

2. If a side of an equilateral triangle is 3, its altitude is $3\sqrt{3}$.

3. A median of a triangle bisects the area of the triangle.

4. The areas of two similar polygons are directly proportional to the squares of any two corresponding sides.

5. The perimeters of two similar polygons have the same ratio as their areas.

6. If the ratio of the corresponding medians of two similar triangles is 1 : 3, the areas of the triangles are in the ratio 1 : 9.

7. The product of the legs of a right triangle is equal to the product of the hypotenuse and the altitude upon the hypotenuse.

8. If the diagonals of a rhombus are 6 and 5, its area is 15.

9. If the area of one square is 9 square feet and the area of another square is 9 square yards, their sides are in the ratio 1 : 3.

10. If the area of a triangle is to remain unchanged when its base is multiplied by 2, its altitude must be multiplied by 2.

11. The area of a square is equal to one-half the product of its diagonals.

12. Corresponding altitudes of two similar rectangles have the same ratio as their areas.

13. If a side of an equilateral triangle is $3\sqrt{3}$, its area is $9\sqrt{3}$.

14. Two equal triangles are congruent.

Completion Test

Write the numbers **1-20** *on your paper. After each number write an expression that correctly completes the corresponding statement. Do not write in this book.*

1. If the bases of two parallelograms are in the ratio 2 : 3, and their altitudes are in the ratio 3 : 4, their areas are in the ratio . . . . .

2. If two triangles are similar and the ratio of similitude is 2 : 3, the ratio of their areas is . . . . .

3. The area of an equilateral triangle having a side x is . . . . .

4. If two parallelograms have equal bases and their altitudes are in the ratio 4 : 9, their areas are in the ratio . . . . .

5. A square constructed on the diagonal of a given square has . . . . times the area of the given square.

6. The altitude of an equilateral triangle having a side m is . . . . .

7. If the side of a square is multiplied by $\sqrt{3}$, the area of the square is multiplied by . . . . .

8. If a line is drawn through the point of intersection of the diagonals of a . . . . , its area is bisected.

9. Doubling the length of the side of a square doubles its . . . . .

10. In the trapezoid formula $\frac{1}{2}h(b_1+b_2)$ if $b_1 = b_2$, the formula becomes the formula for the area of a . . . . .

11. If two rectangles have equal areas and their bases are in the ratio 2 : 3, their altitudes are in the ratio . . . . .

12. If the diagonals of a rhombus are 3 and 4, its area is . . . . .

13. If two polygons are similar and their corresponding sides are in the ratio 9 : 16, their areas are in the ratio . . . . .

14. If two triangles are similar and the ratio of their areas is 3 : 4, the ratio of their corresponding sides is . . . . .

15. If the area of an equilateral triangle is $6\sqrt{6}$, its side is . . . . .

16. A line through the midpoints of two sides of a triangle divides the triangle into a triangle and a trapezoid. The area of the new triangle is to the area of the trapezoid as . . . . .

17. If the side of a square is divided by 4, the area of the square is divided by . . . . .

18. A square constructed on a leg of a right triangle is equal to the . . . . .

19. If the legs of a right triangle are 1 and 2, the area of the square constructed on the hypotenuse is equal to . . . . .

20. The diagonals of a parallelogram divide it into four . . . . triangles.

This is a view of the "big dish" of the 60-foot radio telescope at Harvard University, which is being used to help explain the secrets of the universe. It can be rotated and tilted to focus on any part of the sky. "Whispers" from stars much farther than a hundred million light years away are heard as the radio telescope electronically scans outer space. Note the 24-sided polygons in the central part of the framework and the circle forming the outer edge.

Chapter 16   # REGULAR POLYGONS
AND CIRCLES

A REGULAR POLYGON is both equilateral and equiangular. We shall
learn that the vertices of a regular
polygon are equidistant from the center
of the inscribed circle, its sides are
equidistant from the center of the
circumscribed circle, the inscribed and
circumscribed circles are concentric,
and as the number of sides of a regular
polygon increases, it becomes more
like a circle.

Review Exercises

1. Are equilateral polygons necessarily equiangular? Illustrate.
2. Are equiangular polygons necessarily equilateral? Illustrate.

3. When is a polygon inscribed in a
circle? When is a polygon circumscribed about a circle?
4. When is a circle inscribed in a
polygon? When is a circle circumscribed about a polygon?
5. **a.** Inscribe a circle in a square.
   b. Circumscribe a circle about the
   square in **a.**
6. **a.** What is the formula for the sum
   of the interior angles of any n-gon?
   b. What is the formula for the size
   of each angle of a regular n-gon?
7. How many degrees are there in
each angle of a regular pentagon? a
regular hexagon? a regular octagon?
a regular decagon?

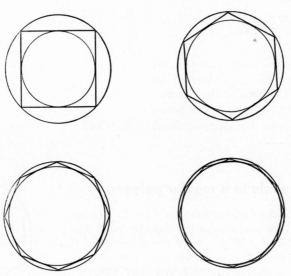

Inscribed and Circumscribed
Circles of Regular Polygons

Fig. 1

Circumscribing a circle about a regular polygon

THEOREM 87.   A circle can be circumscribed about any regular polygon.

Given: Regular polygon ABC .... of n sides.

Prove: A circle can be circumscribed about ABC .....

Plan: Construct a circle through the vertices A, B, and C; and then prove that the other vertices lie on this circle.

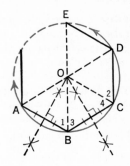

Proof

STATEMENTS	AUTHORITIES
1. Construct a circle through A, B, and C. Draw OA, OB, OC, and OD.	**1.** Why possible?
2. $\angle ABC = \angle BCD$.	**2.** Why?
3. $OB = OC$.	**3.** Why?
4. $\therefore \angle 4 = \angle 3$.	**4.** Why?
5. $\therefore \angle 1 = \angle 2$.	**5.** Why?
6. $\therefore \triangle ABO \cong \triangle CDO$.	**6.** Why?
7. $\therefore DO = AO$.	**7.** Why?
8. Hence a circle with O as center and OA as radius will pass through D. Similarly, all vertices of the polygon can be proved to lie on the circle.	**8.** Why?
9. $\therefore$ A circle can be circumscribed about ABC....	**9.** Why?

Inscribing a circle in a regular polygon

ABC .... is a regular polygon of n sides. In Theorem 87 we learned how to circumscribe a circle about ABC. ..... The sides of ABC .... are equal chords of the circumscribed circle; hence, the sides of ABC .... are equidistant from O. That is, OM, ON, OR, OS, ... are equal. Why? Hence, M, N, R, S, ... lie on a circle whose center is O and whose radius is a perpendicular from O to any side. Why?

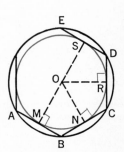

Fig. 2

THEOREM 88.   A circle can be inscribed in any regular polygon.

DEFINITIONS The *center of a regular polygon* is the common center of the inscribed and circumscribed circles.

The *radius of a regular polygon* is the radius of the circumscribed circle. It is the distance from the center to any vertex.

The *apothem of a regular polygon* is the radius of the inscribed circle. It is the distance from the center to any side.

A *central angle of a regular polygon* is the angle between radii drawn to any two consecutive vertices of the polygon.

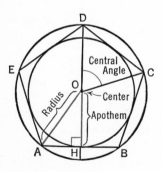

Fig. 3

Exercises

1. Prove that an angle of a regular polygon is bisected by the radius to the vertex of that angle.

2. Prove that the central angle of a regular hexagon equals one-half of one of its angles.

3. Prove that the apothem of a regular polygon bisects the side to which it is drawn.

4. Prove that the apothem of a regular polygon bisects the central angle.

5. How many degrees are there in the central angle of an equilateral triangle? of a square? of a regular pentagon?

6. If a side of a square is 10, find its radius and apothem.

The purity of the glass in this telescope lens is such that only the unpolished rim of the disc is visible in the photograph. A regular polygon of 24 sides has been used to approximate a circle.

COROLLARY   The number of degrees in each central angle of a regular polygon is $\dfrac{360}{n}$.

Regular inscribed and circumscribed polygons

THEOREM 89. **If a circle is divided into three or more equal arcs,**

         (a) the chords of these arcs form a regular inscribed polygon, and

         (b) the tangents at the points of division form a regular circumscribed polygon.

Given: Circle O divided into equal arcs at A, B, C, . . . with **(a)** the inscribed polygon ABC . . . formed by the chords AB, BC, . . . and **(b)** the circumscribed polygon PQR . . . formed by tangents at A, B, C, . . .

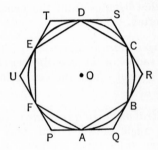

Prove: a. ABC . . . is a regular polygon.

     b. PQR . . . is a regular polygon.

The proof is left for you to do.

COROLLARIES 1. An equilateral polygon inscribed in a circle is a regular polygon.

         2. If the midpoints of the arcs of a regular inscribed polygon are joined to the ends of their chords, a regular inscribed polygon of double the number of sides is formed.

         3. Tangents to a circle at the midpoints of the arcs of the sides of a regular inscribed polygon form a regular circumscribed polygon of the same number of sides.

Exercises

1. Inscribe a regular hexagon in a given circle.
2. Circumscribe a regular hexagon about a given circle.
3. Inscribe a regular triangle in a given circle.
4. Circumscribe a regular triangle about a given circle.
5. Explain how to construct regular inscribed and circumscribed polygons of 8, 16, 32, ... sides.
6. Explain how to construct regular inscribed and circumscribed polygons of 12, 24, 48, ... sides.
7. Prove: An equiangular polygon circumscribed about a circle is regular.
8. Prove: The area of any polygon circumscribed about a circle is

equal to the product of one-half the perimeter of the polygon and the radius of the circle.

9. Prove: An equiangular polygon inscribed in a circle is not necessarily regular.

10. Prove: An equilateral polygon circumscribed about a circle is not necessarily regular.

11. Prove: The radius of an equilateral triangle is twice its apothem, and its apothem is one-third of the altitude.

12. If s is a side of an equilateral octagon inscribed in a circle whose radius is r, show that

$$s = r \sqrt{2 - \sqrt{2}}.$$

Hint: In the adjoining figure, draw $CH \perp OB$. Express CH and BH in terms of r.

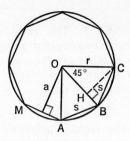

Ex. 12–13

13. If a is the apothem of a regular octagon, show that in terms of the radius r of the circumscribed circle,

$$a = \tfrac{1}{2}r \sqrt{2 + \sqrt{2}}.$$

14. If the radius of a regular octagon is 8.000 cm., find its apothem and the length of one of its sides by using the trigonometric functions. Compare the answers you get with those in Exercises **12** and **13** above.

Similar regular polygons

THEOREM 90. **Two regular polygons of the same number of sides are similar.**

Given: The regular polygons $ABC \ldots$ and $A'B'C' \ldots$, each having n sides.

Prove: $ABC \ldots \sim A'B'C' \ldots$.

Suggestions: Each angle of either polygon equals $\dfrac{(n-2)\,180°}{n}$. Prove that the corresponding sides are proportional.

You write the proof.

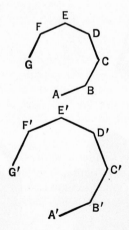

COROLLARIES 1. The ratio of the perimeters of two regular polygons of the same number of sides is equal to the ratio of any two corresponding sides, apothems, or radii.

2. The ratio of the areas of two regular polygons of the same number of sides is equal to the ratio of the squares of any two corresponding sides, the squares of their radii, the squares of their apothems, or the squares of their perimeters.

Exercises

1. The ratio of the corresponding sides of two regular decagons is 3 : 5.
   a. Find the ratio of their perimeters.
   b. Find the ratio of their radii.
   c. Find the ratio of their apothems.
   d. Find the ratio of their areas.

2. The ratio of the areas of two regular octagons is 4 : 9. Find the ratio of their sides, of their perimeters, of their radii, and of their apothems.

3. The area of one regular polygon is 212 square inches, and the area of another regular polygon of the same number of sides is 53 square inches. What is the ratio of their radii? of their apothems? of their sides?

4. The perimeters of two regular polygons of the same number of sides are 24.0 feet and 30.0 feet. A side of the smaller is 3.0 feet. How long is a side of the other?

5. The perimeters of two regular polygons of the same number of sides are 27.0 inches and 36.0 inches. What is the ratio of their areas?

Many regular polygons appear in the polyhedrons of space geometry. There are only five regular polyhedrons and all of them are included in the center model of the upper row; they are known as the Five Platonic Solids. How many different sets of similar regular polygons can you identify in these models made by geometry students?

Area of a regular polygon

THEOREM 91. The area of a regular polygon is equal to one-half the product of its apothem and its perimeter.

Given: Regular polygon ABC . . . . with apothem a, side s, perimeter p, and area A.

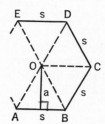

Prove: $A = \frac{1}{2}ap$.

Suggestions: Draw radii to form triangles. Area of each triangle $= \frac{1}{2}as$.

You write the proof.

The area of a square in terms of its radius

The square $ABCD$ is inscribed in circle O, r is the radius of the square, and a is its apothem. (See Figure 4.)

$\angle HAO = \angle AOH = 45°$. Why?

$$a = \frac{r}{\sqrt{2}} = \frac{r\sqrt{2}}{2}. \text{ Why?}$$

$$AB = 2AH = 2a = r\sqrt{2}. \text{ Why?}$$

$$A_{sq.\,ABCD} = \tfrac{1}{2}ap. \text{ Why?}$$

$$= \frac{1}{2} \cdot \frac{r\sqrt{2}}{2} \cdot 4r \sqrt{2}.$$

$$= 2\,r^2.$$

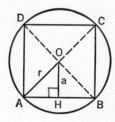

Fig. 4

Can you derive the same formula in other ways?

The area of a square circumscribed about a circle

The square $EFGH$ shown in Figure 5 is circumscribed about circle O of radius r. Show that $A_{sq.\,EFGH} = 4r^2$.

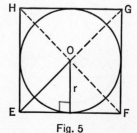

Fig. 5

Exercises

1. What is the ratio of the areas of the inscribed and circumscribed squares of a circle?
2. What is the ratio of the perimeters of the inscribed and circumscribed squares of a circle?
3. What is the ratio of the radius and apothem of a square?
4. The radius of a circle is 6.
   a. What is the area of the inscribed square?
   b. What is the area of the circumscribed square?
5. The side of a square is 8.
   a. What is the radius of the circumscribed circle?
   b. What is the radius of the inscribed circle?
6. What is the area of the right section of the largest square piece of timber that can be sawed from a round log 20.0 inches in diameter?

The area of an equilateral triangle in terms of its radius

(Optional)

The equilateral triangle ABC is inscribed in circle O, r is its radius, and a is its apothem.

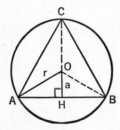

Fig. 6

$\angle HAO = 30°$, and $\angle AOH = 60°$. Why?

$$a = \frac{r}{2}. \text{ Why?}$$

$$AH = \frac{r}{2}\sqrt{3}. \text{ Why?}$$

$$AB = 2AH = r\sqrt{3}. \text{ Why?}$$

$$A_{\triangle ABC} = \frac{1}{2}ap. \text{ Why?}$$

$$= \frac{1}{2} \cdot \frac{r}{2} \cdot 3r\sqrt{3}.$$

$$= \frac{3}{4}r^2\sqrt{3}.$$

Can you derive this formula in other ways?

The area of an equilateral triangle circumscribed about a circle *(Optional)*

Equilateral $\triangle EFG$ is circumscribed about circle O of radius r.

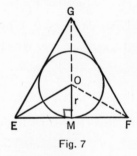

Fig. 7

Show that $A_{\triangle EFG} = 3r^2\sqrt{3}$.

Hint: Since $\triangle EMO$ is a 30°, 60°, 90° triangle, you can find the length of EM in terms of r. The area of $\triangle EFG$ can then be found in one of these ways: multiply the area of $\triangle EMO$ by six; multiply the area of $\triangle EFO$ by three; substitute the length of EF for s in the formula $\dfrac{s^2\sqrt{3}}{4}$.

Exercises (*Optional*)

1. Equilateral triangles are inscribed in and circumscribed about a circle whose radius is r.

   a. Find the ratio of their areas.

   b. Find the ratio of their perimeters.

2. Given an equilateral triangle.

   a. What is the ratio of its radius and apothem?

   b. What is the ratio of its radius and altitude?

   c. What is the ratio of its radius and a side?

   d. What is the ratio of its apothem and altitude?

   e. What is the ratio of its apothem and a side?

3. The radius of a circle is 6.

   a. What is the area of the inscribed equilateral triangle?

   b. What is the area of the circumscribed equilateral triangle?

4. The side of an equilateral triangle is 9.

   a. What is the radius of the inscribed circle?

   b. What is the radius of the circumscribed circle?

5. The side of an equilateral triangle is 12.0 inches.

   a. What is the area of the triangle?

   b. What is the radius of the triangle?

   c. What is the apothem of the triangle?

   d. What is the altitude of the triangle?

The area of a regular hexagon inscribed in a circle (*Optional*)

The regular hexagon $ABCDEF$ in Figure 8 is inscribed in circle O, r is its radius, and a is its apothem.

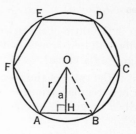

Fig. 8

$\angle HAO = 60°$, and $\angle AOH = 30°$. Why?

$$a = \frac{r}{2}\sqrt{3}, \text{ and } AB = r. \text{ Why?}$$

$$A_{ABCDEF} = \frac{1}{2}ap. \text{ Why?}$$

$$= \frac{1}{2} \cdot \frac{r}{2}\sqrt{3} \cdot 6r.$$

$$= \frac{3}{2}r^2\sqrt{3}.$$

Show that $A_{\text{hex. }ABCDEF} = 6 \cdot A_{\triangle ABO}$.

The area of a regular hexagon circumscribed about a circle
(*Optional*)

The regular hexagon $EFGHIJ$ is circumscribed about the circle with center O and radius r. Show that $A_{\text{hex. }EFGHIJ} = 2r^2\sqrt{3}$.

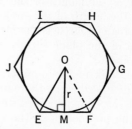

Fig. 9

Exercises (*Optional*)

1. What is the ratio of the areas of the inscribed and circumscribed regular hexagons of a circle?

2. What is the ratio of the areas of the inscribed regular triangle and the inscribed regular hexagon of a circle?

3. What is the ratio of the areas of the circumscribed regular triangle and the circumscribed regular hexagon of a circle?

4. What is the ratio of the radius and the apothem of a regular hexagon?

5. The radius of a circle is 6.
   a. What is the area of the inscribed regular hexagon?
   b. What is the area of the circumscribed regular hexagon?

6. The side of a regular hexagon is 9.
   a. What is the radius of the inscribed circle?
   b. What is the radius of the circumscribed circle?

7. The side of a regular hexagon is 12.0 inches.
   a. What is the radius of the hexagon?
   b. What is the apothem of the hexagon?
   c. What is the area of the hexagon?

Regular polygons and circles

The circumference of a circle is the measure of the length of the circle, or simply, the length of the circle.

The area of a circle is the measure of the area of the plane surface enclosed by the circle.

If we think of the number of sides of regular inscribed and circumscribed polygons as being doubled again and again, the perimeters of the resulting polygons approach nearer and nearer to the circumference of the circle; the apothems approach the radius of the circle; and the areas approach the area of the circle. That is, as the number of sides of the regular inscribed polygon increases indefinitely, the perimeter of the polygon approaches the circumference of a circle of the same radius as a *limit*; the area of the polygon approaches the area of the circle as a *limit*; the apothem of the polygon approaches the radius of the circle as a *limit*; and, in a circle having a given radius; the sides of the polygon get shorter and shorter.

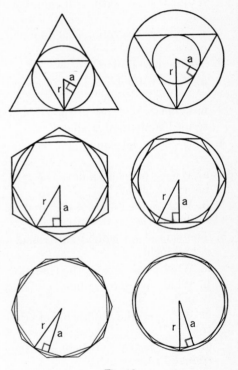

Fig. 10

Thus we see that a circle may be thought of as a regular polygon of the same radius, but with a very great number of sides. The greater the number of sides, the closer the approximation.

POSTULATE 49. Any relationship that is true for regular polygons and which does not depend upon the number of sides of the polygons, is also true for circles.

Circumference and area ratios

The ratio of the perimeters of two regular polygons of the same number of sides is equal to the ratio of their radii, apothems, or sides. That is,

$$\frac{p_1}{p_2} = \frac{r_1}{r_2} = \frac{a_1}{a_2} = \frac{s_1}{s_2}.$$

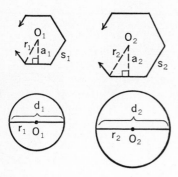

Fig. 11

If C_1 and C_2 are the circumferences of two circles whose radii are r_1 and r_2 and whose diameters are d_1 and d_2, respectively, then by Postulate 49

$$\frac{C_1}{C_2} = \frac{r_1}{r_2} = \frac{d_1}{d_2}$$

COROLLARY   The ratio of the circumferences of two circles is equal to the ratio of their radii or of their diameters.

The preceding corollary may be stated two other ways as follows:
1. The circumferences of two circles are directly proportional to their radii or diameters.
2. The circumference of a circle varies directly as its radius or diameter.

The ratio of the areas of two regular polygons of the same number of sides is equal to the ratio of the squares of their radii, the squares of their apothems, or the squares of their perimeters. That is,

$$\frac{A_1}{A_2} = \frac{r_1^2}{r_2^2} = \frac{a_1^2}{a_2^2} = \frac{p_1^2}{p_2^2}.$$

If $A_{\odot 1}$ and $A_{\odot 2}$ are the areas of two circles whose radii are r_1 and r_2, whose diameters are d_1 and d_2, and whose circumferences are C_1 and C_2, respectively, then by Postulate 49

$$\frac{A_{\odot 1}}{A_{\odot 2}} = \frac{r_1^2}{r_2^2} = \frac{d_1^2}{d_2^2} = \frac{C_1^2}{C_2^2}.$$

COROLLARY   The ratio of the areas of two circles is equal to the ratio of the squares of their radii, the squares of their diameters, or the squares of their circumferences.

Exercises

1. The radii of two circles are 3 and 6.
   a. What is the ratio of their diameters?
   b. What is the ratio of their circumferences?
   c. What is the ratio of their areas?
2. The ratio of the areas of two circles is 4 : 8.
   a. What is the ratio of their radii?
   b. What is the ratio of their diameters?
   c. What is the ratio of their circumferences?

3. The circumferences of two circles are 1.35 inches and 4.05 inches.
   a. What is the ratio of their radii?
   b. What is the ratio of their diameters?
   c. What is the ratio of their areas?
4. By what number must the radius of a circle be multiplied if its area is to be multiplied by 4? by 2? by $\frac{2}{3}$?
5. By what number must the diameter of a circle be multiplied if its circumference is to be multiplied by 4? by 2? by $\sqrt{2}$?
6. What is the effect on the circumference of a circle
   a. If its radius is multiplied by $\frac{4}{9}$?
   b. If its area is divided by $\frac{4}{9}$?
   c. If its area is multiplied by $\frac{2}{3}$?
7. What is the effect on the area of a circle
   a. If its radius is divided by 2?
   b. If its radius is multiplied by 2?
   c. If its radius is multiplied by $\sqrt{2}$?
8. The diameters of two pipes are $\frac{3}{4}''$ and $1''$. What is the ratio of the areas of their right sections?

The area of a circle in terms of its radius and circumference

The area of a regular polygon is one-half the product of its apothem and perimeter. A circle may be thought of as a regular polygon of a great number of sides whose circumference is the perimeter and whose radius is the apothem of the polygon. If $A_\odot$ is the area of a circle, r is its radius, and C is its circumference; then, by Postulate 49, $A_\odot = \frac{1}{2}rC$.

COROLLARY   The area of a circle is one-half the product of its radius and its circumference.

The ratio of the circumference of a circle to its diameter

It can be shown that the circumference C of a circle varies directly as its diameter d. The variation constant is called π (pronounced pi).

Hence $\dfrac{C}{d} = \pi$.

POSTULATE 50.   **The ratio of the circumference of any circle to its diameter is the constant π.**

Since $\dfrac{C}{d} = \pi$, then $C = \pi d$. If we replace d with $2r$, we get $C = 2\pi r$. Since $A_\odot = \frac{1}{2}rC$, then $A_\odot = \frac{1}{2}r \cdot 2\pi r$, or $A_\odot = \pi r^2$. If we replace r with $\frac{1}{2}d$, $A_\odot = \frac{1}{4}\pi d^2$.

COROLLARIES 1. The circumference of a circle is equal to the product of its diameter and π.

2. The circumference of a circle is equal to the product of its radius and 2π.

3. The area of a circle is equal to the product of the square of its radius and π.

4. The area of a circle is equal to the product of the square of its diameter and $\frac{1}{4}\pi$.

The numerical value of π

An approximate value of π may be obtained by dividing the circumferences of circular objects by their diameters. The circumference of a circular object can be found by wrapping a string once around it and then measuring the length of the string.

The Babylonians and Hebrews thought that $\pi = 3$. The Egyptian mathematician Ahmes (1700 B.C.) used $\pi = 3.1605$. By computing the perimeters of inscribed and circumscribed regular polygons of ninety-six sides, Archimedes of Greece (287-212 B.C.) found the value of π to lie between $3\frac{1}{7}$ and $3\frac{10}{71}$. The value of π is not a rational number; hence, it is not a repeating decimal.

Recently the value of π was computed to 2035 decimal places, but for practical purposes we seldom need a value more exact than 3.14159. In computing the circumference and area of the circle, if the number of units in the measure of the radius contains two significant digits, use either $3\frac{1}{7}$ or 3.14 for π; if the radius is measured to three significant digits, use 3.142; etc.

Exercises

In Exercises 1-9, find the unknown values if r is the radius, d the diameter, C the circumference, and A the area of a circle. For the value of π, round off 3.14159 to one more digit than there are digits in the value of the given quantity.

Copy the table on your own paper.

	r	d	C	A
1.	2.2325 ft.	?	?	?
2.	7.00 in.	?	?	?
3.	$\frac{7}{22}$ in.	?	?	?
4.	?	1.80 in.	?	?
5.	?	$\frac{2}{\pi}$	?	?
6.	?	?	5.781 in.	?
7.	?	?	3π	?
8.	?	?	?	265.8 sq. in.
9.	?	?	?	9π

10. If the diameter of a bicycle wheel is 28.0 inches, how many revolutions does it make in going a mile?

11. If an automobile has wheels 30.2 inches in diameter, how far does it travel for each turn of the wheel?

12. If the diameter of a wheel is increased by 1.00 in., what is the increase in the circumference of the wheel?

13. If the diameter of a disc is increased by 1.00 in., what is the increase in the area of the disc?

14. How many revolutions are made by a lawn roller 30.0 inches in diameter as it is pushed the length of a lawn which is 30.0 feet?

15. If the pressure is constant, the amount of water that flows through a pipe depends upon the area of the right section of the pipe. Compare the amounts of water that can flow through two pipes whose radii are 0.50 inches and 0.75 inches.

16. If the drive wheels of a locomotive are 60.0 inches in diameter, how many revolutions per minute do they make when the locomotive is going 75.00 miles per hour?

17. Construct a circle whose circumference is equal to the sum of the circumferences of two given circles.

18. Construct a circle whose area is equal to the sum of the areas of two given circles.

19. Construct a circle whose area is equal to the difference of the areas of two given circles.

20. Construct a circle whose area equals 4 times the area of a given circle.

21. Construct a circle whose area equals 3 times the area of a given circle.

22. Derive the formula for the area of a square inscribed in a semicircle in terms of the radius of the semicircle.

23. Find the ratio of the circumferences of the inscribed and circumscribed circles of an equilateral triangle.

24. Find the ratio of the areas of the inscribed and circumscribed circles of an equilateral triangle.

25. Find the ratio of the areas of the inscribed and circumscribed circles of a square.

26. Find the ratio of the circumferences of the inscribed and circumscribed circles of a regular hexagon.

The length of an arc

If $\angle AOB$ contains x angle degrees, then $\overset{\frown}{AB}$ contains x arc degrees. If C is the circumference, the linear measure S of $\overset{\frown}{AB}$ can be obtained as follows:

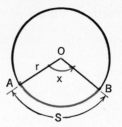

Fig. 12

$$\frac{S}{C} = \frac{x}{360} \quad \text{or}$$

$$\frac{S}{\pi d} = \frac{x}{360}.$$

Hence, $\quad S = \dfrac{x}{360} \cdot \pi d.$

COROLLARY The ratio of the length of an arc of a circle to its circumference is equal to the ratio of the number of degrees in the arc to 360°.

The area of a sector of a circle

DEFINITION A *sector of a circle* is a figure formed by two radii and the arc intercepted by the angle between them.

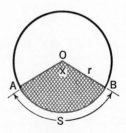

Fig. 13

In Figure 13, if S is the linear measure of $\overarc{AB}$, x is the number of degrees in its central angle AOB, C is the circumference, r is the radius, A_S is the area of the sector ABO, and $A_\odot$ is the area of circle O, then

$$\frac{A_S}{A_\odot} = \frac{x}{360} \cdot \text{Why?}$$

Thus, $\quad \dfrac{A_S}{\pi r^2} = \dfrac{x}{360}.$

Hence, $\quad A_S = \dfrac{x}{360} \cdot \pi r^2.$

However, $\dfrac{x}{360} = \dfrac{S}{C}.$ Why?

Then, $\quad \dfrac{A_S}{A_\odot} = \dfrac{S}{C}.$ Why?

Thus, $\quad \dfrac{A_S}{\pi r^2} = \dfrac{S}{2\pi r}.$

Hence, $\quad A_S = \frac{1}{2}Sr.$

THEOREM 92. **The area of a sector of a circle is equal to one-half the product of the length of its arc and its radius.**

The area of a segment of a circle

The area of the segment ABX of the circle O is equal to the difference of the areas of the sector AOB and the $\triangle AOB$. (See Figure 14.)

Example: Find the area of the segment of a circle bounded by one side of an inscribed equilateral triangle and its arc in terms of the radius r of the circle. (Refer to Figure 15.)

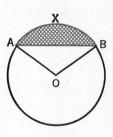

Fig. 14

Solution:
$$\angle OBM = 30°. \text{ Why?}$$
$$OM = \tfrac{1}{2}r. \text{ Why?}$$
$$AB = r\sqrt{3}. \text{ Why?}$$
$$A_{\triangle AOB} = \tfrac{1}{2}AB \cdot OM.$$
$$= \tfrac{1}{2}r\sqrt{3} \cdot \tfrac{1}{2}r. \text{ Why?}$$
$$= \tfrac{1}{4}r^2\sqrt{3}.$$
$$\angle AOB = 120°. \text{ Why?}$$
$$A_{\text{Sector } AOB} = \tfrac{1}{3}\pi r^2. \text{ Why?}$$
Hence,
$$A_{\text{Segment } ABX} = \tfrac{1}{3}\pi r^2 - \tfrac{1}{4}r^2\sqrt{3}.$$
$$= r^2(\tfrac{1}{3}\pi - \tfrac{1}{4}\sqrt{3}).$$
Show that
$$A_{\text{Segment } ABC} = r^2(\tfrac{2}{3}\pi + \tfrac{1}{4}\sqrt{3}).$$

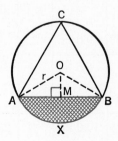

Fig. 15

The area of a ring

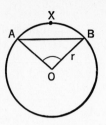

Ex. 1–5

DEFINITION A *ring* is a figure bounded by two concentric circles.

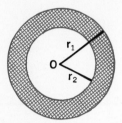

Fig. 16

In Figure 16, the area of the larger circle is πr_1^2, and the area of the smaller circle is πr_2^2. Hence,

$A_{\text{ring}} = \pi(r_1^2 - r_2^2)$. Why?

$\quad\quad\quad = \pi(r_1 - r_2)(r_1 + r_2)$. Why?

Exercises

In Exercises **1-5**, *find the values of the unknown quantities. Copy the table on your own paper and fill in the blanks. Do not write in this book.*

	$\angle O$	Radius r	$\overset{\frown}{BA}$	Area of Sector AOB	Area of Segment ABX
1.	60°	9.0 in.	?	?	?
2.	?	9.0 in.	90°	?	?
3.	120°	9.0 in.	?	?	?
4.	?	10.0 in.	?	25π	?
5.	?	?	120°	12π	?

6. If the diameters of a circular ring are 10.0 inches and 8.0 inches, find the area of the ring.

7. A circular walk is to be built around a water fountain. The width of the walk is to be 6.0 feet, and the diameter of the inside edge of the walk is to be 30.0 feet. Find the cost of the walk at $3.25 per square yard.

8. In a circle whose radius is 5.0 inches, a sector has an area of 25 square inches. Find the area of a sector having the same central angle in a circle whose radius is 3.0 inches.

9. Two sectors have equal central angles, and their radii are 6.0 cm. and 9.0 cm., respectively. What is the ratio of their areas?

10. What is the effect upon the area of a sector of a circle if:
a. Its angle is doubled and its radius is constant?
b. Its arc is divided by n and its radius is multiplied by n?
c. Its radius is multiplied by 3 and its angle is multiplied by 2?
d. Its radius is doubled and its angle is tripled?

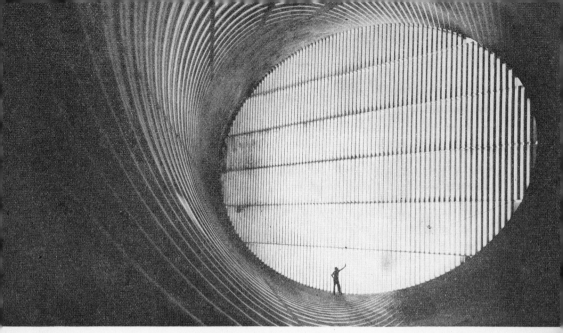

This huge ellipse, 58 feet high and 82 feet wide, is part of the air control system in the giant wind tunnel at Langley Aeronautical Laboratory in Ohio. The curved vanes force the air to turn corners smoothly so that turbulent eddies do not form to interfere with the wind tunnel tests.

The area of an ellipse (*Optional*)

The axes AB and XY of the ellipse are perpendicular bisectors of each other. AB is called the major axis, and XY is called the minor axis of the ellipse.

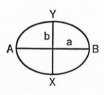

Fig. 17

It can be proved that the area of the ellipse can be found by the formula $A = \pi ab$, where a is $\frac{1}{2}AB$, and b is $\frac{1}{2}XY$.

If $a = b = r$, then πab becomes πr^2. Hence, a circle is a special kind of ellipse.

General formula for the area of a regular inscribed polygon (*Optional*)

If AB is a side of a regular inscribed n-gon $ABC. . .$, then

$$\angle P = \frac{360}{n}. \text{ Also, } \sin P = \frac{h}{r} \text{ or}$$
$$h = r \sin P.$$
$$A_{\triangle ABP} = \tfrac{1}{2}rh. \text{ Why?}$$
$$= \tfrac{1}{2}r \cdot r \sin P.$$
$$= \tfrac{1}{2}r^2 \sin P.$$
$$A_{n\text{-gon}} = \tfrac{1}{2}nr^2 \sin P. \text{ Why?}$$
$$= \tfrac{1}{2}nr^2 \sin \left(\frac{360}{n}\right).$$

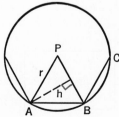

Fig. 18

A line segment divided in extreme and mean ratio

(*Optional*)

DEFINITION **A point divides a given segment in *extreme and mean ratio* when the longer part of the segment is the mean proportional between the whole segment and the shorter part.**

If AB is divided at point C in extreme and mean ratio, then

$$\frac{AB}{AC} = \frac{AC}{CB}.$$

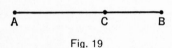

A   C   B

Fig. 19

The ancient Greeks considered the division of a line segment in the extreme and mean ratio to be of mystical significance and called it the "divine proportion." It has also been called the "golden section" because of its practical value in art and architecture.

Rectangular openings in buildings, picture frames, and other rectangular figures are most pleasing to the eye when the length and width have the ratio of the segment divided in extreme and mean ratio. Hence, a rectangle has the most pleasing proportions when

$$\frac{w + l}{l} = \frac{l}{w}.$$

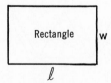

Rectangle   w

l

Fig. 20

Example: If the length of a rectangular picture frame is to be 10.00 inches, what width should be most pleasing to the eye?

Solution: $\dfrac{w + 10}{10} = \dfrac{10}{w}$

$$w^2 + 10w = 100$$

$$w = 6.18.$$

The width should be 6.18 inches.

Exercises (*Optional*)

1. A line segment 10.00 inches long is divided in extreme and mean ratio. Find the length of its segments. What is the ratio of the two segments?

2. The two parts of a line segment of length x divided in extreme and mean ratio are, to three decimal places, $0.618x$ and $0.382x$. Is the ratio of the segments nearer to $\frac{8}{5}$ or $\frac{5}{3}$?

3. A segment x inches long is divided in extreme and mean ratio. Show that the segments of x are $\frac{x}{2}(\sqrt{5} - 1)$ and $\frac{x}{2}(3 - \sqrt{5})$.

4. If the shorter side of a rectangular picture frame is to be 15.0 inches, find the length of the longer side if the frame is to have the most pleasing proportions.

5. Measure the length and width of a window frame of your home or school building. Does the ratio of its length and width conform to the golden section?

6. Check to see how closely the ratios of the dimensions of the prints of camera pictures conform to the golden section.

Constructions based on extreme and mean ratios (*Optional*)

CONSTRUCTION 26   Divide a line segment in extreme and mean ratio. (*Optional*).

Given: Segment AB.

Required: To divide AB in extreme and mean ratio.

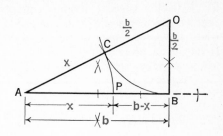

Method:
1. Construct $OB \perp AB$ at B and equal to $\frac{1}{2}AB$.
2. With O as center and OB as radius, draw circle O.
3. Draw AO intersecting circle O at C.
4. With center A and radius AC, draw an arc intersecting AB at P.
5. P is the required point of division; that is, $\dfrac{AB}{AP} = \dfrac{AP}{PB}$.

Proof:
1. $\left(x + \dfrac{b}{2}\right)^2 = b^2 + \left(\dfrac{b}{2}\right)^2$. Why?
2. $x^2 = b^2 - bx$. Why?
   $= b(b - x)$.
3. $\therefore \dfrac{b}{x} = \dfrac{x}{b - x}$. Why?

CONSTRUCTION 27 (*Optional*).   Inscribe a regular decagon in a circle.

Given: Circle O.

Required: To inscribe a regular decagon in circle O.

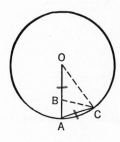

Method:
1. Draw OA and divide it at B so that $\dfrac{OA}{OB} = \dfrac{OB}{BA}$.
2. With A as center and OB as radius, draw an arc intersecting circle O at C.
3. AC is one side of the required decagon.

Proof:
Draw OC and BC, and prove:
1. $\dfrac{OA}{AC} = \dfrac{AC}{BA}$.

2. $\triangle AOC \sim \triangle ACB$.
3. $AC = BC$.
4. $\angle OCA = \angle A = \angle ABC = 2\angle O$.
5. $\angle OCA + \angle A + \angle O = 180°$ or $5\angle O = 180°$.

Hence, $\angle O = 36°$, and AC is the side of a regular decagon.

The length of a side of a regular inscribed decagon in terms of its radius (*Optional*)

Since $\dfrac{OA}{AC} = \dfrac{AC}{BA}$, then $\dfrac{r}{d} = \dfrac{d}{r-d}$.

Hence, $d^2 + rd - r^2 = 0$.

$$d = \frac{-r + \sqrt{r^2 + 4r^2}}{2}$$

$$d = \frac{r}{2}(\sqrt{5} - 1).$$

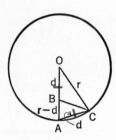

Fig. 21

Explain why the root $\dfrac{-r - r\sqrt{5}}{2}$ is not used.

Other regular polygons (*Optional*)

A regular pentagon can be constructed by joining the alternate vertices of a regular decagon.

The arc of a side of a regular inscribed hexagon is 60°, and the arc of a side of a regular inscribed decagon is 36°. Does this suggest a way to construct a regular polygon of 15 sides?

Exercises (*Optional*)

1. Explain how to construct regular polygons of 20, 40, 80, ... sides.

2. Explain how to construct regular polygons of 30, 60, 120, ... sides.

3. Construct the side of a regular inscribed decagon and a regular inscribed pentagon as follows:

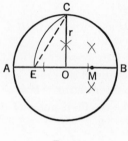

Ex. 3

Draw a diameter AB of circle O, and at O construct $OC \perp AB$.

Construct the midpoint M of OB. With M as center and MC as radius, draw $\widehat{CE}$.

a. Prove that EO is the side of a regular inscribed decagon by proving that $EO = \dfrac{r}{2}(\sqrt{5} - 1)$.

b. It can be proved that the side p of a regular pentagon inscribed in a circle of radius r is given by the formula $p = \dfrac{r}{2}\sqrt{10 - 2\sqrt{5}}$.

Show that EC is equal to the side of a regular pentagon inscribed in circle O.

Space Geometry

Prisms (*Optional*)

The *prism* shown here has four lateral faces $EFF'E'$, $FGG'F'$, $GHH'G'$ and $EHH'E'$. It has two parallel bases $EFGH$ and $E'F'G'H'$. Its lateral edges are EE', FF', etc. The lateral faces are parallelograms. The plane $WRMK$ is perpendicular to each of the edges; and, hence, it is a right section.

In a *right prism* the lateral edges, and hence the lateral faces, are perpendicular to the bases. A *regular prism* is a right prism whose bases are regular polygons. A *parallelepiped* is a prism whose bases are parallelograms. A *rectangular parallelepiped*, or a *rectangular solid*, is a right prism whose bases are rectangles. A *cube* is a rectangular solid having square bases and faces.

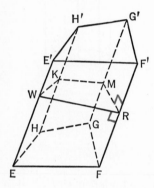

Fig. 22

It can be proved that

1. The lateral area of a prism is equal to the product of the length of one of its edges and the perimeter of a right section.

2. The volume of a prism is equal to the product of the area of a right section and the length of its edge.

3. The lateral surfaces and the total surfaces of similar prisms are directly proportional to the squares of corresponding sides or edges.

4. The volumes of similar prisms are directly proportional to the cubes of corresponding sides or edges.

Exercises (*Optional*)

1. The width, height, and length of a rectangular solid are respectively 3 inches, 4 inches, and 12 inches.

   a. Find the length of one of its diagonals. (The distance from a lower corner to opposite upper corner.)

   b. Find the total area of its surface.

   c. Find its volume.

2. The edge of a cube is 2 inches.

   a. Find the area of its total surface.

   b. Find its volume.

   c. Prove that its diagonals are not perpendicular.

3. A classroom is 24 feet wide, 30 feet long, and 12 feet high.

   a. What is its volume in cubic yards?

   b. If its length and width were each doubled, by what number would its floor area be multiplied?

   c. If all three of its dimensions were doubled, by what number would its volume be multiplied?

4. The edge of a cube is e.

   a. To triple the total surface of the cube, by what number must e be multiplied?

   b. To triple the volume of the cube, by what number must e be multiplied?

5. The areas of the total surfaces of two cubes are in the ratio 1 : 4.

   a. What is the ratio of their edges?

   b. What is the ratio of their volumes?

6. The base of a right prism is a right triangle whose legs are 0.75 inch and 1.00 inch. The altitude of the prism is 2.00 inches.

   a. Find the area of the lateral surface of the prism.

   b. Find the total area of the prism.

   c. Find the volume of the prism.

7. Each side of the base of a regular triangular prism is 1.0 inch, and its altitude is 4.0 inches.

   a. Find the area of the lateral surface of the prism.

   b. Find the area of the total surface of the prism.

   c. Find the volume of the prism.

8. How many gallons of water are needed to fill a swimming pool 60.0 feet wide if the dimensions of a right section are as indicated in the figure? (1 gallon = 231.0 cubic inches.)

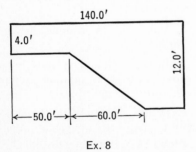

Ex. 8

Cylinders *(Optional)*

A *right circular cylinder* is a cylinder whose bases are circles lying in parallel planes which are perpendicular to the axis of the cylinder.

In Figure 23, MK is not only the axis of the cylinder, but also its altitude. The radius of each base is r.

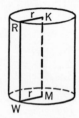

Fig. 23

Exercises *(Optional)*

1. The cylinder W-MK-R is a right circular cylinder.

   a. Write a formula for finding the area of its lateral surface.

   b. Write a formula for finding the area of its total surface.

   c. Write a formula for finding its volume.

2. A metal tank is in the form of a right circular cylinder. The radius of its base is 7.0 inches, and its altitude is 5 feet 6 inches.

   a. If 10% of the area of its total surface must be allowed for waste and seams, how many square inches of metal are required to make the tank?

   b. Find the volume of the tank in gallons. (1 gallon = 231.0 cubic inches.)

3. Two cylindrical tin cans are similar. The ratio of similitude of the cans is 2 : 3.

a. What is the ratio of their altitudes?

b. What is the ratio of the areas of their bases?

c. What is the ratio of the areas of their lateral surfaces?

d. What is the ratio of their volumes?

4. Consider two right circular cylinders.

a. If they are similar, write a formula for comparing their volumes.

b. Write a formula for comparing their volumes if they have equal altitudes, but the radii of their bases are unequal.

c. Write a formula for comparing the areas of their lateral surfaces if the radii of their bases are equal, but they have unequal altitudes.

d. Write a formula for comparing the areas of their lateral surfaces if they have equal altitudes, but the radii of their bases are unequal.

e. Write a formula for comparing their volumes if the radii of their bases are equal, but they have unequal altitudes.

5. A right section of a cylindrical pipe is a ring whose radii are 12.0 inches and 13.0 inches. The pipe is 36.0 inches long. Find its volume.

Pyramids (*Optional*)

The pyramid in Figure 24 has five lateral faces VLK, VLM, etc. The pentagon $LMNJK$ is its base. The intersections VK, VL, etc., of the lateral faces are the lateral edges. The perpendicular VO from the vertex V to the plane of the base is its altitude.

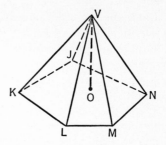

Fig. 24

A *regular pyramid* is a pyramid whose base is a regular polygon and whose altitude is perpendicular to the plane of the base at its center. The faces of a regular pyramid are congruent isosceles triangles. The *slant height* of a regular pyramid is the altitude to the base of any one of the lateral faces.

It can be proved that

1. The volume of a pyramid is equal to one-third the product of the area of its base and its altitude.

2. The areas of the lateral surfaces of two similar pyramids are directly proportional to the squares of any two corresponding edges, sides, or altitudes.

3. The volumes of two similar pyramids are directly proportional to the cubes of any two corresponding sides, edges, or altitudes.

Exercises (*Optional*)

1. A regular pyramid has a square base whose side is 8.00 inches. The altitude of the pyramid is 3.00 inches.

a. Find the volume of the pyramid.

b. Find the slant height of the pyramid.

c. Find the lateral edge of the pyramid.

d. Find the lateral area of the pyramid.

e. Find the total area of the pyramid.

f. If the dimensions of the pyramid were doubled, by what number would its total area be multiplied?

2. The base of a triangular pyramid is an equilateral triangle 2.0 inches on a side, and its altitude is 4.0 inches.

   a. Find the volume of the pyramid.

   b. If the pyramid is a regular pyramid, what is its lateral area?

   c. If the pyramid is a regular pyramid, what is its total area?

3. The volumes of two similar pyramids are in the ratio 8 : 27.

   a. Find the ratio of the areas of their bases.

   b. Find the ratio of two corresponding lateral edges.

   c. Find the ratio of their lateral areas.

4. A regular pyramid has a hexagonal base 3.00 inches on a side. Its altitude is 5.00 inches.

   a. Find the length of one of its lateral edges.

   b. Find the length of its slant height.

   c. Find its lateral area.

   d. Find its total area.

   e. Find its volume.

Cones (*Optional*)

A *right circular cone* is a cone whose base is a circle and whose altitude is the perpendicular from the vertex to the plane of the base at the center of the circle.

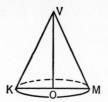

Fig. 25

If the radius of the base of a circular cone is r, and the altitude of the cone is h, its volume is $\frac{1}{3}\pi r^2 h$. If the radius of the base of a right circular cone is r, and its slant height is s, its lateral area is $\pi r s$.

Exercises (*Optional*)

1. The slant height KV of a right circular cone is 13.0 inches, and the radius KO of the base is 5.0 inches.

   a. Find the lateral area of the cone.

   b. Find the total area of the cone.

   c. Find the volume of the cone.

   d. If the dimensions of the cone were tripled, by what number would its total area be multiplied?

   e. If the dimensions of the cone were tripled, by what number would its volume be multiplied?

2. If the volumes of two similar cones are in the ratio 1 : 8, what is the ratio of their altitudes?

3. In a right circular cone, a right section is midway between the vertex and the plane of the base.

   a. What is the ratio of the radius of the right section to the radius of the base?

   b. What is the ratio of the area of the right section to the area of the base?

c. What is the ratio of the volume of the cone whose base is the right section to the volume of the original cone?

4. A right circular cone can be made from a sector of a circle.

a. If the radius of the sector $AA'O$ is 5.0″, and the central angle O is 120°, find the radius AP of the base of the cone which can be made from this sector.

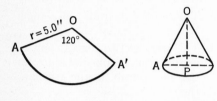

Ex. 4

b. Find the angle and the radius of the sector from which a right circular cone can be made if the diameter of the base is equal to the slant height of the cone, and if the altitude of the cone is to be 10.0 feet.

c. How many square feet of canvas would it take to make the cone in **(b)** if 10% of the lateral area is allowed for waste?

5. Draw the pattern necessary to make a lamp shade with the dimensions shown in the figure; that is, find the radius and the angle of a sector from which the pattern can be cut.

Ex. 5

Spheres (*Optional*)

If r is the radius of a sphere, it can be proved that

1. The area of the sphere is $4\pi r^2$.
2. The volume of the sphere is $\frac{4}{3}\pi r^3$.

Exercises (*Optional*)

1. The radius of a sphere is 3.00 inches.
  a. Find the area of the sphere.
  b. Find the volume of the sphere.

2. The ratio of the radii of two spheres is 1 : 2.
  a. What is the ratio of their areas?
  b. What is the ratio of their volumes?

3. The ratio of the volumes of two spheres is 8 : 27.
  a. What is the ratio of their radii?
  b. What is the ratio of their areas?

4. Prove: If the radii of two small circles of a sphere are equal, their planes are equidistant from the center of the sphere.

5. Prove: If the planes of two small circles of a sphere are equidistant from the center of the sphere, the radii of the circles are equal.

6. To the nearest 100 miles, the radius of the earth is 4000 miles.
  a. What is the radius of the 30° parallel of latitude?
  b. What is the radius of the 45° parallel of latitude?
  c. What is the radius of the 60° parallel of latitude?

7. The ratio of the areas of two spheres is 1 : 2.
  a. What is the ratio of their radii?
  b. What is the ratio of their volumes?

Review of Chapter 16

True-False Test

Write the numbers **1-10** *on your paper. After each number write* **True** *if the corresponding statement is always true; write* **False** *if the corresponding statement is not necessarily true.*

1. The perimeter of a regular polygon of n sides inscribed in a circle is less than the circumference of the circle.

2. All regular polygons are similar.

3. The ratio of the areas of squares constructed on the diameters of two circles whose circumferences are in the ratio 1 : 4 is 1 : 16.

4. The area of a circle is equal to the square of the circumference divided by 4π.

5. The apothem of an equilateral triangle is one-half the altitude.

6. If two regular polygons have the same number of sides, they are similar.

7. The ratio of the areas of two circles whose radii are in the ratio 4 : 9 is 2 : 3.

8. The ratio of the areas of two similar regular polygons is equal to the ratio of the squares of the circumferences of their inscribed circles.

9. The area of a regular polygon of n sides inscribed in a circle is less than the area of a regular polygon of $4n$ sides inscribed in the same circle.

10. If the central angle of the arc of a segment is 90°, the area of the segment is $\frac{1}{4}r^2(\pi - 2r^2)$.

Completion Test

Write the numbers **1-13** *on your paper. After each number write an expression that correctly completes the corresponding statement. Do not write in this book.*

1. If the ratio of the areas of two circles is 4 : 9, the ratio of their circumferences is . . . . .

2. The apothem of an equilateral triangle is . . . . of its altitude.

3. The ratio of the radius of a regular hexagon to its apothem is . . . . .

4. The areas of two regular polygons of the same number of sides have the same ratio as the squares of their . . . . .

5. The ratio of the circumference of a circle to its diameter is a number called . . . . .

6. The ratio of the radius of a square to its apothem is . . . . .

7. The circumferences of two circles have the same ratio as . . . . .

8. The ratio of the areas of the inscribed and circumscribed squares of a circle is . . . . .

9. The areas of two circles have the same ratio as . . . . .

10. If x units are added to the radius of a circle, its circumference is increased by . . . . units.

11. The regular polygon in which each vertex angle is three times the size of each central angle has . . . . sides.

12. The area of a circle whose radius is exactly 1 unit is exactly . . . . square units.

13. If the radius of a circle is $\sqrt{2}$, the area of the inscribed square is . . . . .

ACKNOWLEDGMENTS

The authors gratefully acknowledge the help of the following individuals and organizations whose cooperation in supplying illustrative material for this book has been of great value: (The numbers indicate the pages on which the illustrations appear.)

Aero Service Corporation 418, 425

Bell Telephone Laboratories 280

Bettmann Archive 46

Boeing Aircraft Corporation 216

Margaret Bourke-White . . . . Binding Case Photograph of
George Washington Bridge

Corning Glass Works 372, 461

Philip Gendreau . . . . 12 (both), 108, 113, 304, 313, 332, 348, 375, 458

General Electric Company 2

General Motors Corporation 182

S. C. Johnson & Son, Inc. 258

Lever Brothers Company 225

National Advisory Committee for Aeronautics 475

Standard Oil of New Jersey 37, 162, 365, 421

United Aircraft Corporation 163

United States Plywood Corporation 432

United States Steel Corporation 74

W. M. Welch Manufacturing Company 41, 161, 218, 239, 265

Westinghouse Electric Corporation 128, 400

Wide World Photos, Inc. 14

Students of Bexley, Ohio, High School 9, 127, 211, 266

Students of Garden City, N. Y., High School 464

Two angles are equal if: 1. they are complements of the same angle (58); **2.** they are complements of equal angles (59); **3.** they are supplements of the same angle (59); **4.** they are supplements of equal angles (59); **6.** they are alternate interior angles of parallel lines cut by a transversal (83); **10.** their sides are parallel right to right and left to left (92); **15.** their sides are perpendicular right to right and left to left (158); **17.** they are angles opposite equal sides of a triangle (192); **33.** they are base angles of an isosceles trapezoid (230)

Two angles are supplementary if: 8. they are interior angles on the same side of a transversal cutting two parallel lines (87); **11.** their sides are parallel right to left and left to right (92); **16.** their sides are perpendicular right to left and left to right (158); **23.** they are consecutive angles of a parallelogram (220)

Two angles are unequal if: 63. one is an exterior angle and the other is a remote interior angle of a triangle (337); **64.** they are opposite unequal sides of a triangle (338); **66(b).** they are central angles of unequal arcs in the same or in equal circles (342)

Angle sums: 12. The sum of the angles of a triangle is 180° (149); **13.** The sum of the interior angles of a polygon is (n − 2) 180° (154); **14.** The sum of the exterior angles of a polygon (formed by extending the sides in succession) is 360° (156)

Angles measured by their intercepted arcs: 58. An inscribed angle is measured by one-half its intercepted arc (308); **60.** An angle formed by a tangent and a chord is measured by one-half its intercepted arc (314); **61.** An angle formed by two chords is measured by one-half the sum of the intercepted arcs (317); **62.** An angle formed by two secants, or a secant and a tangent, or two tangents is measured by one-half the difference of the intercepted arcs (319)

Two segments are equal if: 18. they are sides opposite equal angles of a triangle (192); **20.** they are segments of a segment intersected by a line through two points each equidistant from the ends of the other (204); **24.** they are opposite sides of a parallelogram (221); **25.** they are segments of a diagonal formed by the other diagonal of a parallelogram (221); **31.** they are diagonals of a rectangle (226); **34.** they are diagonals of an isosceles trapezoid (230); **35.** they are the legs of a trapezoid having equal base angles (230); **36.** they are segments of a transversal cut by parallel lines which cut off equal segments on another transversal (233); **40.** they are chords of equal arcs in the same or in equal circles (262); **42.** they are segments of a chord intersected by a diameter perpendicular to it (265); **45.** they are the distances from the center of equal chords in the same circle or in equal circles (269); **46.** they are chords equidistant from the center in the same or in equal circles (269); **51.** they are tangent segments to a circle from an external point (275)

One segment is one-half another if: 19. one segment is the side opposite the 30° angle and the other is the hypotenuse of a 30°, 60° right triangle (202); **37.** one is the segment joining the midpoints of two sides of a triangle and the other is the third side (235); **38.** one segment is the median of a trapezoid and the other is the sum of the bases (238); **39.** one segment is the median to the hypotenuse and the other is the hypotenuse of a right triangle (239)

Two segments are unequal if: 65. they are opposite unequal angles of a triangle (339); **66(c).** they are chords of unequal minor arcs in the same or in equal circles (342); **67.** they are the distances from the center of unequal chords in the same or in equal circles (343); **68.** they are chords unequally distant from the center in the same or in equal circles (343)

Two arcs are equal if: 41. they are arcs of equal chords in the same or in equal circles (262); **42.** they are segments of the arcs of a chord intersected by a diameter perpendicular to it (265); **43.** they are segments of the arcs of a chord intersected by a diameter that bisects the chord (266); **44.** they are segments of the arcs of a chord cut by the perpendicular bisector of the chord (267); **57.** they are intercepted arcs of a circle cut by two parallel lines (288)

Two arcs are unequal if: 66(a). they are intercepted arcs of unequal central angles (342); **66(d).** they are minor arcs of unequal chords in the same or in equal circles (342)

Two lines are parallel if: 5. they are cut by a transversal and the alternate interior angles are equal (81); **7.** they are cut by a transversal and the interior angles on the same side of the transversal are supplementary (86); **9.** they are parallel to the same line (90); **37.** one is a side of a triangle and the other is the segment joining the midpoints of the other two sides (235); **38.** one is the median of a trapezoid and the other is one of its bases (238); **70.** one is a side of a triangle and the other is a line that divides the other two sides proportionally (366)

Two lines are perpendicular if: 20. one line passes through two points each equidistant from the ends of the other (204); **43.** one is a diameter bisecting a chord that is not a diameter (266); **48.** one is a diameter and the other is the tangent to the circle at one end of the diameter (272)

A line passes through the center of a circle if: 44. it is the perpendicular bisector of a chord (267); **49.** it is perpendicular to a tangent at the point of contact (274)

A line is tangent to a circle if: 47. it is perpendicular to a diameter at one end of the diameter (271)

A line intersects a tangent at the point of contact if: 50. it is a diameter perpendicular to the tangent (274)

A quadrilateral is a parallelogram if: 26. the opposite sides are equal (223); **27.** two sides are equal and parallel (223); **28.** the diagonals bisect each other (223); **29.** the opposite angles are equal (223); **30.** the consecutive angles are supplementary (224)

A parallelogram is a rectangle if: 32. it has equal diagonals (226)

Loci in a plane: 21. The locus of points equidistant from two given points is the perpendicular bisector of the segment joining the points (205); **22.** The locus of points equidistant from the sides of an angle is the bisector of the angle (208); **59.** The locus of the vertex of the right angle of a right triangle which has a fixed hypotenuse is a circle with the hypotenuse as diameter (311)

Lines are concurrent if: 52. they are bisectors of the angles of a triangle (280); **53.** they are respectively perpendicular to two intersecting lines (282); **54.** they are perpendicular bisectors of the sides of a triangle (283); **55.** they are altitudes of a triangle (285); **56.** they are medians of a triangle (286)

Ratios of segments: 69. If a line parallel to one side of a triangle intersects the second and third sides, the ratio of the segments of the second side equals the ratio of the corresponding segments of the third side (362); **71.** If a line bisects an angle of a triangle, the ratio of the segments of the opposite side equals the ratio of the adjacent sides (368); **72.** If the bisector of an exterior angle of a triangle meets the extension of the opposite side, the ratio of the segments into which it externally divides that side equals the ratio of the adjacent sides (369); **73.** The ratio of the perimeters of two similar polygons equals the ratio of any two corresponding sides (374)

Ratios of areas: 81. The ratio of the areas of two rectangles equals the ratio of the products of their bases and altitudes (435); **85.** The areas of two similar triangles have the same ratio as the squares of any two corresponding sides (446); **86.** The areas of two similar polygons have the same ratio as the squares of any two corresponding sides (446)

Products of segments: 74. If two chords intersect within a circle, the product of the segments of one chord equals the product of the segments of the other (384)

Mean proportional between segments: 75. If a tangent and a secant are drawn to a circle from an external point, the tangent is the mean proportional between the whole secant and its external segment (385); **76.** If the altitude is drawn to the hypotenuse of a right triangle, (a) the altitude is the mean proportional between the segments of the hypotenuse, (b) each leg is the mean proportional between the whole hypotenuse and the segment adjacent to that leg (390)

If two polygons are similar: 73. the ratio of the perimeters equals the ratio of any two corresponding sides (374); **79.** they can be separated into the same number of triangles similar each to each and in corresponding positions (401)

Two polygons are similar if: 80. they are composed of the same number of triangles similar each to each in corresponding positions (402); **90.** they are regular and have the same number of sides (463)

Right triangle relationships: 19. If the acute angles of a right triangle are 30° and 60°, the side opposite the 30° angle is one-half the hypotenuse (202); **76.** If the altitude is drawn to the hypotenuse of a right triangle, (a) the altitude is the mean proportional between the segments of the hypotenuse, (b) each leg is the mean proportional between the whole hypotenuse and the segment adjacent to it (390); **77.** The square of the hypotenuse equals the sum of the squares of the legs (391); **78.** If the sum of the squares of two sides of a triangle equals the square of the third side, the triangle is a right triangle (392)

Circles and regular polygons: 87. A circle can be circumscribed about any regular polygon (460); **88.** A circle can be inscribed in any regular polygon (461); **89.** If a circle is divided into three or more equal arcs, (a) the chords of these arcs form a regular inscribed polygon, (b) the tangents at the points of division form a regular circumscribed polygon (462)

Areas: 82. The area of a parallelogram equals the product of its base and altitude (437); **83.** The area of a triangle equals one-half the product of its base and altitude (439); **84.** The area of a trapezoid equals one-half the product of its altitude and the sum of its bases (443); **91.** The area of a regular polygon equals one-half the product of its apothem and perimeter (465); **92.** The area of a sector of a circle equals one-half the product of the length of its arc and its radius (473)

INDEX

Abscissa: 129

Accuracy: 163

Algebra: deductive reasoning in, 60; equations of form $x^2 = a$, 352; graphic solution of simultaneous equations, 132; numerical geometry problems, 155, 180, 214; solution of quadratic equations, 388-390. *Also see* Equations

Alidade: 402-403, 421

Altitude(s): of equilateral triangle, 395; as mean proportional in right triangle, 390; of parallelogram, 218; to sides of triangle, 159-160, 284-285; of triangle, in terms of side, 442

Ambiguous case (of triangle construction): 172-174, 185

Analogy: 175

Analysis: 64

Angle(s): 24; acute, 30; adjacent, 33-34; alternate exterior, 77; alternate interior, 77, 81-83; bisector, 32, 112, 159, 208; central, 25-26, 261-262, 342; complementary, 33-34; construction, 112; corresponding, 76; degree, 25; of depression, 428; dihedral, 43; drawing, 27; dynamic, 28-29; of elevation, 428; equal, 30, 308; exterior, of polygon, 152; exterior, of triangle, 337; formed by lines meeting outside circle, 318-319; formed by tangent and chord, 314; formed by transversal, 76-77; formed by two chords, 316-317; how to name, 24; identifying, 78; inequality relations, 339-342; inscribed, 307-308; and intercepted arcs, 305-306; interior, 76; interior, on same side of transversal, 77, 86-87; kinds, 30; locus of points equidistant from sides, 208; measure, 25, 27; measurement of, in circles, 304-331; negative, 29; obtuse, 30; overlapping, 196; with parallel sides, 91-92; positive, 29; reflex, 30; right, 30, 36; of rotation, 28-29; sides, 24; with sides respectively perpendicular, 157-158; size, 24; static, 28; straight, 30, 35; summary, 104; supplementary, 35-36, 158, 220, 224; symbol, 24; trigonometric functions, table of, 423; trisection, 195-196; vertex, 24; vertical, 37

Applications (of geometry): aircraft, 216-217, 247; art, 476; astronomy, 290, 298; carpentry, 3, 105, 210-211, 242-243, 298, 399, 405; design, 126-128, 266; finding distance to horizon, 386; indirect measurement, 243, 404, 428-429; industrial, 113; machine shop, 162-163, 298; mapmaking, 365, 402-404, 421; mirror problems, 150, 295-297, 403; navigation, 247, 304, 327-328, 330, 426; physics, 6-7, 10, 32, 427; rigid figures, 3, 142-143; road-building, 297; slingshot, 297; surveying, 418, 425; of tangents, 290; using circles, 258-259; vectors, 245-250

Approximate numbers: computation with, 166-167; measurement with, 161-165

Arc(s) of circle: 22-23; construction, in which given angle can be inscribed, 326; degree of, 23; equal, 261; intercepted, 25, 287-288; length, 472; major, 23, 260; minor, 23, 260; minute of, 23; positive and negative, 321-323; second of, 23; unequal, 342

Arch: 22

Area(s): 432-457; circle, 20, 470; cone, 482; continuity of formulas, 444; by coordinate geometry, 445; cylinder, 482; ellipse, 475; equal, 433; equilateral triangle, 440, 466; irregular figures, 453-455; parallelogram, 437; polygon, 433, 444; prism, 479; quadrilateral, 440; ratios, 435-440; rectangle, 433-434; regular hexagon, 467; regular inscribed polygon, 475; regular polygon, 465, 475; rhombus, 440; ring, 474; sector of circle, 472-473; segment of circle, 473; similar triangles, 446; sphere, 483; square, 465; surface, 433; surface of pyramid, 481; trapezoid, 443; triangle, 432, 439-442; by trigonometry, 444-445; unit of, 433

Assumptions: 7, 15-16; concerning lines and points, 17; hidden, 176; unstated, 67. *Also see* Axioms, Postulates

Auxiliary lines: 89

Axiom(s): 15; basic, 38; inequalities, 334; on powers and roots, 352

Bisector(s): angle, 32; of angles of quadrilateral, 231; of angles of triangle, 159-161, 279-280, 368-369, 443; construction of,